Economic Report
of the President

Transmitted to the Congress
January 1993

TOGETHER WITH

THE ANNUAL REPORT

OF THE

COUNCIL OF ECONOMIC ADVISERS

UNITED STATES GOVERNMENT PRINTING OFFICE

WASHINGTON : 1993

For sale by the U.S. Government Printing Office
Superintendent of Documents, Mail Stop: SSOP, Washington, DC 20402-9328
ISBN 0-16-041592-6

CONTENTS

Page

For a detailed table of contents of the Council's Report, see page 11.

ECONOMIC REPORT
OF THE PRESIDENT

Economic Report of the President

To the Speaker of the House of Representatives and the President of the Senate:

The last 4 years have challenged the American economy, and the economy is meeting those challenges. The longest peacetime expansion in America's history ended in the second half of 1990. While the 1990–91 recession was relatively short (8 months compared to a postwar average of 11), the recovery was quite slow by historic standards but accelerated in the second half of 1992, with real gross domestic product growth over 3 percent and unemployment falling.

It is important to understand that the interruption to growth was temporary. An unusual confluence of forces—the delayed effect of the tight monetary policy in 1988–89 designed to head off an incipient rise in inflation, the oil price shock related to the Gulf War, the credit crunch, the problems in financial institutions, the overbuilding in commercial real estate, the fiscal imbalances, and the substantial current and prospective defense downsizing—all hit the economy in a relatively short period of time. These events occurred in the midst of a worldwide slowdown among the industrialized countries which temporarily slowed America's export boom— Canada and the United Kingdom were in far steeper recessions than the United States, with unemployment rates rising to over 10 percent, and Germany and Japan entered recession in 1992.

While the consolidation and transition were painful, the policies of my Administration have worked with the natural forces of the private economy to lay a foundation for stronger growth ahead. Inflation and interest rates are at their lowest levels in a generation. Consumers have trimmed their installment debt and have taken advantage of low interest rates to refinance their mortgages. Corporations have been raising equity, on balance, for the first time in several years. And, despite the economic slowdown abroad, America is once again the world's leading exporter and is more internationally competitive than it has been in many years, with productivity once again rising at a respectable rate.

In addition to these short-term problems and challenges, which the economy has been successfully weathering, the United States faces serious challenges in sustaining the economic recovery and simultaneously providing a firmer basis for long-term growth in productivity, income, and employment opportunities. Throughout my Administration, I have presented a series of interrelated and comprehensive programs to achieve these goals. I strongly believe my proposals—some of which I was able to implement unilaterally, others of which I have worked with the Nation's Governors to advance, others of which have been partially adopted by the Congress, and others of which the Congress has thus far refused to enact—reflect sound principles. These principles define the appropriate, though limited role for government in improving the foundations and performance of our economy. My fundamental reform agenda included:

- *Fiscal Reform.* In addition to the existing spending limits, I have proposed setting new caps on the growth of mandatory spending to reduce future budget deficits; restore tax incentives for saving, investment, and entrepreneurship to spur economic growth; and reforming the budget process itself, most notably by giving the President a line item veto and enacting a balanced budget Constitutional Amendment.

- *Trade Liberalization.* In a series of multilateral, regional, and bilateral initiatives, this Administration has set forth a forward-looking program, opening markets not closing them, in order to expand trade and growth for our Nation and the world. The North American Free Trade Agreement is an historic achievement that offers us the opportunity to create a more prosperous and stable Western Hemisphere. The United States has taken the lead in the Uruguay Round of GATT. Bringing the Uruguay Round to a successful conclusion remains essential to advancing U.S. and global economic prosperity.

- *Regulatory Reform.* The Federal, State, and local governments regulate too much, and often in inflexible, inefficient, costly, and unnecessary ways. While some government regulation is necessary, it should be limited to only those areas where serious market failures require attention and should provide maximum flexibility for the private sector to comply with the regulations. My Regulatory Moratorium, for example, saved American businesses and consumers over $20 billion a year.

In addition to these general areas of economic policy, I have made important proposals that would provide choice-based education reform; a more balanced approach to tort, malpractice, and civil justice reform; job training and insurance reform; market-based health care reform to control costs and provide access for the uninsured; and regulatory reform of the banking system. I would especially like to note my innovative proposals to spread hope and opportunity to the least advantaged in our society. Proposals such as enterprise zones and home ownership form the basis of my program to provide millions of disadvantaged Americans with the opportunity to live free of crime and drugs, in safe neighborhoods, and with productive employment. These citizens need and deserve the opportunity to have a stake in their communities and in society.

Americans should take great satisfaction in the fact that totalitarian, centrally planned economies all over the world are moving toward pluralistic democratic capitalism. The pace differs and the road will not be easy. But our advice, encouragement, and assistance has been essential. America has illuminated the advantages of freedom and market economies. Not so long ago it was fashionable to argue that all the world's economies were converging toward some form of socialism; the Communist regimes would ease some restrictions and allow market forces to play a role in their economies, and the democratic capitalist regimes would continue their headlong rush toward ever-larger bureaucratic welfare states. But history has rendered its judgment. The world's economies have opted decisively for various forms of democratic capitalism, not socialism or central planning. Our form of economic organization—a dynamic market economy based on individual initiative, entrepreneurship, personal freedom, and respect for private property—has made America the largest and most productive economy in the world, providing our citizens with the highest standard of living of any industrialized country. Our economic success continues to inspire market-oriented reforms in regions as diverse as the former Soviet Union, Eastern Europe, Latin America, and China.

America's future can and should be bright. We have the strongest, largest, most successful economy in the world, with the highest standard of living. But we cannot take continued economic growth for granted. The reform proposals I have put forward during my Administration, if enacted, would greatly enhance long-term economic growth, providing the foundation for higher living standards, a better legacy of prosperity for our children, improved social and economic mobility for the disadvantaged, more resources to pay for nontraditional goods and services such as a healthier environment, and for maintaining America's economic and geopolitical leadership into the twenty-first century.

George Bush

THE WHITE HOUSE
JANUARY 13, 1993

THE ANNUAL REPORT
OF THE
COUNCIL OF ECONOMIC ADVISERS

LETTER OF TRANSMITTAL

COUNCIL OF ECONOMIC ADVISERS,
Washington, D.C., January 8, 1993

MR. PRESIDENT:

The Council of Economic Advisers herewith submits its 1993 Annual Report in accordance with the provisions of the Employment Act of 1946 as amended by the Full Employment and Balanced Growth Act of 1978.

Sincerely,

Michael J. Boskin
Chairman

David F. Bradford
Member

Paul Wonnacott
Member

CONTENTS

11

LIST OF TABLES, CHARTS, AND BOXES

Charts

Boxes

18

CHAPTER 1

Perspectives on the Economy and Economic Policy

THE AMERICAN ECONOMY IS THE largest and most productive in the world. Not only does it have the highest per capita
levels of productivity and output of any industrialized country, but
even its modest growth in 1992 surpassed the performance of the
other major industrialized countries. The American economy faces
serious short-term problems and long-term challenges, however. As
past *Economic Reports* of this Administration have stated, the
Nation cannot take sustained, long-term economic growth for
granted. It must pursue wise economic policies that improve the
foundation and performance of the economy. *Such policies are by
nature limited but not passive.* Activist economic policy reforms can
greatly improve the performance of the American economy, laying
a better foundation for the economic growth that provides expanded employment opportunities, not just for new entrants into the
labor force but for those seeking upward economic mobility, a
higher standard of living, a richer legacy of prosperity for our children, the resources to help pay for nontraditional goods and services such as a healthy environment, and assurance that America's
economic and geopolitical leadership will extend into the next century.

Because the last 4 years have been so challenging to the American (indeed, to the world) economy and more recent economic performance has not been what Americans have come to expect, two
currents of opinion have gained currency, based on a lack of accurate information and faulty analysis. The first, which can be la-
belled "declinism," puts forth the notions that America has been in
substantial decline, that America is lagging behind its economic
competitors, that economic collapse is just around the corner, that
the United States is deindustrializing, or that foreigners will soon
own all (or at least too much) of America. These complaints cannot
survive a thorough scrutiny based on readily available factual information and sound economic analysis. To be sure, the American
economy does, indeed, face serious challenges, but it does so from a
position of great strength and with the tools and experience needed
to overcome them. On one point, however, the prophets of declin-

ism and the authors of this *Report* fully agree: the Nation cannot and should not take continued economic growth for granted.

The second current of opinion, which can be labeled "revisionism," uses the recent problems of the American economy to argue that the general changes in economic policy of the last 12 years have somehow been a calamitous mistake, responsible for all the problems in the economy and none of its remarkable achievements; indeed, the economy would have performed better if the policies of the 1960s and 1970s had been continued. Again, to be sure, policies of the last 12 years were far from perfectly implemented. But, on balance, economic policy since 1980 has been much superior to that of the late 1960s and the 1970s. And the performance of the economy, fairly evaluated, generally reflects that major improvement in policy direction.

THE DECLINISTS MEET THE FACTS

Contrary to the claims of the declinists, the United States remains the largest, richest, and most productive economy in the world. With less than 5 percent of the world's population, the Nation produces about a quarter of the world's total output of goods and services. The American economy is about 2½ times the size of the next largest economy, Japan. The average standard of living of Americans—as measured by gross domestic product (GDP) per capita—exceeds that of any other major industrialized country. Productivity, or output per worker, in the American economy is also higher than in these other nations.

While it is true that the fortunes of particular industries have ebbed and flowed, America is not deindustrializing. Total employment in manufacturing has fluctuated within a modest range depending on economic conditions since 1960. In fact, manufacturing's share of total economic output has been roughly constant for the last 30 years. *And the United States accounts for an even larger share of the industrial output of the countries of the Organization for Economic Cooperation and Development (OECD)—the 24 largest industrial market economies—than it did in 1970.*

Neither is America losing its overall competitive edge. The United States is the world's leading exporter; indeed, it is more internationally competitive than it has been in decades. From 1987 to 1991, exports rose from 8 to over 11 percent of GDP. This strong export performance prevented the recent recession from having a far greater negative impact on U.S. employment and has helped sustain the economy through a difficult period of sluggish economic growth. Although many U.S. manufacturers face stiff competition in markets with high volume and low profit margins, America has maintained its technological edge in areas that are allegedly at risk, including microprocessors, advanced telecommunications, and biotechnology.

Some declinists play on fears of foreign investment, in the same way that many West Europeans of the 1950s and 1960s played on fears of the American investment that helped rebuild their economies. These fears are unfounded. Foreign investment helps to build plants and equip workers, leading to higher productivity and improved standards of living. Increasing global integration and the general strength of the American economy are among the reasons for the long-term growth of foreign investment in the United States. Foreign investment is a sign of strength and future prospects, not a symptom of decline. In any event, foreign investment in the United States is a quite modest share of GDP relative to foreign investment in most other industrialized countries.

What about the recent problems of the American economy? (These problems are discussed in more detail in Chapters 2 and 3 of this *Report*.) No economic system is immune to disruption. Even well-functioning market economies run the risk of temporary setbacks due to external shocks, policy mistakes, or other disturbances. The American economy, which had already experienced a few quarters of slow growth, fell into a recession in the second half of 1990 that was shorter (8 months, compared with a postwar average of 11) and slightly less severe (output declined 2.2 percent relative to a postwar average of 2.8 percent; unemployment rose 2.8 percent, less than the postwar average of 3.4 percent) than other postwar recessions. More troubling was the anemic pace of the recovery that began in March 1991. Unfortunately, the Administration's prediction that this would be the slowest recovery since World War II proved to be correct. Growth was so sluggish, in fact, that job creation was insufficient to prevent unemployment from rising even months after the recovery had begun.

The declinists worry that America is losing the competitive economic race with Germany and Japan and perhaps with other countries as well. This argument must seem somewhat remarkable to the other major industrialized countries, which not only started out behind the United States in terms of productivity and per capita income but have experienced far more severe economic problems recently. The recessions in Canada and the United Kingdom were much steeper than the U.S. recession, with unemployment rising to over 10 percent. Germany and Japan entered recession in 1992, as the American economy was moving from anemic to modest growth. Inflation in some of these countries is still a serious concern, while inflation and interest rates are at their lowest levels in a generation in the United States.

The American economy still faces many challenges. To improve the prospects for long-term growth in productivity, primary and secondary education badly need improvement; legal, tax, and regulatory obstacles to entrepreneurship and business expansion must be removed; and expanding federal entitlement spending, which has contributed to large structural budget deficits, must be brought under control. But the view that the Nation is already in decline or must inevitably falter does not accord with the facts. The future is neither bleak nor predetermined, and America has the ability to solve the problems that lie ahead.

Basing policy on a faulty analysis of the economy's problems and prospects will not improve economic performance. The economy does not need answers to false problems. The declinists attribute the economy's alleged ills to fundamental flaws in the free market system. Their response to trade problems is protectionism or "managed trade," and they would solve the problems of particular industries with an industrial policy that mandates volumes of new government regulations; government subsidies; tax breaks; and new government spending on projects the private sector would eventually undertake itself if free to do so. These notions, while appealing to declinists, avoid the fundamental fact that private markets and an open trading system—not government regulation and subsidies—have been the fundamental source of the remarkable economic progress industrial nations have made in the postwar era.

The usual argument of the industrial policy proponents is that Japan's Ministry of International Trade and Industry (MITI), has been the driving force behind Japan's remarkable progress in the post-World War II era. MITI did play a powerful role in Japan's economic progress immediately after the war, but the country's success is attributable primarily to classic prescriptions: its high saving and investment rates and the hard work of its labor force. Indeed, MITI attempted to prevent SONY from entering the consumer electronic business. In each case, the Japanese firms sensibly avoided making what would have been very expensive mistakes, not just for themselves but for the Japanese economy.

In fact, there is no reason to believe that bureaucrats or politicians are better able than private individuals or firms to allocate resources to their most productive uses. In the United States, the Federal Government's Synfuels program of the early 1980s, which was terminated without ever producing a commerically viable product, offers a $3 billion example of the government's inability to second-guess the markets. Another classic example is the French and British Concorde SST, which became a multimillion dollar commercial flop and wasted taxpayers' resources in those countries. The very nations the declinists envy so much are currently moving away from heavy government intervention in the workings of the economy. Many of the more advanced social welfare states in Western Europe, including Sweden, France, and the United Kingdom, have, to various degrees, pulled back from their reliance on nationalized industry, outsized transfer payments systems, excessive bureaucratic regulation, and high rates of taxation.

In short, the declinists are wrong on the facts. America still has the largest and strongest economy in the world. It is neither deindustrializing, nor losing some overall economic competition with other countries. Although it can improve its competitive position in specific industries, America still enjoys the highest standard of living of the major industrialized countries. But again, the declinists and the authors of this *Report* agree on one point: The Nation cannot take continued economic growth for granted.

THE REVISIONISTS MEET THE FACTS

The second group of skeptics argues that the changes in economic policy most closely associated with the last 12 years (some of which actually began earlier) misdirected the American economy and led to its current problems. Economic policy in the last 12 years has aimed primarily at reducing inflation and maintaining it at low levels; restraining growth in regulation; lowering tax rates to restore incentives to produce income and wealth; controlling government spending and targeting it more effectively; expanding international trade; and providing for a strong national defense.

What is not generally understood is that this approach was a logical outcome of postwar U.S. economic history. Its policies did not entirely succeed but rather left a legacy of impressive accomplishments, as well as some notable failures and an important unfinished agenda.

The quarter century of rapid productivity growth that followed World War II led to substantial increases in living standards and wages for the American people. Most economists describe the rapid productivity growth of this period as extraordinary, far above the long-term trend. In part, this growth can be traced to the pent-up demand left over from the Great Depression and World War II; to opportunities to export and help rebuild war-ravaged nations, especially in Europe; and to the dissemination of major technological breakthroughs that had been promulgated during the war, from jet airplanes to communications.

With relatively low unemployment and inflation, rising productivity growth, and generally improving economic performance, America in the 1960s turned its attention to a variety of other concerns, including a noble, if controversial, attempt to improve the condition of the disadvantaged in society through substantial in-

23

creases in social welfare spending. In the last half of the 1960s and the first half of the 1970s the introduction of medicare and the vast expansion of Social Security benefits unrelated to need put in place a variety of forces that caused problems during this period, set in train serious problems for future government budgets, and created enormous controversy about the most appropriate way for the government to assist those in need.

The economy went through a series of profound changes and disruptive internal and external shocks throughout the 1960s and 1970s, including the Vietnam War, rising inflation coupled with stagnating growth, two significant oil price hikes, and a significant increase in government regulation and spending—as well as in the marginal tax rates facing ordinary American workers. By 1980 inflation had soared to double digits, and the Nation was caught in a sharp but brief recession.

The major goal of the 1980s and beyond was clearly to restore healthy, noninflationary economic growth. This objective required an economic environment with a rate of monetary expansion that was slower, more predictable, and more stable than it had been in the 1970s; reduced growth in government spending; and a concerted effort to remove those disincentives from the tax and regulatory systems that obstruct working, saving, investing, innovating, and entrepreneurship. In short, the economic objectives of the 1980s required a serious reorientation of monetary, fiscal, regulatory, and trade policies.

Deregulation did not just begin in the 1980s but had its roots in the Carter and, to some degree, the Ford Administration. However, social regulation—regulation of health, safety and the environment—expanded at an accelerating pace throughout the 1970s. With inflation at double digit levels, the Federal Reserve committed itself to a disinflationary policy in late 1979, and while the resulting disinflation was quite costly—the unemployment rate peaked at 10.8 percent in 1982—inflation rates dropped to the 4- to 5-percent range with a loss of output that was only about a third of what many economists and policymakers had predicted.

The tax system was dramatically reformed in 1981 to improve economic performance. Tax brackets were indexed for inflation and marginal tax rates reduced. Capital consumption allowances were accelerated, the investment tax credit was expanded, and universal individual retirement accounts were introduced. In 1986, a major tax reform was enacted with the idea of lowering marginal tax rates and broadening the tax base while removing special incentives. Unfortunately, the slowdown in depreciation, full taxation of capital gains, elimination of investment incentives, and some other specific changes (including a more onerous corporate alternative minimum tax) would prove to be major problems in the coming years. The tax reforms stabilized revenues as a share of GDP, while government expenditures rose relative to GDP. The budget deficit grew substantially to become a key focus of concern.

When the President took office in 1989, he faced many economic challenges, not the least of which was the prospect that the already large budget deficit would grow over time. Several attempts to control the Federal deficit had already been undertaken, such as the Gramm-Rudman-Hollings budget law. In 1990 the Congress passed and the President signed a set of comprehensive budget reforms, but these reforms were not sufficient to control growth in the largest and most rapidly expanding area of the budget—so-called entitlement spending for programs such as medicare and medicaid.

Some progress was made in slowing the growth of regulation, although perhaps the most important reform, the risk-based deposit insurance reform proposed by Vice President Bush's Task Force on Regulatory Relief, was not enacted. The intransigence on this issue would greatly aggravate the costs of cleaning up the savings and loan industry later on. Major new regulatory programs, such as the 1990 Clean Air Act Amendments and the Americans with Disabilities Act, while designed for the admirable purposes of creating a healthier environment and bringing the disabled into the mainstream of American life, were much costlier and more cumbersome than necessary. While some innovations were implemented to reduce the costs imposed by the amendments to the Clean Air Act, such as the emissions allowance trading program on sulfur dioxide, it became increasingly clear that such regulation would lead to substantial economic disruption. Budgetary constraints on direct government spending to achieve health, safety, and environmental goals led lawmakers to impose new and excessive regulations as an alternative.

The growth of regulation leads to litigation as various groups seek to have regulations overturned or recast by the courts. In fact, the courts have developed into a new economic policy forum for the interpretation of important rules and regulations. Regulatory advocates have emerged whose activities have distorted the original legislative intent of many programs, imposing heavy direct costs and increasing uncertainty about private investment decisions. The regulatory reform initiative implemented in the last year of the Bush Administration forcefully laid out the principles of sound regulation and carried out some reforms within the constraints of existing statutes. The regulatory system was finally pointed in the right direction. The reforms implemented during the first year of the moratorium indicate how great the rewards of a more sensible regulatory policy can be.

While the Administration was moving in the direction of a less economically disruptive regulatory policy, congressional micromanagement of the economy increased greatly. New regulation is but one example. More serious are new laws that increasingly prescribe the precise methods of achieving regulatory outcomes rather than allowing private firms and households greater flexibility to achieve the same results at far lower costs.

THE ECONOMY'S PERFORMANCE AFTER 1980

A major success of the economic policies of the past decade was the reduction of inflation to its lowest level in a generation. Inflation held remarkably steady (excluding an occasional run-up or collapse of energy prices) into the late 1980s. By then, however, incipient inflationary pressure was beginning to emerge. In a welcome break from previous policy, the Federal Reserve attempted to prevent a rise in inflation and, indeed, to reduce inflation further. This program of early intervention—the second round of disinflation of the 1980s—brought the inflation rate down to the 3-percent range that had prevailed during the 1950s and 1960s. This success augers well for future expansion. As discussed in Chapters 2 and 3 of this *Report* and in the last two *Economic Reports of the President*, however, the additional disinflation, which occurred during a time of adjustment to severe structural imbalances, and the oil shock resulting from the Gulf War ushered in a prolonged period of sluggish growth.

Partially in response to lower tax rates, the defense buildup, and reduced inflation in the early 1980s, the economy commenced the longest peacetime expansion in the Nation's history. While the 1981–82 recession had been deep, the recovery was exceptionally strong. Output grew by 3.9 percent in 1983 and 6.2 percent in 1984, the fastest rate since the 1950s. Between 1982 and 1990, the economy's growth averaged 3.3 percent per year. The expansion of the economy created 21 million additional jobs and 5 million new businesses. The rate of unemployment declined from its peak of 10.8 percent at the end of 1982 to 5.2 percent in June 1990, declining for all major industrial, occupational, and demographic categories.

These achievements were accompanied by serious strains—for example, friction in world trade, a buildup of household and corporate debt relative to income and profits, and budget deficits that were large for a prosperous peacetime—all of which threatened to impede future growth.

In addition to the remarkable growth in employment, several other labor market developments deserve particular note. Real labor compensation continued to grow slowly. The wage premium for highly skilled relative to younger, less educated workers rose substantially. The wage gap between men and women closed by one-fourth, and for the first time in recorded history unemployment rates were no worse for women than for men.

Productivity growth rebounded somewhat during the expansion of the 1980s from what it had been in the 1973–81 period, especially in manufacturing. There is strong evidence that the inability to separate out improvements in quality from true inflation in the price increases in the service sector have led to a systematic understatement of long-run productivity growth. Improving the Nation's productivity growth is the highest long-term economic priority— higher output per worker hour is *the* foundation of rising wages and living standards.

In summary, the change in the basic orientation of economic policy was exactly what was needed, given the economic problems of the period. However, while highly desirable, this change was imperfectly implemented. The biggest problem was the failure to control the growth of government spending. Second, while the lower marginal tax rates represented a significant achievement, an opportunity was missed in the 1986 Tax Act to continue the progress toward removing the tax impediments to saving, investment, and entrepreneurship that began in the late 1970s and was the hallmark of the 1981 Tax Act. Worse yet, the tax treatment of investment and entrepeneurship moved in the wrong direction, with deleterious consequences. Third, trade policy was disappointingly protectionist. Finally, insufficient progress was made in reforming regulation.

A more limited role for government, sound money, expanded world trade, reduced and more effective and efficient regulation, and lower tax rates were, and still are the correct thrust of economic policy and were partially responsible for the fact that the economy performed much better in the last decade than it did in the 1970s. Even the deep recession of 1981–82 was a consequence of the disinflation made necessary by the policies of the 1970s, which had led to double-digit inflation. But numerous problems remain. This course of policy was enacted imperfectly, and some parts not at all. New problems emerged and some old problems persisted.

THE REAL ECONOMIC PROBLEMS

The American economy is neither in long-term decline nor short-term contraction. It is emerging slowly from a period of sluggish growth and a short, about average, recession after the longest peacetime expansion in history. But it does face serious problems and challenges.

The fundamental challenge facing the American economy is the slowdown in the rate of productivity growth, which began in the late 1960s and worsened in the early 1970s. Even small differences in the rate of productivity growth compounded over long periods of time can lead to dramatic differences in future standards of living.

With its productivity growing half a percentage point less rapidly than that of the United States, the United Kingdom went from the highest standard of living in the world in the late 19th century to a standard of living only two-thirds that of the United States today. Such is the power of compounding. Simply put, raising the rate of productivity growth is essential to raising income per capita and is the foundation of rising real wages. To lay the foundations for higher and more sustained productivity growth, the following issues must be addressed.

First, a highly skilled labor force is essential to America's future. The deplorable state of public elementary and secondary education in the United States is perhaps the Achilles' heel of America's economic future. Our future labor force first acquires knowledge and skills, or at least the foundation upon which future knowledge and skills must be based, in the schools. On international test after international test, America's students do not stack up well. They will not be able to earn as much as or more than their peers tomorrow if they do not learn as much as or more than their peers today.

Second, the Nation saves and invests too little. A higher rate of capital formation and more efficient capital allocation are essential to raising labor productivity. The Nation's tax, regulatory, and legal systems, as they now stand, pose severe obstacles to a more efficient and higher rate of capital formation. There is also legitimate concern about the appropriate role of government in financing public investment, such as infrastructure and research and development. The economic criteria that should be used to determine the appropriate role of government are straightforward: there is a role for government when there are investments that the private sector will not undertake, perhaps because individual firms cannot fully appropriate the returns to making them, and when the benefits to society are likely to outweigh the costs of the investment.

Third, throughout history, the expansion of international trade has increased the pace of world economic growth and the contraction of international trade has led to worldwide contractions, most notably the Great Depression. After several successful rounds of tariff reductions in the General Agreement on Tariffs and Trade (GATT), new forms of trade barriers and problems—bilateral, regional, and multilateral—have emerged. Expanding world trade and opening trade and investment markets worldwide will be enormously important to the future economic growth of the American and world economies. Opportunities are substantial, but difficult political obstacles remain.

After the need to raise productivity growth, a second major problem is the sluggish short-term performance of the economy and the inadequate pace of job creation. The economy has been through several challenging years. While heightened concern during a period of slow growth is understandable, the 1990–91 recession must be placed in historical perspective. There have been nine recessions in the United States since World War II, and each downturn has been followed by a phase of renewed growth. It appears now that the economy is emerging from a period of sluggishness to a period of modest, self-sustaining growth.

An unusual confluence of forces, including the delayed effect of the tight monetary policy pursued in 1988 and 1989 (which was designed to head off an incipient rise in inflation), the oil price shock related to the Gulf War, the credit crunch, the problems in financial institutions, the overbuilding in commercial real estate (worsened by the credit crunch and the wild swings in the tax rules), the fiscal imbalances, and the substantial current and prospective defense downsizing all hit the economy in a relatively short period of time. These events occurred during a worldwide slowdown among the industrialized countries, slowing America's export boom.

While the consolidation and transition were painful, and earlier economic policy might well have been somewhat more aggressive in dealing with the short-term problems, unless the economy falters badly in its current or prospective state, fiscal and monetary policy should be directed primarily by the long-term goal of enhancing noninflationary economic growth. If the economy falters badly, and unemployment rises or appears likely to do so, it would be wise to combine any short-term fiscal stimulus with simultaneously enacted long-term spending cuts to reduce future budget deficits. This strategy would help allay fears in financial markets and decrease the likelihood that a rise in interest rates would offset much of the benefit from short-term fiscal stimulus. It would also help promote long-term investment. Monetary policy, now that it has achieved the lowest inflation rates in a generation and broken the previous cycle of ever-higher inflation at corresponding stages of successive expansions, should be directed toward maintaining low and stable inflation while providing sufficient money and credit to support economic expansion. *The last thing the economy needs after having gone through two rounds of disinflation—the first in the early 1980s and the second in the early 1990s—is excessive money growth that would rekindle inflation and a return to the boom/bust cycles of the 1970s.*

A third major problem confronting America is the economic condition of the disadvantaged. For several decades the rate of economic growth greatly reduced the poverty rate. But a combination of demographic, social, economic, and policy factors has led to a situation where many Americans have little opportunity or incentive to improve their condition and have a standard of living far below that of most Americans. As noted in previous *Economic Reports*, economic growth is essential to provide rising employment opportu-

29

nities for new entrants into the labor force and those seeking upward economic mobility. But economic growth, by itself, will not be sufficient to make major inroads in the poverty rate in the United States.

Fourth, the Nation's health care system costs too much and fails to insure too many Americans. Because of its importance to both the economy and the welfare of all citizens, problems in the health care system pose a special threat to future increases in income and living standards. While Americans enjoy rising life expectancies and probably the highest quality of health care in the world, health care expenditures, which now account for one-eighth of the economy, are rising rapidly. Estimates suggest that one out of every seven or eight Americans is not covered by health insurance. The system of health insurance and third-party payment and the lack of incentives to use health services wisely are only a few of the factors that are driving up health care costs. Chapter 4 of this *Report* describes these issues and proposed solutions in far greater detail.

In summary, the economy has short-term problems and long-term challenges. Each of these is discussed in much more detail in subsequent chapters in this *Report*, and each is amenable to policy reforms that would greatly strengthen the American economy.

AGENDA FOR REFORM

In order to surmount the challenges, solve the problems, and take advantage of the opportunities confronting the American economy, government policy in numerous areas needs to be reformed. Successful implementation of this reform agenda would greatly enhance the prospects for a stronger economy, higher living standards, and greater economic and social mobility for the disadvantaged. It is an activist agenda, but one that points to more limited government. This is far from a contradiction. The private sector of the economy is where most of the jobs are created and income earned. Sometimes the government can play an effective role in dealing with problems, but too often in the past the government has overplayed that role, creating costly, ineffective, inefficient bureaucracies and unnecessarily wasteful spending. The answer is not to let the existing programs continue indefinitely, nor is it always to eliminate government involvement. It is to seek reform based on sound economic principles in a primarily pluralistic democratic capitalist and federal system, consistent with individual initiative, freedoms, and responsibilities.

A comprehensive agenda for reform has been presented during the course of the Bush Administration. Some of the reforms had their roots in proposals made during the Reagan Administration, while others were entirely new. The President was able to implement some of them unilaterally; some of them were partially adopted by the Congress; and others the Congress refused to enact, at least in a form acceptable to the President. The appropriate though limited role for government in improving the foundations and performance of the economy includes, in addition to maintaining a sound monetary system with low and stable inflation:

FISCAL REFORM

- *Removing Tax Penalties on Saving, Investment, and Entrepreneurship.* Despite the substantial and desirable reduction in marginal tax rates achieved in the 1986 Tax Reform, disincentives to saving, investment, and entrepreneurship in the current tax system were worsened. Restoring tax incentives, such as a capital gains differential, more neutral capital cost recovery or other investment incentives, and elimination of the double taxation of saving, should be a high priority. Further, this could be accomplished either by reforming the income tax or by moving to a consumed income tax, as discussed in Chapter 6. It should be done in the context of tax simplification. The corporate tax also ought to be explicitly or implicitly integrated with the personal tax to eliminate the double taxation of corporate source income, reduce the bias favoring debt as opposed to equity finance, and restore investment incentives. Further, the corporate alternative minimum tax, which was greatly expanded in 1986, should be substantially reformed or repealed.
- *Limiting and Redirecting Growth of Federal Government Spending.* Bringing the budget under control requires limiting the growth of the mandatory spending that forms the bulk of the budget. This will mean a substantial reduction in the growth of entitlements, especially for health care. The best place to start would be with entitlement payments to well-off individuals. It is also desirable to continue to reorient spending to productive investment in infrastructure and research and development.
- *Reforming the Budget Process.* A good start would be giving the President a line-item veto.

TRADE LIBERALIZATION

- *NAFTA.* The North American Free Trade Agreement (NAFTA) offers the opportunity to create a more prosperous and stable Western Hemisphere. It should be adopted by the respective legislatures as rapidly as possible. It will be phased in over many years, so the fear of economic dislocation is greatly exaggerated.

31

- *Completing the Uruguay Round.* To bring the Uruguay Round of GATT to a successful conclusion remains essential to advancing U.S. and global economic prosperity. (Each of these is discussed in more detail in Chapter 7.)

REGULATORY REFORM

- *Utilizing Market Incentives.* Wherever possible, command-and-control approaches that prescribe particular ways of meeting the objectives of regulation should be replaced by performance standards allowing far greater flexibility to workers, firms, and consumers to meet sensibly chosen standards.
- *Reform Risk Assessment and Management.* There needs to be a fundamental reexamination and reform of the Federal Government's risk assessment and risk management systems. Current procedures result in biased estimates of risk and in uneven standards of risk minimization, with unrealistically strict requirements in some areas and missed opportunities for major reductions in risk in others.

EDUCATION REFORM

- *School Choice.* Low- and middle-income families should be given the opportunity to send their children to schools of their choice, whether public or private. School choice will create competition, forcing schools to improve their quality in order to attract students, in much the same manner as do American universities, which are the best in the world.
- *National Educational Standards.* Families and educators need objective, widely accepted standards that define children's skill levels in key areas. Without such standards in place, it is impossible to evaluate the quality of schools or assess children's academic performance.

HEALTH CARE REFORM

- *Improving Access to Health Care.* Reforms are needed to provide insurance to low-income people. The best way to do this is to provide them with tax credits tied to the purchase of health insurance to enable them to choose among the options available in the health care market.
- *Pooling Health Risks.* To lower the cost of health care for those with chronic illnesses, it is important to pool risks among the healthy and the chronically ill. Risk pooling should be accomplished through the use of health risk adjusters and not through mechanisms that discourage insurers from providing insurance to those in poor health.
- *Access to Health Insurance for Employees in Small Businesses.* Regulatory reform is needed to enable small businesses to gain

access to the health insurance market and to reduce the cost of this insurance. Small businesses should be encouraged to pool their health insurance buying power and should be made exempt from state benefit mandates and premium taxes.

• *Malpractice reform.* The malpractice litigation crisis must be ended and the system overhauled. Litigation over medical malpractice raises costs directly and encourages the practice of costly defensive medicine.

EMPOWERING THE DISADVANTAGED

• *Enterprise Zones.* To improve the employment opportunities of the disadvantaged in distressed urban and rural communities, enterprise zones should be created. Businesses locating within the enterprise zone would be eligible for a tax incentive to encourage employment of low-income residents.

• *Weed and Seed.* To control violent crime, and to provide social and economic support to areas where high crime rates and social ills are prevalent, neighborhoods should be given assistance through job training, drug treatment and prevention, and educational activities.

• *Housing and Homeownership.* Reforms are needed to increase the possibilities for low-income families to own their own homes in order to have a stake in their communities.

CONCLUSION

Continuing the activist, appropriate, but limited governmental role demonstrated by the Bush Administration is the proper basis of economic policy for the 1990s and beyond. Such a role will foster the spirit of vitality, creativity, productivity, and resourcefulness that has so often described America and its accomplishments in the past. The major need is for a steady, coherent, coordinated, long-term policy framework.

Without abandoning government's substantial accomplishments, such as greatly mitigating the economic distress attributable to unemployment and poverty, government spending must be made much more cost conscious and target effective. Without deluding themselves about the prospects of instantly promoting the rate of economic growth, policymakers must unravel the disincentives for capital formation and new business creation that government regulatory and tax policies have created. Without forgetting the genuine needs for greater health, safety, and environmental protection, Americans must begin to clean up the regulatory morass that hinders the country's economic progress. Without ignoring important national interests, America must resist the lure of protectionism and managed trade and complete the work of liberalizing trade throughout the world. Without neglecting the fact that markets sometimes do not work perfectly, it must be recognized that this is the exception and not the rule, and that governments often fail to improve on imperfect market outcomes.

America's economic success sends an important message that free political institutions, free markets, and economic progress are linked. Responding to economic challenges to enhance the Nation's long-term economic growth in an open world trading system is the single most important thing Americans can do to ensure the prosperity of future generations and influence decisively the evolution of many of the world's economic and political systems toward democratic capitalism.

CHAPTER 2

Recent Developments and the Economic Outlook

OVER THE LAST SEVERAL years, the U.S. economy has been struggling through a period of consolidation and transition. In addition to the oil price shock in the second half of 1990, various structural relationships and imbalances contributed to the recession and the sluggish economic performance including defense downsizing; a boom-bust cycle in commercial real estate aggravated by wide swings in the tax laws and bank regulation; credit market constraints resulting from the balance sheet, capital, and regulatory difficulties that financial institutions faced; and a buildup in corporate debt relative to profits and household debt relative to income. The working off of these imbalances added to the economy's cyclical difficulties. Changing demographic trends that have slowed the underlying rate of household formation and the more recent trend toward corporate downsizing also have played a role in slowing the economy. The sluggish economic performance has not been confined to the United States: In recent years, Australia, Canada, and the United Kingdom have been in recession, and Japan and Germany entered recession during 1992. Other European countries are verging on recession. Although some countries are adopting policies to help stimulate their economies, the general slowdown in the international economy will act as a drag on U.S. exports and growth for some time.

As the Nation's economic difficulties are resolved—as the drag associated with corporate and household indebtedness is reduced; banks improve their capital position, become less cautious about lending, and face a more-balanced regulatory environment; the adjustment to defense cuts progresses; and the supply of developed real estate is brought into balance with demand—conditions for a stronger, sustained expansion are being laid. Other developments that promise to enhance the prospects for a sustained expansion include low and stable inflation, low interest rates, and rising productivity. Interest rates and core inflation—consumer price inflation excluding the volatile food and energy components—are at their lowest levels in a generation.

In the late 1970s, inflation climbed to disturbing double-digit levels, exceeding 13 percent during 1979 and 12 percent during

35

1980. Inflation imposed a heavy burden on the economy, complicating saving and investment decisions and adding to the economic uncertainties that many Americans faced. Additionally, because tax brackets were not indexed for inflation at that time, increases in nominal income that barely kept pace with inflation automatically pushed taxpayers into higher tax brackets. The severe recession that followed in the early 1980s, the country's worst economic performance since World War II, was largely a direct consequence of the disinflation policies—in particular tight monetary policy—that successfully reduced inflation from the double-digit levels of 1979–80 to less than 4 percent in 1982. Inflation remained in the 4- to 5-percent range for the rest of the decade. While the recession of the early 1980s was deep, the loss of output was not nearly as severe as many economists had predicted it would have to be in order to achieve such a sharp reduction in inflation.

The lower rate of inflation was a significant improvement, and the economy grew strongly, producing over 21 million new jobs between 1982 and 1990. But concern mounted that progress toward lower inflation had stalled. It seemed that a rate of 4 to 5 percent might be a new floor below which inflation would be unlikely to fall. In the early 1970s, such rates of inflation had been considered unacceptably high; in response to such rates, the Nixon Administration imposed wage and price controls to bring inflation down, in what proved to be an unsuccessful effort with costly side effects. In the late 1980s, as the economy continued to expand and the unemployment rate fell to its lowest level in 15 years, incipient inflationary pressures raised fears of a resurgence in inflation. This raised the possibility of another round of rapidly accelerating inflation—and the costly efforts required to fight it—much like the severe events of the late 1970s.

The Federal Reserve was determined to avoid the mistakes of the past and to act before a new inflationary spiral developed. In order to prevent a substantial increase in inflation and to resume the progress toward lower inflation that had begun early in the decade, the Federal Reserve pursued a strategy that tightened monetary policy gradually in an attempt to contain the growth of nominal output and reduce inflation without causing an actual decline in real output. This has sometimes been called a "soft-landing" strategy. Short-term interest rates rose from about 7 percent in early 1988 to about 10 percent in early 1989. By acting in a timely manner with forward-looking monetary policies, the Federal Reserve improved the prospects for a reduction in inflation without a costly economic downturn.

As growth slowed in 1989 and early 1990, the Federal Reserve began gradually lowering interest rates as evidence of poor economic performance and lower inflationary pressures accumulated.

36

Interest rates fell gradually from the spring of 1989 until the beginning of 1990. In the last quarter of 1990, after it was evident that the economy had indeed entered a recession, the Federal Reserve became more aggressive in lowering interest rates, which continued to fall through 1991 and much of 1992. During this period, the reserves of banks and other depository institutions grew substantially. However, the broader money supply measures grew at surprisingly low rates and appeared largely unresponsive to increases in bank reserves and reductions in short-term interest rates (Chapter 3). Moreover, the economy did not respond to the decline in interest rates as rapidly or as strongly as the Federal Reserve and many private observers had anticipated.

The soft-landing strategy involved inevitable risks because it slowed aggregate demand growth and made the economy more vulnerable to potential adverse developments. This strategy might have worked if large shocks and other unforeseen factors depressing economic activity had not emerged or if the drag they exerted on the economy had been readily observable and easily offset by changes in policy. However, policies are always conducted in an uncertain environment, and it takes time to recognize problems and implement policies—and for those policies to take effect.

At the time the various problems facing the economy began to emerge, it was difficult to determine their severity or the kind of stimulus that would be required to offset them without reversing progress toward lower inflation. With the benefit of hindsight, a more rapid reduction in interest rates might have reduced the downward pressures on output and contributed to a healthier recovery without reviving inflationary pressures—although the progress in reducing inflation could have been slowed. In any event, too much reliance was placed on monetary policy, and the economy would have benefited from fiscal stimulus (primarily tax incentives), regulatory relief, and policies oriented toward trade expansion.

If the soft-landing strategy failed to avert a recession as a result of unexpected events, the strategy was highly successful in reestablishing progress toward lower inflation. The rate of core inflation declined from 5.2 percent during 1990 to about 3.5 percent during 1992. Following the decline of inflation from the double-digit levels of the late 1970s to the 4- to 5-percent range in the mid- to late-1980s, the more recent decline represents the second round of a long-term disinflation effort started over a decade ago. The current low and stable inflation rate means that households will be able to save with reduced concern that inflation will erode the purchasing power of their nominal assets, while businesses will be able to commit themselves to long-term projects with less uncertainty that inflation might render their investments unprofitable. As a result of reduced inflationary pressures and the credibility the Federal Reserve has gained from its inflation fight, the economy may be spared the need for the policy reversals—so prevalent from the late 1960s through the early 1980s—that resulted in the upward ratcheting of inflation and wide swings in output and employment.

During the recent period of disinflation, the U.S. economy has gone through several fairly distinct phases: a period of slow growth starting in early 1989 and continuing through the first half of 1990; a recession for the next three quarters, with real gross domestic product (GDP) falling a total of 2.2 percent; and three quarters of very sluggish recovery, with real GDP growing about 1.2 percent at an annual rate. During 1992, the U.S. economy remained in a modest and uneven recovery, with the rate of growth picking up to the 2.5- to 3-percent range.

Last year's Administration forecast correctly predicted that, by historical standards, the economy would grow at a quite modest pace during 1992. Through the middle of the year, employment and income growth remained sluggish, and consumer and business confidence were low. Export growth slowed, restricting what had been a source of strength for the U.S. economy for many years. However, by midyear the outlook began to improve as unemployment began a gradual decline, nonfarm payrolls began to edge up, income growth picked up, and consumer and business confidence stabilized and then began to rise.

The current Administration forecast predicts that real GDP will grow about 3 percent during 1993. Growth is expected to continue in the 3-percent range through the mid-1990s. Sustained growth will require, among other things, a fiscal policy oriented toward spending restraints to reduce the structural budget deficit over time and tax incentives that enhance growth, a monetary policy that provides sufficient growth in money and credit to sustain the expansion while maintaining low inflation, regulatory reform that provides greater room for the use of market incentives to minimize the negative impacts of regulation on economic growth, and trade policies that succeed in opening markets worldwide and in supporting growth in the international economy.

The unemployment rate is expected to decline slowly but steadily during 1993, averaging 6.9 percent for the year (compared with 7.4 percent for 1992) and to continue its slow decline through the mid-1990s. Inflation likely will remain low in 1993 and in coming years, with consumer prices rising in the range of about 3 percent per year. With moderate growth and low inflation, short-term interest rates are expected to remain low in 1993, and long-term interest rates are expected to decline. In coming years, short-term rates are likely to increase slightly as the economy continues to expand, and long-term rates are expected to stabilize as inflation remains low.

However, the outlook for interest rates in general and long-term rates in particular depends on fiscal and monetary policies. Policies that would lead to higher spending and deficits or higher inflation, relative to what is currently expected, could boost long-term interest rates and retard economic growth in the future.

The economy is expected to improve in coming years. But challenges remain. Short-term cyclical performance remains uncertain, various structural imbalances have yet to be worked out, and a high rate of productivity growth must be maintained to sustain increases in Americans' living standards. Of the various short-term cyclical concerns that remain, the most important center on the need for improved employment prospects and the related bolstering of consumer confidence. Corporate restructuring and military downsizing are significant structural adjustments that could hamper job growth.

This Administration has recognized throughout its term, and stated explicitly in each of its previous *Economic Reports*, that *the Nation faces serious economic challenges and cannot take economic growth for granted.* The Administration's policies and policy proposals have been designed to support sustained increases in the Nation's standard of living by raising long-term productivity growth while boosting the job base. Unfortunately, the Congress did not enact many of the Administration's key growth proposals in an acceptable form. Included in these proposals were pro-growth fiscal measures designed to enhance incentives for entrepreneurship, saving, and investment and to increase economic growth, as well as spending controls aimed at reducing the multiyear structural budget deficit. This Administration also has promoted a trade policy designed to open markets worldwide, contributing to more vigorous growth, and pursued regulatory reforms to reduce unnecessary burdens on businesses and consumers.

The Nation has been through difficult economic times over the past several years, but despite these difficulties, the U.S. economy remains the strongest and most resilient in the world. The recovery from the recent recession has been slow and protracted, but the performance of the economy during the last 4 years has not been uniformly weak. Broad-based, readily available information does not support the argument that the country's recent economic performance has been the worst since World War II. Economic conditions, including inflation, interest rates, unemployment, and real growth, have been better during the past 4 years than they were during the 1978–82 period. Core inflation and interest rates are now at their lowest levels in a generation, well below the double-digit rates that prevailed 12 years ago. At its recent peak the unemployment rate was 7.7 percent, considerably lower than the peak of nearly 11 percent in the early 1980s and the 9-percent peak during the 1973–75 recession. And in terms of real GDP and income, the slow growth of the past 4 years still exceeds the average growth from 1978 to 1982.

The soaring inflation and interest rates of the late 1970s condemned the U.S. economy to years of declining output, falling incomes, and rising unemployment. Yet these adjustments, painful as they were, set the stage for the sustained expansion of the 1980s. For the last several years, the economy has been going through a similar but much less severe period of consolidation and transition, with structural adjustments and disinflation restricting economic growth. This period once again has meant substantial hardship for millions of Americans. But the numerous structural adjustments of recent years have been laying the basis for a solid, sustained expansion in the 1990s. As the drag associated with household and corporate indebtedness is reduced, consumer spending and investment in plant and equipment will increase. As banks improve their balance sheet positions and banking regulation and supervision become more balanced, credit conditions will improve. Over time, shifting resources from defense to civilian industries will strengthen the private economy and provide new employment opportunities. Enhanced productivity already has boosted the Nation's competitive position in international markets, and low and stable inflation will reduce the need for policies that could restrict future growth. Together, these factors will help create a strong, sustainable recovery, more jobs, and higher incomes in years to come.

AN OVERVIEW OF THE ECONOMY IN 1992

The pattern of real GDP growth reveals the slow and uneven nature of the economy's recent performance (Chart 2-1). The recession of 1990–91 ended in March 1991, following 8 months of decline (Box 2-1). Beginning with the second quarter of 1991, real GDP grew for six consecutive quarters, although growth averaged only 2 percent at an annual rate. Furthermore, the pattern of growth was uneven. During the final three quarters of 1991, the pace of recovery was particularly slow; in the fourth quarter of 1991, the economy was essentially flat, with real GDP increasing at only a 0.6-percent annual rate. During the first three quarters of 1992, the economy grew at a stronger pace, but still well below the average for previous recoveries.

Uneven growth during a recovery is not unusual. Indeed, every previous postwar recovery has shown a "saw-tooth" growth pattern with weaker quarters following, or sandwiched between, stronger quarters. The underlying growth rate was low for much of 1991 and 1992—too low, in fact, to increase employment appreciably. While real GDP increased for six consecutive quarters after its

40

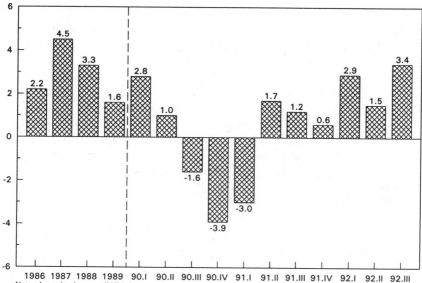

Chart 2-1 **Real Gross Domestic Product Growth**
Real GDP has grown for six consecutive quarters, following three quarters of decline during the recession.

Percent change

Note: Annual values are IV/IV change. Quarterly values are seasonally adjusted at an annual rate.
Source: Department of Commerce.

trough in the first quarter of 1991, the unemployment rate increased by 1.2 percentage points, reaching an 8-year high of 7.7 percent in June 1992 before trending down for the remainder of the year (Chart 2–2). Nonfarm payroll employment remained almost flat after the recession ended, declining slightly in late 1991 and early 1992, before growing slowly through the end of 1992 (Chart 2–3).

EARLY IMPROVEMENT

The economy picked up in the first quarter of 1992, with real GDP expanding at an annual rate of 2.9 percent—the strongest growth in 3 years. Real consumer spending posted its best quarterly performance in over 5 years, rising 5.1 percent at an annual rate. Real final sales—real GDP less the change in business inventories, a measure of aggregate demand in the economy—rose at an annual rate of 4.7 percent in the first quarter. Real per capita disposable personal income also increased, recording its largest gain in 2 years. Consumer confidence, as measured by the Conference Board's Consumer Confidence Survey, reached an 18-year low early in the year but then rose more than 50 percent through the spring

41

Box 2-1.—Recessions and Business Cycle Dating

For the past year and a half the question of whether the economy has been in a slow recovery or has continued in recession has been hotly debated. The National Bureau of Economic Research (NBER), a private economic research organization, is the official arbiter determining the beginning and ending dates for recessions and expansions—the turning points of the business cycle. In late December 1992, the NBER Business Cycle Dating Committee determined that the recession that began in July 1990 ended in March 1991, indicating the recession lasted only 8 months.

During a recession, the economy is in a decline of significant depth, duration, and diffusion (that is, spread across various industries and sectors); during a recovery it regains the output lost during the recession. A recovery is typically followed by a sustained expansion. To say that the recession ended in March 1991 does not mean that the economy was doing well after that date; rather, it means that the period of decline had ended and output had begun to increase. The recovery was complete by the third quarter of 1992, when real GDP climbed above the prerecession peak of the second quarter of 1990.

Key economic variables must be examined to determine the beginning or end of a recession. The components of the Department of Commerce's index of coincident indicators—nonfarm payroll employment, industrial production, real personal income less transfer payments, and real manufacturing and trade sales—generally serve that purpose well. Industrial production and real manufacturing and trade sales hit their low point in early 1991. Real personal income less transfer payments and nonfarm payroll employment also reached their initial lows in early 1991 but then flattened out, even dipping slightly in late 1991 and early 1992.

The debate also was clouded somewhat by the methodology used to construct the index of coincident indicators. This methodology results in a downward bias that would generate a declining index even if the economy were growing very slowly. The Department of Commerce has begun publishing an alternative coincident index based on revised methodology that shows a trough—the low point in economic activity—in March 1991, a result consistent with the NBER dating of the end of the recession.

(Chart 2-4). Civilian employment and labor force participation—the percentage of the working-age population working or actively seek-

Chart 2-2 Civilian Unemployment Rate

The unemployment rate fell steadily during the second half of 1992. The recent peak of 7.7 percent in June 1992 was well below the 10.8 percent peak following the 1981-82 recession.

Percent

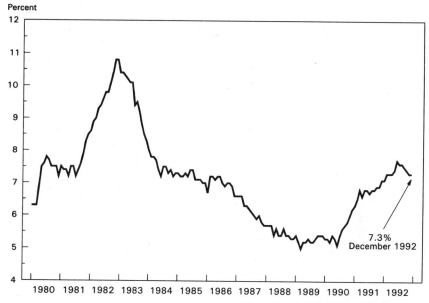

Source: Department of Labor.

Chart 2-3 Nonfarm Payroll Employment

Nonfarm payroll employment grew slowly during 1992, after being stagnant for much of 1991 following the recession.

Thousands

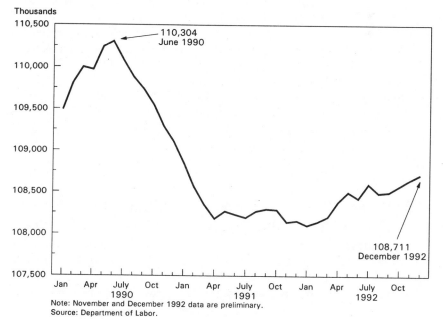

Note: November and December 1992 data are preliminary.
Source: Department of Labor.

43

ing work—rose as the economy appeared to be moving into a sustainable recovery and job prospects appeared brighter. After-tax corporate profits surged nearly 11 percent in the first quarter, the largest increase in 4 years.

Chart 2-4 **Consumer Confidence**
Consumer confidence has been extremely volatile over the last 2 years, turning up again in the final months of 1992.

Index, 1985 = 100

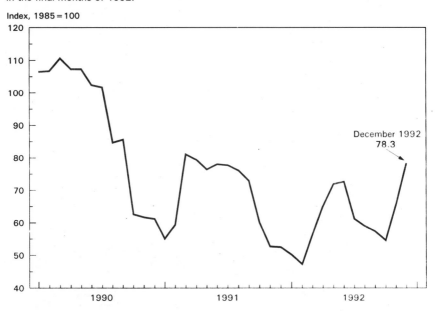

Source: The Conference Board.

Other indicators also pointed to an improved economic outlook in early 1992. Lower mortgage rates helped boost housing construction, with housing starts surging 20 percent over the first 3 months of the year. Orders for durable goods rose 7.4 percent between December 1991 and April 1992, and industrial production—the output of the Nation's factories, mines, and utilities—rose 2.2 percent between January and May. The improved economic outlook was reflected in five consecutive monthly increases in the index of leading indicators, a measure designed to predict the economy's short-term performance.

MIXED PERFORMANCE AND UNCERTAINTY

Growth slowed after the initial surge, and the economy expanded at a modest 1.5-percent annual rate in the second quarter. Real final sales declined slightly in the second quarter, indicating that aggregate demand was weak. Hence, the change in inventory investment more than accounted for the growth in the economy in

44

the second quarter. Inventory investment often increases significantly and adds to growth during recovery periods as firms increase stocks in anticipation of increased sales. However, in the recent recovery, better management of inventories coupled with slow and uneven demand led businesses to be more efficient and, at the same time, more cautious in managing inventories. In such an environment, the degree to which inventory accumulation is due to lower-than-expected demand—and is therefore undesired—and the degree to which it is a desired buildup in anticipation of increased sales remain unclear.

The final expenditure components of real GDP—consumption, investment, government purchases, and net exports (exports of goods and services minus imports of goods and services)—showed uneven performance in the second quarter. Consumer spending stalled. Fixed investment increased strongly, with spending for producers' durable equipment and residential investment showing solid gains. Government purchases declined slightly. Net exports fell significantly as imports rose and exports declined slightly. The deterioration in net exports in the second quarter had a significant negative effect on real GDP, directly reducing the annual growth rate by 1.8 percentage points.

Consumer confidence also began to fall again in the middle of the year. Although mortgage rates remained low compared to earlier years, they moved up somewhat from their January low, and housing starts and housing sales fell back after their earlier surge. New orders for durable goods, retail sales, industrial production, and the index of leading indicators flattened out.

The lack of significant improvement in the labor market was a particularly important factor underlying the continued sluggish performance of the economy throughout 1992. While employment rose in the first half of the year, too few jobs were created to absorb the increased number of job seekers. As a result, the unemployment rate rose from 7.1 percent in January to 7.7 percent in June, as the number of unemployed persons rose from just under 9 million to nearly 10 million. The optimism of the first few months of the year was replaced with pessimism as employment prospects stagnated.

The weak labor markets reflect, in part, increases in efficiency. The strong performance of corporate profits noted earlier reflected vigorous cost-cutting efforts that often involved layoffs or restricted hiring in response to slow growth in aggregate demand. While such cost-cutting measures may help boost productivity and profits and, eventually, strengthen the economy, they also contribute initially to sluggish labor markets and slow income growth for a large proportion of households.

Because sustained income gains are the basis for continued growth in consumption, the immediate effect of sluggish performance in the labor market, with the accompanying reduced prospects for income gains, is decreased prospects for a pickup in spending. Wages and salaries and "other" labor income—primarily employer contributions to private pension and welfare funds—account for nearly two-thirds of all personal income. From March 1991 through September 1992, aggregate weekly hours worked by private nonagricultural production workers were essential flat, increasing only 0.3 percent, and real average gross hourly earnings for private nonagricultural workers actually fell, decreasing 0.7 percent. Total real wages and salaries rose less than 1 percent over the same period. Because consumer spending accounts for two-thirds of the spending stream constituting GDP, its growth is crucial to a sustained economic expansion.

SECOND-HALF REVIVAL

The economy revived in the second half of the year, with real GDP growing at a 3.4-percent annual rate in the third quarter, the highest rate in over 3½ years. The performance of the major components of real GDP shows that the revival was broad based in the domestic economy. Consumer expenditures rose at an annual rate of 3.7 percent, with solid contributions from increased spending on services and both durable and nondurable goods. Investment spending also made a significant contribution to third-quarter growth, rising at an annual rate of 6.5 percent as producers increased purchases of durable equipment and inventories surged, offsetting a decline in spending on structures. Government purchases more than made up for the second-quarter decline, rising at a 3.8-percent annual rate. The only major component to have a negative effect on growth was net exports, which continued to decline because of an increase in imports that more than offset an increase in exports. Commerce Department estimates for the fourth quarter had not been released when this *Report* was written. Initial data and private forecasts indicate that real GDP likely continued to grow at a moderate pace in the fourth quarter, supported primarily by a further large increase in consumer spending.

In the second half of the year, various indicators pointed to an improving economy. Retail sales climbed steadily. Consumer confidence declined slowly into the fall but then rose strongly in the final months of the year. After having slipped back in the summer, housing starts increased into the fall. New orders for durable goods and industrial production picked up. Initial claims for unemployment insurance trended down and by the end of the year had reached their lowest level in over 3½ years. The index of leading indicators increased in the fall after having been flat during the summer.

SPECIAL FACTORS—HURRICANES

The effects of Hurricanes Andrew and Iniki were among the most important of the special factors affecting the economy in 1992. In August, Hurricane Andrew swept across southern Florida, the Gulf of Mexico, and into Louisiana, causing enormous damage. In September, Hurricane Iniki struck Hawaii. Department of Commerce estimates show that Hurricane Andrew destroyed or severely damaged over 100,000 private residences, Hurricane Iniki over 6,500. Insurance covered three-fourths of the more than $9.1 billion in residential property losses, one-half of the $1.2 billion in proprietors' property losses, and four-fifths of the $3.5 billion in corporate property losses. Hence, total property loss was nearly $14 billion, of which about three-fourths was covered by insurance. Hurricane Andrew also disrupted several major industries—oil and gas extraction, petroleum refining, and petrochemicals—contributing to a reduction in industrial production. The hurricanes also initially reduced personal income through lost wages, uninsured losses of personal and business property, and crop damage. The cost of benefit payments made by insurance companies had a significant negative effect on corporate profits in the third quarter.

Ironically, the subsequent rebuilding and new purchases resulting from the hurricanes will have a net positive effect on real GDP. GDP measures production, not the stock of wealth or capital. While the hurricanes destroyed wealth and capital and, in the short run, disrupted production and income, the increased expenditures and production required by rebuilding will boost real GDP. Given the magnitude of the rebuilding effort, the contribution to real GDP growth at the end of 1992 and in early 1993 could be as high as 0.25 to 0.5 percentage point of growth at an annual rate per quarter over several quarters. The effect on real growth in each quarter will depend on how the purchases and rebuilding are distributed through time.

LOW INFLATION

During 1992 inflation fell to the lowest rate in a generation. Through November consumer price inflation during 1992 was 3.1 percent at an annual rate, and core inflation was 3.5 percent (Chart 2-5), the lowest yearly rate since 1972. Producer price inflation was somewhat higher during 1992 than during 1991; it had been unusually low during 1991 as a result of declining oil prices from their peaks during the Gulf conflict.

Various fundamentals helped keep consumer and producer price inflation low and contributed to the decline in core inflation. The

Chart 2-5 **Consumer Price Inflation**
Consumer price inflation has fallen over the past 2 years, with core inflation nearing its
lowest level in two decades.

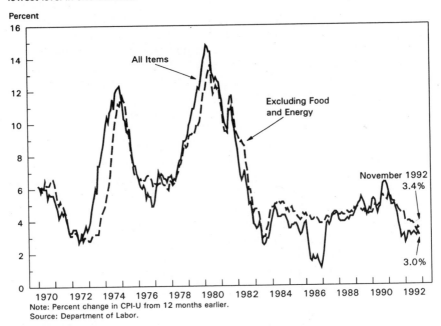

Percent

Note: Percent change in CPI-U from 12 months earlier.
Source: Department of Labor.

recession and slow recovery in the United States and the sluggish international economy have resulted in only modest growth of aggregate demand. Slow money growth over the past several years contributed to, as well as reflected, the sluggish economy and waning inflationary pressures. Primary commodity prices have not increased as they typically do during a recovery. These fundamentals are likely to keep inflation well below the 4.5- to 5-percent range of the mid- to late-1980s. In fact, the average expected 12-month change in consumer prices, measured by the Michigan Surveys of Consumers, has declined over the past several years, falling from over 5 percent in early 1989 to about 3½ percent in late 1992.

Low inflation not only benefits the economy but helps set the stage for sustained economic expansion. Lower inflation helps to maintain the purchasing power of Americans' savings and wealth. Low inflation has also helped bring nominal interest rates to their lowest levels in a generation. Low interest rates have helped households and businesses reduce the cost of paying off existing debt. Low mortgage rates helped to make housing more affordable in 1992 than it had been at any time in the past 18 years and created a burst of refinancing activity. Over the past 4 years, the interest rate on 30-year fixed-rate mortgages declined by over 2½ percentage points; for a $100,000 30-year mortgage, that interest rate decline translates into savings of over $2,000 per year. Household debt-service payments as a percent of disposable income have fallen from a high of over 18 percent in late 1990 and early 1991 to about 16½ percent, improving household finances and freeing up funds for spending or saving. These lower interest rates also mean that interest income will be lower and that some of the economic benefits of lower interest rates will be offset. For some specific groups such as retirees, lower interest rates mean a significant decline in income.

THE INTERNATIONAL SLOWDOWN

Even though U.S. export growth has slowed gradually over the last several years, exports have made a significant contribution to economic growth, rising from 8 percent of real GDP in 1987 to over 11 percent in 1991. In 1992 slower export growth and a significant increase in imports caused the Nation's trade balance to deteriorate. Because the dollar's low foreign exchange value has bolstered the economy's international competitive position, the slowdown in export growth and deterioration of the U.S. trade balance appear to be the result of the sluggish economic performance of our major trading partners and the recent growing demand within the United States.

Despite the economic difficulties that the U.S. economy has had to face, over the past year and a half it has performed better than the economies of the other large industrial economies that belong to the Group of Seven (G-7)—Canada, France, Germany, Italy, Japan, and the United Kingdom. The German and Japanese economies, which grew strongly in 1990 and 1991 (with average annual real growth exceeding 4 percent) slowed markedly and entered recession during 1992. Canada and the United Kingdom were in recession in 1991, with real output declining by about 2 percent in each country; in 1992, growth in the Canadian economy resumed at a slow pace, but the United Kingdom continued in recession. France and Italy experienced sluggish economic performance in both 1991 and 1992, with real annual growth rates in the 1- to 2-percent range. Because the other G-7 countries account for almost one-half of all U.S. merchandise exports, slow growth or recessions in their economies can have a significant negative effect on U.S. exports.

U.S. exports to the newly industrialized economies of the Pacific Rim have been increasing, with the share to Korea, Taiwan, Singapore, and Hong Kong increasing from 8 percent in 1986 to nearly 11 percent in 1991. The outlook for real growth in those four economies is good and to some degree may offset the decline in demand for U.S. goods and services among G-7 members. Prospects also are good for expanded trade with Latin and South America, and the North American Free Trade Agreement (NAFTA) should boost trade with Mexico. In the past 6 years, U.S. exports to Mexico have roughly tripled. While real growth in Mexico has slowed over the past 2 years, growth in 1992 and 1993 likely will compare favorably to the stagnant performance of the mid-1980s. (Chapter 7 of this *Report* has a detailed discussion of international financial and trade issues.)

LONGER TERM STRUCTURAL ADJUSTMENTS AND SHORT-TERM PERFORMANCE

As discussed earlier, the structural imbalances and adjustments of the past several years have been a major cause of the sluggish performance of the economy. In the 1970s and early 1980s, shifting demographic trends related to the postwar baby boom boosted household formation, increasing residential investment and spending on big-ticket durable goods such as cars, appliances, and furniture. However, by the late 1980s the share of the population in the age groups that traditionally form households had begun to decline, reducing the demand for new housing and related durable goods relative to other goods and services.

As the Cold War wound down, so did the defense buildup of the mid-1980s; moderate cuts in defense have been followed by more significant cuts that are likely to continue through the mid-1990s. Federal defense spending shifted from being a large net stimulus to the economy to being a sizable drag. Over the 1982–87 period Federal defense purchases directly contributed an average 0.35 percentage point annually to real GDP growth. Over the 1987–91 period, however, the direct effect was negative: –0.05 percentage point. In 1992 real Federal defense purchases were running nearly $20 billion (in 1987 dollars) below their 1991 level, resulting in a direct negative effect of nearly 0.4 percentage point on the growth rate of real GDP. Yet the actual impact of defense cutbacks has been greater than these data indicate. Because the data on purchases relate primarily to the delivery rather than the production of goods, the decline in purchases in 1992 from 1991 does not account for the additional decline in manufacturers' inventories of defense capital goods, which fell by $6 billion from October 1991 to October 1992. In addition, the data reflecting the effect on the Nation as a whole understate the short-term effect on local communities in the regions where defense industries are concentrated. Indirect effects contribute significantly to the overall effect of defense cutbacks.

Problems in the financial sector have had a significant effect on the recent economic situation because of the integral role the sector plays in ensuring a growing, healthy, and flexible economy. When functioning properly, financial institutions help allocate capital efficiently and thus promote economic growth. Structural problems, like the recent constraints on credit that have resulted in a "credit crunch," impair the ability of financial institutions to function efficiently and, as a result, reduce growth. Credit crunches used to occur from time to time because regulations fixed an upper limit on the interest rates that could be paid on deposits. Those interest rate caps made it more difficult for depository institutions to attract deposits and forced them to cut back on loans. Over the past several years, however, restructuring of depositories' balance sheets—in part market driven and in part to meet new capital standards—as well as the overreaction of examiners to the earlier excesses of banks and savings and loans, have contributed to credit constraints. In addition, the Congress passed two bills—the Financial Institution Reform, Recovery, and Enforcement Act of 1989 and the FDIC Improvement Act of 1991—which contained several features that inadvertently contributed to the credit crunch and restricted bank lending (Chapter 5). Balance sheet restructuring, in combination with an unusually steep yield curve, resulted in declining commercial and industrial loans by banks and increased growth of bank holdings of government securities (Chapter 3). The reduced lending created particular difficulties for small and medium-sized businesses that typically rely heavily on banks as a source of funds. In addition, a variety of other financial intermediaries have suffered asset quality and capital problems that have reduced their willingness and ability to lend at precisely the same time that banks and thrifts have reduced lending.

Other factors, including the overbuilding of commercial real estate and high levels of consumer and corporate debt, have constrained both private investment and consumption. As these imbalances are gradually worked off, the drag on the economy will be reduced, allowing the economy to operate closer to its potential. (Chapter 3 contains an in-depth discussion of these issues.)

MONETARY AND FISCAL POLICY IN 1992

Desires to balance the need for short-term stimulus with long-term objectives governed monetary and fiscal policies in 1992. The Federal Reserve lowered interest rates in response to accumulated evidence of abating inflationary pressures and continued sluggish economic performance. Interest rates fell during the year, while the reserves of banks and other depository institutions grew rapidly. However, growth rates for the broader monetary aggregates were below the lower bound of the Federal Reserve's target ranges for most of the year. When the need for a fiscal policy that would provide immediate stimulus became increasingly clear in late 1991,

51

the President, in January 1992, responded by proposing tax incentives and other measures to encourage short-term growth and job creation as well as long-term investment and productivity (the program was not adopted by the Congress). (A broader discussion of monetary and fiscal policies in an historical context is presented in Chapter 3.)

Monetary Policy and Interest Rates

As a result of sluggish economic performance and monetary policy actions, short-term interest rates have been on a downward trend over the last 3½ years. Growth of the broader monetary aggregates, however, has remained consistently weak. The M2 monetary aggregate—which includes currency, checking accounts, money market accounts and funds, savings and small time deposits, and a few other items—stayed below the lower bound of the Federal Reserve's target range for much of 1992 (Chart 2-6).

Chart 2-6   M2 Money Stock and Growth Target Ranges
Growth in the M2 money stock has been near or below the lower bound of the Federal Reserve's target range for much of the past 2 years.

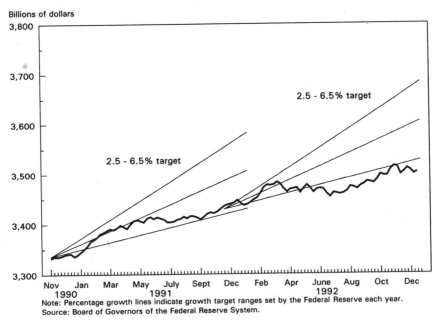

Billions of dollars

Note: Percentage growth lines indicate growth target ranges set by the Federal Reserve each year.
Source: Board of Governors of the Federal Reserve System.

While the long-term relationships between money—specifically M2—and nominal GDP have been relatively stable in the past, the short-term relationships have not been as stable. Furthermore, particularly in the short and medium terms, the Federal Reserve can only influence, not control, the quantity of money. However, because it can directly affect the Federal funds rate—the rate banks charge each other for overnight loans— this rate tends to be the focus of short-term monetary policy. The Federal Reserve generally increases the Federal funds rate when inflationary pressures appear to be rising and lowers it when inflation appears to be waning and the economy is weak. Changes in the Federal funds rate, however, do not necessarily signal a fundamental shift in policy toward loosening or tightening because of the natural tendency for market interest rates to decline when the demand for credit falls during a period of sluggishness or to rise when demand for credit increases in a strong economy.

The slow growth of money and credit in recent years, at a time when the Federal Reserve has been lowering interest rates and boosting bank reserves, reveals significant changes in the relationship between short-term interest rates and the growth of money and credit. Traditionally, reductions in Treasury bill and other money market interest rates have led people to want to hold more of the deposits and currency included in M2, since the income forgone by holding M2 balances is reduced. But during 1992 nominal GDP grew at a rate of around 5 percent, while the M2 monetary aggregate grew at a much lower rate—less than 2½ percent—demonstrating that the relationship between the growth of money and credit and the growth of the economy had changed during this period.

Economists have not been able to agree on the reasons for the slow growth of M2 in the presence of falling short-term interest rates and rapidly rising bank reserves. M2 growth may have been constrained as households and firms moved funds away from low-yielding M2 assets to seek higher returns in long-term bonds and equities or to repay outstanding debts. Because the gap between long-term bond yields and short-term deposit rates has become especially large—and because of increased investment opportunities for small investors—M2 assets may be less responsive to short-term interest rates than they have been in the past. Additionally, the decrease in bank lending that has occurred due to more cautious lending by banks as well as to reduced loan demand by firms and households may have led banks to compete less aggressively for time and savings deposits by lowering interest rates, reducing advertising, or taking other actions to lower the growth of these components of M2.

Declining interest rates on time and savings deposits and money market accounts not only have weakened demand for M2 assets in total but also have reduced the opportunity cost of holding checking deposits or currency—included in the narrower M1 aggregate— that pay lower interest rates or no interest at all. Holdings therefore have shifted from time deposits and money market accounts (included in M2 but not in M1) to transactions accounts within M1, as well as to bonds and equities not included in M2, as noted above. In consequence, M1 growth has been very strong in the past few years, also reflecting increased currency demand from abroad and the higher demand deposits associated with mortgage refinancings, even as M2 growth has lagged. Depository institutions are required to hold reserves of 10 percent against the bulk of deposits included in M1, but the reserve requirements do not apply to the nontransactions deposits included in M2. Hence, banks have needed the large increases in reserves over the past year in order to meet their reserve requirements on rapidly growing M1 deposits; excess reserves have been low and stable.

The changing relationship between M2 and economic activity has complicated the process of monetary policymaking, making it harder to judge the extent to which current monetary policy is stimulating or restraining the economy, and added to uncertainties about the impact prospective monetary policy actions will have on the economy in the future.

These complications may have been all the more important because it was difficult at the time to perceive the changing relationship between M2 and the level of economic activity. As in most economic relationships, the link between M2 and the economy has been variable, so that a period of a few months in which M2 is lower than expected is not sufficient to indicate that the fundamental relationship between M2 and the economy has changed. In fact, the growth of M2 did not fall substantially and consistently below what the Federal Reserve Board staff's statistical models predicted until late 1990, after the recession already had started. Even now, there is no definitive explanation as to why M2's relation to nominal GDP changed.

Given these difficulties, concerns have been raised as to whether M2 was the appropriate monetary aggregate to target in recent years—and whether it is the best aggregate to target at present. The most important criterion used to evaluate the appropriateness of an aggregate for monetary targeting is the predictability of its relationship to GDP. Recent research indicates that M2 continues to be the most useful aggregate available; in spite of recent changes, its relationship to GDP is still more predictable than that of other monetary aggregates. While the Federal Reserve always looks at a set of indicators for implementing monetary policy, it may be appropriate in this uncertain environment for the Federal Reserve to place greater weight on more direct indicators of production, income, and prices in addition to monetary aggregates. If a more predictable relationship between M2 or some other aggregate and GDP is reestablished in the future, the Federal Reserve could return to placing greater emphasis on that aggregate.

During 1992, following the sizable reductions at the end of 1991, the Federal Reserve initially held short-term interest rates relatively steady but near midyear began to lower them again in response to accumulating evidence that the economy remained sluggish and as the growth of the broader monetary aggregates continued to be slow. The most significant cut in interest rates took place in early July, when the Federal Reserve cut both the discount rate—the rate the Federal Reserve charges banks for loans to cover shortfalls in monetary reserves—and the target for the Federal funds rate by 0.5 percentage point, to 3 percent and about 3.25 percent, respectively. Those cuts, which brought interest rates to their lowest levels in nearly three decades, were followed by an additional reduction of 0.25 percentage point in the targeted Federal funds rate in September.

Other interest rates that also have been falling for several years were at low levels in 1992. The prime rate—the interest rate banks charge for loans to their best business customers—ended the year at its lowest level in nearly 20 years, falling from more than 11 percent in mid-1989 to just 6 percent. The rate on 30-year fixed-rate mortgages also fell to a 20-year low in September, declining below 8 percent from its mid-1989 high of more than 11 percent. Yields on long-term government and corporate bonds also dropped, although the decline was less pronounced than it was for short-term securities. As a result, the yield curve—a curve plotting the yields of comparable securities according to their term to maturity—became much steeper as the difference between long-term rates and short-term rates increased. Such a result is typical during recessions and early recoveries, although the yield curve has been unusually steep recently.

Fiscal Policy in 1992

During periods of slow growth or recession, fiscal policy typically shifts to assume a more stimulative role in the economy. To compensate for reduced private spending, government spending increases and tax collections are reduced. Some of this happens because of automatic stabilizers; spending for some programs (such as unemployment compensation) automatically increases during recessions, and tax collections are reduced as incomes and expenditures grow slower or even decline. In addition, Federal spending can be boosted or taxes lowered through discretionary changes to existing programs and policies. Typically, these actions provide a significant stimulus to the economy. During the recent recession and early recovery, Federal spending and taxes were modestly stimulative, mainly because of the automatic stabilizers. However, Federal spending and taxes did not provide as large a boost as typically occurred in earlier recessions and recoveries. The Budget Enforcement Act of 1990, the ongoing defense downsizing, and a political stalemate between the Administration and the Congress played important roles in keeping fiscal policy from being more stimulative (Chapter 3).

The need for a fiscal policy that would provide more direct economic stimulus became increasingly apparent when the already sluggish recovery showed signs of faltering in late 1991. In January 1992 the President submitted a set of proposals designed to provide a short-term stimulus to the economy as well as to enhance long-term growth. The proposals for short-term stimulus included a cut in the capital gains tax rate, a temporary investment tax allowance, simplified and enhanced depreciation for companies paying taxes under the corporate alternative minimum tax (AMT) rules, a temporary tax credit for first-time homebuyers, allowing individual retirement account (IRA) balances to be used for first-time home purchases, and two additional proposals aimed at providing a boost to real estate investment and values. Additional proposals were directed at boosting the Nation's long-term economic performance through higher investment and enhanced productivity. The Congress did not pass the President's proposals.

The President was, however, able to take unilateral steps that did not require the consent of the Congress, including the reduction of tax withholding and the acceleration of spending for certain programs already in place. If the President's broad set of proposals had been adopted, growth and employment would have been higher—and unemployment lower—than they actually were during 1992. The positive benefits of the proposals would have carried through to future years, boosting investment, productivity, economic growth, and the Nation's standard of living.

A key factor in preventing fiscal policy from being more stimulative in the recent downturn has been the mounting concern over the budget deficit. The size of the deficit and the level of public debt in recent years has given rise to fears of a resurgence of inflation or of dramatic tax increases if the growth of government spending is not controlled. These fears are manifested in higher long-term interest rates and would be heightened if a fiscal policy were adopted that increased the short-term deficit without simultaneously legislating a credible program to reduce future deficits substantially. Hence, if the economy's recovery falters in the coming months and a period of very sluggish growth and rising unemployment appears likely, an appropriate response might be to adopt tax cuts and incentives to spur growth immediately, while at the same time adopting larger reductions in future government spending. Such a policy combination would allay concerns in financial markets about future budget deficits and prevent the rise in long-term interest rates that could otherwise offset much of a direct fiscal stimulus.

SUMMARY

- The economy experienced modest and uneven growth during 1992. Consumer spending provided a significant boost to the economy. Investment spending also contributed to growth, but government purchases made little or no contribution, and a significant decline in net exports subtracted from growth.
- The labor market was sluggish throughout the year, with employment remaining relatively stagnant and the unemployment rate rising until the summer, when it began declining.
- In 1992 core inflation and interest rates were at their lowest levels in a generation. Low inflation and interest rates help put the economy on track for a sustained expansion.
- Slow growth in the international economy could limit U.S. export growth and reduce prospects for a return to strong economic growth in the near term.
- The Federal Reserve lowered interest rates during 1992, but growth of the broad monetary aggregates remained sluggish. Various structural changes as well as weak demand for funds have restricted M2 growth. Historical relationships among interest rates, the monetary aggregates, and GDP have shifted, making the implementation of policy more difficult.
- Fiscal policy recently has provided only a modest stimulus to the economy. The President proposed a set of tax incentives and other initiatives in January 1992 designed to provide further short-term stimulus to the economy as well as to boost investment and productivity. Additional fiscal stimulus, if needed, should be coupled with simultaneously enacted future reductions in government expenditures.

RECENT ECONOMIC PERFORMANCE IN HISTORICAL CONTEXT

Following the longest peacetime expansion in history, the Nation has been through difficult economic times over the last several years, with a slow and protracted recovery following a recession that was somewhat shorter and shallower than average. Comparisons with the average of previous recessions and recoveries are informative, even if there is no such thing as a typical or average recession or recovery. For example, the regional pattern of economic activity or the relative contributions to growth from increased labor hours and increased productivity can vary significantly across business cycle experiences.

SLOW RECOVERY

As the forecasts of this Administration correctly anticipated, the pace of growth during the recent recovery has been much slower than it was during other postwar recoveries (Table 2-1). In the first year and a half following previous troughs, growth in real GDP averaged nearly 10 percent; growth ranged from a low of 3.4 percent during the short four-quarter recovery of 1980-81 to a high of 16 percent in 1949-51. If the extraordinary recovery of 1949-51 is excluded, growth averaged about 9 percent during the first year and a half after previous troughs. In the year and a half following the most recent trough, however, real GDP increased only 2.9 percent, less than one-third the postwar average.

TABLE 2-1.—*Recovery Comparisons*

First Year and a Half of Recovery [1]

Recovery	Real Output [2] Percent Change	Payroll Employment Percent Change	Unemployment Rate Change Percentage Points
1949-51	16.0	11.7	-4.8
1954-55	11.6	5.4	-1.7
1958-59	9.3	4.8	-1.7
1961-62	10.5	4.5	-1.2
1970-72	8.6	4.4	-.2
1975-76	8.0	4.5	-1.0
1980-81 [3]	3.4	2.0	-.6
1982-84	11.1	6.1	-3.4
Recovery Average	9.8	5.4	-1.8
1991-92	2.9	.1	.7

[1] Changes in variables determined from NBER designated trough.
[2] Real output changes are determined from historical GNP or GDP series with base year near the recovery period: for 1949-51 and 1954-55, GNP measured in 1954 dollars was used; for 1958-59 and 1961-62, GNP in 1958 dollars; for 1970-72 and 1975-76, GNP in 1972 dollars; for 1980-81 and 1982-84, GNP in 1982 dollars; for 1991-92, GDP in 1987 dollars. A fixed-weight measure of real output based on the prices of a more recent year (for example, GDP in 1987 dollars) generally changes less than one based on prices of an earlier year. This property creates problems in long-term comparisons of real output. See 'Alternative Measures of Change in Real Output and Prices,' Survey of Current Business, April 1992. Caution should be used in interpreting these data because of definitional changes made to the output measures over time.
[3] Recovery after 1980 recession is through peak in July 1981 (four quarters).
Note.—Upcoming data revisions may affect the values reported in this table.
Sources: Department of Commerce, Department of Labor, and National Bureau of Economic Research.

The sluggish nature of the recovery was particularly evident in the labor market. During the first 18 months after previous postwar troughs, nonfarm payroll employment increased, on average, by 5.4 percent, ranging from a low of 2 percent in 1980-81 to a high of nearly 12 percent in 1949-51. In comparison, for the 18 months following the March 1991 trough, nonfarm payroll employment was essentially flat, increasing only 0.1 percent. Unemployment rate data also show the effects of the slow recovery in the labor market. After 18 months of expansion in previous postwar recoveries, the unemployment rate was, on average, 1.8 percentage points below its level at the trough, with a range of declines from 0.2 percentage point in 1970-72 to 4.8 percentage points in 1949-51. In contrast, from March 1991 to September 1992, the unemployment rate *increased* by 0.7 percentage point.

THE RECESSION IN HISTORICAL CONTEXT

The slow recovery followed a recession that was somewhat shorter and shallower than average (Table 2-2). Initial data had suggested that the 1990-91 recession was relatively mild, but subsequent data revisions—released more than a year after the end of the recession—showed that real GDP fell by 2.2 percent (Box 2-2). The decline was less than the average of previous postwar recessions and less than those of the previous three recessions of 1973-75 (4.9 percent), 1980 (2.3 percent), and 1981-82 (3.3 percent). In terms of duration, the 8-month recession of 1990-91 was shorter than the average of 11 months for previous postwar recessions.

TABLE 2-2.—*Recession Comparisons*

Recession	Duration[1]	Real Output[2]	Payroll Employment	Unemployment Rate		
				Change	High	
	Months	Percent Change	Percent Change	Percentage Points	Percent	Months After Trough
1948–49	11	−1.4	−5.2	4.5	7.9	0
1953–54	10	−3.7	−3.5	3.6	6.1	4
1957–58	8	−3.9	−4.3	3.8	7.5	3
1960–61	10	−1.6	−2.2	2.3	7.1	3
1969–70	11	−1.0	−1.5	2.7	6.1	9
1973–75	16	−4.9	−2.9	4.4	9.0	2
1980	6	−2.3	−1.4	2.2	7.8	0
1981–82	16	−3.3	−3.1	3.6	10.8	1
Recession Average	11	−2.8	−3.0	3.4	7.8	3
1990–91	8	−2.2	−2.0	2.7	7.7	15

[1] Duration based on National Bureau of Economic Research dating of business cycle peaks and troughs.
[2] Real output changes are determined from historical GNP or GDP series with base year near the recession period: for 1948–49 and 1953–54, GNP measured in 1954 dollars was used; for 1957–58 and 1960–61, GNP in 1958 dollars; for 1969–70 and 1973–75, GNP in 1972 dollars; for 1980 and 1981–82, GNP in 1982 dollars; for 1990–91, GDP in 1987 dollars. A fixed-weight measure of real output based on the prices of a more recent year (for example, GDP in 1987 dollars) generally changes less than one based on prices of an earlier year. This property creates problems in long-term comparisons of real output. See 'Alternative Measures of Change in Real Output and Prices,' Survey of Current Business, April 1992. Caution should be used in interpreting these data because of definitional changes made to the output measures over time.
Note.—Changes determined from series-specific peaks and troughs. Upcoming data revisions may affect the values reported in this table.
Sources: Department of Commerce, Department of Labor, and National Bureau of Economic Research.

The 1990-91 recession also had a somewhat less severe effect on payroll employment and the unemployment rate than on average in previous postwar recessions. The decline in nonfarm payroll employment associated with the 1990-91 recession was 2 percent, about two-thirds the average decline of previous recessions (but the Bureau of Labor Statistics recently reported that this likely overstates the true decline). Similarly, the increase in the unemployment rate resulting from the 1990-91 recession was 2.7 percentage points, below the recession average of 3.4 percentage points.

However, other measures indicate that the effect of the 1990-91 recession and subsequent slow growth period on labor markets was more severe than the absolute change in employment or the unemployment rate indicated. The unemployment rate peaked at 7.7 percent—slightly below the average peak for previous recessions—15 months after the end of the recession. Typically, the unemployment rate hits its peak an average of only 3 months after the end of a recession. In addition, the percentage of unemployed who lost their jobs permanently rather than being temporarily laid off, reached its highest level on record, eroding workers' long-term job security and limiting prospects for the quick rebound in employment that usually occurs during a recovery (Chart 2-7).

Chart 2-7   Ratio of Permanent Job Losers to Total Unemployed
The fraction of unemployed workers not expecting to be recalled to a job has been on an upward trend over the past several decades. In 1992 it rose to its highest level on record.

Percent

42.4%
December 1992

Source: Department of Labor.

Additionally, as highlighted in last year's *Report*, the relative proportions of unemployment among white-collar, blue-collar, and sales and services workers has shifted, making the relative effect on white-collar workers somewhat more severe. Because of job losses in finance, insurance, and real estate, white-collar workers recently have accounted for a larger proportion of total unemployment—relative to blue-collar or sales and services workers—than they did in recent recessions. Nonetheless, blue-collar unemployment still accounted for a larger share of total unemployment than white-collar unemployment.

REGIONAL DISPARITIES

The regional disparities in labor market performance also indicate that the effects of the recession and slow recovery were widely

Box 2-2.—Data Revisions and the Severity of the Recession

Various government agencies and private groups release a steady stream of data about the economy. Typically, the data are released in preliminary form, subject to subsequent revision. Most monthly data, for example, are released in preliminary form, and are subject to revision for 2 or 3 months. Also, once a year, data series are usually revised to take account of additional information from comprehensive annual surveys and to reestimate the regular seasonal patterns in the data.

During 1992, the annual revisions to several key data series showed that the recession was more severe than initial data had indicated. In July the Department of Commerce released revised data for real GDP as part of its regular revisions to the national income and product accounts (NIPAs). Prior to the revisions Department of Commerce estimates had shown a total decline in real GDP (measured in 1987 dollars) over two consecutive quarters—the fourth quarter of 1990 and the first quarter of 1991—of 1.6 percent. The revised estimates showed a decline over three consecutive quarters totaling 2.2 percent, with the estimated change in real GDP in the third quarter of 1990 revised down from a small increase to a significant decline.

In a separate set of annual revisions, the Department of Labor reported that nonfarm payroll employment declined in early 1991 by much more than was originally estimated. The revised data resulted in a larger estimated decline in nonfarm payroll employment during the recession; the absolute size of the decline increased by about 0.5 percentage point. However, recent research by the Bureau of Labor Statistics indicates that the bulk of the revisions resulted from non-economic factors—mainly, improved employment reporting procedures instituted in early 1991.

The data discussed above represent important sources of information for policymakers and the general public, and their reliability is crucial. Policy might have been conducted in a different fashion if the true severity of the recession had been known earlier. At a time of fiscal constraint, government statistical agencies often must attempt to handle an increased workload with dwindling resources. The need for improved quality of statistics was the motivation behind the Economics Statistics Initiative developed by an interagency working group and approved by the President in November 1989. Work began on the programs in 1991, although the lack of full funding will delay their full implementation.

334-230 O—92——3 (QL3)

dispersed and differed from the regional effects of the 1981–82 recession. Chart 2–8 plots the average unemployment rate in each State for November 1982, the month the unemployment rate peaked at the end of the 1981–82 recession. Unemployment rates generally were much lower on the East Coast (with the exception of the Carolinas and Rhode Island) than in the Midwestern industrial States and some parts of the South, which were hit hard by problems in manufacturing.

Chart 2–9 plots unemployment rates for June 1992, the month of the recent unemployment rate peak. The unemployment rate for the Nation as a whole was lower than it was during the 1981–82 recession. Following the 1981–82 pattern, several States in the industrial heartland fared worse than other parts of the country, especially Illinois and Michigan. The Northeast (Massachusetts, New York, and Rhode Island, in particular) and other widely dispersed states such as Alaska, California, Florida, Mississippi, New Jersey, and West Virginia experienced relatively high unemployment rates. This regional distribution reveals the structural adjustments underway in the economy. Restructuring in the domestic auto industry hurt Michigan and Illinois. New England and California were particularly hard hit by ongoing defense cutbacks. Overbuilding in commercial real estate and restructuring in the finance and insurance industries had disproportionately negative effects on California, Florida, and the Northeast.

EMPLOYMENT AND PRODUCTIVITY TRENDS

The relatively stagnant labor market performance at a time when output was increasing reveals that *real growth during the recovery resulted exclusively from labor productivity gains.* It is not unusual to see labor productivity surge when the economy is in a recovery phase because firms tend to keep their most productive workers on the payroll during downturns and use the existing workforce more intensively during the initial phase of an upturn. In the first year and a half of previous recoveries, labor productivity growth averaged 3.0 percent at an annual rate, about twice the average annual rate of labor productivity growth of the past three decades.

Over the first six quarters of the recent recovery, labor productivity in the nonfarm business sector grew at an annual rate of 2.5 percent, only slightly less than the average for previous recoveries (Chart 2–10). However, the unusual thing about the past year and a half is that all of the gain in output resulted from labor productivity gains. In previous recoveries, the split between the increase in labor productivity and the increase in labor hours worked was much more balanced, with labor productivity gains and the in-

62

Chart 2-8 Unemployment Rates by State, November 1982

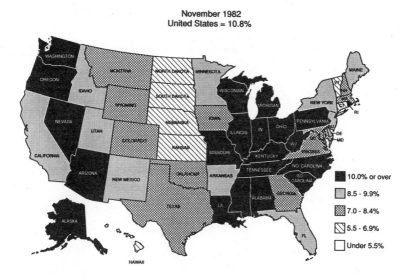

November 1982
United States = 10.8%

10.0% or over
8.5 - 9.9%
7.0 - 8.4%
5.5 - 6.9%
Under 5.5%

Source: Department of Labor.

Chart 2-9 Unemployment Rates by State, June 1992

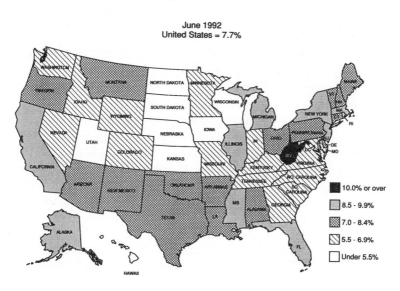

June 1992
United States = 7.7%

10.0% or over
8.5 - 9.9%
7.0 - 8.4%
5.5 - 6.9%
Under 5.5%

Source: Department of Labor.

63

crease in labor hours accounting for roughly equal shares, on average.

Chart 2-10 **Growth in Output per Hour, Nonfarm Business Sector**
Productivity has rebounded strongly over the past year and a half, typifying the strong gains that usually occur during a recovery.

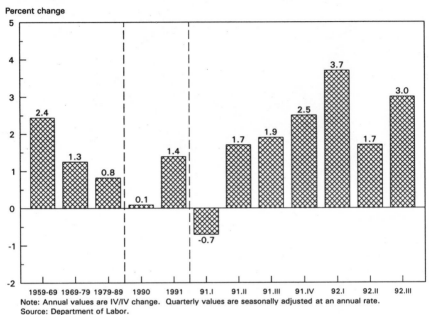

Percent change

Note: Annual values are IV/IV change. Quarterly values are seasonally adjusted at an annual rate.
Source: Department of Labor.

The increase in labor productivity is expected to continue as the economy settles into a sustained expansion and higher investment boosts the stock of productive capital. Labor productivity growth had been slipping in recent decades, but several factors suggest that it is likely to improve over the experience of the past two decades. The average age of the population and the workforce will continue to increase, and evidence suggests that a move toward a more experienced work force is usually associated with higher productivity growth. Also, during the past two decades, oil price shocks diverted spending into energy-saving rather than labor-saving capital equipment and, as a result, the economy is less vulnerable now to energy shocks than it was during the 1970s. The labor force is expected to grow slowly, making labor relatively less abundant. Over time, this likely will increase real wages, promoting higher capital investment and faster growth in labor productivity. In addition, low real interest rates reduce capital costs and the anti-inflation credibility that the Federal Reserve has earned reduces uncertainty premiums in interest rates. Prospects for reducing the structural budget deficit over time would also likely promote lower interest rates and borrowing costs, helping to boost investment and contributing to labor productivity.

SUMMARY

- In terms of output and employment, the recovery of 1991–92 has been the slowest of the postwar era.
- Compared with previous postwar recessions, the recession of 1990–91 was somewhat shallower and shorter. In labor markets, however, the effects of the recession were less straightforward. While the effects on employment and the unemployment rate were milder than average, nonfarm payroll employment remained relatively stagnant for over a year following the trough, and the unemployment rate peaked more than a year after the decline in real GDP had ended.
- State unemployment rates show that the coastal States and the Northeast were hit relatively hard in the recent recession and slow recovery, while the heartland was disproportionately affected by the 1981–82 recession.
- All of the gain in output during the past year and a half resulted from increases in labor productivity. The outlook for continued productivity gains is good.

THE ECONOMIC OUTLOOK

Factors such as low interest rates and low inflation provide a strong foundation for continued short- and long-term economic growth. While structural adjustments have slowed the economy for the last several years, economic performance is expected to improve as structural imbalances are resolved.

THE ADMINISTRATION'S ECONOMIC PROJECTIONS

Table 2–3 shows Administration projections for key economic variables for the period from 1992 through 1998. At the time of this writing, estimates of GDP for the fourth quarter of 1992 and for 1992 as a whole were not available. Data from the first three quarters and preliminary information for the fourth quarter indicate that real GDP grew at a rate of around 2.5 to 3 percent from the fourth quarter of 1991 to the fourth quarter of 1992. During 1993, the economy is expected to grow at a moderate pace early in the year and then pick up later in the year, with real GDP growing around 3 percent during the year. Growth is expected to continue in the 3-percent range through the mid-1990s but then to slow slightly in the second half of the decade. The slight slowing of growth later in the decade reflects the movement of the economy toward full employment of available resources without increased inflationary pressure.

TABLE 2-3.—*Administration Forecasts*

Item	1992	1993	1994	1995	1996	1997	1998
	Percent change, fourth quarter to fourth quarter						
Real GDP...	2.6	2.9	3.1	3.0	2.9	2.8	2.7
GDP deflator, 1987=100.............................	2.5	2.6	2.7	2.8	2.8	2.8	2.8
Consumer price index, CPI–U.........................	2.9	2.8	2.9	3.0	3.0	3.0	3.0
	Calendar year average						
Unemployment rate, percent.........................	7.4	6.9	6.2	5.7	5.4	5.3	5.3
Interest rate, 91–day Treasury bills, percent..	3.4	3.5	4.2	4.4	4.4	4.4	4.4
Interest rate, 10–year Treasury notes, percent	7.0	6.4	6.1	6.0	6.0	6.0	6.0
Civilian employment, millions	117.7	119.9	122.3	124.6	126.6	128.4	130.1

Sources: Council of Economic Advisers, Department of the Treasury, and Office of Management and Budget.

Sustained higher economic growth will improve employment prospects. The unemployment rate is expected to decline during 1993, averaging 6.9 percent for the year, down from 7.4 percent for 1992. In the mid-1990s, with the economy expected to continue in a sustained expansion, the unemployment rate is expected to decline steadily, reaching a level of 5.3 percent by 1997.

Inflation is expected to remain low in 1993 and in coming years, not only because of excess capacity and underemployment of resources in the immediate future, but also because of the Federal Reserve's ongoing efforts to keep inflation in check. The Administration projections show consumer prices rising about 3 percent annually; the implicit price deflator for GDP is expected to rise at a rate slightly below 3 percent annually.

With moderate growth and low inflation, short-term interest rates are expected to remain low in 1993 and long-term interest rates are expected to decline. As the economy moves back toward full employment of resources, short-term rates are likely to rise. In the middle and later years of the projection, long-term rates are expected to stabilize as inflation remains low. However, the outlook for interest rates in general—and long-term rates in particular—depends critically on the outlook for fiscal policy. The adoption of policies that would lead to higher structural budget deficits, relative to what is currently expected likely would boost long-term interest rates and retard economic growth in subsequent years.

Economic forecasting is an imprecise science. Unexpected developments can cause forecasts to go awry, and changes in policies can cause actual events to differ substantially from the forecast. Ultimately, economic forecasts are based largely on predictions about human behavior, usually taking the previous patterns of behavior as a guide. But human behavior is complex, difficult to predict, and subject to change. People do not always respond in the same way, or with the same speed, in what appear to be similar circumstances.

Changes in the general state of the economy can also affect the relative accuracy of forecasts. Forecasting becomes much more difficult when the economy shifts from expansion to recession or from recession to recovery. Despite a difficult forecasting environment, this Administration's forecasts generally have been accurate by forecasters' standards. Using a broad set of variables—real growth, consumer price inflation, the unemployment rate, and the Treasury bill rate—from the annual forecasts presented in the *Budget of the U.S. Government*, this Administration's (1990–92) short-term forecasts for the year under consideration have been more accurate than either the Carter (1978–81) or Reagan Administration (1982–89) forecasts. The average absolute error of Bush Administration forecasts is over 20 percent smaller than Reagan Administration forecasts and over 30 percent smaller than Carter Administration forecasts. Each Administration—in its entirety—had to forecast in periods of comparable difficulty, as there were business cycle turning points at some point during each of their terms. However, forecasts for the individual terms of the Reagan Administration were produced during significantly different economic environments. There was a deep recession following high and volatile inflation during the early years of the first Reagan term, while during the second Reagan term, the economy was in the midst of a sustained expansion with moderate inflation. This Administration's forecasts were about 30 percent more accurate than those of the first Reagan term and about 10 percent more accurate than those of the second Reagan term.

This Administration's short-term forecasts also have matched up relatively well with the individual and "consensus" (really the average) Blue Chip forecasts, although the accuracy of specific forecasts of this Administration relative to individual Blue Chip forecasts, has varied. The first forecast of this Administration—the mid-session forecast in 1989—was more accurate than any of the individual Blue Chip forecasts as well as the consensus. The Budget forecast for 1990, prepared in late 1989, was less accurate than the consensus and the bulk of individual Blue Chip forecasts. However, the mid-session forecast prepared in mid-1990 was as accurate as the consensus and in the middle of the pack of individual forecasts. The Budget and mid-session forecasts for 1991 also were as accurate as the consensus and in the middle of the pack of individual forecasts. Both the Budget and mid-session forecasts for 1992 (prepared in late 1991 and mid 1992 respectively) were more accurate than the consensus and the vast majority of individual forecasts (based on data currently available).

General interpretations of the economic situation and public comments also matter. In late 1990, when the Council of Economic Advisers reported that the Nation was in a recession, it was the first time in any of the nine postwar recessions that an Administration had acknowledged that the Nation was in a recession before the data on even one quarter of decline in real output were available. At that time the Administration forecast for 1991 correctly predicted that real output would continue to decline in the first quarter of 1991 and then grow slowly in the remaining quarters of the year. That forecast also correctly predicted that the recovery would be the slowest on record.

The uncertainties of forecasting can be seen in the range of projections provided in Table 2–4. The higher growth alternative is consistent with a sharper and faster rebound in economic activity than in the Administration's projection, reflecting the uncertainty about the positive potential for growth. Over the past several years, the recession and slow growth have pushed the economy well below its potential level of output. A high level of excess capacity of productive plant and equipment currently exists in the economy and labor is less than fully utilized, as indicated by the current level of the unemployment rate. Because of the underutilization of resources, there is significant upside potential for growth. The economy has been working its way through many structural problems for several years, and as the drag from those structural difficulties is reduced, economic growth likely will improve further; the extent and timing of that improvement are uncertain. Consumer and business confidence have been lower than justified by economic fundamentals, and as consumer and business confidence rebound, consumer spending and business investment may pick up more strongly than expected.

The lower growth alternative is consistent with continued sluggish activity, reflecting uncertainty about the downside risks for growth. The drag from ongoing defense downsizing and other structural adjustments may be larger and more persistent than expected. Slower-than-expected growth in the international economy may hinder U.S. exports, increase the trade deficit, and reduce economic growth in the United States relative to what is expected in the Administration projection. Adoption of improper policies could adversely affect the performance of the economy.

The lower section of Table 2–4 shows projections for the Federal budget deficit for the Administration forecast and the higher and lower growth alternatives. The deficit projections are significantly affected by changes in the projected rate of economic growth. Under the higher growth alternative, the Federal budget deficit is projected to decline somewhat faster than under the Administration projection and then to stabilize at a level about $40 to $60 bil-

TABLE 2-4.—*Alternative Forecasts and Deficit Projections*

Item	1992	1993	1994	1995	1996	1997	1998
	Percent change, fourth quarter to fourth quarter						
Alternative Forecast							
Real GDP							
Higher growth	2.6	3.5	4.0	3.7	3.4	3.2	3.0
Lower growth	2.6	2.0	2.2	2.4	2.5	2.5	2.5
Consumer Price Index, CPI–U							
Higher growth	2.9	3.1	3.5	4.0	4.5	4.7	5.0
Lower growth	2.9	2.3	2.2	2.3	2.3	2.3	2.3
	Percent, annual average						
Unemployment rate, civilian							
Higher growth	7.4	6.7	6.0	5.6	5.3	5.1	5.0
Lower growth	7.4	7.6	7.6	7.4	7.0	6.7	6.5
Interest rate, 91-day Treasury bill							
Higher growth	3.4	4.0	5.0	5.6	6.3	7.0	7.5
Lower growth	3.4	2.7	2.7	2.8	2.8	2.9	3.0
	Billions of dollars, fiscal years						
Deficit projections							
Higher growth	290	328	287	240	201	207	194
Administration	290	332	297	265	241	266	265
Lower Growth	290	340	322	307	300	338	344

Sources: Council of Economic Advisers, Department of the Treasury, and Office of Management and Budget.

lion below that of the Administration projection; the cumulative effect on the debt is about $200 billion over the 6 years of the projection. Under the lower growth alternative, the Federal budget deficit remains at much higher levels—in excess of $300 billion—throughout the projection, with a cumulative effect approaching $300 billion of additional debt relative to the Administration projection.

ACCOUNTING FOR GROWTH

Overall growth of real GDP can be decomposed into four components: (1) labor force growth, or growth in the number of people available for work each year; (2) the change in the share of the labor force that is employed, or the employment rate; (3) the growth in the number of hours an employed person works each year, represented as the growth in average weekly hours; and (4) labor productivity growth, or the growth in the average amount of goods and services produced per hour of labor.

Table 2–5 shows the contribution of these factors in average real GDP growth for various periods. The first three columns provide historical comparisons for periods from business cycle peak to business cycle peak. The final column shows the contributions for the period, incorporating actual data since the recent business cycle peak (in the third quarter of 1990) along with estimates for the forecast period to 1998. Economic growth is projected to average 2.3 percent a year from the business cycle peak in 1990 through the end of the forecast in 1998.

69

TABLE 2-5.—*Accounting for Growth in Real GDP, 1960–98*

[Average annual percent change]

Item	1960 II to 1981 III	1973 IV to 1981 III	1981 III to 1990 III	1990 III to 1998 IV
1) Civilian noninstitutional population aged 16 and over	1.8	1.8	1.1	0.9
2) PLUS: Civilian labor force participation rate	.3	.5	.4	.3
3) EQUALS: Civilian labor force	2.1	2.4	1.6	1.2
4) PLUS: Civilian employment rate	−.1	−.4	.2	.0
5) EQUALS: Civilian employment	2.0	2.0	1.8	1.3
6) PLUS: Nonfarm business employment as a share of civilian employment[1]	.1	.1	.2	−.1
7) EQUALS: Nonfarm business employment	2.1	2.1	2.0	1.1
8) PLUS: Average weekly hours (nonfarm business sector)	−.6	−.7	.0	.0
9) EQUALS: Hours of all persons (nonfarm business)	1.5	1.3	2.0	1.2
10) PLUS: Output per hour (productivity, nonfarm business)	1.7	.6	.8	1.4
11) EQUALS: Nonfarm business output	3.3	1.9	2.8	2.6
12) LESS: Nonfarm business output as a share of real GDP[2]	.1	−.2	.2	.3
13) EQUALS: Real GDP	3.2	2.1	2.6	2.3

[1] Line six translates the civilian employment growth rate into the nonfarm business employment growth rate.
[2] Line 12 translates nonfarm business output back into output for all sectors, or GDP, which includes the output of farms and general government.
Note.—Data may not add due to rounding.
Time periods are from business cycle peak to business cycle peak to avoid cyclical effects.
Sources: Council of Economic Advisers, Department of Commerce, Department of Labor, Department of the Treasury, and Office of Management and Budget.

This projection assumes an average rise of 1.2 percent a year in the labor force over the 1990–98 period, a lower rate than during the prior three decades. Slower labor force growth results from slower growth in the working-age population and from smaller increases in projected labor force participation rates.

The civilian unemployment rate is projected to fall to 5.3 percent at the end of the forecast, only slightly below the unemployment rate at the business cycle peak in the third quarter of 1990. Hence, only a slight contribution (rounded to 0.0 in Table 2–5) is attributed to changes in the civilian employment rate from the previous peak of the business cycle through the end of the forecast. The largest contribution from a falling unemployment rate during the forecast occurs between 1992 and 1995. As the economy nears full employment in the later years of the forecast, increases in the employment rate make smaller contributions.

A key assumption underlying the 2.3-percent forecasted average growth rate of real GDP is that the increase in labor productivity will average 1.4 percent a year. That rate of productivity growth is higher than the rates experienced during the 1970s and 1980s, but substantially lower than those of the 1960s. As discussed earlier in this chapter, labor productivity growth has been quite strong over the past year and a half, and various factors—including a more experienced and slower growing labor force and likely higher investment resulting from low real interest rates and lower and less volatile inflation—point to a higher rate of productivity growth in coming years in comparison with the low rates of the past two decades.

SUMMARY

- In the short term, the economy is expected to show continued gradual improvement, with real growth at about 3 percent during 1993. During 1993 the unemployment rate is expected to decline gradually as the economy improves, and inflation and interest rates are expected to remain relatively low.
- Real growth is expected to continue in the 3-percent range through the mid-1990s before slowing gradually to the 2¾-percent range later in the decade. The unemployment rate is expected to show steady but gradual declines over the next 4 years. Current fundamentals point to only slight increases in inflation and short-term interest rates, with long-term interest rates declining slightly before stabilizing.
- The uncertainties of economic forecasting indicate that growth could be higher or lower than currently anticipated. With higher real growth, the projected level of the Federal budget deficit falls significantly; with lower growth, the Federal budget deficit increases.

CONCLUSION

Following 8 months of recession and 1½ years of recovery, there are signs that the economy is entering a period of solid and sustained expansion. The extended period of slow growth—which appears to be largely over—reflected the economy's response to serious structural imbalances and long-term trends. The process of improving household and corporate balance sheets, adjusting to reductions in defense expenditures, and bringing the supply of commercial and multifamily residential real estate into balance with demand resulted in a protracted period of sluggish economic growth. As well, the implementation of the second round of disinflation since 1980, which brought inflation to its lowest level since the early 1970s, was also accompanied by painful adjustments.

These adjustments, costly as they were and as they continue to be for millions of Americans, have laid the foundation for strong and sustained economic growth. In particular, a more secure outlook for low inflation will provide enhanced incentives to save and invest during the economy's future expansion.

However, the Nation cannot take this expansion for granted. Even as the recovery appears to be picking up steam, unemployment continues to be too high and job growth too low. This sluggish performance in the labor market reflects the continued process of adjustment by firms to more competitive conditions and changing

71

patterns of product demands. To put Americans back to work, it is necessary to continue to strengthen the fundamental dynamism and resilience of the Nation's economy in the face of change, to create an environment conducive to new business formation and small business expansion, and to promote the entrepreneurial process that only a sound market economy can produce.

The gains from recent adjustments can only be fully exploited if they are coupled with appropriate policies. These include provision of sufficient money for sustained growth consistent with maintaining low inflation; a fiscal policy directed toward the long-term control of government spending and tax incentives to save, innovate, and invest; continued movement toward free and open trade throughout the world; and growth-enhancing regulatory reform to ensure sustained progress toward more smoothly functioning markets at home.

CHAPTER 3

Monetary and Fiscal Policy in the Current Environment

THE EFFORTS AND ACCOMPLISHMENTS of households and businesses produce the economic growth that leads to improved living standards. An environment that includes an open trading system, a strong market system with well-designed and efficient regulation where necessary, and legal protection of property rights fosters such progress. Monetary and fiscal policies also shape the environment within which households and businesses make their decisions. These policies are important tools used to pursue the goals of the Employment Act of 1946, which charges the Federal Government with promoting "maximum employment, production, and purchasing power."

Monetary and fiscal policies can be best understood in the context of the events, both historical and recent, that shaped them. Such an analysis can assist in choosing policies that improve rather than disrupt short- and long-term economic performance. Of particular interest are the circumstances and policies surrounding the recent recession, which began in July 1990 and lasted until March 1991. While the decline in output was less than the average for other post-World War II recessions, by most measures the recovery was the weakest in postwar history.

Monetary policy refers to actions taken by the Federal Reserve (the Fed) that influence bank reserves, the money stock, and interest rates. An expansionary monetary policy tends initially to lower short-term interest rates by increasing the availability of money and credit. Lower interest rates encourage spending, particularly on investment projects. When the economy is operating well below capacity, increased spending is likely to lead to increased output. Once the economy is at or near capacity, however, rapid monetary expansion is likely to lead to inflation (a sustained increase in prices) rather than output growth. Conversely, contractionary, or tight, monetary policy reduces the growth rate of the money stock, increases short-term interest rates, and eventually lowers inflation.

Fiscal policy refers to the spending and taxing policies of the Federal Government. Fiscal policy can influence total demand in the economy by changing taxes and government spending. Expansionary fiscal policy, for example, implements tax cuts, government

73

spending increases, or both, in order to increase economic activity during downturns. Fiscal policy can also affect incentives to work, save, invest, and innovate. Changes in taxes on capital, for example, affect the after-tax return on investment in physical assets and thus the incentive for capital accumulation. Evaluations of fiscal policy changes must take into account the effects of both consumer and business demand and supply-side incentive effects.

MACROECONOMIC POLICY IN HISTORICAL CONTEXT

The dominant feature of per capita real gross national product (GNP), or output, since 1870 has been its steady growth, but there have been noticeable interruptions in growth as well (Chart 3-1). The "business cycle" refers to fluctuations of output around a long-term trend—that is, recessions followed by recoveries and expansions. However, nothing is very regular about the timing and magnitude of these fluctuations.

Chart 3-1 **Gross National Product Per Capita, 1870-1990**
While there have been occasional interruptions, real GNP per capita has been rising since 1870.

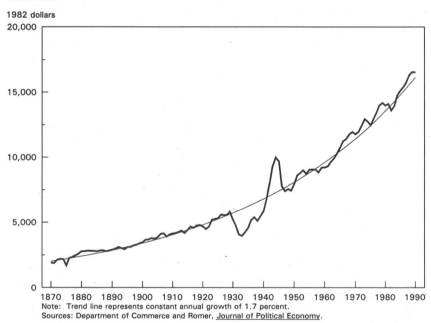

1982 dollars

Note: Trend line represents constant annual growth of 1.7 percent.
Sources: Department of Commerce and Romer, Journal of Political Economy.

In the long run, aggregate output grows because of increases in the quality and quantity of physical capital, the knowledge and skill of workers, the size of the labor force, advances in technology, improved resource allocation through trade expansion and a more dynamic market system, and the entrepreneurial process that creates new businesses and products. These factors do not grow at a constant rate; this explains a small part of the variations in output. The major short-term fluctuations, however, do not reflect primarily changes in the productive capacity of the economy, but changes in its rate of utilization. For example, during economic declines the labor force is not fully utilized, as indicated by high unemployment rates.

The Great Depression, which began in late 1929, was the largest decline in economic activity in recorded U.S. history. Output fell by nearly 30 percent during the first 3 years of the Depression. The unemployment rate had risen to 25 percent by 1933 and remained well above 10 percent until the early 1940s (Chart 3-2). By comparison, output has fallen an average of 2.7 percent during post-World War II recessions. In the most severe of these, which began in the fourth quarter of 1973, real output fell 4.9 percent and the unemployment rate peaked at 9.0 percent. The 1981-82 recession, which began in an already weak economy, involved a smaller decline in output of 3.3 percent, but the unemployment rate reached 10.8 percent. In contrast, in the recent recession, output declined 2.2 percent and the unemployment rate later peaked at 7.7 percent. (The basis for cyclical comparisons is discussed in detail in Table 2-2.)

The relative stability of the postwar era may reflect fewer or less severe disturbances. But it also may be due to the development of public and private institutions and policies designed to offset temporary disruptions or to help the economy adjust. These institutions are particularly important in light of the fact that the costs of recessions are not shared evenly across the population. For most families, incomes remain roughly the same or continue to grow during a recession; the economic and social costs of recessions fall disproportionately on those who experience or are threatened with unemployment or reduced employment.

The experience of the United States is not unique. All modern industrial economies grow at uneven rates. Recessions in the United States often coincide with slowdowns in the economies of its trading partners because many of the factors affecting the economy, such as oil price changes, affect other economies as well. Trade and capital flows that link national economies also transmit purely domestic economic shocks from one country to others.

CAUSES OF RECESSIONS

Can carefully chosen policies eliminate recessions entirely? The answer, unfortunately, is that they almost certainly cannot, although well-designed policies may reduce the frequency and severity of economic downturns. To understand the limitations of policy,

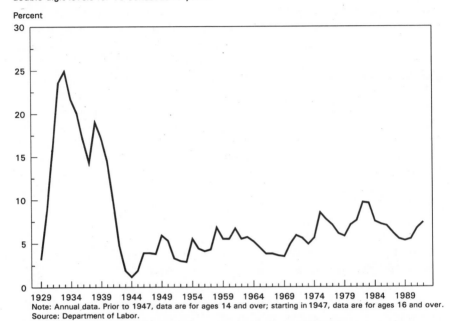

Chart 3-2 **Civilian Unemployment Rate**
During the Great Depression the unemployment rate reached 25 percent and remained at double-digit levels for 10 consecutive years.

Percent

Note: Annual data. Prior to 1947, data are for ages 14 and over; starting in 1947, data are for ages 16 and over.
Source: Department of Labor.

the factors that contribute to recessions must be taken into account. They can be broadly classified as structural adjustments, external events (also called shocks), and policy mistakes. At any given time, the economy may be struggling to overcome one or more of these adverse factors. Recessions occur when a number of unfavorable factors exist simultaneously or an unusually large problem arises.

A sharp reduction in expenditures on national defense, for example, gives rise to structural adjustments in production and employment. Such reductions followed World War II, the Korean and Vietnam wars, and are now taking place in response to the end of the Cold War. The Nation on the whole is better off when a conflict ends and the resources devoted to national defense can be put to other uses. Nonetheless, large decreases in military spending disrupt production and employment as production patterns adjust to meet changing demands. The temporary declines in output and increases in unemployment following World War II and the Korean war illustrate the costs that are incurred while resources are reallocated.

External shocks in the form of large and sudden oil price increases have been an important factor in several recent recessions. The partial embargo on oil exports by the Organization of Petroleum Exporting Countries in 1973 tripled world oil prices. Since oil is an important input in production, oil price shocks may lead industries to change their production patterns. For example, oil-fueled plants may be refitted to run on coal. Further, since the United States is a net oil importer, it would pay more for its imported oil, thereby transferring income and wealth to oil exporting countries and reducing the overall demand for domestic output.

In some instances policy mistakes have contributed to economic downturns. The Great Depression is perhaps the best example. Even after production and prices had begun to decline sharply, monetary policy remained contractionary by most measures. The 1930 passage of the Hawley-Smoot Tariff Act raised tariffs on many imports, leading our trading partners to retaliate and disrupting global trade flows. With the economy still mired in depression in 1932, a tax increase was enacted in an effort to balance the budget. But by reducing disposable income and household spending, the tax increase deepened the Depression. This series of policy blunders turned what could have been a moderate or severe recession into the Great Depression.

Even if no policy mistakes are made, however, structural adjustments and external shocks may cause occasional periods of declining output. It is unrealistic to expect that well-chosen policies can always compensate completely for all types of disturbances and eliminate recessions entirely.

THE LIMITS OF POLICY

The extent to which fiscal and monetary policies can mitigate short-term economic fluctuations has been the subject of debate. Views on this subject have evolved considerably in recent decades, and will undoubtedly continue to evolve as circumstances change and new policies are tried.

The Activist Approach

The Keynesian view, which reached its peak of influence in the 1960s, advocated government spending increases and tax cuts, supported by expansionary monetary policy, to stimulate overall demand whenever output fell below the economy's estimated capacity to produce. More restrictive policies were advocated when inflation became a greater concern. Many economists believed that a stable tradeoff existed between unemployment and inflation rates: Expansionary policies would lower unemployment at the cost of somewhat higher—but not continually rising—inflation. It was believed that "activist" or "fine-tuning" policies could increase demand whenever the economy was below capacity, reducing business cycle fluctuations and at the same time increasing long-term growth in the economy's capacity. Such policies frequently changed course in response to short-term economic developments.

Impediments to Fine-Tuning

The foundation of the activist approach was discredited by the historical experience of the 1960s and 1970s. Output grew rapidly in the 1960s, but inflation, as measured by the rate of change in the consumer price index, rose from 0.7 percent during 1961 to 6.2 percent during 1969. In the 1970s the economy experienced many difficulties, including large simultaneous increases in both inflation and unemployment. This development contradicted the idea that a stable tradeoff existed between inflation and unemployment and led to a rethinking of the efficacy of fine-tuning.

It has become clear that a number of factors, including delays, forecasting difficulties, and uncertainty about the economy's response, make fine-tuning unreliable at best. Furthermore, well-intentioned policies may actually increase business cycle fluctuations.

Policymaking is complicated by a number of delays, or lags. The information available on the current state of the economy is imperfect; most data for a particular month or quarter are not available until the next month or quarter and are often revised substantially. As a result, policymakers learn that the economy has changed direction only after the fact, resulting in a recognition lag. But even after it becomes clear that the economy has weakened, delays in the political process create lags in implementing specific policies. For instance, most fiscal policies require time-consuming congressional action and then must be approved by the Administration, creating an action lag between the time problems develop and action is taken. Finally, even after new policies are implemented, further lags may occur before economic activity is affected. A reduction in tax rates, for example, may initially have little effect on consumption or investment because time elapses before consumers and businesses can respond fully. Thus, expansionary countercyclical actions will have their intended effect only if the economy would have remained weak well into the future.

Because of the various lags, policymakers must rely on economic forecasts in setting policies. Economic forecasting is an imprecise science; it is particularly difficult around business cycle turning points. Fortunately, market economies have many self-correcting tendencies that eventually reduce the effects of external shocks or structural imbalances. As noted, disturbances such as oil price shocks or reductions in defense spending create a need for changes in patterns of production. Growth in output tends to fall as these adjustments begin but resumes as they are completed. While these self-correcting tendencies are a desirable feature of market economies, the pace at which adjustments occur is unpredictable, compli-

78

cating the forecasting process and raising the possibility that a recovery may be well under way before the economy receives significant stimulus from policies introduced to fight the recession. In this case, such policies may cause higher inflation but only small gains in production.

A further impediment to fine-tuning is uncertainty about how the economy will respond to changes in fiscal and monetary policy. The economic response to a particular policy change depends in part on people's expectations about future policies. For instance, firms and households may view economic policies as temporary under a fine-tuning regime because policy changes can be expected to occur relatively frequently. Unpredictable policies may complicate the task of long-term planning for firms and households, discouraging investment and undermining long-term economic growth.

Fine-Tuning and Inflation

The costs of high and variable inflation are considerable but more subtle than the costs of recessions. In a market economy, prices provide essential information about the relative scarcity of goods and services. High and volatile inflation obscures this information and distorts the allocation of resources. Furthermore, unexpected inflation arbitrarily redistributes income and wealth. It hurts lenders and people on fixed incomes and helps borrowers, since the real value of interest and principal payments is eroded by inflation.

Inflation also has unintended effects on the tax structure that affect incentives to work, save, and invest. The Economic Recovery Tax Act of 1981 indexed income tax brackets for inflation beginning in 1985, but some taxes on capital income are still affected by inflation. For example, capital gains are not indexed for inflation, and depreciation allowances are effectively reduced by inflation because they are based on original rather than replacement cost. These features of the tax system cause inflation to both reduce the real after-tax return on capital assets and discourage investment.

The late 1940s and early 1950s were marked by dramatic changes in inflation rates associated with the aftermath of World War II and the beginning of the Korean war (Chart 3-3). From 1952 into the mid-1960s, however, inflation never exceeded 3 percent. The rate of inflation then began to increase, albeit erratically, reaching double digits in 1974 and again in 1979 and 1980. *In fact, from 1960 to 1980 inflation was higher at each successive business cycle peak, and each recovery also began with a higher inflation rate than the preceding one.*

Why did the fine-tuning policies pursued during this period contribute to rising and variable inflation? If expansionary policies stimulate demand when the economy is already approaching capac-

79

Chart 3-3   Consumer Price Inflation
During the 1960s and 1970s the inflation rate reached a higher level at each successive
business cycle peak. This upward trend was reversed in the 1980s.

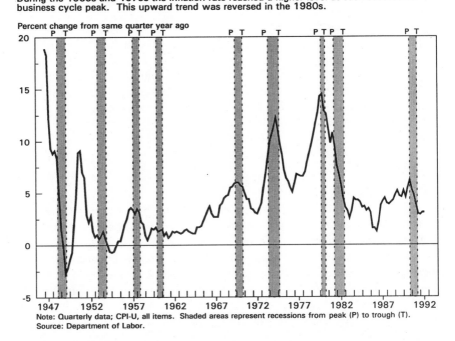

Note: Quarterly data; CPI-U, all items. Shaded areas represent recessions from peak (P) to trough (T).
Source: Department of Labor.

ity, they may increase output temporarily but then, after some lag,
increase prices. In particular, a monetary policy that produces
growth in money that persistently exceeds growth in real output
inevitably leads to inflation. If expansionary policies are expected
to continue, people may anticipate higher future inflation rates as
well, complicating the process of reversing inflation.

One danger of fine-tuning is that expansionary policies may
become addictive. Political considerations can cause policymakers
to favor short-term stimulus to expand output and employment relative to policies to control inflation. This is one of the reasons why
inflation was higher at the end of each recession between 1960 and
1980. Policymakers may also simply overestimate the economy's capacity, especially when structural adjustments or external shocks
are temporarily slowing the growth of capacity. If expansionary
policies persist after the economy is near capacity, output and employment will increase very little, but inflation will continue to
rise.

Because of the considerable costs of inflation, episodes of high
and variable inflation lead to policy actions to contain or reverse it.
Reducing inflation—that is, disinflating—after an extended period

80

of rising or high inflation tends to result in reduced output growth and increased unemployment. The recession of 1981–82, during which unemployment rates rose to almost 11 percent, was in part a consequence of the policies introduced to reverse the rising inflation that had developed throughout the 1960s and 1970s. An important accomplishment of the past 12 years has been the reduction and subsequent containment of inflation, achieved in part by adherence to a credible, systematic monetary policy.

Alternatives to Fine-Tuning

Fine-tuning is complicated by a number of factors such as variable and uncertain lags, the need for accurate forecasts, and the temptation to pursue overly expansionary policies. Furthermore, frequent policy changes complicate the task of long-term planning for firms and households, discouraging investment and undermining long-run economic growth.

An alternative to fine-tuning that avoids some of these difficulties is the establishment of systematic and clearly stated policy plans consistent with the long-term objectives of high and stable output growth and low and stable inflation. Credibility is achieved over time both as plans are carried out and long-term objectives are accomplished. Even if policymakers aim to follow a systematic policy, however, it is not always possible to specify all contingencies, and changes in the economy may occasionally require that plans be revised. For example, if the relationship between money growth rates and output shifts, the targets for monetary growth will need to be adjusted. Similarly, high and persistent budget deficits may necessitate changes in fiscal policies.

Fine-tuning policies can be likened to a weathervane. Just as the weathervane changes direction with the wind, fine-tuning policies frequently shift in response to changes in the economy. Adhering to systematic policies, on the other hand, is much like following a course laid out by a compass. Just as travellers deviate from the compass headings only if an obstacle such as a mountain lies in their path, policymakers deviate from their plans only if a severe or protracted economic contraction or rising inflation is at hand. In contrast to fine-tuning, systematic policies do not change in response to small, temporary variations in the rate of growth. Any deviations from the announced plans are explained in the context of long-term policy goals, so as not to undermine future credibility. One might call such a policy "gross-tuning," to distinguish it from both fine-tuning and from the notion that policies should be set according to rigid rules which are mechanically followed regardless of actual and prospective developments in the economy.

SUMMARY

- The United States and other modern industrial economies experience occasional periods of recession when output declines and unemployment rises.
- Recessions can result from a number of factors that impede growth, including unavoidable structural imbalances, external disturbances, and government policy errors.
- Monetary and fiscal policies may be able to mitigate recessions, but they cannot eliminate business cycle fluctuations completely. Overly aggressive attempts to do so are likely to lead to higher inflation and impede long-term growth in output.

RECENT ECONOMIC DEVELOPMENTS

Recent monetary and fiscal policies have been heavily influenced by the legacy of the preceding two decades, most notably by the rising inflation of the late 1960s and 1970s and the emergence of large budget deficits during the long expansion of the 1980s. Many structural imbalances, some of which had their roots in the 1970s, worsened the recent recession and slowed the subsequent recovery. In addition, the economy was buffeted by an oil price shock after Iraq invaded Kuwait in August 1990.

MACROECONOMIC POLICIES AND ECONOMIC PERFORMANCE IN THE 1980s

The economy entered the 1980s with declining production and high inflation. After rising rapidly in the late 1970s, inflation reached a peak of 13.3 percent during 1979—the highest rate since the aftermath of World War II. Faced with high and rising inflation, the Federal Reserve announced new measures that were intended to signal its unwillingness to finance a continuing inflationary process. The 1979 Annual Report of the Board of Governors of the Federal Reserve System noted that "the System's day-to-day operating procedures would be altered in a way expected to make the achievement of growth targets for the monetary aggregates more certain. Specifically, policy would be conducted with greater emphasis on supplying reserves to member banks at a rate believed consistent with growth objectives for monetary aggregates; and less attention would be focused on short-term interest rates as a guide for open market operations." Focusing on short-term interest rates "had become less reliable in an environment of rapid and variable inflation."

Efforts to curb inflation were costly. The economy suffered a brief but steep recession from January to July of 1980, during which output fell by 2.3 percent and unemployment rose to 7.8 percent. Inflation edged downward slightly to 12.5 percent during 1980. After a brief period of growth, the economy entered another recession in July 1981 that lasted until November 1982. This recession was unusually severe, with unemployment rates climbing above 10 percent for the first time since 1941.

While the recession was painful, the loss of output was actually far below the levels that many models had predicted would be necessary to achieve the dramatic reduction in inflation that occurred. By the time the economy emerged from the recession of 1981–82, core inflation—which excludes the volatile food and energy components—had fallen below 5 percent. One reason models overestimated the loss in output was that they neglected to take into account the fact that credible policies could lower inflationary expectations and lead to a faster and less costly reduction in inflation.

After a difficult 3-year period, the longest peacetime expansion in modern U.S. history began in late 1982. As is often the case, the early phase of recovery was marked by rapid growth in output as idle resources came back into use. In 1983 real gross domestic product (GDP) grew by 3.9 percent. GDP growth increased to 6.2 percent in 1984, faster than during any year since 1951. By the end of 1984, many of the previously idle resources had been brought back into use and real output expanded at a rate of about 3 percent from 1985 to 1989. Job growth in the 1982–89 period was remarkable. Nonagricultural payrolls increased by 18 million, from 90 million in 1982 to 108 million in 1989, exceeding the combined increase in employment in Western Europe and Japan, with their much larger total population, over the same period.

Fiscal and Monetary Policy in the 1980s

Growth in government expenditures on programs such as defense and medicare contributed to demand during the 1980s. Federal Government spending as a share of GDP rose from 20.2 percent in 1979 to 23.4 percent by 1985. Substantial changes in the tax structure in 1981 increased incentives to work and invest. Total tax receipts, however, changed little as a percentage of GDP. By the mid-1980s, the combination of growing government spending and stable tax receipts had resulted in budget deficits that were large relative to the size of the economy, particularly for a peacetime expansion. The Federal budget deficit averaged about 5 percent of GDP from 1984 to 1986.

In response to growing concern about the deficit, the Federal Government in 1985 adopted (and later amended) the Balanced Budget and Emergency Deficit Control Act, known as Gramm-Rudman-Hollings (GRH), which seemed to be somewhat successful in slowing the growth of government expenditures. While the original deficit targets under the GRH were never met, deficits did fall to about 3 percent of GDP by 1989. Still, containing spending growth and reducing the deficit remained major fiscal policy issues as the economy entered the 1990s.

While real output and employment grew steadily following the 1981–82 recession, the rate of inflation—in contrast to the 1970s— remained relatively stable. Core inflation hovered around the 4- to 5-percent range from 1982 to 1988. While low compared to the rates of the late 1970s, these rates would have been deemed unacceptable just two decades earlier. Many argued in favor of a second round of disinflation. However, the Fed had eased credit conditions in late 1987 and early 1988 in order to counter any economic weakness and to ensure the smooth functioning of financial markets in the wake of the stock market crash of October 1987. It soon became clear that the economy had remained strong in spite of the crash, with unemployment rates hovering around 5½ percent and monetary aggregates growing at rates near the top of their target ranges in early 1988. Concerns about inflationary pressures rose relative to concerns about the possibility of recession.

A Shift in Policy

Mindful of the cost of reversing rising inflation in the early 1980s, the Fed tightened reserve conditions in a series of steps beginning in March 1988 and continuing into 1989. The Fed target for growth in M2, a key measure of the money stock, was lowered from the 4- to 8-percent range in 1988 to the 3- to 7-percent range in 1989. The Federal funds rate (a key short-term interest rate) rose by more than 3 percentage points between March 1988 and March 1989. This policy change is often referred to as the "soft-landing" strategy. Its presumed objective was a slow deceleration of the economy that would head off an incipient rise in inflation, and possibly even lower it, without causing a recession. This strategy represented a welcome break from the policies of the 1960s and 1970s, which typically had reacted to inflation only *after* it had risen significantly, thereby imposing greater costs in terms of lost output and higher unemployment during the disinflation process.

The soft-landing strategy was laudable but went unappreciated by many observers. Preemptive measures to contain inflation may go unnoticed whereas measures to reduce inflation after it has already risen are painfully obvious. The latter may receive more praise, even though the former may reflect a much wiser policy.

STRUCTURAL IMBALANCES IN THE ECONOMY

Even though the economy experienced strong growth in the mid- to late-1980s, several structural imbalances were building that would contribute to the most recent recession and subsequent slow recovery. Problems in the financial sector led to a credit crunch, high debt levels burdened households and corporations and inhibited spending, the end of the Cold War led to reductions in defense spending, corporate restructuring hindered employment growth, overcapacity in commercial real estate discouraged new construction, and budget problems constrained the spending of State and local governments.

The Credit Crunch

After a period of relatively easy credit in the mid-1980s, bankers and bank regulators appear to have adopted much more stringent standards near the end of the decade, although regional credit problems had occurred earlier. Companies that could easily obtain financing in the past had difficulty finding new bank loans; they faced a "credit crunch." In practice, it is difficult to quantify a credit crunch. A reduction in bank lending during a recession can be caused by weak demand, limited supply, or a combination of the two. Nevertheless, there is evidence that a credit crunch has been at work in the latest recession and recovery.

Banks play a unique role in financial markets, specializing in obtaining and analyzing information on the creditworthiness of small firms that often have difficulty obtaining credit elsewhere. As a result, the effects of the recent credit crunch were concentrated on small businesses and some types of commercial real estate that have limited alternative funding sources. Medium-sized and large corporations appear to have been less affected, since they can borrow in the commercial paper and bond markets, where firms obtain financing by issuing securities directly to investors. The effects were also concentrated geographically, with California and the Northeast experiencing the tightest credit conditions.

One reason for the shift in bank lending practices was a shift in regulatory policy. During the steady growth of the 1980s, regulators were perhaps too sanguine, exerting insufficient control on risk-taking by banks and savings and loans (S&Ls). By the late 1980s, however, the situation had changed. The magnitude of the S&L problems had come to light, and it became clear that the government-backed insurance fund for savings and loans (the Federal Savings and Loan Insurance Corporation, or FSLIC) would go bankrupt, causing heavy taxpayer losses. The economy was beginning to slow, and bad loans were weakening many banks. Recognizing that banks were also susceptible to large losses, regulators became concerned about the strength of all insured financial institutions. The Congress passed two bills—the Financial Institution Reform, Recovery, and Enforcement Act of 1989 and the FDIC Improvement Act of 1991—which contained several features that inadvertently contributed to the credit crunch and restricted bank lending (Chapter 5).

Regulators worldwide focused on the need to rebuild bank capital (Box 3-1). A bank's capital is the difference between the value of its assets (reserves, loans, and securities) and the value of its liabilities (primarily deposits). In 1988 the industrialized nations agreed to a common set of capital standards for financial institutions, known as the Basle Accords. While most U.S. banks already met the new risk-based capital standards, some fell short. Furthermore, the new rules failed to mandate adequate reserves for government bonds in comparison with commercial loans, unintentionally providing an incentive for banks to shift their assets into government bonds and away from commercial loans—a tendency some have suggested contributed to the decline in commercial lending (Chart 3-4).

Chart 3-4 **Loans and Securities Held by U.S. Commercial Banks**
Commercial banks have shifted their assets into government securities and away from commerical loans.

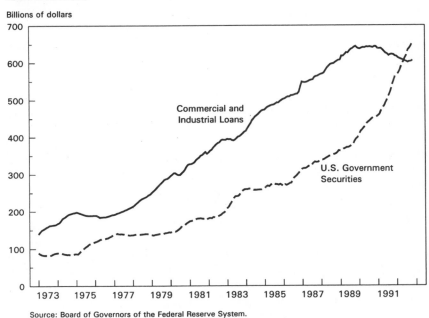

Source: Board of Governors of the Federal Reserve System.

The combination of higher capital standards and lower asset values created a "capital crunch" for banks. To increase capital, banks had to reduce their asset holdings, raise more capital, or both. Since raising capital quickly is often expensive, many banks chose to reduce assets by cutting back on lending, which increases the ratio of capital to assets because capital remains approximately the same while assets shrink. In this sense, the capital crunch for banks appears to have contributed to the credit crunch for businesses.

Box 3-1.—The Role of Bank Capital

Bank regulators set minimum capital standards for two reasons. First, capital absorbs losses that would otherwise have to be paid by the Federal Deposit Insurance Corporation (FDIC) or taxpayers (if the losses were large enough). Another important motive for ensuring that banks have sufficient capital is to reduce the perverse incentives caused by deposit insurance. When a bank is close to bankruptcy, it may invest in risky projects that have a high rate of return if they succeed. Because the FDIC will absorb any insured losses, the bank is willing to take a gamble that could keep it from failing.

The underlying weakness in the capital position of U.S. financial institutions in recent years can be traced to a number of causes. For the S&Ls, the problems can be traced back to losses suffered in the late 1970s, when rising inflation and rising interest rates caused the value of their mortgage loans to plummet and their funding costs to rise. These difficulties were compounded by losses on risky investments made in the 1980s following deregulation, a situation discussed in Chapter 5.

The problems facing commercial banks were more varied and on the whole not as severe. In the early 1980s, large banks suffered major losses on loans to Third World countries. While these had become less of a problem by 1990, the banks soon experienced a new wave of losses. The average commercial bank loan has become more risky in recent years, in part because established firms can borrow at more favorable terms from sources such as the commercial paper market. Losses from defaults on real estate loans, particularly in regions where property values were falling, further eroded bank capital. Conversely, many believe that tighter credit conditions contributed to the fall in property values by creating a shortage of financing for real estate investments.

Bank capital increased markedly in 1992 due to record banking industry profits and improvements in loan performance. However, a continuing challenge for bank regulators is to strike a balance between the need to ensure that banks have sufficient capital and the need to allow banks the necessary flexibility to provide the credit essential for economic growth.

The Buildup of Household and Corporate Debt

In addition to the constraints on the supply of credit, a number of factors contributed to unusual softness in the demand for credit.

Consumers entered the 1990s with high levels of outstanding debt relative to their income. The ratio of household interest payments to income remained between 14 and 16 percent from mid-1960 until 1983 but had grown to 18 percent by the end of the 1980s (Chart 3-5). An increase in corporate indebtedness in the 1980s was brought about by a wave of financial restructurings. Tax laws that continued to heavily favor debt over equity encouraged this trend. The rise in the share of income devoted to interest payments began to act as a constraint on private sector spending as income declined and prospects for future growth dimmed.

Chart 3-5   Debt Service Payments as Percent of Disposable Income
Household interest payments climbed from 14.2 percent of disposable income in 1983 to 18.1 percent in 1990.

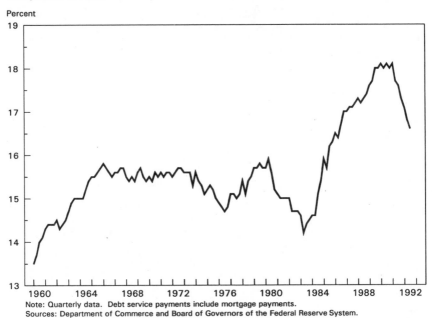

Percent

Note: Quarterly data. Debt service payments include mortgage payments.
Sources: Department of Commerce and Board of Governors of the Federal Reserve System.

Recently corporate and household balance sheets have begun to strengthen. In 1992 corporations issued a record volume of new equity, increasing their ability to borrow in the future. Much existing corporate debt has been refinanced at lower rates, and new bond issues have been on the rise. The ratio of household interest payments to income has fallen back to approximately 16½ percent.

Defense Spending Reductions

Outlays on defense, which had increased substantially during the first half of the 1980s, peaked at 6.5 percent of GDP in 1986, then flattened and began to decline slightly (Chart 3-6). Soon thereafter, it became apparent that defense spending was likely to be cut substantially during the 1990s due to reforms in the Soviet Union and Eastern Europe. The President's budget for fiscal 1993 calls for defense outlays in fiscal 1997 to fall to an estimated 3.7 percent of GDP.

Chart 3-6 **National Defense Outlays**
After rising to 6.5 percent of GDP in fiscal 1986, national defense outlays are projected to decline to 3.7 percent of GDP in fiscal 1997.

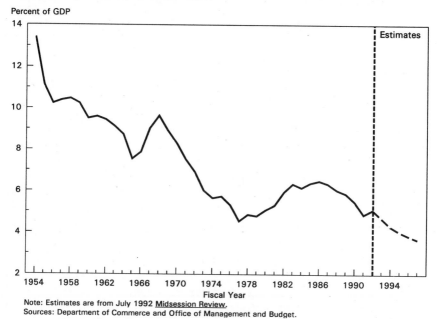

Note: Estimates are from July 1992 Midsession Review.
Sources: Department of Commerce and Office of Management and Budget.

Reductions in defense spending have many ramifications. Overall the Nation will benefit, since more resources will be available to provide other goods and services. As mentioned earlier, however, certain transitional problems are associated with drawdowns. Workers no longer needed in the defense industry will not be hired immediately by nondefense firms, resulting in some transitional unemployment.

Some have argued that the recent and prospective reductions in defense spending will have little effect on economic performance, even in the short run, since they represent a smaller share of GDP than previous reductions and are scheduled over a longer period of time. However, the short-term impact of defense spending reductions is evident in the changes in unemployment rates across States. Unemployment in the four States most heavily dependent on defense industry purchases—Connecticut, Virginia, Massachusetts, and California—rose by 4.1 percentage points between 1988 and September 1992. Meanwhile, the combined unemployment rate for all other States rose by only 1.5 percentage points. These figures indicate that defense reductions are a substantial drag on the economy today. Although the level of defense spending should be shaped by national security needs rather than concern about temporary economic dislocations, such dislocations will increase in the event of even deeper budget cuts.

The short-term impact of current defense reductions may be larger than many expected for several reasons. First, the relatively gradual rate of spending reductions may be misleading. Because businesses plan for the future, they are likely to adjust their work forces and equipment purchases as soon as they are aware of impending reductions, rather than waiting until the cuts actually occur. In addition, defense industry workers fearing the possibility of permanent job loss are likely to reduce their spending today. Uncertainty about the nature and size of the reductions increases the number of workers who feel vulnerable. Finally, the increasingly specialized nature of defense and commercial production suggests that defense industry workers—including highly skilled scientists and engineers—and perhaps some military personnel may have greater difficulty finding comparable nondefense employment now than they would have 20 years ago.

The changes in State unemployment rates show that the short-term impacts of defense reductions will be severe in some regions. In some instances, defense spending reductions have coincided with property deflation and banking problems. Southern California is a prime example. By reducing employment opportunities and income substantially in certain regions, the defense drawdown exacerbated declines in property values. As noted in Box 3-1, falling property values combined with increased default rates on real estate loans have eroded bank capital. Until these structural problems begin to be resolved and credit conditions ease, high unemployment may persist in regions such as Southern California.

Industry Restructuring

Defense downsizing is an example of industry restructuring in which long-term adjustment occurs in response to changing conditions. In this case, restructuring is a response to a lessening of the threat to national security. Although in other cases the underlying sources of change may be more difficult to identify, restructurings occur continuously in a market economy; some industries grow rapidly while others decline. Technological breakthroughs, shifts in consumer preferences, fluctuations in input prices, changes in domestic and international competition, and countless other influences require firms and industries to adjust constantly in order to remain profitable.

The degree of industry restructuring appears to have been un-usually great during the recent recession. Chart 2-7 in Chapter 2 shows that the percentage of unemployed workers who have per-manently lost their current jobs rather than just being laid off reached an all-time high of over 45 percent in October 1992. This job loss is in part a result of the weak economy, but it is also an indication that U.S. industries are making the painful long-term adjustments necessary to increase their productivity and remain competitive in international markets. Productivity in the nonfarm business sector has been rising rapidly in the last six quarters, partly because of these restructurings (Chart 3-7). History shows that the Nation's living standards are ultimately linked to produc-tivity levels, so these adjustments are a positive long-term develop-ment. In the short run, however, restructurings are likely to in-crease the length of time workers remain unemployed, since dis-placed workers must find new employment rather than simply waiting to be recalled to their former jobs.

Chart 3-7 **Output per Hour, Nonfarm Business Sector**
The recent period of strong productivity growth is the largest six-quarter gain in nonfarm business productivity since 1982-83.

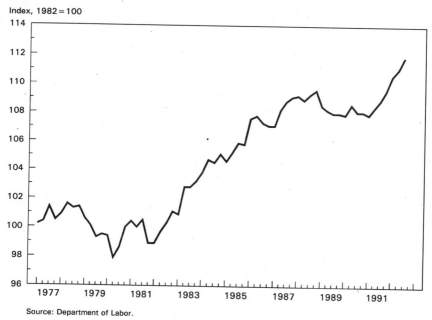

Index, 1982 = 100

Source: Department of Labor.

Slowdown in Commercial Construction

Investment spending in general and construction in particular undergo more severe fluctuations than the rest of the economy. Be-

91

cause of the long life of structures, small changes in interest rates or tax policies strongly affect demand for this type of investment.

Commercial real estate has recently undergone a pronounced cycle of "boom and bust." Changes in the tax code in 1981 greatly increased the incentive to invest in new commercial real estate. The annual average rate of spending on nonresidential structures from 1981 through 1985 rose 25 percent in real terms over the previous 5-year period, in spite of the steep recession of 1981–82. The 1986 tax act reversed and in fact further reduced the incentives for commercial real estate introduced in the 1981 law. As the new measures were phased in, the real estate boom gradually ended. The overbuilding that occurred during the first half of the 1980s and the credit crunch in recent years would probably have ended this boom even without the tax changes. Vacancy rates for commercial office space, for example, had risen sharply by the mid-1980s in many metropolitan areas.

Changes in tax laws, interest rates, and demographics contributed to a slowdown in the construction of multifamily housing units. The 1986 tax reforms reversed the incentives not only for commercial real estate but also for multifamily housing units. Increases in interest rates in the late 1980s raised the cost of financing new construction projects. Furthermore, as the "baby-boom" generation matured, the rate of household formation declined. The number of multifamily housing units under construction rose from 379,000 in 1981 to 670,000 in 1985, before falling back to 373,000 in 1989.

Reduced residential construction tends to reduce the purchase of consumer durables, such as furniture and home appliances, as well. Housing starts and building permits in 1992 were well above their 1991 levels, but demographic trends suggest that neither household formation nor housing starts will return to the levels of the 1960s and 1970s anytime soon.

State and Local Fiscal Developments

Most States are prohibited from running a budget deficit, and local budgets showed relatively large surpluses in the mid-1980s. However, State and local government expenditures have risen substantially in recent years. Because tax revenues failed to keep pace with expenditures, combined State and local government surpluses had fallen to half the level of the mid-1980's by 1990. These budget problems meant that expenditures could not easily be increased and taxes could not easily be reduced.

EXTERNAL EVENTS

By 1990 many structural adjustments were adversely affecting output growth: Banks had grown more cautious in their lending policies, high debt levels had reduced household and business spending, the defense industry was contracting, industry restructuring was hindering employment growth, construction had slowed considerably, and State and local fiscal spending was constrained. Of these factors, it was clear that at least two—reduced defense spending and the glut of commercial real estate—would be continuing drags on the economy for some time to come.

The effects of these structural adjustments were aggravated by external events. The Iraqi invasion of Kuwait in August 1990 caused world oil prices to double. This oil price shock was a further drag on growth in the United States and other oil-importing industrial economies. Economic slowdowns that developed in some foreign countries made economic recovery in the United States more difficult by reducing demand for U.S. exports.

The Oil Price Shock

In the wake of the Iraqi invasion, the world price of oil soared, roughly doubling between July and October 1990. Consumer and business confidence plummeted, reflecting uncertainty about the standoff in the Persian Gulf. In October 1990 the Conference Board's index of consumer confidence reached its lowest level since 1974 (Chart 3–8). In an uncertain environment, it is natural for firms to postpone spending until they begin to feel more confident about the future. Similarly, many households postpone purchasing big-ticket items until they have solid information about their own employment situation. Oil price increases also disrupt the production process as firms seek to economize on energy.

Real output in the economy declined in the third and fourth quarters of 1990 and the first quarter of 1991. Civilian nonagricultural employment peaked at just over 115 million in May 1990 and then fell gradually below 114 million by January 1991. The oil price shock put upward pressure on energy prices, but weak demand muted the impact on other prices. The annual rate of core inflation rose by less than one-half percentage point between the first and second half of 1990.

As the Persian Gulf conflict was resolved, oil prices fell back to pre-crisis levels and consumer and business confidence increased sharply. These developments led to a sudden burst of consumer spending (Chart 3–8) and gains in production. The short-lived euphoria after the Persian Gulf crisis was not sufficient to generate a strong recovery, however, because the structural problems had not been satisfactorily resolved. Debt burdens remained high, commercial and industrial lending were declining, and it became apparent that defense reductions would accelerate due to marked changes in the relationship between the United States and the Soviet Union.

Although real output began to grow again in the second quarter of 1991, employment hovered between 113 and 114 million for the rest of the year. Output grew slowly, but only because output per worker increased; employment changed little.

93

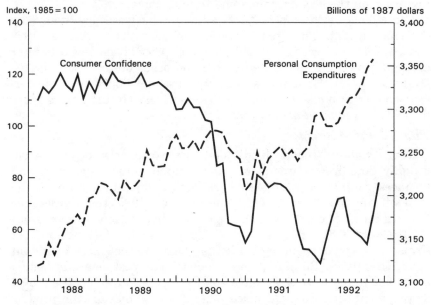

Chart 3-8   **Consumer Confidence and Personal Consumption Expenditures**
Driven in part by the drop in consumer confidence during the Gulf War, personal consumption expenditures fell in late 1990 before beginning to rise in early 1991.

Index, 1985 = 100   Billions of 1987 dollars

Sources: Department of Commerce and the Conference Board.

The Worldwide Slowdown

Exports provided a source of growth in output in the United States throughout the 1980s and even during the recession of 1990–91. Unfortunately, many major U.S. trading partners began experiencing recession or slower growth just as the U.S. economy was beginning to recover (Chart 3-9). Recessions in Canada and the United Kingdom that were associated with, among other causes, very tight monetary policies intended to secure large reductions in inflation, began about the same time as the U.S. recession, but have been much more severe, with unemployment rates exceeding 10 percent. Although Germany and Japan continued to grow faster than the United States in 1990 and 1991, recent data indicate that they have both entered recession. As a result of these foreign economic slowdowns, the demand for U.S. exports has been lower than it otherwise would have been.

Some of the same structural problems that slowed the U.S. economy were affecting foreign economies as well. In Japan, the huge increase in stock prices during the 1980s was reversed at the end of the decade, with the Nikkei stock market average plummeting 58.6 percent between December 1989 and August 1992. Real estate

Chart 3-9   International Real GDP Growth
As the U.S. economy began to recover, output growth in Germany and Japan weakened considerably.

Percent change, IV/IV

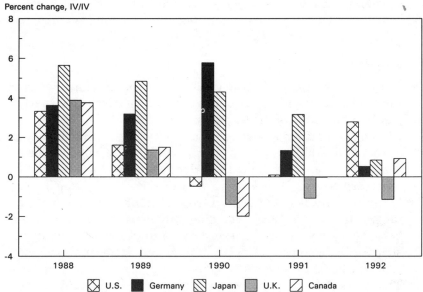

Note: Data for Japan and Germany are for GNP. Changes for 1992 are 1992.III/ 1991.IV at an annual rate.
Sources: Organization for Economic Cooperation and Development and The Economist.

prices also fell: Residential land prices in the six largest cities decreased 20.6 percent from the second half of 1990 to the first half of 1992. These developments may depress Japanese spending by lowering household wealth and could constrain lending since many loans are collateralized with real estate. The Japanese slowdown appears to be worsening; output declined 0.4 percent in the third quarter of 1992.

Germany has had to confront the high costs of unification. Government spending on income assistance programs has soared since east and west were united in 1990, putting upward pressure on both output and prices. Union wage demands have exceeded productivity growth, putting more upward pressure on costs and prices. Fearing an increase in inflation, the Bundesbank (Germany's central bank) pursued a tight monetary policy, forcing other European countries to adopt tighter monetary policies in order to maintain parities under the European Monetary System. Output growth has slowed significantly throughout Europe in recent years.

Recent Developments

As indicated in Chapter 2, the U.S. economy has made modest improvements over the past year. Output has grown in each quar-

95

ter since the first quarter of 1991, although the somewhat erratic growth has been insufficient to support substantial increases in employment. Meanwhile, the rate of core inflation has fallen to levels not seen in this country for 20 years. These recent developments, viewed against the backdrop of the structural adjustments and external shocks that have affected the economy, provide the context in which recent policy choices must be evaluated.

SUMMARY

- Output grew rapidly during 1982–86, but the development of a relatively large Federal budget deficit during this period placed constraints on fiscal policy.
- Although inflation was reduced dramatically at the beginning of the 1980s, the Fed became concerned about a possible resurgence in 1988, leading to the adoption of a more restrictive monetary policy.
- Many structural imbalances were contributing to a slowdown in growth by mid-1990, including problems in financial markets, heavy debt burdens, the defense drawdown, industry restructuring, commercial overbuilding, and State and local government budget problems.
- The oil shock contributed to a recession beginning in the summer of 1990. The persistence of several structural problems and the slowdown in foreign economies weakened the recovery.

THE CHANNELS OF MONETARY POLICY

The goals and limitations of monetary policy can be best understood by first considering the basic channels through which monetary policy operates. Monetary policy is conducted by the Federal Reserve System (the Fed), which is the central bank of the United States. The Full Employment and Balanced Growth Act of 1978 directs the Fed to set ranges for the growth of monetary and credit aggregates (the money supply) taking into account "past and prospective developments in employment, unemployment, production, investment, real income, productivity, international trade and payments, and prices." The Fed is also responsible for maintaining the orderly functioning of the payments system and is one of several Federal banking regulators.

The Fed, whose 7 governors are chosen by the President with the consent of the Congress to serve staggered 14-year terms, is independent in the sense that its decisions do not have to be ratified by either the Administration or the Congress. This independent status allows the Fed to pursue the goal of low and stable inflation more effectively (Box 3–2). Nevertheless, the Fed sets policies that reflect the government's overall policy objectives and makes periodic reports to the Congress.

SHORT-TERM EFFECTS OF MONETARY POLICY

In setting monetary policy, the Fed states its objectives in terms of targets for short-term interest rates and target ranges for the growth rate of several measures of the money supply. Short-term interest rate targets are called "operating targets" because the Fed monitors interest rates almost continuously and generally can exert a high degree of control over them.

Interest and Exchange Rates

The Fed most frequently uses open market operations to influence short-term interest rates and credit conditions. To put downward pressure on interest rates, it buys U.S. Treasury securities in the open market. The increased demand for securities causes their prices to rise, or equivalently, their rates of return to fall. In paying for these purchases, the Fed increases the monetary base—the money financial institutions have on deposit at the Fed plus the currency in circulation.

While lower interest rates tend to stimulate spending on average, some groups cut spending in response to lower rates. Lower rates benefit borrowers but hurt savers. For example, senior citizens living off interest income from their savings suffer when interest rates fall.

As well as spurring increased domestic investment and spending, lower interest rates tend to increase demand by lowering the exchange value of the dollar. Lower U.S. interest rates encourage investment to be shifted to other countries where rates of return are higher, causing demand for U.S. dollars to drop and reducing the dollar's exchange value against foreign currencies. U.S. goods become cheaper for foreigners, encouraging U.S. exports, and foreign goods become more expensive for Americans, encouraging consumption of domestic products.

LONG-TERM CONSEQUENCES OF MONETARY POLICY

Expansionary policies increase nominal GDP, which is the total dollar value of goods and services produced in a year. Because the change in nominal GDP is the sum of the change in the price level and the change in the quantity of real output, an increase in nominal GDP may reflect higher output, higher prices, or a combination of the two. When the Fed pursues an expansionary monetary policy, the hope is, of course, to increase real output rather than inflation.

As discussed earlier, in response to an increase in demand firms tend, on average, to increase production when they have excess capacity and to increase prices when production approaches capacity. In a recession, many firms find themselves with excess capacity, so that monetary expansion is likely to show up predominantly as an increase in output. The closer the economy is to its capacity, the more likely it is that an increase in aggregate demand will increase inflation. But because monetary policy has long and variable lags, excessively high money growth today may not show up as inflation for many months or even years.

Monetary policy affects both current and future interest rates, in part because it affects people's expectations about future inflation. Distinguishing between real and nominal interest rates is essential to understand the effect of inflation on interest rates (Box 3-3). Nominal, or market, interest rates increase with the rate of anticipated inflation. Although the Fed may be able to temporarily reduce short-term interest rates by adding reserves to the banking system, this action may cause an increase in inflationary expectations that results in higher short-term interest rates in the future.

Box 3-3.—Real and Nominal Interest Rates

The promised return on a corporate bond, a mortgage, a government security, or a savings account is called a "nominal interest rate." A nominal interest rate is simply a promised rate of return, or dollars received tomorrow per dollar invested today. The expected real interest rate is the return after adjusting for expected inflation, or the nominal interest rate less the expected rate of inflation. For instance, if the bank offers a return of 10 percent on 1-year certificates of deposit, but prices are expected to increase by 6 percent over the course of the year, the expected real return is only about 4 percent, since it is anticipated that the money received will buy 6 percent less than it did when it was deposited. When inflation rates declined at the beginning of the 1980s, the gap between nominal and real interest rates declined as well (Chart 3-10).

Although the Fed may be able to use monetary policy to influence real interest rates in the very short run, broader market forces are generally believed to be the fundamental determinants of real interest rates. For instance, the destruction caused by Hurricane Andrew put upward pressure on real interest rates as firms and households sought funding to rebuild the damaged areas. The large Federal deficit also puts upward pressure on real interest rates, because the government competes with private borrowers for limited savings. The real interest rate is also affected by international developments such as the increased demand for capital due to German unification. Finally, tax policy affects the real after-tax return received by investors.

At any point in time, interest rates vary with the maturity of the debt obligation. For instance, on November 13, 1992, the market rate for 6-month Treasury bills was 3.3 percent, for 5-year Treasury bonds 6.0 percent, and for 30-year Treasury bonds 7.6 percent. This relationship between maturity and interest rates is called the "yield curve." Expansionary monetary policy tends to depress very short-term rates, such as the overnight Federal funds rate. Medium- and long-term rates respond less predictably to changes in monetary policy, in part because they reflect expectations about future inflation.

Concern about how policy changes will influence expectations and, hence, long-term interest rates is a factor the Fed must consider in setting policy. Since both short-term and long-term rates affect the economy, the Fed must be careful that in lowering short-term rates it does not inadvertently increase long-term rates. In

Chart 3-10   Real and Nominal 3-Month T-Bill Rates
The real rate of interest is approximately equal to the nominal 3-month T-Bill rate minus
the inflation rate as measured by the consumer price index.

Percent per year

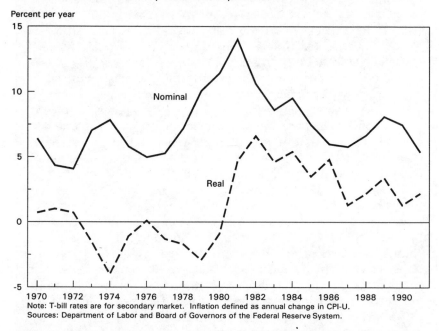

Note: T-bill rates are for secondary market.   Inflation defined as annual change in CPI-U.
Sources: Department of Labor and Board of Governors of the Federal Reserve System.

fact, over the last 3 years, virtually every time the Fed lowered the
short-term Federal funds rate, long-term interest rates either declined or were unchanged, although the declines in long-term rates
were substantially less than the declines in short-term rates.

Some observers focus almost exclusively on relatively high long-
term interest rates as the reason for the limited effectiveness of the
recent loosening of monetary policy. Since November 1990, the Federal funds rate has fallen by 4.7 percentage points, while the 10-
year Treasury bond rate has fallen by only 1.8 percentage points.
The relatively high long-term rates may slow the growth of long-
term business investments and mortgage borrowing. On the other
hand, evidence suggests that many borrowers easily substitute
short-term financing for long-term debt. For instance, many firms
finance a large proportion of their capital expenditures with short-
term bank debt, and many families now finance their homes with
adjustable rate mortgages. Furthermore, at the beginning of past
recoveries, relatively high long-term rates did not appear to discourage increased investment spending. For these reasons, it is
doubtful that the weaker-than-expected demand for credit is due
exclusively to the level of long-term rates.

INDICATORS OF MONETARY POLICY

The Fed uses several measures, or monetary aggregates, to quantify what is popularly called money. The monetary base, or M0, is the only monetary aggregate that can be controlled with precision through open market operations. In setting target ranges for money growth rates, the Fed focuses on several broader aggregates. Until 1982 the Fed's primary target was M1, the funds generally used for transactions, including currency in circulation, checking accounts, and travelers checks. Since 1982, the primary monetary target has been M2—M1 plus a number of short-term financial assets such as savings accounts.

Monetary aggregates are "intermediate targets." Unlike operating targets such as short-term interest rates, monetary targets are adjusted infrequently. They are intermediate to more fundamental goals such as maintaining a low and stable inflation rate. An important consideration in choosing a monetary target is whether it exhibits a predictable relationship with nominal GDP; that is, a predictable velocity. The velocity of money is the ratio of nominal GDP to the money stock. Velocity measures the average number of times the money stock is spent each year in generating the transactions that constitute nominal GDP. If velocity were perfectly predictable for a monetary aggregate under Fed control, then the Fed could set the growth rate of nominal GDP.

In addition to interest rates and monetary aggregates, the Fed relies on many other types of information to judge whether its policy is having the intended effect, including exchange rates, the unemployment rate, the level of inventories, the capacity utilization rate, commodity prices, and changes in the price level. Statistical data that provide information about the current situation and the effects of past policies also provide some insight into the future. For instance, an increase in inventories often reflects a cutback in sales and signals a fall in future production, and gold prices and long-term interest rates reflect the market's expectations about inflation. Unfortunately, no perfect indicator or set of indicators exists that can accurately predict the future consequences of current policies under all circumstances.

SUMMARY

- In the short run, the Fed can use monetary policy to increase the availability of credit and to lower interest rates. In the long run, an excessively expansionary monetary policy will lead to inflation and higher nominal interest rates.
- Interest rates, monetary aggregates, and many other indicators help the Fed assess the effects of its actions. No set of indicators, however, provides a reliable forecast of the future consequences of current policy choices.

MONETARY POLICY SINCE 1970

An important indicator of Fed policy is the growth rate of monetary aggregates, although these do not always move together over time (Chart 3-11). Prior to 1982 the Fed's primary target was M1 but since then it has dropped its M1 target and focused on M2. The reason is clear from Chart 3-12: After a steady increase, the velocity of M1 dropped sharply in 1981 and became much more variable, making its relationship with nominal GDP much less predictable. The velocity of M2, on the other hand, has generally been more predictable, although its velocity also dropped sharply in 1980-82.

Starting in late 1979 the Fed made a strong commitment to reducing inflation. Although monetary policy was perceived as tight during this period, in fact the growth rates of both M1 and M2 were approximately the same as they had been in the late 1970s (Chart 3-11). This episode illustrates that monetary policy cannot be evaluated simply by looking at the growth rate of the money supply in the abstract; rather, it must be evaluated relative to the current economic situation. Given that the economy was in the midst of a sharp recession during this period, some would argue that, by maintaining the previous growth rate of money, the Fed was running a tight policy.

As mentioned earlier, fear of growing inflationary pressure in the late 1980s led the Fed to try to engineer a soft landing. To do this, the Fed had to balance the risk that reducing the growth rate of money would increase the chances of a recession against the risk that maintaining money growth at the same rate would increase inflation. Starting in early 1988, the Fed began to raise short-term interest rates. The target growth range for M2 was revised downward in 1989, and its growth rate often remained near the bottom of the target range and sometimes even below it (Chart 3-13). As inflationary pressures eased and inflation in fact declined in a soft economy, the Fed cut short-term interest rates gradually from mid-1989 to late 1990 and then cut rates more aggressively, for a cumulative decline of about 4 percentage points since December 1990.

Some have argued that the Fed's policy in these years was the primary cause of the most recent recession and slow recovery, but this conclusion appears to be unwarranted. Although a somewhat more expansionary policy may have been appropriate during the recession and early in the recovery, many other factors—some unforeseeable, others of a severity and duration that would have been hard to predict—were acting as a drag on the economy. Furthermore, the fact that the growth of M2 remained at the low end of the target range came as somewhat of a surprise to the Fed. From January 1991 to October 1992, M1 grew at an annual rate of 12.0 percent, but M2 lagged behind, growing at an annual rate of only

Chart 3-11 Growth Rates of Monetary Aggregates
The growth rates of the various monetary aggregates are quite variable. In the past 2 years, M1 growth has accelerated, while M2 growth has declined.

Percent change, 4-quarter moving average

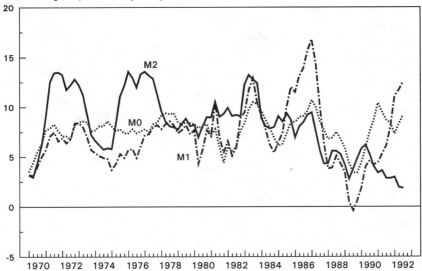

Source: Board of Governors of the Federal Reserve System.

Chart 3-12 Velocities of Monetary Aggregates, 1970-92
In the early 1980s, the predictability of the relationship between M1 and GDP weakened significantly. As a result, M2 became the Federal Reserve's primary monetary target.

Index, 1970=100

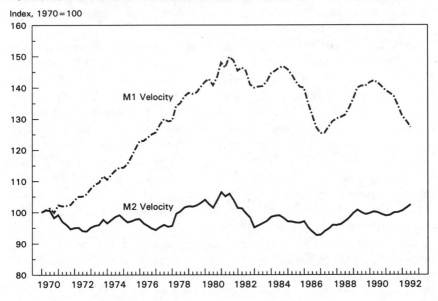

Sources: Department of Commerce and Board of Governors of the Federal Reserve System.

103

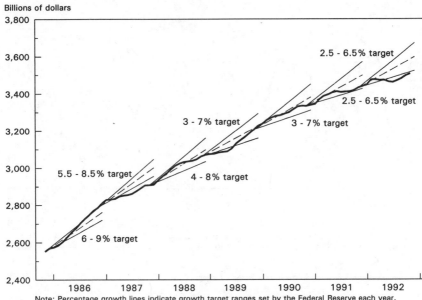

Chart 3-13 **M2 Money Stock and Growth Target Ranges**
Since the mid-1980s, the Federal Reserve repeatedly has lowered the target range for M2 growth. M2 generally has been in the lower part of the target cones.

Billions of dollars

2.5 - 6.5% target

2.5 - 6.5% target

3 - 7% target

3 - 7% target

5.5 - 8.5% target

4 - 8% target

6 - 9% target

Note: Percentage growth lines indicate growth target ranges set by the Federal Reserve each year.
Source: Board of Governors of the Federal Reserve System.

about 2.6 percent. This divergence in growth rates was accompanied by an increase in the velocity of M2 and a decrease in the velocity of M1 (Chart 3-14).

Although there is no simple explanation for the divergence in the growth rates and velocities of M1 and M2, the fall in the general level of interest rates and the steep yield curve appear to have been contributing factors. When interest rates drop, the difference between the returns on checking accounts and savings accounts generally narrow, so investors become less inclined to move money from checking to savings, explaining in part the recent drop in the velocity of M1, which consists largely of checking accounts. When long-term rates rise above short-term rates, people tend to shift savings out of the short-term assets included in M2 and into assets with higher yields, such as Treasury bonds, reducing the M2 money stock and increasing its velocity.

The change in M2's velocity has again raised the question of whether it is appropriate for the Fed to focus on a single monetary aggregate or whether it should attach some weight to a range of other indicators. Researchers have examined a number of alternatives, including the behavior of MZM (M2 less time deposits such as

104

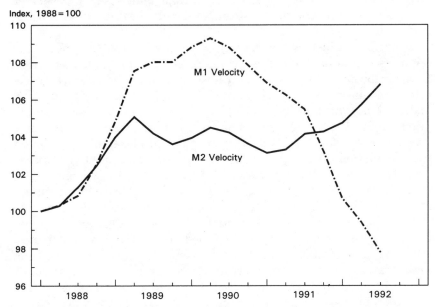

Sources: Department of Commerce and Board of Governors of the Federal Reserve System.

certificates of deposit). MZM is intended as a fairly broad measure of money that includes only accounts which can be withdrawn immediately without penalty. Unfortunately, the velocity of MZM is more variable than that of either M1 or M2, and it does not appear to be a better predictor of GDP.

Others have suggested a nominal GDP target, under which the Fed would increase the growth rate of the monetary base when nominal GDP growth falls below the target range and reduce it when GDP growth exceeds the target range. Since nominal GDP is measured infrequently and responds to monetary policy often with a considerable lag, however, nominal GDP targeting would increase the risk that policy actions would be taken too late. More fundamentally, even if nominal GDP growth could be controlled fairly precisely, the division of nominal GDP growth between price increases and real output increases is difficult to predict or control. None of the other alternatives to an M2 target is obviously superior either, making it likely that the Fed will have to rely on a variety of imperfect measures that include M2, other monetary aggregates, and other indicators of the future path of inflation and output.

RECENT COMPLICATIONS FOR MONETARY POLICY

How much and how quickly spending increases in response to lower interest rates depends on a number of factors, most of which are beyond the Fed's control. Although short-term interest rates have fallen a total of about 4 percentage points since December 1990, demand has grown at a disappointingly weak pace for most of this period.

A number of factors appear to have tempered the response to interest rate cuts in the last few years relative to previous recoveries. Despite lower market interest rates, borrowers had difficulty obtaining loans because of the troubled condition of many financial institutions. The high business and household debt levels accumulated in the 1980s weakened demand for new borrowing. The capital-intensive sectors that usually respond most rapidly to interest rate reductions were beset by other problems that hampered growth. In particular, the excess supply of and high vacancy rates in commercial real estate damped the demand for new buildings, and a slowdown in the rate of household formation lowered the demand for residential construction. As a result, it appears that lower interest rates have so far failed to generate as much new spending as expected. Firms and households have benefited from lower rates, however, as interest burdens have been reduced by record levels of refinancing of corporate debt and mortgages in the last few years.

While problems such as the credit crunch and overbuilding are likely to diminish over time as the economy adjusts, other developments may have a more lasting impact on the effectiveness and channels of monetary policy. One such development is the increased integration of world capital markets.

First, monetary policy cannot control interest rates and exchange rates independently because the two are interrelated. Decreases in U.S. interest rates lower the dollar's value as investors seek higher returns in other countries. In the early 1980s, our relatively tight monetary policy was one of the factors that strengthened the dollar. Now, the tough anti-inflationary policies of the German Bundesbank have had the effect of strengthening the deutsche mark and the currencies linked to it. These exchange-rate swings may lead to unwanted effects on both the balance of trade and price levels, limiting monetary policy options. For instance, a sharp appreciation of the dollar could raise the trade deficit and cause job losses in export-producing and import-competing industries.

Second, as capital markets become more integrated, capital tends to flow more quickly into those countries that offer the highest rate of return. The Fed has an increasingly limited ability to control real U.S. interest rates, since attempts to unilaterally lower rates cause foreign investors (and some American investors) to move their money abroad (Box 3-4). This outflow tends to push U.S. interest rates back up, since new investors must be found.

Box 3-4.—International Interest Rate Differences and Capital Flows

Investors deciding between different types of assets will choose those investments offering the highest rate of return after risk is taken into account. Capital tends to flow from countries offering lower expected rates of return to those offering higher expected rates of return. By reducing the supply of capital in the countries offering low returns and increasing it in those with higher rates, this process tends to equalize expected returns across national borders.

Investors consider expected exchange-rate movements as well as relative interest rates when comparing international investments. For example, a 1-year bond in the United Kingdom may offer an 8-percent interest rate, while an American bond may offer only 4 percent interest. However, if the pound's value in terms of dollars is expected to decline by 5 percent over the year, the British bond's return, in dollars, would be only about 3 percent, making it the less attractive investment. Since investors compare investments in different countries taking into account expected changes in exchange rates, the exchange-rate adjusted expected returns on similar assets tend to be equalized across countries.

Finally, not all of the increased demand generated by reduced interest rates will benefit domestic producers. Both foreign and domestic companies can borrow in the United States to finance operations abroad that do not contribute to U.S. GDP. At the same time, some domestic borrowing will be used to finance expenditures on imports. Similarly, U.S. borrowers benefit when foreign interest rates fall, because money can then be borrowed abroad to finance domestic investment.

SUMMARY

- The goal of using monetary policy to increase output without increasing inflation is inherently difficult to achieve. When the Fed increases or decreases bank reserves, the path from reserve changes to interest rates to output and prices is often unpredictable.
- In recent years, a number of factors have further complicated the task of setting monetary policy. The weakening in the relation among M2, interest rates, and nominal GDP has decreased

the reliability of monetary aggregates as indicators of policy, at least in the recent period.

- Transitory problems in financial markets and structural changes in the global economy have altered the response of the U.S. economy to the Fed's policies.

FISCAL POLICY

In light of the economy's performance over the last 2 years, it is natural to ask what role Federal fiscal policy played in the recession and slow recovery. Was policy in part responsible for the poor economic performance, or did policy make the economy stronger than it otherwise would have been?

TOOLS OF FISCAL POLICY

As mentioned earlier, fiscal policy refers to changes in Federal spending and the tax system that influence demand and incentives to work, save, and invest. Federal purchases of goods and services, which make up nearly 8 percent of GDP, contribute directly to total spending. Changes in transfer payments and income taxes affect spending indirectly through their impact on disposable (after-tax) income. Since households typically save a portion of additional income, their spending tends to change by less than their disposable income. Consequently, changes in transfers and taxes affect total spending less than changes in purchases of an equal magnitude.

The Federal budget distinguishes between two main types of expenditures: mandatory and discretionary. Nearly all mandatory spending is in the form of "entitlements," or programs such as medicaid, medicare, and unemployment insurance which use preset criteria to determine eligibility and benefit levels. Discretionary spending, on the other hand, refers to government spending that requires annual budget appropriations. The distinction is important for fiscal policy, because short-term changes in mandatory spending are heavily affected by short-term economic conditions.

Automatic Stabilizers

Discussions of fiscal policy often divide Federal taxing and spending activities into two kinds: automatic stabilizers and discretionary policy. Automatic stabilizers act as buffers when the economy weakens by automatically reducing taxes and increasing government spending. Mandatory spending for programs such as unemployment insurance, food stamps, welfare programs, and medicaid increases when the economy slows down since benefit criteria depend on income or employment status. These transfer payments help consumers maintain spending.

The tax system as a whole also acts as an automatic stabilizer. In an economic slump, personal income and corporate profits are lower, so tax payments fall, helping to reduce the decline in after-tax incomes that would otherwise occur. Likewise, government revenues from excise and other sales-based taxes fall when purchases decline. In fact, taxes typically change by a larger proportion than GDP, primarily because average income tax rates fall with income levels. This feature of the tax system makes after-tax income more stable than pretax income, which helps insulate consumption spending from changes in income.

Discretionary Fiscal Policy

Discretionary fiscal policy refers to changes in discretionary spending and new tax legislation. Many classic examples of discretionary fiscal policy are new tax initiatives. For example, tax cuts in 1964 were intended to stimulate spending and economic expansion, while the income tax surcharge of 1968 was designed to curb rising inflation.

Since the change in total annual expenditures determines whether policy has been expansionary or contractionary, it is difficult to attribute expansionary fiscal policy to specific acts of spending. For example, increased spending on highways in a given year is expansionary only if it is not offset by a decline in some other part of the annual appropriations. Nonetheless, changes in discretionary spending have potentially significant effects on the economy, as evidenced by the economic responses to the defense buildups and drawdowns over the past 50 years.

RECENT BEHAVIOR OF EXPENDITURES AND TAX RECEIPTS

While expansionary and contractionary policies are easy to describe, they are difficult to measure. Automatic stabilizers cause the Federal budget deficit to rise during recessions and fall during expansions, even without discretionary fiscal actions. For this and other reasons discussed in Chapter 6, changes in the budget deficit are an imperfect measure of discretionary fiscal policy.

More than in the past, large Federal budget deficits and budget problems at the State and local levels have constrained fiscal policy. Real Federal purchases, which fell 0.8 percent during the recent recession and recovery, rose an average of 2.1 percent during earlier recessions and recoveries (Chart 3-15). Real Federal purchases have fallen only once before during a similar business cycle phase—the recession and recovery of 1969-71—and then by a much greater amount, 15.4 percent. In both cases, defense drawdowns were occurring; recently because of the end of the Cold War, and earlier because of the winding down of the Vietnam conflict.

Real defense purchases fell by 4.2 percent during the recent period, well below the decline of 20.3 percent during 1969–71.

Chart 3-15 Real Federal Spending and Taxation in Recent Recoveries
During the recovery of 1991-92, Federal Government purchases and transfers did not increase as much as they had in past recoveries.

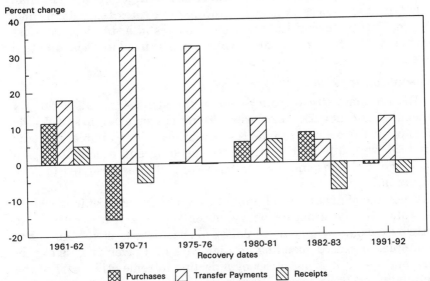

Percent change

Recovery dates

☒ Purchases ▨ Transfer Payments ▨ Receipts

Note: National Income and Product Accounts basis. Change is from trough of recession to fourth quarter of recovery.
Source: Department of Commerce.

Federal nondefense purchases increased 8.6 percent in the recent period, almost twice the average for previous recessions and recoveries. This increase only partially offset the defense cuts, however, since defense purchases are 2½ times the level of nondefense purchases. Increases in State and local government purchases, which are about 1½ times greater than Federal purchases, were also below average. Federal, State, and local government purchases combined rose just over 1 percent during the recession and recovery of 1990–92—about 40 percent of the average increase during other recessions and recoveries since 1959. Federal transfers have also grown more slowly recently than they did during earlier slowdowns, but State and local transfers have grown at twice their normal rate. The combined change in transfer payments for all levels of government during the recent period was 15.5 percent, compared to the 18.6 percent average increase during previous recessions.

While the bottom line is that recent fiscal policy has been less expansionary than fiscal policy during previous recessions and early recoveries, it does not necessarily follow that more expansionary policies were either possible or desirable. Growing government expenditures and large Federal budget deficits acted as a constraint on traditional forms of fiscal stimulus.

THE BUDGET PROCESS

The budget process itself also limits the potential of fiscal policy to stimulate the economy. Each January or February the President submits a budget for the fiscal year beginning in October, with 13 appropriations proposals for discretionary spending. Mandatory program expenses and interest payments on outstanding debt do not require annual appropriations but are estimated in the budget. Both houses of the Congress make separate modifications to the President's proposal and then meet to resolve their differences on any appropriations bills. Once this is done, the House and Senate must pass the appropriations bills and forward them to the President to be signed into law or vetoed.

Because the Federal budget process begins well in advance of actual spending, and because downturns are difficult to forecast, annual appropriations are usually not an effective means of fighting recessions. New legislation can be introduced to modify appropriations during the fiscal year, but there may still be legislative delays in the Congress and further delays between appropriation and actual expenditure. For example, government procurement procedures can involve time-consuming regulations intended to ensure fairness in contract awards. In contrast, monetary policy changes can be implemented more rapidly, since open market operations do not require congressional action and the extended delays it sometimes imposes.

Reducing growth in government expenditures and budget deficits were important long-term objectives of this Administration's fiscal policy. Escalating government spending and budget deficits are believed to be partly responsible for the decline in conventional measures of national saving and investment rates during the 1980s. Modifications to the budget process introduced as part of the Omnibus Budget Reconciliation Act of 1990, known as the Budget Enforcement Act (BEA), were intended to improve on the GRH and bring government spending and budget deficits under control. Like any credible deficit reduction plan, however, the BEA restricted expansionary countercyclical policy actions by placing constraints on new mandatory spending programs, tax decreases, and all discretionary spending. These restrictions help explain the recent behavior of expenditures and receipts.

Absent special circumstances, the BEA requires that any new mandatory spending program be offset by some combination of decreases in other mandatory spending programs or by a tax increase. Similarly, any tax bill projected to decrease total govern-

111

ment revenue would trigger across-the-board spending cuts unless it was matched by specific cuts in spending programs. These constraints on new mandatory spending programs and tax initiatives are known as the "pay-as-you-go" provisions of the BEA.

A problem with these provisions is that the method used to estimate the effects of tax changes on revenues is very imprecise. A change in tax law can cause a series of changes—often referred to as feedback effects—in the consumption, investment, and saving decisions of individuals and firms. Current government methods of estimating changes in revenue allow for a very narrow range of feedback effects. While a full accounting of the feedback effects that new tax proposals could have is currently impractical, the absence of fully dynamic estimates has limited the usefulness of the estimating process in tax policy debates.

The BEA also established legally binding caps (adjusted for inflation and certain technical factors) that impose a "flexible freeze" on discretionary spending growth. Originally, separate caps prohibited transfers of funds across three categories of spending: domestic, defense, and international. These "firewalls" expire after fiscal 1993, when a single cap will be applied to total discretionary spending.

The discretionary spending caps and pay-as-you-go rules in the BEA are much more difficult to circumvent than the GRH budget deficit targets. The GRH required the Administration to estimate total receipts and expenditures at the start of the fiscal year to determine if the deficit would be below the target for the upcoming year. However, it was not difficult to pass legislation later in the year that increased the deficit. Another weakness of the GRH was that the deficit was estimated only for the upcoming year, so that legislation significantly increasing deficits in subsequent years did not conflict with the provisions of the GRH. For the most part, the BEA solved both of these problems by requiring the Administration to show, within days of its passage, whether legislation signed by the President increased or decreased the deficit over both 1- and 5-year time horizons. Legislation that violated the BEA targets resulted in across-the-board spending cuts to restore compliance.

Although an effective deficit reduction plan necessarily requires constraints on fiscal expansion, the BEA does not eliminate expansionary actions completely. First, the automatic stabilizers implicit in mandatory spending programs and the tax code are allowed to operate, since the BEA deficit targets are adjusted for changes in short-run economic conditions. Second, the BEA constraints on policy changes can be waived under either of two conditions: (1) in the event of a "low-growth scenario"—two consecutive quarters of less than 1 percent growth or a forecast of two or more consecutive quarters without growth or (2) when the President declares an emergency (such as a weak economy that does not qualify as a low-growth scenario or humanitarian relief efforts). Finally, economic activity can be stimulated by policy changes that strengthen economic incentives without increasing spending or reducing total receipts, such as an appropriately designed reduction in capital gains tax rates.

LIMITATIONS OF COUNTERCYCLICAL FISCAL POLICY

Even in the absence of procedural constraints, the ability of countercyclical fiscal policy to stimulate a weak economy may be limited. The effect of changes in purchases, transfers, and taxes on total spending is complex and uncertain.

Expectations

People's actions depend not only on their current situation but also on their expectations for the future. For example, many people in their 50s and early 60s, anticipating retirement, save a large share of their incomes. Fiscal policy can affect people's behavior by changing their current disposable income, but changes in spending will also depend on people's expectations about their future disposable income. For instance, a temporary income tax cut will affect consumption less than a permanent cut. If people think a cut in income tax rates will last, they are likely to respond by consuming most of their additional after-tax income. They have little reason to save more, because they expect the higher after-tax income to last into the future. But if they expect that a tax cut will soon be reversed, they may save most of their temporary windfall to spend when taxes rise again and their disposable income falls. Given current concerns about large budget deficits, unless income tax cuts are linked to reductions in future government spending, people may be more likely to believe any current tax cut will be offset by higher taxes in the future. If so, tax cuts will have little effect on current spending.

People's expectations about the future can affect other tax initiatives as well. For example, when the government introduces a temporary investment tax allowance, businesses have an incentive to shift investment expenditures to the period in which the temporary tax credit applies. In contrast to a cut in personal income taxes for families—which will have little effect on spending if it is temporary—an investment tax allowance will have a stronger short-run effect if it is temporary. If businesses know the investment tax allowance is permanent, they have no reason to change the timing of expenditures. The long-term effects of a permanent investment tax credit or more neutral depreciation are discussed in Chapter 6.

The amplified response to a temporary investment tax allowance may appear to make it an excellent tool for fiscal policy. But the role of people's expectations in determining the response to an investment tax allowance has far-reaching implications for policy. Once businesses know that an investment tax allowance is being considered, they may defer investment spending so that they are better able to take advantage of the investment tax allowance at a later date. Similarly, if in the past the government has introduced a temporary investment tax allowance during recessions, people may defer investment at the first hint of a slowdown in the future, hoping to benefit from another tax credit. This deferral of spending may exacerbate fluctuations in output.

Crowding Out

Changes in government purchases may also have limited effects on total spending. For example, if the appropriation for the construction of a new highway system is not accompanied by a corresponding increase in tax revenues, the budget deficit and government borrowing will increase. Increased government borrowing may put upward pressure on interest rates and discourage investment spending, offsetting at least part of the increase in total demand resulting from the construction project. This reduction in private investment associated with an increase in government spending is known as "crowding out."

How important is crowding out? Unfortunately, it is difficult to distinguish the effect of changes in government spending from the many other factors that influence interest rates and private investment. At present, interest rates may be particularly sensitive to changes in fiscal policy, raising concern about crowding out. Given the already large budget deficit, further increases in spending now may seriously undermine the credibility of fiscal policy and create expectations of higher future deficits and tighter conditions in credit markets, resulting in higher long-term interest rates now.

Actions need not increase the current government budget deficit in order for crowding out to occur. Actions that make higher spending more likely in the future may increase interest rates now, even if they have no effect on current deficits. For example, if a law passed today increased government spending beginning in the year 2000, expectations of tighter conditions in credit markets in the future could raise long-term interest rates and reduce investment today.

Resource Allocation

Countercyclical fiscal policies also have long-term effects on the allocation of resources that should be taken into account. For example, policymakers may decide to construct a highway system to stimulate spending in an economic downturn. The benefits the highway system will provide may not justify the costs incurred; if they did, the project should have been undertaken long before the idle resources provided additional incentive. History shows that, in

114

a market economy, idle resources typically are brought back into use in the private sector after a period of transition. And unlike government projects, these private activities are sustainable only if they meet the stringent test of the market: sufficient consumer demand to ensure that the value of the activity exceeds its cost. If a downturn is expected to be brief, relying on the safety net of unemployment insurance and other programs while waiting for idle resources to be brought back into private activities could maximize their economic value. If, on the other hand, a recession is expected to be long or severe, there is a stronger case for short-run fiscal stimulus.

SUMMARY

- Automatic stabilizers increase spending and reduce taxes automatically when the economy weakens.
- During the recent recession and recovery period, fiscal policy appears to have been less expansionary than it was in previous recession and recovery periods.
- The Budget Enforcement Act places constraints on spending growth and tax reductions. Expansionary measures are limited to automatic stabilizers, increases in spending or tax cuts that are allowed under special circumstances, and initiatives that increase incentives.
- Factors such as expectations and crowding out increase uncertainty about the response of the economy to fiscal policy. Short-term stimulus is likely to be effective only in the event of a downturn that is expected to be long-lived or severe.

WOULD DIFFERENT POLICIES HAVE HELPED?

During the past 4 years, the economy experienced a slowdown in growth in 1989, a recession in late 1990 and early 1991, and then an unusually weak recovery beginning in March 1991. Only recently has the economy shown sufficient vigor to reduce the unemployment rate for several consecutive months. In light of this experience, would earlier and more expansionary fiscal or monetary policies have been desirable during the recession and early recovery? The answer, in our opinion, is a qualified yes. Given that many of the factors responsible for the slow growth in the U.S. economy—defense reductions, commercial overbuilding, and the slowdown in foreign economies—were expected to persist into the future, there appeared to be little danger that inflation would rise as a result of a moderately more expansionary policy, although it may well have fallen more slowly.

The conclusion that more stimulative policies would have been desirable does not come simply with hindsight. The Administration proposed fiscal policies in early 1992 that would have provided a modest stimulus to the economy. These initiatives included unilateral measures such as a reduction in excess income tax withholding and several proposals requiring congressional action, including a temporary investment tax allowance to speed up spending on productive assets, a temporary tax credit for first-time homebuyers, and a reduction in the tax rate on capital gains.

The Administration's proposals would have provided short-term stimulus to the weak economy primarily by using tax incentives to encourage business and residential investment. Reductions in excess withholding taxes were intended to stimulate household spending, while the temporary investment tax allowance would have stimulated business investment. The cut in capital gains taxes would have increased the value of capital assets and thus, wealth, thereby providing short-term stimulus to spending in addition to long-term incentives for investment and entrepreneurship.

The Administration's proposals were designed to avoid increasing the already large deficit. By emphasizing investment incentives, the fiscal proposals would have increased capital formation and the potential for long-term growth. Unfortunately, only the unilateral measures were implemented, since the Congress did not pass the President's proposals in an acceptable form.

A fiscal plan with even stronger tax incentives merited consideration, subject to one very important condition—that legislative action (not just the development of general plans) be taken at the same time to reduce both future government spending growth and future budget deficits. Any policy initiative had to take into account both the short-term problem of recession and slow recovery and the long-term problem of low productivity growth that is due, in part, to insufficient national saving and investment. While the recession could have provided an argument for short-term fiscal expansion, such action would have been both less effective and inappropriate if it had sacrificed long-term goals by increasing expectations of future government spending and budget deficits.

Some have argued that, given the slow growth of M2 and the overall weakness in the economy, monetary policy has been the predominant cause of the recent recession and weak recovery. As noted earlier, a number of unforeseen problems complicated the task of setting monetary policy. It is not clear to what extent the slow growth of M2 reflected inadequate expansion of the monetary base, weak demand, or portfolio shifts away from the assets that constitute M2 (undermining its usefulness as an indicator of monetary policy).

While it would have been desirable for monetary policy to have been somewhat more expansionary than it in fact was during the recession and early recovery in order to further cushion the declines in output and employment, such a policy could have delayed progress on reducing inflation. Furthermore, in the presence of uncertainty about the effectiveness of fiscal and monetary policy tools, there are advantages to using both to reduce the uncertainty about the overall response of the economy. During this period, too much responsibility for strengthening the economy was left to monetary policy. Greater help from fiscal incentives, regulatory relief, and trade liberalization was needed.

Overall, it appears that recent fiscal and monetary policy have been less expansionary than in the typical postwar recession and early recovery. It should be remembered, however, that in many cases past policies proved to be too expansionary and worsened inflation in the subsequent recovery. Nonetheless, the weakness of the economy—indicated by both the fall in output during the recession and the substantial decline in core inflation over the past year—and the prospects that the weakness would continue made a case for somewhat greater stimulus from fiscal and/or monetary policies during the recession and early recovery. Even perfect policies probably could not have prevented a recession, given the myriad factors impeding growth during this period, but they may have softened the recession and speeded up the recovery.

CONCLUSION

This chapter has emphasized the difficulties inherent in using monetary and fiscal policies to offset short-term fluctuations in the economy. The experience of the 1960s and 1970s has shown that fine-tuning can be destabilizing and may even erode long-term growth rates by increasing the uncertainty associated with long-term planning and impeding the reallocation of resources.

In response to the apparent failure of fine-tuning, some have taken the opposite position that there is no benefit to countercyclical policies, even when the economy experiences a protracted recession. This argument is based on the belief that the primary effect of policy changes in response to short-term conditions is increased uncertainty among private decision-makers, with possible negative impacts on output.

A more balanced view recognizes the limitations of fine-tuning, without precluding the possibility that policy may need to be adjusted occasionally. In this view, policies are designed primarily with long-term objectives in mind. Because sound money is indispensable to a well-functioning economy, monetary policy targets are guided by the goals of maintaining low and stable rates of inflation and facilitating the reliable provision of credit. Spending policies are guided by cost-benefit analysis, taking into account future effects as well as short-run economic conditions. Tax policies are structured to minimize interference with market incentives to work, save, invest, and innovate. In the present situation, fiscal policy should also aim for gradual reduction in the growth of government expenditures and the budget deficit.

In certain circumstances, however, it may be necessary to change policies. First, it is possible that relationships between policy targets, such as the growth target for M2, and policy objectives, will change. In that case, targets for M2 may need to be adjusted and/or supplemented or replaced by targets for other monetary aggregates or other indicators. Second, if structural adjustments, external shocks, or other factors are expected to weaken the economy for an extended period, then more expansionary policies may be appropriate to facilitate the economic adjustment process. To the greatest extent possible, the circumstances under which policies might change should be specified in advance, so that credibility is enhanced rather than compromised by such deviations. The low-growth scenario provisions of the BEA are an example of this kind of "recession escape clause." When policy must deviate from the established targets, actions should be consistent—and understood to be consistent—with the long-term objectives of high and stable output growth and low and stable inflation.

While the economy has endured a period of protracted weakness during which more expansionary policies would, in our judgment, have been desirable, economic developments in 1992 and current indicators of future activity suggest that a more self-sustaining recovery consistent with maintaining low inflation is finally underway and that additional short-term fiscal and/or monetary stimulus may be unnecessary. If the modest recovery were to falter, any short-term fiscal stimulus should be tied to long-term spending reductions in order to minimize upward pressure on interest rates, thereby increasing the effectiveness of the short-term stimulus and reducing future deficits. Monetary policy should remain focused on sustaining a recovery consistent with low and stable inflation. Interest rates and inflation rates are now at their lowest levels in two decades, providing the foundation for long-term, noninflationary growth in output and employment.

CHAPTER 4

The Economics Of Health Care

AMERICANS ARE LIVING LONGER, healthier lives than ever before. Since 1960, average life expectancy has increased by more than 5 years. American physicians have access to the best technology in the world and more than one-half of the world's medical research is funded by private and public sources in the United States. At the same time, the share of the Nation's income devoted to health care has been growing rapidly, and today more than 35 million Americans lack health insurance. Growing concern about rising expenditures and reduced access to insurance has led to the development of a wide variety of proposals for health care reform, from the Administration's market-based approach to calls for a government-run national health insurance program.

The success of any of these proposals will depend on how well it addresses the reasons behind the increase in expenditures and decline in insurance. Economics is very helpful in understanding these developments. It suggests that most health care in the United States is financed and delivered in ways that give both health care providers and their insured patients many incentives to increase the quality of health care but little reason to be concerned about its cost.

HEALTH CARE IN THE UNITED STATES

In many respects, the health care industry resembles other service industries such as transportation and legal services. It supplies a service—health care—in response to consumer demand. But the demand for health care is different from the demand for many other services because most people do not pay for their care directly. Instead, the government and private insurers pay most health care expenses. The supply of health care also differs from that of many other service industries. Consumers rely on providers for information about health care services and these providers are heavily regulated, primarily by other health care providers. Finally, many people believe that health care is inherently different from other goods and services. They believe that everyone should be entitled to at least some health care, although they may not believe that everyone has a similar entitlement to goods in general.

THE HEALTH OF THE U.S. POPULATION

Americans buy health care to improve their health, but recent research suggests that the connection between health care and health is not a simple one. In fact, increases in life expectancy in developed countries are not strongly related to increases in the number of physicians or hospital beds per capita, nor are they primarily a consequence of increasing utilization of these services. *Studies show that increases in life expectancy are mainly related to changes in behavior and improvements in medical technology.* Between 1960 and 1990, life expectancy at birth, which is strongly affected by changes in infant mortality, rose from 67 years to 72 years for men and from 73 years to 79 years for women. The life expectancy of older Americans, a group that may be more strongly affected by improvements in medical technology, increased by 3 years between 1960 and 1990, a larger increase than occurred between 1900 and 1960.

Changes in Behavior

Changes in behavior offer great promise as a way to prevent disease and preventing disease is often less costly than treating it. Many Americans have adopted increasingly healthy lifestyles. During the 1980s, the rate of smoking among adults decreased from 33 to 26 percent, more Americans exercised regularly, and deaths associated with alcohol abuse declined substantially. Traffic accident deaths per capita have declined by over 30 percent since 1970, in part because of greater use of seat belts.

Medical Technology

Improvements in medical technology (a term that includes drugs, vaccines, and knowledge about treatments as well as medical equipment) reduce the incidence of disease and improve the effectiveness of treatment. For example, over 33,000 cases of polio were reported in the United States in 1950, but polio has been all but eradicated since the development of the polio vaccine. Only 25 years ago, childhood leukemia was nearly always fatal; today the long-term survival rate for children diagnosed with leukemia is about 65 percent. New drugs have greatly improved the well-being of those with ulcers and virtually eliminated the need for surgery to treat this medical problem. Similarly, coronary bypass surgery has greatly improved the quality of life of those with angina.

Continuing Problems

Despite the many medical advances of recent years, cures for many diseases have yet to be discovered and new diseases continue to emerge. For example, the rate of mortality from breast cancer has not improved since 1950 despite the development of new screening methods and new treatment therapies. Acquired immune deficiency syndrome, or AIDS, has claimed the lives of over 160,000 Americans. Tuberculosis, a disease that had almost disappeared in the United States, has reemerged. Among young people, homicide and drug abuse exact an enormous toll.

A further problem is the persistence of serious disparities in health across income and race categories. For example, black babies are more than twice as likely as white babies to have low birthweight. While many ascribe these differences in health to differences in the ability to pay for care, evidence from the United States and other countries casts doubt on the belief that health insurance alone can greatly narrow these disparities. Studies in the United Kingdom have found that the gap in mortality between rich and poor has actually increased since the introduction of national health insurance. This result is consistent with evidence showing that increased utilization of medical services has relatively little effect on health.

PROVIDING AND PAYING FOR HEALTH CARE SERVICES IN THE UNITED STATES

The U.S. health care industry as defined in government statistics includes services provided in hospitals, nursing homes, laboratories, and physicians' and dentists' offices. It also includes prescription and nonprescription drugs, artificial limbs, and eyeglasses, as well as the services of nontraditional practitioners. But many goods and services that may strongly affect health, such as fitness club services and food, are not included in the usual definition.

The U.S. health care industry employs 9 million people, including over 600,000 physicians; by comparison, the automobile manufacturing industry employs about 800,000 people. Inpatient services are provided by approximately 6,500 hospitals containing over 1 million hospital beds. One-half of these hospitals are private, nonprofit institutions, some 30 percent are operated by Federal, State, and municipal governments, and the remainder are operated privately on a for-profit basis.

Health care expenditures averaged $2,566 per person in 1990 and were divided among health care services in almost the same proportion as in 1960. The largest part of each health care dollar, about 38 cents in 1990, was spent on hospital care, which covers all services billed through a hospital, including those of some physicians, such as medical residents and radiologists. More than 1 in every 10 Americans was admitted to a non-Federal short-stay hospital (a hospital in which the average length of stay is less than 30 days) in 1990, for an average stay of 6 days; over 10 percent of these admissions were for maternity care. Physician services are the second largest category of expenditures, accounting for about 19 percent of health care expenditures. In 1990, the average

American made 5.5 visits to a doctor. Most of the remaining 43 percent of health care expenditures was divided among drugs, nursing home care, dental services, vision products, and home health care services.

In most other developed countries, the government plays a larger part in financing and, in many cases, in delivering health care than in the United States. Boxes 4-1, 4-2, and 4-3 describe the health care systems in Canada, Germany, and the United Kingdom.

Box 4-1.—Canada

Since 1971, all Canadians have been covered by public health insurance plans administered by the Provinces. In Canada, it is illegal to sell private insurance for services provided by the public plans and participating physicians and hospitals may not accept direct payment from patients for those services. While the Provinces differ in the methods they use to finance health care, most funding comes from general tax revenues.

Physicians are paid by the provincial governments on a fee-for-service basis according to a fee schedule negotiated by the provincial governments and physician associations. There have been very substantial increases in the utilization of physician services since the introduction of public health insurance. Attempts to cut total costs by limiting physicians' fees have been partially thwarted by these continuing increases in utilization.

Hospitals receive annual lump sum, or global, budgets that are not tied directly to hospital expenditures. Hospitals cannot purchase new equipment without government approval and many types of high-technology equipment are less common in Canadian than in U.S. hospitals. The global budget reimbursement system and restrictions on the purchase of equipment have led to waiting lists for some nonemergency hospital services.

Financing Health Care

Since 1960, U.S. health care financing has undergone a major change (Chart 4-1). In 1960, most medical care was paid for directly by consumers, but by 1990 only 23 percent of health care expenses were paid for directly by consumers. Thirty-two percent were covered by private health insurers and 41 percent by the government. This change can be traced to three developments: the expansion of employer-provided benefits, the development of medicare (a government program that finances care for the elderly and disabled), and the initiation of medicaid, a program that extended and formalized

Box 4-2.—Germany

All working Germans and their families are required to have health insurance. Those with low and middle incomes must participate in one of the approximately 1,100 not-for-profit health insurance plans known as sickness funds. Most blue-collar workers are assigned to a specific plan, while most white-collar workers may choose among plans. In addition, about 26 percent of the population earn incomes high enough to allow them to opt out of the sickness funds and purchase private insurance; over one-third of those eligible do so. Out-of-pocket payments in the sickness funds are very low. The sickness funds are financed primarily from payroll taxes, and premium rates can vary substantially according to the fund. General revenues are used to fund coverage for the nonworking poor, who are insured through the sickness funds.

German physicians belong to regional associations that negotiate lump-sum budgets with the sickness funds. Individual physicians are then reimbursed by the physicians' associations on a fee-for-service basis, with the fees adjusted retroactively to comply with the negotiated budget. Hospitals are paid operating costs negotiated between the hospitals and sickness funds and pay the salaries of their staff physicians out of these operating costs. Hospital capital investments are mainly paid for by State governments.

Germans make many more physician visits per year than Americans, but the average visit is much briefer. Germans also spend more days in the hospital, on average, than do Americans. The ratio of hospital staff to patients, however, is much lower in Germany than in the United States, and Germany does not have as much high-technology equipment. Physicians spend, on average, more time with privately insured patients than with those enrolled in the sickness funds, and hospitals provide special facilities for these patients.

existing programs to finance health care for the poor. *People no longer bear most of the financial responsibility for their own health care decisions; instead most Americans have relatively little exposure to the cost implications of these decisions.*

EMPLOYER-PROVIDED BENEFITS

Large numbers of American employers first began offering health insurance benefits to their employees during World War II. During and after the war, Federal wage and price controls led businesses to expand nonwage benefits such as health care—which

Box 4-3.—United Kingdom

In the United Kingdom, the National Health Service (NHS) finances and delivers health care. All residents are eligible to receive care through the NHS, although a small but growing private insurance market also exists. The NHS is financed primarily from general revenues and only very low copayments are required for a limited number of goods and services.

Almost all physicians are employed by the government, which also owns most of the hospitals. Office-based primary care physicians who are part of the NHS are compensated in part through payments for each patient, adjusted according to the patient's age. Specialists are salaried and may only see those patients who have been referred by a general practitioner.

Expenditures per person are much lower in the United Kingdom than in other developed countries. Health care in the United Kingdom is characterized by a much lower level of high technology and fewer physicians per capita than in Canada, Germany, or the United States. There are long waiting lines for many high-cost, nonemergency procedures, and physician visits are very short.

were exempt from the controls—in order to attract workers. By 1960, private employers were paying for about 13 percent of national health care expenditures, and today, most Americans receive health insurance benefits through their employers (Chart 4–2).

Tax Treatment of Benefits

Tax provisions that exempt employer-provided health insurance from Federal and State income taxes encourage the spread of such insurance. Employees do not pay tax on the share of their compensation that comes to them in the form of employer-paid health insurance. This preferential tax treatment is effectively a government subsidy. The amount of the subsidy depends on the worker's tax rate: the higher the tax rate, the greater the subsidy. The greater the subsidy, the more likely workers are to want a larger part of their compensation in the form of health insurance.

Firms can increase the generosity of a health insurance package by lowering deductibles (the fixed amounts that policyholders must pay toward bills each year before any insurance payments are made), copayment rates (the share of medical bills that must be paid by policyholders), or the employee's share of premiums. Employers may also expand the range of services included in policies, as they did during the 1980s, when an increasing proportion began to offer vision and home health care benefits. Between 1972 and

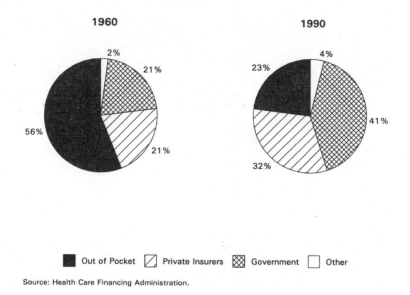

Source: Health Care Financing Administration.

1989 the total cost of all deductibles, copayments, and employee-paid insurance premiums remained almost constant as a share of after-tax income, at about 5 percent, despite the sharp increase in overall health care expenditures.

As tax rates have changed over time, so has the proportion of health care expenditures funded by employer payments. In 1965, when the marginal combined Federal tax rate of the median worker (including the Federal income tax and the employee's and employer's shares of the Social Security and medicare tax) was 17 percent, private employer contributions for private health insurance accounted for 14 percent of U.S. national health care expenditures. By 1982, when the combined marginal rate reached 38 percent, 21 percent of U.S. health expenditures were accounted for by private employer contributions for private insurance. During the 1980s, the marginal combined tax rate of the median worker fell (to 30 percent in 1990) and the share of national health care expenditures paid for by private employer contributions stopped rising, remaining at about its 1982 level, although the dollar amount of employer health care expenditures continued to increase.

125

Chart 4-2   **Health Insurance Coverage**
Most Americans receive health insurance through their employers.

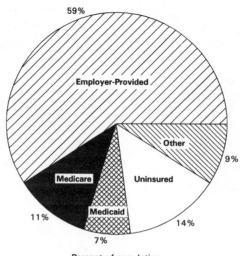

Percent of population
by insurance provider

Note: Other includes, for example, privately purchased health insurance and the Department of Veterans Affairs.
Sources: Department of Commerce and Congressional Research Service.

Employer-sponsored insurance is also exempt from State income taxes in most States, but these taxes are not included in the above figures. State income taxes currently range between 0 and 12 percent, so that for most people the entire tax subsidy is greater than the Federal subsidy.

By not taxing benefits as income, the government is effectively forgoing revenues that could be used to lower tax rates. If all the health insurance benefits expected to be provided in 1993 were counted as part of Americans' taxable income, the Federal Government would collect approximately $65 billion in additional revenues.

Insurance Costs and Money Wages

A firm's cost of health insurance must be passed along to someone—customers, owners, employees, suppliers, or some combination of these groups. *In most cases, employers are constrained in their ability to pass along these costs to their customers, owners, and suppliers. In general, when health insurance costs rise, firms must raise the cash component of wages less than they otherwise would in order to meet the higher health insurance costs.*

Between 1973 and 1989, employers' contributions to health insurance absorbed more than one-half of workers' real gains in compensation. Much of the growth in compensation reported for the 1980s took the form of higher health insurance premiums.

THE GOVERNMENT'S ROLE

Until the mid-1960s, the government's role in the provision and financing of health care was limited primarily to prevention and medical research. Some government health care spending continues to be targeted to these areas. The Federal Government spent over $22 billion in 1992 on preventive health efforts, including $594 million spent for AIDS prevention and $297 million for childhood immunizations. In 1990 the Federal Government spent about $10 billion to fund medical research. Since the mid-1960s, the government has also taken an active role in providing health insurance.

Medicare

Medicare, a nationwide Federal health insurance program that began in 1966 for people over 65 and for those with disabilities, is comprised of a hospital insurance program and a supplementary medical insurance program. Most Americans over the age of 65 are eligible for medicare hospital insurance benefits, which they receive without paying a special premium. Some disabled persons under 65 and most people who suffer from chronic kidney disease are eligible for medicare hospital benefits.

Medicare hospital benefits cover all reasonable costs for 60 days of inpatient hospital care per year, after a $676 deductible; days 61 through 90 are covered with a daily copayment of $169. In addition, those insured through medicare have a 60-day lifetime reserve for hospitalizations exceeding 90 days, during which they must contribute $338 a day toward the cost of their care. (These deductible and patient payment amounts are for calendar year 1993.) Medicare hospital insurance also provides limited coverage for posthospital nursing services, home health care, and hospice care for the terminally ill.

Participation in the medical insurance portion of medicare is voluntary. For a monthly premium of $36.60, people 65 and over and all others eligible for hospital benefits may purchase medical insurance. When the medicare program began, premium income financed half the cost of supplementary medical insurance but today premiums cover only about one-quarter of the costs of these benefits and general tax revenues cover the remainder. Medicare medical insurance covers physician services, laboratory and other diagnostic tests, and outpatient hospital services. It generally pays 80 percent of the approved amount for each service with an annual deductible of $100.

127

Many medicare beneficiaries purchase additional private insurance, called medigap insurance, to cover deductibles and copayments that are not paid by medicare. In 1990, 77 percent of medicare beneficiaries had medigap insurance. Of these, some 44 percent purchased such insurance directly; another 40 percent were retirees receiving medigap coverage through their former employers. For medicare recipients below the poverty level, another government program, medicaid (discussed below), provides this additional coverage. A recent change in Federal law requires that all medigap insurance must cover all patient payments for hospital and medical care except the deductibles. Purchasers of medigap insurance have relatively few out-of-pocket expenses for hospital and physician bills. New medicare beneficiaries (those who have just turned 65) are guaranteed the right to purchase medigap insurance at the same rate regardless of their health status.

Medicaid

Medicaid is a Federal-State matching entitlement program that provides medical benefits to low-income individuals including the elderly, blind, disabled, children, adults with dependent children, and some pregnant women. Eligibility for medicaid has been tied to participation in the aid to families with dependent children (AFDC) or supplemental security income program. In 1986, the Congress extended medicaid coverage to pregnant women and children under 6 whose family incomes fall below 133 percent of the Federal poverty level. States may choose to cover all pregnant women and all children under the age of 1 with family incomes of up to 185 percent of the Federal poverty level, and 29 States currently do so. By 2002, the medicaid program will be required to provide coverage for all children under 18 whose families are below the Federal poverty line.

For some senior citizens whose incomes are below the poverty line and who receive medicare benefits, medicaid pays deductibles and copayments for physician and hospital expenses. Medicaid also covers long-term nursing home care: some 25 percent of all medicaid expenses in 1987 were for nursing home care for those over 65.

Each State administers its own medicaid program according to Federal eligibility guidelines. The Federal Government contributes 50 percent of the State's administrative costs and a percentage of the medical expenses based on a matching formula that gives more money to poor than to wealthy States. The Federal share of medicaid costs ranges from a low of 50 percent to a high of 79 percent. Federal law mandates that medicaid beneficiaries can be required to pay only small copayments.

In 1990, 25.3 million persons received medicaid benefits. *Expenditures for the aged, blind, and disabled, who account for only 27 per-*

cent of the caseload, made up about 70 percent of the outlays. Dependent children accounted for only 14 percent of medicaid outlays.

RECENT CHANGES IN THE PROVISION OF CARE

Until the late 1970s, most providers of health care in the United States were paid using a system called retrospective reimbursement that paid for each service provided, encouraging providers to increase their services. Hospitals and physicians had incentives to counsel patients to accept more and costlier treatments, and insured patients had little reason to question these recommendations because services were paid for largely by insurance. Physicians and hospitals competed for patients by improving the quality of their services, driving up prices.

During the 1980s, some attempts were made to control expenditures by encouraging physicians and hospitals to compete in ways that keep costs down. Competition among insurers led to an increase in the use of innovative payment methods that, in turn, have begun to create an environment in which competition among providers may lead to lower health care costs.

Institutional Responses: Capitation and Coordinated Care

Under retrospective reimbursement, insurers paid physicians and hospitals for the costs of services after the fact. There were few restrictions on payments, and providers had little reason to compare the costs and benefits of services for insured patients. Insurers using the retrospective reimbursement system responded to rapidly rising expenditures by reviewing physician behavior more closely. This oversight has taken different forms, including increased monitoring, or case management, for more costly cases (a procedure used by an estimated 67 percent of employers in 1991) and requirements that patients seek a second opinion before undergoing surgery (used by about 49 percent of employers in 1991).

As health care expenditures rose during the 1970s and 1980s, however, insurers also experimented with alternative reimbursement strategies that would create incentives to control expenditures while ensuring quality care. One major innovation was the expansion of coordinated care programs that use capitation-based reimbursement and direct review of the utilization of medical and hospital services (Box 4-4).

Under capitation-based reimbursement, physicians receive an annual payment for each patient in their care, regardless of the services a patient uses during the year. Coordinated care organizations, which include health maintenance organizations (HMOs) and preferred provider organizations, often use the capitation system to pay providers. By 1990, 33 million Americans were receiving care through HMOs, over 5 times as many as had 15 years earlier.

129

Box 4-4.—Coordinated Care

The term "coordinated care" describes a variety of arrangements that increase coordination and management of health care services. The best-known form of coordinated care is the HMO, which provides its services through a single group of doctors and other health care providers. Individuals enrolled in an HMO pay a specific annual fee, regardless of the services they receive, although a small copayment is sometimes charged for services.

Another popular form of coordinated care is the preferred provider organization, which contracts with a group of providers who are reimbursed for services based on a negotiated fee schedule. Preferred provider organizations usually incorporate programs to monitor the use of services to ensure that physicians do not offset lower fees with increased volume.

Coordinated care programs have been shown to reduce expenditures while maintaining the quality of care. Some studies have found that coordinated care programs reduced the cost of care by as much as 30 percent.

Although coordinated care has become increasingly common in the private sector, it has not been as popular in public insurance programs. Medicare began entering into contracts with HMOs in the mid-1980s. Because medicare beneficiaries have few incentives to join HMOs, however, very few have done so. Congressional restrictions on the use of coordinated care by State medicaid programs have impeded the growth of such arrangements for medicaid recipients and fewer than 10 percent of medicaid beneficiaries currently receive care through these arrangements.

These innovations, which have occurred largely in the private insurance market, have reduced health care expenditures while offering health care that is at least as good as that of traditional retrospectively reimbursed medicine. In fact, capitation-based payment gives physicians a financial incentive to invest in preventive care, because they benefit financially when their patients remain healthy. *Studies show that costs have risen more slowly in health care markets where there is vigorous competition among many coordinated care providers.*

Diagnosis-Related Groups

In an effort to control rising hospital expenses, which make up the bulk of medicare payments, the Federal Government in 1983 replaced the existing retrospective payment system with a prospec-

130

tive payment system. The new system reimburses hospitals with a fixed amount for each patient based on the patient's diagnosis, rather than on the services provided. A medicare patient admitted to a hospital is now classified as belonging to one of 470 diagnosis-related groups (DRGs) that form the basis for payment.

In principle, hospitals could compete to offer care for a particular DRG at the lowest price. The medicare program, however, has set fees for each DRG, limiting the opportunities for price competition among hospitals. Payment for each DRG is based on the average cost of treatment but may vary according to region and type of hospital. Hospitals that can provide care at less than the average cost profit from this system.

Hospitals have responded to the new incentives the DRG system provides. The length of the average hospital stay has fallen significantly. A study that compared hospital costs under DRGs with estimates of what costs would have been without DRGs suggests that the system led to a one-time decline of about 20 percent of the cost of hospital care paid for by medicare. The DRG system may also slow increases in expenditures by removing the incentive that operated under retrospective reimbursement to add costly services. Finally, a substantial amount of evidence suggests that the DRG system has not reduced the quality of care medicare patients receive, even though it provides hospitals with an incentive to limit the services provided to a patient with a particular diagnosis.

The Resource-Based Relative Value Scale for Paying Physicians

In response to the increases in physician expenditures during the 1980s, the medicare program in 1992 began implementing a new fee system for physicians. The old system had reimbursed physicians the customary fee, a practice that could lead to cost spirals. If one physician raised fees, the average would rise, and this increase could be included in the next fee schedule.

With the new resource-based relative value scale, the Federal Government sets the fee medicare pays for each service according to the complexity and duration of the treatment. The current scale has greatly increased the reimbursement for evaluative functions and reduced the reimbursement for surgery.

Unfortunately, the method used to determine the new fee schedule may not be sound. Theoretically, fees should reflect not only time and effort but also demand for the service and the willingness of physicians to perform it. Unless a fee schedule takes into account these fundamental economic forces, it is likely to lead to shortages and surpluses in particular specialties, especially those with changing technology.

SUMMARY

- Improvements in technology and behavioral changes have led to significant improvements in Americans' overall health. Americans are living longer, healthier lives, free from many life-threatening illnesses. Many serious problems have developed, however, including AIDS and a recurrence of tuberculosis.

- The government's share of total health expenditures has increased and the share of patient out-of-pocket spending in total health expenses has been falling. People have much less responsibility for the financial consequences of their health care decisions than they did thirty years ago.

- Most Americans are insured through their employers. Employer-provided insurance benefits have increased dramatically since World War II, in part because such benefits are excluded from employees' taxable income. Employees pay for increases in health care costs mainly through lower wages. Individual expenditures for deductibles, copayments, and insurance premiums remained roughly constant as a share of after-tax income between 1972 and 1989.

- Insurers have responded to cost increases with innovative changes in the financing of care, moving away from fee-for-service, retrospective reimbursement of independent providers to prospective, capitation-based reimbursement of networks of providers.

RISING EXPENDITURES, DECLINING INSURANCE COVERAGE

The impetus for health care reform is driven by two concerns: the rapid rise in health care expenditures and the increasing percentage of Americans who lack health insurance.

TRENDS IN HEALTH CARE EXPENDITURES

Chart 4-3 shows the change in spending on health care since 1960. Some increases were due to the expansion of health insurance benefits through the establishment of the medicaid and medicare programs in the mid-1960s. Health care spending has continued to escalate since then.

Studies that examine patterns of health care spending across countries show that the share of income countries devote to health care usually rises with national income. Health expenditures in the United States are no exception. Expenditures rose more quickly than incomes between 1960 and 1990, from 5 percent of gross national product (GNP) in 1960 to 12 percent.

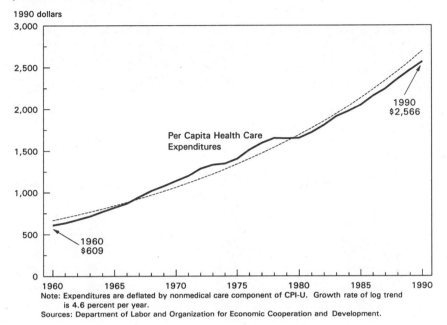

Chart 4-3   Real Per Capita Health Care Expenditures

Real per capita health care expenditures have been rising at an average annual rate of 4.6 percent since 1960.

Note: Expenditures are deflated by nonmedical care component of CPI-U. Growth rate of log trend is 4.6 percent per year.

Sources: Department of Labor and Organization for Economic Cooperation and Development.

Health expenditures are not greatly affected by short-term changes in economic conditions. *Health care costs often continue to grow during economic downturns, so that the share of national income devoted to health care may rise during a recession and fall when prosperity returns.*

HEALTH CARE EXPENDITURES IN OTHER DEVELOPED COUNTRIES

America is not alone: Germany, the United Kingdom, Canada, and other industrialized countries all experienced large increases in health care spending between 1960 and 1990. As Chart 4-4 shows, spending in Germany increased rapidly between 1960 and 1980, but slowed sharply in the 1980s. In Canada, the United Kingdom, and the United States, expenditures increased rapidly in all three decades. Although outlays for health care have increased substantially in all four countries, per capita health care spending in the United States has historically been considerably higher than in the other three countries. The United States currently spends about 1.5 times as much on per capita health care as Canada, about 1.7 times

133

as much as Germany, and about 2.6 times as much as the United Kingdom.

Chart 4-4 **Growth in Real Per Capita Health Care Expenditures in Selected Countries**
Other countries have also experienced substantial increases in health care expenditures since 1960.

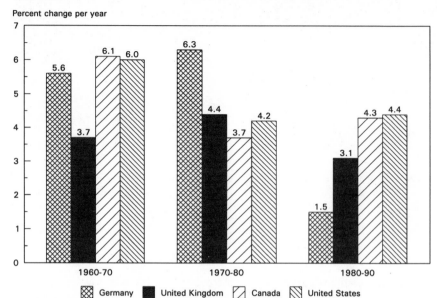

Percent change per year

Note: Expenditure in national currency deflated by GDP price indexes for all items.
Source: Organization for Economic Cooperation and Development.

The rapid growth in health care spending in the United States, Canada, Germany, and the United Kingdom is somewhat surprising because these countries have very different systems of health care financing and provision. As health care expenditures continue to increase, each of these countries is considering health care reform. *In some cases, these reform proposals include incorporating features of U.S. health care financing and provision. The United Kingdom and Canada have been experimenting with coordinated care systems, the United Kingdom has been developing versions of DRGs, while Germany has been increasing the use of patient copayments.*

THE UNINSURED

Besides rising costs, the other major problem in U.S. health care has been the increasing number of Americans who lack insurance—over 35 million people, according to current estimates. Because so many Americans receive health insurance through their employers, the percentage of Americans without health insurance is affected by changes in employment. The number of uninsured, however, increased during the 1980s, even during periods of economic growth.

Who Are the Uninsured?

Although medicaid covers many of the very poor, about 47 percent of those with incomes below the poverty line, the probability of being uninsured is highest among those with low incomes. As incomes rise, so does the probability of having health insurance.

Those in the 18–35 age group are more likely to be uninsured than those of other ages. These young adults, most in good health, may have been covered previously by their parents' health insurance. Young adults who work are more likely than other workers not to accept health insurance coverage even when their employers offer it, and young adults who lose their jobs are the least likely to pay to retain their health insurance.

Most uninsured people report that their health is good or excellent relative to others of the same age. The population of uninsured Americans, however, also contains a group that is much sicker than average, with serious chronic health conditions. The chronically ill, who are very likely to incur high health care costs, may find it very costly to obtain insurance.

Other Problems with Insurance Coverage

Health insurance is also a concern for people with limited insurance coverage and for those whose insurance ties them to a specific employer. Some people with insurance are susceptible to large out-of-pocket expenses, either as copayments or for services that their insurance does not cover. Estimates from the mid-1980s suggest that 7 percent of privately insured Americans under the age of 65 face a 1-percent chance of spending at least one-fifth of their family income on health care. Over 20 percent of those over 65 have not purchased supplementary medigap policies that cover medicare copayments and do not qualify for medicaid; they also may be subject to substantial financial burdens if they become seriously ill.

Those whose health insurance ties them to a specific employer face a different problem. Most private health insurance contracts contain preexisting condition clauses limiting or excluding coverage for conditions that began before the policy went into effect. These restrictions can force people with chronic conditions to stay with one job when they would prefer to move to another. Even those without chronic conditions may avoid changing jobs because they prefer to stay with one insurer. A recent survey found that over 25 percent of American households included a family member who stayed in a job because of health coverage.

Gaps in Employer-Provided Health Insurance Coverage

Although not having a job greatly increases the probability that an individual is not insured, the majority of uninsured Americans are workers or their dependents. Workers may lack health insurance because their firm does not offer it, because they do not work enough hours to qualify for benefits, or because they have been offered insurance and have chosen not to take it. While almost all large firms in the United States offer health insurance to their workers, small firms are far less likely to do so (Chart 4–5).

Chart 4-5 **Employer-Provided Health Insurance, by Firm Size: 1990**
Employees of large firms are much more likely than employees of smaller firms to have health insurance.

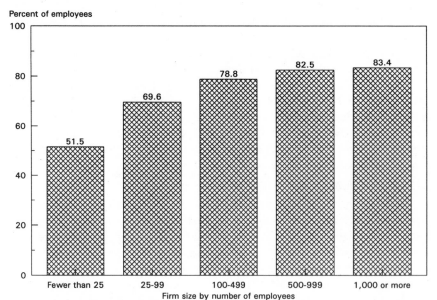

Percent of employees

Firm size by number of employees
Note: Data for persons aged 18-64.
Source: Employee Benefit Research Institute.

Three factors affect the ability and willingness of small firms to provide health insurance. First, the administrative costs of health insurance per employee rise rapidly as the size of a firm declines. Second, small firms are less able to self-insure their health insurance coverage—that is, pay expenses from their own funds rather than contracting with a commercial insurance company. About 65 percent of all firms self-insured the health costs of their employees rather than purchasing commercial insurance in 1991, but only 41 percent of firms with fewer than 500 employees self-insured their costs. Because small firms often purchase State-regulated commercial insurance, they incur costs associated with State-mandated benefits (for example, coverage for chiropractic services) and pay State insurance premium taxes. These mandates can be quite costly and may affect the probability that a small employer will offer insurance. Self-insured plans, on the other hand, are exempt-

136

ed from providing State-mandated benefits and paying State premium taxes under the Federal Employee Retirement Income Security Act (ERISA). Third, risk-spreading, which keeps costs down by pooling the cost of possible serious health problems among a large group is more difficult in smaller firms. When one employee of a small enterprise becomes seriously ill, the cost of premiums for the entire group increases much more than it would in a larger group.

This last observation is a matter of concern. The purpose of insurance should be to spread risk so that premiums do not increase in small groups when an employee becomes ill. To improve risk-spreading, small firms could purchase health insurance policies that remained in force for 5 or 10 years, rather than the 1-year contracts that are now customary. High employee turnover rates and high business failure rates in small firms, however, may make it costly for insurers and firms to make such contracts. Furthermore, continuing changes in medical technology may make it risky for insurance companies to offer long-term contracts.

Firms are considerably less likely to offer health insurance to their part-time employees than to their full-time employees, mainly because coverage for a part-time employee costs as much as it does for a full-time employee and accounts for a much higher share of part-time workers' total compensation.

HOW THE UNINSURED USE HEALTH CARE SERVICES

Those who lack insurance do not necessarily forgo all health care. They may pay for care directly or may receive it for free, primarily through hospitals. In 1989, U.S. hospitals provided over $10 billion worth of free, or uncompensated, care. People without health insurance do use less health care than those with similar health problems who are insured, however.

People without health insurance are far more likely than those with insurance to report that they did not receive health care during an illness because of financial constraints. Those who do seek care are more likely to receive it in inappropriate and costly settings such as emergency rooms. The uninsured are likely to be sicker when they are admitted to a hospital; they are also likely to be discharged from the hospital earlier than their insured counterparts.

New estimates suggest that out-of-pocket health expenditures among the uninsured are lower than they are among insured people with similar incomes and are far less than the cost of purchasing a basic health insurance policy. Some uninsured people may be consciously choosing to rely on emergency room care and personal savings rather than purchasing costly health insurance coverage.

RECENT CHANGES IN THE NUMBER OF UNINSURED

Many of the uninsured are unemployed. Although the Consolidated Omnibus Budget Reconciliation Act allows those who leave jobs to continue their coverage for up to 18 months through their employer's health care plan by paying the full cost of the premium, only about 20 percent of those eligible do so. Structural changes in the American labor market have also affected insurance coverage. Workers are most likely to be covered by health insurance if they are unionized or employed in the manufacturing sector. But employment in manufacturing fell from 23 percent to 18 percent of total employment during the 1980s, while the fraction of private sector workers represented by a union fell from 19 percent to 13 percent between 1983 and 1991.

These changes in the composition of the labor force, however, explain only a small percentage of the increase in the number of uninsured. As health insurance becomes more costly, more people may find it makes sense for them to seek higher wages rather than health insurance from their employers, relying instead on emergency care.

Low-Wage Jobs and Health Insurance

For employers offering jobs at low wages, increases in the cost of health insurance make it especially difficult to offer coverage. These employers cannot lower wages to help pay for health insurance, because wages would then fall below the legal minimum. *Studies suggest that, in 1989, about one-third of all uninsured American workers earned wages which, if reduced by the cost of health insurance, would fall below the legal minimum. Requiring employers to provide these workers with health insurance is likely to lead to increased unemployment among low-wage workers.*

SUMMARY

- Spending on health care has been rising steadily, both in absolute terms and as a share of national income. Since 1960, spending on health care has also risen rapidly in other developed countries, but the per capita cost of health care is much higher in the United States than in other developed countries.
- The number of uninsured has increased recently. Part of this increase is due to the economic slowdown, while part is due to a long-term decline in employer-sponsored health insurance.
- The uninsured are poorer and younger, on average, than the insured. Although most are in good health, some are chronically ill. The uninsured do receive some health care, but they receive less than those with insurance and often receive care in emergency rooms. Out-of-pocket health expenditures among

the uninsured are lower than among insured people with similar incomes.
- Many of the uninsured are workers employed by small firms. A substantial fraction of uninsured workers earn wages which, if reduced by the cost of health insurance, would fall below minimum wage. Requiring employers to provide insurance to these workers would lead to increased unemployment.

ECONOMIC THEORY OF THE HEALTH CARE MARKET

Economic analysis can help explain much of the recent performance of the American health care market and the problems that have emerged. Providers and purchasers of health care services respond to the incentives and restrictions they face, which stem from both the nature of health care itself and the way it is financed and delivered.

PROVIDING HEALTH CARE SERVICES

Two features of health care provision have significant implications for costs. First, it is difficult for consumers to evaluate the quality of health care services. They rely on the advice of the provider of the service in deciding what to buy. While the lack of independent information is not unique to the health care market (car owners may rely on mechanics), it can lead to the unwitting purchase of unnecessary, poor quality, or high-cost services.

Second, to protect consumers from unscrupulous or incompetent providers, licensing boards in every State regulate those who work in health care. The licensing procedure can increase the price of services by restricting the number of providers and limiting the ways that they may compete.

PROBLEMS OF MEASURING QUALITY

Physicians have much more information about treating a particular illness than their patients do. Patients may find it difficult to evaluate their treatment; if they get better, they may not be able to tell whether they have enjoyed a natural recovery or especially effective treatment. Lack of information can make it difficult for people to make decisions about purchasing health care. A physician could charge a low fee either because the services are provided in the most cost-saving way or because they are not performed properly.

People have tried to overcome this problem by evaluating a primary care physician—asking for recommendations from friends, for example—and then accepting the primary care physician's advice on further treatment. But friends may not be able to assess quality accurately; their advice may be particularly deficient in evaluating the services of a group of doctors in a coordinated care organization.

Information about provider quality is especially important because of the enormous variation in the way American doctors treat patients with similar problems. For example, rates of use of some discretionary procedures, such as tonsillectomies, can be ten times as high in one county as in a neighboring county with a similar population. In many cases, the use of such procedures deviates substantially from what experts recommend. Rates of mortality for patients with similar problems also differ considerably among hospitals.

These variations suggest that if consumers could better evaluate their care, the quality of care could be improved substantially and costs could be reduced. Physicians and hospitals that offer low-quality care at high prices would face stronger incentives to improve quality and reduce costs.

Improving the Quality of Information

Without a reasonably accurate way to measure quality, health care plans, hospitals, and providers have a difficult time competing on the basis of the price of services they offer. But developing such information may not make economic sense for any single health care provider or insurer, since setting up a system of gathering and disseminating information would be costly and, once developed, might well be copied. The tax treatment of employer-provided insurance and the government's growing role in health care provision have also limited the incentives for private insurers and providers to develop ways to compete by providing high-quality, low-cost care.

Despite these impediments, insurers and employers have recently been working together to develop systems for measuring the quality of health care provided. The Federal Government has launched a major initiative with the publication of mortality rates (adjusted for the severity of patient illness) for medicare patients in U.S. hospitals. A variety of other groups are providing information in health care markets, including a group that publishes an annual guide to Washington-area Federal employee health plans; the Pennsylvania Health Care Cost Containment Council, which publishes information about hospital charges and mortality rates; and a group of employers in Cleveland that sponsors the Cleveland Health Quality Choice Project, which is developing measures to compare the quality of care in Cleveland-area hospitals.

THE SUPPLY OF PROVIDERS

In many industries, costs rise when the necessary skilled personnel and materials are in short supply. In most cases, such short-term shortages cause wages to rise, attracting new supplies of skilled workers. Shortages and the high wages that they produce are unlikely to persist over time. High physician incomes might persist, however, without leading to an increased supply of doctors, because the medical profession can, to some extent, regulate the number of new physicians receiving licenses each year.

In the past, physicians' associations have also kept doctors from competing on the basis of price. Until 1982, these organizations restricted their members' ability to advertise services. For many years, professional associations controlled the types of fee arrangements that doctors could accept, stifling the growth of coordinated care. These problems are less serious today. The number of practicing doctors has increased greatly and the profession's ability to limit price competition has declined.

HEALTH INSURANCE

The need for health care depends, in part, on somewhat unpredictable and costly events, such as a serious illness or accident. People can respond to the risk of such possibilities by self-insuring, or saving money to pay for potential expenses; by investing in preventive health care; or by purchasing health insurance.

Insurance is most valuable when it protects people against uncertain events that carry a high risk of substantial financial loss. Thus, early insurance plans were set up to cover costly hospital expenses. By 1960, insurance covered most hospital care, but people generally paid for other services themselves. In recent years, however, insurance coverage has expanded to cover other services. The share of out-of-pocket expenses for relatively predictable and inexpensive services (such as physician services, dental care, and pharmaceuticals) has been declining steadily (Chart 4–6).

Insurance can Lead to Overconsumption of Services

All insurance, whether privately or publicly provided, affects the incentives of the insured. Because they are protected against the full cost of a serious illness or injury, the insured have less incentive to take steps to limit the losses associated with such events. The change in incentives that results from the purchase of insurance is known by economists as "moral hazard." To economists, the term carries no connotation of dishonesty.

Moral hazard typically refers to a reduction in the incentive to avoid undesirable events. For example, people insured against car theft may leave their doors unlocked, increasing the chance that their cars may be stolen. People with health insurance may be just as careful as the uninsured about avoiding health risks, but they also respond to the incentives produced through insurance by using more health care services. They are likely to go to the doctor more often and choose more complex procedures. Among health econo-

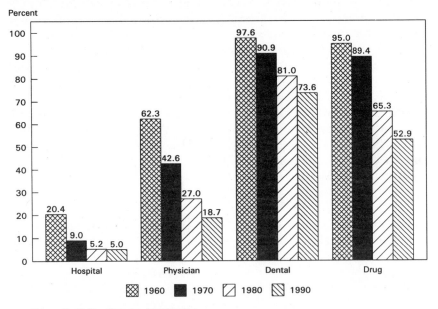

Chart 4-6 **Share of Health Care Expenses Paid Out of Pocket**
The share of expenses paid out of pocket varies considerably among services but has been declining since 1960 for all services.

Percent

Source: Health Care Financing Administration.

mists, the term moral hazard has come to include this incentive for the overconsumption of health care services, which adds to total health care costs.

Studies suggest that the overconsumption of services due to moral hazard is an important factor in rising health care costs. One study in the 1970s gave one group of randomly selected families health insurance policies that provided them with full insurance for all health care services and another group a catastrophic health insurance plan and a corresponding cash payment (for example, a health insurance policy with a $1,000 deductible together with a cash payment of $1,000). Although both families were equally well indemnified, those who were fully insured used nearly 30 percent more services than those with the catastrophic insurance plan. According to most measures of health status, families in both groups were equally healthy at the end of the 3 to 5-year experiment.

Responses to Moral Hazard

Because people with insurance pay less than the full cost of insured services, moral hazard suggests they may use services that they would not have chosen to purchase if they had to pay the full cost. But by using these additional services, policyholders drive up the cost of insurance. Ultimately, they pay the full expected cost of these additional services through higher insurance premiums. Yet many consumers would prefer less expensive insurance policies that encourage them to use only those services that they value most highly.

Insurers have two well-known ways to limit the potential response to moral hazard in their policies and keep premium costs down. Traditionally, they have required those with insurance to pay for part of their services through deductibles and copayments. Even with deductibles and copayments for a particular service, however, the price an insured patient pays for services will generally be less than the full cost.

Another response to moral hazard involves monitoring policyholders to ensure that they are taking appropriate preventive measures and to cap the services that they can use if an illness or injury occurs. By monitoring services and encouraging preventive care, the insurer can try to restrict the policyholder to only those services that are worth their full cost. Coordinated care organizations take this approach. These organizations typically charge low copayments and deductibles but closely monitor the utilization of health care services among those who are ill and often provide free preventive care services. Conventional insurers have also begun to adopt these monitoring practices, for example, by requiring a second opinion for surgery.

Using Private Information in Purchasing Insurance

People usually know more than insurance companies about their own health and their need for health care services. This asymmetry of information has important implications for the health insurance market. An insurer charges a premium based on the average need for health care services. For those who anticipate that their need for health care services will be higher than average, health insurance is a bargain. But those who anticipate that their need for health care services will be below average may find health insurance a poor investment. They may choose to pay for their health care themselves or to purchase a health insurance policy with very high deductibles and copayments. This process is known as adverse selection.

If those at low risk drop out of the health insurance market, the average premiums for the remaining purchasers will rise. In theory, if the adverse selection process continues, the market for insurance may disappear altogether as healthier people decline increasingly expensive insurance. Alternatively, people may sort themselves into high- and low-risk groups and purchase different kinds of insurance. If this occurs, *those at high risk will purchase comprehensive health insurance plans and face premiums that re-*

143

flect the full costs associated with their true health status. Low-risk individuals will purchase less comprehensive insurance, paying low premiums that reflect both the type of plan they purchase and their health status.

Economic theory suggests that adverse selection can lead to lower levels of health insurance coverage for the relatively healthy. Studies also support this finding. Among firms offering multiple health insurance plans, premiums for comprehensive coverage are much higher than premiums for plans with high deductibles and copayments. These higher premiums are not fully explained by the fact that comprehensive plans offer additional services or by the effects of moral hazard. Rather, evidence suggests that those who choose the comprehensive plans are in poorer health than those who choose plans requiring high out-of-pocket payments.

The theory of adverse selection can also explain some characteristics of the uninsured. For example, the uninsured appear to have a low propensity to use medical services. When currently uninsured people obtain insurance, they use, on average, fewer services than those who are continuously insured.

CONCERNS OVER THE DISTRIBUTION OF MEDICAL RESOURCES

Asymmetries of information, whether between insurers and policyholders or providers and patients, can cause problems in the health care market. Consequently, some people will not be able to purchase insurance, and some patients willing to pay for better care will not be able to find it. But even if these asymmetries could be eliminated, health care would still be costly. Some Americans, especially those who are poor or who have chronic health conditions, would still find it very difficult to purchase health insurance.

Risk Selection

Private insurers compete to offer people the lowest price for their health coverage. One way to offer a better bargain to people with lower-than-average health risks is to adjust the price of insurance offered to them to reflect only the cost of the health services they can be expected to purchase. If insurers can observe the risk characteristics of those they insure, they can charge these low-risk people low premiums. People at high risk would be charged high premiums that reflect all the costs they could be expected to incur.

People with chronic health conditions may be excluded from commercial health insurance coverage due to preexisting condition clauses. If they are able to find coverage, they are likely to be charged very high rates that correspond to their expected health costs. Ironically, improvements in diagnostic and management technology may make it even harder for some people to obtain

144

health insurance, as insurance companies become better able to diagnose and screen out those with chronic health problems.

If insurers are required to charge all purchasers of health insurance in a community the same premiums (a practice known as community rating), they are prevented from responding to even readily observable health characteristics by raising or lowering prices. Yet these insurers will still try to compete by offering low prices to those at low risk. They may do this by directly refusing to provide coverage to those at high risk, a practice called risk selection. Alternatively, they may use adverse selection to their advantage, selling low-priced insurance contracts with restricted services or high copayment rates that appeal to those at low risk but would not be chosen by those at high risk.

Health Care for the Poor and Ill

The unequal distribution of health care is an important policy concern. Most Americans believe that everyone should be entitled to at least basic health care, regardless of income or health status. This belief distinguishes the health care sector from most other parts of the U.S. economy and explains why charitable organizations have always played an important role in health care. Public and voluntary hospitals continue to provide, to some extent, a health care safety net that ironically causes other problems in the health insurance market.

First, because this safety net operates principally through hospital emergency rooms, most of the uninsured receive care only when their conditions are quite serious, although more effective care could often be provided earlier in the course of their illness. Furthermore, providing emergency care through hospitals is likely to be much more costly than providing preventive care in an outpatient setting.

Second, although most Americans agree that everyone should receive basic health care, the safety net does not force all Americans to share the burden of this care equally. Instead, the costs may fall on those who use hospitals that charge high fees to paying patients in order to cover the cost of the uninsured.

Finally, the existence of the safety net may discourage some people from purchasing health insurance, especially those with serious health conditions who must pay very high premiums and those in very good health who do not expect to use services at all. For these people, remaining uninsured may be better than purchasing insurance because they know that they will not be turned away if and when they need care.

Unfortunately, programs that help low-income people purchase health insurance can also have some undesirable effects. As family incomes rise, support under income-tested health programs is phased out. As with similar provisions in other government programs (such as aid to families with dependent children), this phase-out means that poor families may face a very high marginal "tax" rate. Small increases in their income are accompanied by large reductions in the value of the health care and other support they receive. Such high taxes may discourage people from trying to increase their incomes.

SUMMARY

- A lack of information may lead patients to spend money on services they might not choose if they were fully informed. Private and public initiatives are underway to improve the quality of health care information.
- Health insurance reduces the price of health care services for policyholders. Thus it can lead to the overconsumption of health care—that is, the use of services whose full costs exceed their benefit to the consumer.
- When policyholders have more information about their own health status than do insurers (or than insurers are permitted to use), adverse selection—which may cause the healthiest people to opt out of the health insurance market—may occur.
- The existing safety net for the uninsured is problematic. The uninsured receive insufficient and often inappropriate forms of care and have few incentives to purchase insurance.

WHY ARE HEALTH CARE EXPENDITURES INCREASING?

An economic analysis of the structure of the U.S. health care market can help to explain why health care expenditures have risen so sharply. The tax subsidy for health insurance has encouraged employers to provide employees with coverage that includes very low copayments and deductibles and covers relatively predictable and inexpensive services. Most people covered by government insurance programs (medicare and medicaid) also make low out-of-pocket payments. Although substantial out-of-pocket payments are required in the medicare program, most beneficiaries have medigap policies that cover many of these costs. Out-of-pocket payments for health care as a share of all health expenditures have been falling, reducing the incentive for consumers to limit their use of health care services. For example, studies show that, at current levels, medigap insurance increases health care utilization by up to 24 percent.

The open-ended nature of health insurance contracts means that most new nonexperimental technologies will be covered by existing policies. As a result, expensive new technologies covered by insurance may be introduced before consumers would otherwise be willing to pay for them, further contributing to the escalation of costs.

PRICES AND QUANTITIES OF HEALTH CARE

The Health Care Financing Administration, the Federal agency that administers medicare and medicaid, has developed a price index for personal health care expenditures that measures the cost of all health care services, regardless of who pays for them. Dividing total spending on health care by this price index produces a composite measure of the quantity of the various health care services people consume, including physician visits, hospital care, and drug purchases.

Two factors affect the price index: changes in the economy's general inflation rate and deviations in the price of health care services from the general rate of inflation. Table 4-1 provides measures of changes in total health care expenditures and divides these into changes in economywide prices, real health care expenditures, health care prices in excess of economywide inflation, and quantities of health care consumed.

TABLE 4-1.—*Average Annual Percent Change in Personal Health Care Expenditures Per Capita, Prices, and Quantities: 1960-90*

Item	1960-70	1970-80	1980-90
1) Personal health care expenditures per capita	9.2	11.9	9.2
2) MINUS: Economywide inflation	2.2	6.2	4.6
3) EQUALS: Expenditures per capita corrected for inflation	6.9	5.4	4.4
4) MINUS: Health care price increases in excess of inflation	1.7	1.6	2.3
5) EQUALS: Quantity of health care per capita	5.1	3.8	2.2

Note.—Columns do not sum both because of rounding and because the price-quantity interaction terms have been omitted.
Source: Health Care Financing Administration.

This price index for health care expenditures, like other price indexes, is constructed by examining the cost of a basket of commodities or services over time. The personal health care price index basket includes hospital care, physician services, drugs, and other health-related products. The index reflects changes in the cost of this broad basket, not the price of a particular service provided by a hospital or physician.

The price index does not adequately reflect improvements in the quality of the commodities or services, which usually appear as price increases. For example, total expenditures for a hospital day go up if the number of nursing visits made during that hospital day increases. While such a change implies that the quality of a day in the hospital has improved, it appears only as an increase in the health care price index. An alternative way to measure changes in health care expenditures is described in Box 4-5.

147

RECENT INCREASES IN HEALTH CARE EXPENDITURES

U.S. health care expenditures have risen continuously since the 1960s, not only because health care prices have gone up but because Americans are using more services. In the 1980s, real health care spending grew more slowly than it had during the preceding two decades. Growth was split evenly between increases in the quantity of health care consumed (2.2 percent annually) and increases in the health care price index in excess of general inflation (2.3 percent annually) (Table 4-1).

Economic theory suggests that when prices rise people usually consume less of a good or service. Yet the price of health care and the quantity purchased rose in tandem during the 1980s (as well as in earlier decades). These concurrent increases in price and quantity are consistent with the view that the quality of health care changed during the 1980s. Consumers in 1990 were probably not buying more 1980-style health care at 1990 prices; rather, they were willing to pay more for 1990-style health care than they had been willing to pay for 1980-style health care. The changes that were measured in quantity and price hid underlying changes in quality.

148

The quantity of health care services consumed increased primarily because of greater use of outpatient and physician care in the 1980s. The growth rate of inpatient hospital spending declined between 1982 and 1986, largely because of changes in the system of medicare reimbursement. Although inpatient hospital services are now paid prospectively, outpatient services for medicare continue to be paid on a less constraining retrospective basis, giving hospitals a considerable incentive to move procedures from an inpatient to an outpatient setting.

The health care sector responded in a flexible and rapid way to this changed incentive. In 1980 only 16 percent of surgeries in short-stay hospitals were performed on an outpatient basis, but by 1989, 49 percent were conducted on an outpatient basis. The potential for such responses needs to be taken into account in the development of health policy.

COMPONENTS OF PRICE INCREASES IN THE 1980s

The health care price index increased throughout the 1980s. Price increases measured were due, in part, to increased use of expensive technologies and to changes in the cost and types of labor used in health care. As insurers and providers competed by offering more generous coverage, technology, and high quality care, costs rose.

Physician Costs in the 1980s

In the late 1980s, physician costs rose more rapidly than other major components of health care spending, in part because of an increase in the use of outpatient diagnostic and treatment facilities, some of them owned by physicians. Studies suggest that physicians order more tests when they own a share in diagnostic and treatment facilities. These private facilities may be more convenient, but physicians may also be motivated by the incentives created by the traditional insurance system, which pays physicians for each service they provide—including those provided by diagnostic and treatment facilities that they own.

This practice may be curtailed by regulations stemming from the 1988 Clinical Laboratory Improvement Amendments. The act, intended to improve the quality of laboratory tests, imposes very costly regulations on the operation of laboratories. But these regulations may not significantly improve the quality of health care and, in fact, may impose additional costs on patients whose physicians operate small-scale office-based laboratories.

U.S. physicians became, on average, more highly specialized during the 3 decades leading up to 1990, especially before 1980. In 1965 24 percent of U.S. physicians were general practitioners. By 1990 only 12 percent of U.S. physicians were general practitioners; the other 88 percent were specialists, a much higher percentage than in other countries, such as Canada. Specialists are usually more highly paid than general practitioners, and the pay differential expanded during the 1980s as the demand grew for new diagnostic and surgical procedures only specialists can provide.

Nursing Costs in the 1980s

In the early 1980s, salaries for nurses were low compared with those for other occupations requiring similar levels of skill, discouraging some qualified applicants from entering nursing school. In an effort to attract more nurses, hospitals increased nurses' real wages. Between January 1980 and January 1990, the real hourly earnings of private hospital employees rose about 25 percent (excluding the value of nonwage compensation), while the earnings of all private sector workers changed little. Registered nurses were among those hospital employees receiving the largest pay increases during the 1980s. At the same time, reductions in the length of the average hospital stay and increased use of outpatient surgery meant that patients who were admitted and kept in hospitals were, on average, sicker than those admitted in 1980. Hospitals were forced to increase the ratio of highly skilled registered nurses to patients in order to maintain the quality of their services.

Medical Technology in the 1980s

Increased use of costly medical technology also had an important impact on measured health care prices in the 1980s. *Between 1980 and 1990, for instance, the number of computerized axial tomography (CAT) scans performed in short-stay hospitals in the United States increased over 400 percent. The number of community hospitals with magnetic resonance imagery equipment rose 500 percent between 1984 and 1991.* Many of these new technologies also proliferated in nonhospital settings.

The use of new surgical techniques flourished in the 1980s. For example, *in 1980, 1 in every 400 American men aged 65 and over had coronary artery bypass surgery. In 1990, about 1 in 100 American men in the same age group had this form of surgery.*

The Costs of Malpractice Litigation

The increasing costs associated with medical malpractice suits have been an important factor in rising health care costs. Between 1982 and 1989, doctors' liability premiums, the principal source of payment for malpractice claims, grew at 15 percent annually, faster than any other component of medical practice costs. Another more insidious effect of malpractice suits is that they may compel physicians to perform tests that are not cost-effective simply to protect themselves from legal actions. The costs of defensive medical practices have been estimated at over $20 billion in 1989 alone, or almost 18 percent of total physician expenditures. Finally, malpractice insurance costs have caused some physicians to drop out of some specialties, such as obstetrics, making such specialists hard to find in some communities.

Although insurers and physicians spend large sums defending themselves in malpractice suits, relatively little of this money makes its way to those injured through negligence. A recent study of malpractice cases in New York found that 16 times as many patients suffered an injury from negligence as received compensation from the tort liability system. In 1984, only about 60 percent of the money expended on malpractice litigation was actually paid to injured plaintiffs.

Administrative Expenditures

The administrative costs of the U.S. health care industry, which are estimated at $80 billion in 1991, have been widely criticized and unfavorably compared to the costs of administering the government-run systems in many other countries. Private insurance companies incur costs marketing their products, reviewing and processing claims, and screening and establishing the health status of potential enrollees. Billing individual patients or insurance companies raises costs for physicians and hospitals.

Recent studies find, however, that shifting to a system that eliminates the functions of the U.S. private insurance industry would result in few overall cost reductions. Most of the administrative cost savings would be offset by increases in utilization that would come from the elimination of features of the current system that reduce overall expenditures, such as patient payments and insurance company oversight. In other countries with multiple insurers, such as Germany, administrative costs as a share of total health expenditures are comparable to those in the United States.

Private insurance companies compete, in part, on the prices of the services they offer. A competitive insurance company, like any other firm, can increase administrative expenses only if the benefits of these expenditures exceed the new expense. *In health insurance, much of the increase in administrative expenditures has come from the expansion of programs that monitor service utilization, and health insurance that offers these features is cheaper than insurance that does not—despite the administrative costs associated with oversight programs.* Nonetheless, some of these costs, such as the costs of assessing the health status of new enrollees, may raise aggregate health care expenditures.

PROJECTIONS OF FUTURE COST INCREASES

Many analysts expect that unless the health care market is substantially reformed, costs will continue to rise rapidly into the next century. Recent projections suggest that health care, which consumed 12 percent of the GNP in 1990, may rise to as much as 16 percent of GNP by the year 2000 and to 26 percent by 2030 (Chart 4-7).

Chart 4-7 **Projected Health Care Expenditures as Percent of GNP**
Most forecasts suggest that health care expenditures will continue rising, mainly due to increases in prices and in the use of services.

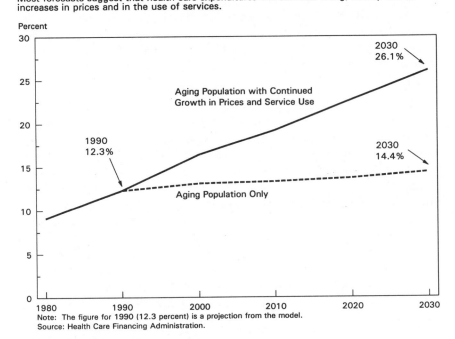

Note: The figure for 1990 (12.3 percent) is a projection from the model.
Source: Health Care Financing Administration.

These projected increases are due primarily to an expected continuation of the historic trends of increasing health care prices and volume consumed, as well as improving quality. Because most projections of health care expenditures are based mainly on mechanical extrapolations of past trends, *they do not take into account changes in government programs or other individual and institutional responses to the rising cost of health care.* During the 1980s, as health care expenses rose rapidly, insurers, employers, consumers, and the government responded through innovations in the financing and delivery of care. Such changes in behavior, which cannot be captured by the modeling techniques currently in use, could have profound effects on the cost of health care.

Demographics

Projected increases in health costs are, to a small extent, a consequence of the aging of the population. Population aging alone is expected to cause health care expenditures to increase from 12 percent of GNP in 1990 to about 14 percent by 2030, explaining about one-seventh of the total projected increase in health care costs (to 26 percent of GNP). The number of Americans over age 64, the age

152

group for which health care spending is the highest, will increase through 2030, especially after the turn of the century.

Those over age 64 consume about 3½ times as much health care as those between the ages of 19 and 64, and those over age 84 consume almost 2½ times as much health care as those between the ages of 65 and 69 (Chart 4-8). Health care spending is higher among those over age 64 due primarily to the increased probability of death at this age. Health care spending is especially high in the last year of life. The 5 percent of aged beneficiaries who were in their last year of life accounted for 29 percent of medicare expenditures in 1979.

Chart 4-8   Per Capita Personal Health Care Expenditures, by Age: 1987
Health care expenditures, especially for nursing home care, rise rapidly with age.

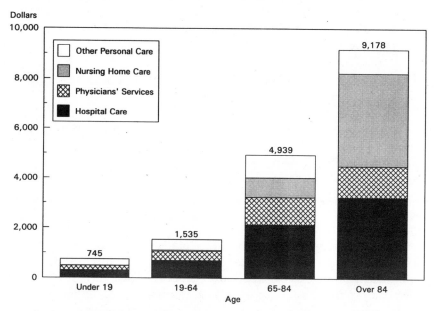

Source: Health Care Financing Administration.

Another important reason for the high costs of caring for those over age 64, and especially for those over age 84, is nursing home care. But because people who pay directly for much of this care, as well as State governments, which both pay for care and license nursing homes, have strong incentives to limit spending, most analysts expect the growth in spending for nursing home care to be slower than the changing age composition of the population would suggest.

SUMMARY

- Both the price of health care and the quantity of services consumed increased during the 1980s. Part of the apparent increase in price was due to improvements in the quality of care. Labor costs, the costs of new equipment, and the use of new treatments all contributed to the growth in expenditures during the 1980s.
- Changes in administrative expenditures are unlikely to have been an important contributor to overall expenditure growth. Most administrative expenses reduce overall health care costs.
- Litigation over medical malpractice raises costs directly and encourages the practice of costly defensive medicine.
- Simple extrapolations of health care expenditures—which do not take cost-cutting measures into account—suggest that they will consume as much as 26 percent of gross national product by 2030. A small part of this increase is due to the aging of the population.

PROPOSALS FOR REFORM OF THE HEALTH CARE MARKET

Increasing health care expenditures and the growing number of uninsured in the United States have led to a proliferation of proposals for health care reform. In the past year, some 70 bills have been introduced in the Congress. While most of these plans seek to alleviate the symptoms of trouble in the health care market, relatively few address the underlying causes of the cost increases and insurance gaps.

As the response to the diagnosis-related group payment system in hospitals has shown, changes in incentives can lead to major modifications in health care provision. *Because the health care sector is flexible and responsive, health reforms that address underlying economic problems and provide sound incentives can be very effective. On the other hand, reforms that ignore the economics of health care are likely to lead to unexpected and undesirable results.* Table 4–2 provides a summary of the main proposals for health care reform that are discussed below.

ADMINISTRATION PROPOSAL

This Administration's health care reform proposal is a comprehensive, market-based reform plan that builds on the strengths of the existing market. It includes components designed both to expand access to health insurance and to improve market functioning.

TABLE 4-2.—Side-by-Side Comparison of Health Insurance Plans

Issue	Administration Proposal	Managed Competition Proposal	Pay-or-Play and Rate Setting	National Health Insurance and Global Budgets
Cost containment				
Moral hazard	Encourages managed care for public programs.	Promotes use of basic benefit package.	—	—
Other	Increases competition in small group market and public programs. Improves availability of health care quality information. Simplifies recordkeeping and billing. Reduces malpractice litigation costs.	Increases competition in small group market.	Provider and hospital fee schedule.	Global budgets. Physician and hospital fee schedule.
Access				
Poor	Provides low and middle income people with insurance certificate/deduction.	Mandates coverage through employers. Provides subsidies to low income people who are not employed and to part-time workers.	Requires employers to offer insurance or pay into public plan.	Universal coverage.
Ill Health	Implements health risk adjusters for high-risk people in individual and small group health insurance markets.	Provides age-adjusted community-rated coverage in individual and small group health insurance markets.	Covers employed persons in ill health.	Universal coverage.

Access to Care Under the Administration Proposal

An important objective of health care reform is to provide better access to health care for the poor and those with chronic illnesses. The Administration's plan would address this objective by providing these groups with the funds to purchase health insurance within the existing health care market at a reasonable price. It would provide low-income Americans with a transferable tax credit, ranging from a maximum of $1,250 for single persons to $3,750 for families of three or more, for purchasing health insurance. Those who do not file tax returns would receive the credit in the form of a transferable health insurance certificate. Middle-income people would be eligible for a tax deduction for health insurance.

The U.S. Treasury estimates that, when fully phased in (in 1997), the health insurance tax credit and deduction could benefit about 90 million people. About 25 million of these potential beneficiaries would be low-income people receiving the maximum applicable credit. The credit or deduction would be reduced for those with higher incomes: 10 million people with incomes between 100 and 150 percent of the poverty level would receive a partial credit or deduction, and 56 million middle-income individuals would receive a partial deduction.

States would develop basic insurance packages equal to the value of the health insurance credit. Each State would ensure that at least two insurers offered such a package. Because low-income

155

Americans would be able to purchase basic insurance using their tax credits, they would no longer have to rely on the public hospital safety net. At the same time, the fixed-dollar nature of the credit or deduction would not encourage overconsumption of health insurance. While the credit or deduction could be used toward the purchase of plans offering other than the basic benefits, the purchaser would bear any additional cost of these plans.

The President's plan encourages States to fold their existing medicaid programs into the new program. Those eligible for medicaid would receive the full individual tax credit and could then purchase basic benefit coverage through one of the plans offered in the State. This scheme would allow even the poorest Americans a choice in their purchase of health insurance.

The plan would further expand health insurance coverage by helping small firms buy insurance. It would promote the use of health insurance networks to act as group purchasing agents for smaller employers, obtaining more favorable premiums and reducing administrative expenditures. Insurance purchased through these networks would be exempt from State-mandated benefits and premium taxes.

The plan would incorporate health risk pools that would spread the cost of serious health problems among all those purchasing health insurance with the tax credit or deduction or through the small group health insurance networks. These pools would employ health risk adjusters (Box 4-6). This feature of the plan addresses the concern that those with poor health conditions should be able to purchase health insurance. Low- and middle-income people with chronic health problems would have greatly improved access to health care through this combination of tax credits and deductions and health risk pools.

Although health risk pools would not wholly eliminate the problem of adverse selection, they would enable people with poor health to purchase health care at reasonable cost. Under the Administration's plan, people would not be required to purchase health insurance. Those who know that their health is unusually good and are eligible for only a partial credit or deduction could choose to forgo the credit or deduction, not purchase health insurance, and continue to pay their own expenses or rely on the existing health care safety net. The only way to eliminate this problem completely would be to require everyone to purchase some health insurance.

Finally, the plan prohibits all insurers from excluding any individual or group from health insurance coverage because of a preexisting condition and requires insurers to renew the coverage of any previously insured group that complies with its insurance contract. These features of the plan would reduce existing impediments to labor market mobility among those with preexisting health condi-

Box 4–6.—Health Risk Adjusters

The health risk pools envisioned under the President's plan would incorporate a system of health risk adjusters intended to equalize the cost of insuring those who differ only with regard to health status. Insurers serving a pool each cover different groups of people. Those providing coverage to groups with more than the average number of health problems would receive a payment from the pool equal to the difference between the expected average expenditures of that group and the average expenditures of all people in the pool. An insurer providing coverage to a relatively healthy group would make a corresponding payment into the pool.

These payments would be age-group specific. Thus, younger people, who tend to be quite healthy, would face lower average premiums than older people, who tend to have more health problems. That means that implementation of a health risk adjuster system would not give younger people additional incentives to leave the health insurance market or increase transfers from the young to the old. (Chapter 6 contains a discussion of current intergenerational transfers.) At the same time, the health risk adjuster system would leave all people with the incentive to save money for their old age.

Health risk adjusters have two advantages over community rating. First, because the payments are based on average rather than actual expenditures, everyone has incentives to monitor his or her own use of care. People who consistently use more than the expected average amount of health care for someone of their health status would face higher rates than those who economized on their use of care. Under community rating, the actual costs of this additional care would be spread among all people with insurance. Second, under a system of health risk adjusters, insurers would have no incentive to deny coverage to people with chronic health conditions. Firms that insure only low-risk people would have to make payments into the health risk pool to subsidize firms that insure high-risk people. Under community rating, insurers could profit by discriminating against people with chronic health conditions.

Under the Administration's reform proposal, health risk adjusters would be phased in over a period of 5 years. Premium bands would be implemented during the phase-in period. Premium bands limit the difference in premiums that insurers can charge groups with different average health status. Further limits on rate increases would also be in effect during the transition to health risk pools and risk adjusters.

157

tions and lower some of the administrative costs associated with the screening of prospective enrollees in small-group plans.

Cost Control Under the Administration Plan

Other aspects of the Administration's proposal are designed to improve the functioning of both private and public insurance in the health care marketplace. The plan would increase incentives to use coordinated care delivery systems within the medicare and medicaid frameworks. It would provide both HMO and alternative coordinated care options to medicare beneficiaries and increase financial incentives for beneficiaries to join the HMOs. The plan would require States either to shift all nonelderly medicaid beneficiaries into coordinated care programs or to fold all medicaid beneficiaries into the tax credit and deduction program.

To improve the performance of the private health insurance industry, the Administration's plan would address the lack of information in health care markets by requiring States to implement programs to help make information about the cost and quality of medical services available to consumers. The Federal Government would assist the States by developing prototype systems to assist in data gathering and outcome comparison. Informed patients are more likely to choose providers and insurers who provide high quality services at reasonable prices.

Under the Administration's plan, administrative costs would be reduced in both the private and public health insurance sectors. The proposal calls for the Federal Government to work with the private sector in developing record-keeping and billing forms. These reductions in billing costs, in combination with the savings from reduced health status screening, could lower the total administrative costs of the health care system significantly.

The Administration's proposal would encourage competition among health plans. Because recipients of tax credits or deductions (including former medicaid recipients) would be able to choose between at least two plans available in every geographic area, competition between the plans would help ensure an adequate level of service. If one plan provided poor-quality service, those insured could choose another plan. States would also be encouraged to remove existing impediments to competition, such as regulations limiting coordinated care arrangements and mandating the inclusion of certain benefits in insurance plans.

Malpractice costs would be reduced under the proposal's comprehensive liability reform plan. The plan would provide States with incentives to cap the amount of allowable losses for damages other than loss of income and the cost of health care associated with an injury. States would be encouraged to employ systems of alternative dispute resolution, which may reduce the cost of adjudicating disputes. The Federal Government would also intensify existing efforts to create guidelines and quality standards for health care that, when adopted by a State, could be used by the courts to determine negligence. If the legal system relied on such standards, physicians would no longer have to practice defensive medicine. Standards could also improve the quality of care by keeping physicians informed about state-of-the-art treatments for particular conditions.

The most important component of the Administration's proposal with respect to improving health is its emphasis on prevention. The proposal calls for substantially increased spending for Federal preventive care programs and for an expansion of primary care health services to low-income communities. It also increases funding for programs aimed at encouraging Americans to make healthier choices with respect to smoking, physical fitness, and diet.

MANAGED COMPETITION

Managed competition reforms are intended to improve the operation of the marketplace and expand the availability of employer-sponsored health insurance. Although managed competition has many market-oriented features, it would greatly increase the role of the government in the health care system and would limit the range of health insurance options available to Americans. Many types of managed competition proposals exist; the discussion that follows examines one version.

Managed competition is built around the "accountable health partnership," an organization similar to an HMO that would provide both health benefits and consumer information. Each accountable health partnership would be registered with a national health board that would monitor the insurance market.

The national health board would define a set of "uniform effective health benefits" that accountable health partnerships would be required to provide. *All insurers, both private and governmental, would be required to offer the same basic benefit plan. Competition would focus on providing these benefits in a cost-saving and medically effective fashion.*

With managed competition almost everyone would have health insurance coverage. The proposal would mandate employer-provided insurance for all full-time employees. Employers would be required to make a flat contribution to an insurer for each of their employees of between 50 and 100 percent of the cost of the minimum benefit package offered by the cheapest accountable health partnership in the area. An employee could use this money to buy this plan, a more generous plan, or a plan from a different accountable health partnership. Even healthy employees would no doubt find it in their best interest to purchase health insurance at only half the premiums, so the 50-percent minimum contribution requirement would help to limit adverse selection.

Small firms would purchase insurance through collective purchasing agents in each State. These purchasing agents would pool risks and charge community rates across all small employers, although premiums could be age adjusted. Only those small employers who joined these organizations would be able to claim tax exemptions for health insurance premiums.

States would contract with the collective purchasing agent to insure all part-time employees and other unemployed and uninsured people. For these people, the premium costs of the cheapest available plan would be subsidized using revenues from taxes on part-time employees and on those with independent incomes.

Each State's collective purchasing agent could contract with many accountable health partnerships, creating competition among them. The national health board would be responsible for ensuring that the agent and each participating accountable health partnership met accounting, insurance, and benefit standards.

The mechanism for cost containment under managed competition is competition among accountable health partnerships over the price of the minimum benefit package. Although people could choose any insurance package offered by any participating accountable health partnership as long as it included at least the minimum benefits, they would not be able to deduct from their taxable income more than the cost of the minimum benefit package offered by the cheapest accountable health partnership. This limit on the tax subsidy would encourage people to choose less comprehensive health insurance and efficiently run insurance plans, since they would face the full additional cost if they chose a plan whose price exceeded that of the lowest-priced plan. Requiring that insurers offer at least this benefit package would mean that low-risk people could not engage in adverse selection by purchasing minimal benefit packages that would never be chosen by those at higher risk.

Because of the central role of the minimum benefit plan in this proposal, the kinds of benefits and deductible and copayment levels included in the plan would be very important. The benefits would have to be designed to fit the services offered by both traditional health insurers, which typically use deductibles and copayments to limit moral hazard, and coordinated care organizations, which use fewer deductibles and copayments but tend to monitor service utilization directly.

To avoid risk selection, the national health board would either need to specify benefits in a way that would limit the ability of accountable health partnerships to avoid sicker-than-average people or implement a system of health risk adjusters. Unless they did so, insurers could avoid such people, for example, by locating their offices in buildings without elevators, or by contracting only with physicians who do not specialize in the care of costly conditions.

With managed competition the government would take an active role in selecting the basic benefit package and in defining the type of insurance that most people would be likely to purchase. These governmental decisions could change the insurance arrangements of many Americans, because the accountable health partnerships envisioned in the proposal are similar to HMOs, while most Americans are currently enrolled in traditional fee-for-service health insurance plans. These decisions will also have a profound effective on the financial future of providers and insurers, who are likely to press for benefits to be defined as broadly as possible, limiting the ability of managed competition to contain costs.

PLAY-OR-PAY

Play-or-pay proposals for health care reform are structured around requirements that firms either provide basic health insurance to employees and their dependents ("play") or pay a payroll tax to cover enrollment in a public health care plan ("pay"). Most play-or-pay proposals would also offer sliding subsidies to those who are not attached to the work force.

Play-or-pay proposals focus on improving access to health insurance. But while play-or-pay would improve access to health insurance for some workers with low incomes or poor health status, it could reduce the incomes and employment opportunities of many other low-income people. Competitive firms would probably have to pass along the costs of health insurance to their workers in the form of lower wages. Thus, mandating health insurance through the workplace could lead to lower wages among currently uninsured employees and to increased unemployment among employees whose wages are at or near the minimum.

To the extent that employers choose to "play" rather than "pay," play-or-pay reform would retain some of the competitive aspects of the current health care market. Firms offering benefits similar to those offered in the public plan, however, would be able to switch to the "pay" option if the cost of their health insurance premiums is greater than the payroll tax. If the tax is set too low, everyone will eventually be enrolled in a single public plan. If the tax is too high, small employers will be forced to buy costly insurance, which will increase the plan's potential to lead to layoffs.

Play-or-pay alone does not directly address the problem of controlling health care expenditures. The effect of play-or-pay on costs would depend greatly on the structure of the public health insurance program, because a play-or-pay system would greatly increase participation in this program. Medicaid includes only limited provisions to reduce moral hazard. It has only recently launched managed care initiatives and, because it covers a population in poverty, currently incorporates few patient payment requirements. The public program in a play-or-pay system would need to include more patient payment requirements and managed care initiatives if costs are to be contained. Otherwise, play-or-pay could lead to increased overconsumption of medical resources, driving up health care costs.

Play-or-pay would provide health insurance to those with poor health conditions who may not be able to afford insurance in the current market. These people, however, are likely to be insured through the public program. Firms that hire workers with serious health conditions can avoid paying high insurance premiums by switching to the public plan. As a consequence, the cost of providing care in the public plan is likely to rise, and payroll tax rates may have to be raised to offset this increase. As the cost of health care rises, firms that are required to provide health insurance may begin laying off workers, especially low-skilled workers (as described above).

NATIONAL HEALTH INSURANCE PROPOSALS

Proposals for national health insurance envision replacing the private health insurance market with a single national health insurer. This national health insurer would be funded through taxes and care would be either free (as in Canada) or provided at a low cost-sharing level. National health insurance would provide Americans, regardless of income or health status, with access to a centrally determined set of health care services, at no direct cost to the insured. Because everyone would have exactly the same health insurance, national health insurance avoids the problems of risk selection and adverse selection.

Although national health insurance would ensure access to health insurance for everyone, it provides few incentives for consumers to limit their use of services and could lead to an explosion in cost unless other substantial reforms were undertaken. National health insurance greatly reduces existing incentives for consumers to limit their use of care. In most proposals, the cost of health care is shared among all taxpayers with few deductibles and copayments. The Canadian experience and other evidence suggest that substantial increases in utilization would be likely to accompany such reductions in deductibles and copayments.

Some proposals for national health insurance envision saving money by reducing administrative costs, but since reductions in administrative costs are likely to be accompanied by increased overconsumption of services, net health care costs may not decrease. National health insurance plans can control costs mainly by controlling the quantity and quality of health care supplied, often through price or budget controls (discussed below). An alternative way to control costs would be to fund only selected services, a method that has been proposed for the State of Oregon's medicaid program (Box 4-7).

Controls on supply and reductions in administrative costs are easiest to achieve in national health insurance programs that do not allow people to opt out by purchasing private health insurance. Adding any degree of choice to a national health insurance program—by allowing people to purchase alternative insurance, for instance—may reduce the cost savings achieved through supply controls and would be likely to increase administrative costs.

Box 4-7.— Oregon Medicaid Waiver Proposal

The State of Oregon has developed an innovative proposal that would extend medicaid insurance coverage to all Oregonians with incomes below the Federal poverty line. The plan would extend coverage to this broad group of people by restricting the treatments available to those covered. As proponents of the plan put it, services, not people, would be rationed.

In order to determine which services would be provided, the Oregon Health Services Commission undertook an extensive process that included research and analysis as well as consultations with the public. Initially, the commission identified 709 "condition-treatment" pairs, such as appendicitis-appendectomy. Next, the commission classified each pair into 1 of 17 categories according to the outcomes that could be expected from the treatment, such as "prevents death with full recovery," and ranked the pairs within each of the categories according to their impact on the quality of life. Finally, the commission submitted the ranked list of 709 pairs to the State legislature.

The legislature appropriated funds to cover services 1–587 on the list. These condition-treatment pairs would be included in the basic medical plan. Those condition-treatment pairs ranked 588–709 would not be covered for those insured by medicaid in Oregon.

Because medicaid is funded jointly by the Federal Government and the States, Oregon had to apply for a waiver from the Federal Government in order to implement this plan. This waiver was denied to the current version of the Oregon plan in August because of concerns that it violated the rights of the disabled under the Americans with Disabilities Act.

RATE SETTING

Some play-or-pay and national health insurance proposals incorporate provisions for rate setting. Rate setting, currently in use for hospital billing in some States, means that a governmental agency sets a single schedule of health care prices on which all payments, whether private or public, are based. In practice, increases in utilization often accompany such restrictions on prices in the health care market, limiting their effectiveness as a method of cost control. Because of the difficulty of measuring prices and quantities of health care, providers of health care services can easily change the quantity of health care services they report to accommodate lower prices. For example, an increase in the number of diagnostic tests provided to a patient will appear to be an increase in the per-visit price if all the tests are provided during one visit. This same increase will appear as an increase in quantity, rather than as a price hike, if the tests are spread over multiple visits.

Problems in measuring units of health care services make the enforcement of price controls in this sector troublesome. The Canadian experience suggests that the implementation of price controls in a fee-for-service physician payment system is likely to be accompanied by large increases in office visits. For example, physicians could require their patients to make office visits to get the results of tests, rather than simply conveying this information over the phone or by mail. Doctors could refuse to do more than one procedure per visit, requiring the patient to come back again for a second procedure, in order to get a second fee from the government. Studies of the Canadian system suggest that very substantial amounts of patient time are wasted through unnecessary trips to the doctor.

Experience from other industries suggests that if price controls could be enforced, they would likely lead to shortages of desired services. Initially, rates may be set to reflect the availability and need for services. But over time, the bureaucratic process of setting rates may mean that changes in the provision of, or demand for, services are not captured by new rates. When conditions change, the old rates are likely to cause shortages.

GLOBAL BUDGETS

A frequently recommended proposal for controlling expenditures in the health care system has been global budgets that cover all health costs. Global budgets would fix the sums health care providers throughout the U.S. economy can spend.

It would be very difficult to implement global budgets in the fragmented health care sector that now exists. For example, a global budget would have to account for out-of-pocket payments made by consumers, fee-for-service payments made by conventional insurers, per capita payments made by HMOs, and the provision of uncompensated care in emergency rooms. They would have to allocate funding across regions, States, and cities, although currently spending varies considerably in different localities. Most global budget plans would begin by implementing price controls—for example, setting payment levels for diagnosis-related groups and for HMOs—but as noted above, such controls are likely to lead to increases in utilization.

Global budgets could also be applied to individual hospitals, independent of the amount of service provided. Such budgets would create incentives to reduce the services within a hospital and could lead to delays in admitting patients, or reductions in the use of effective but costly medical technologies.

Under global budgets there would be few incentives for providers to compete by developing better ways to deliver care. Improvements in health care delivery would be made primarily by government mandate. The government would take a very active role in deciding how much health care would be provided, stipulating the number of practicing physicians, the number of hospital beds, and the availability of new medical technologies and treatments.

Such government-determined supply-side controls could also lead to inappropriate decisions at the level of the individual provider. For example, hospitals are likely to find it easier to stay within their annual budgets if they keep their hospital beds filled with patients who have already recovered, rather than admitting sicker patients. Global budgets for physicians may lead doctors to restrict their hours and increase their vacation days rather than providing cost-effective care. Efficient physicians can be penalized if global budgets lead to across-the-board cutbacks in spending on care.

POLITICS AND HEALTH CARE

Most proposals for reform of the health care market envision a larger governmental role. For example, under the Administration's proposal, the Federal Government would define a basic benefit plan that could be purchased by recipients of the tax credit or deduction (although they could choose other plans). Under the managed competition proposal, government boards would define accountable health partnerships and the basic benefits people could purchase and still remain eligible for the tax subsidy. Such government-determined allocation decisions are likely to become politicized. Decisions about which services to cover and payments to make may be affected by the political influence of provider groups rather than by appropriate medical and economic considerations.

Governments already play an enormous role in the U.S. health care industry as regulators, purchasers, and employers. Federal, State, and local governments regulate virtually every aspect of the

165

industry, from the supply of insurance to the practice of medicine to the sale of pharmaceuticals. In 1990 including the value of health-related tax subsidies, governments paid for about the same share of the output in this industry as in the aerospace industry. The three levels of government together employed more than twice as many health and hospital workers as postal workers.

Using government bureaucracies rather than markets to determine industry outcomes is usually wasteful and inefficient. The ordinary problems of regulation are magnified in the health care context for two reasons. First, setting quantities is difficult because of the enormous variation in people's need for and attitude toward medical care, a product that is constantly changing. Second, regulators have to rely on producer groups (including insurers, doctors, and hospital employees) and some consumer groups for information and support, and these groups share a proclivity to expand public and private expenditures at the expense of the general public.

SUMMARY

- The Administration's proposal for health care market reform would expand the insurance coverage available to low-income and middle-income Americans.

- The use of health risk adjusters in the Administration plan can reduce differences in the cost of health insurance between people in good health and people in poor health. Unlike community rating plans, health risk adjusters limit the incentive for insurers to exclude those in poor health.

- Managed competition proposals would encourage competition among health insurers providing a basic benefit package. Managed competition requires that the government play a substantial role in the private health insurance market, monitoring insurers and defining the benefits that most Americans would receive.

- Play-or-pay proposals focus on improving access to insurance by mandating that employers provide basic health insurance or pay a tax to cover enrollment in a public plan. These proposals do not directly address the problem of rising costs and may cause firms to lay off low-wage workers.

- National health insurance proposals would provide insurance for all Americans through a single national insurer. Without substantial restraints on the quality and quantity of care provided, national health insurance could lead to a cost explosion.

- Attempts to regulate the price of health care are often ineffective in reducing expenditures because of offsetting increases in utilization. If rate regulation succeeds in holding down prices, it may lead to reductions in the quality of health care and to waiting lines for services.

CONCLUSION

The U.S. health care market provides a very high standard of health care to most Americans. The cost of care in this market has, however, been growing very rapidly, and many Americans have inadequate health insurance coverage. Careful analysis of this market indicates that it is subject to many of the same economic forces as other sectors and establishes certain guiding principles that must be heeded if reform is to be successful.

As government and employer-provided health insurance programs have expanded, Americans have been paying for less of their health care out of their own pockets. Because people with health insurance do not face the full cost of their health care decisions, they overconsume health care services. Over time, the quantity and quality of services consumed by Americans have been increasing rapidly.

Because of the high cost of health care, many of the poor and chronically ill find that they cannot afford health insurance. These uninsured individuals often resort to hospital emergency rooms, resulting in a very costly and inefficient use of resources. Most Americans believe poor and unhealthy people should not have to choose between paying high premiums for health insurance or going without any insurance at all.

Because of the complexity of the health care industry, no reform plan can address all features of the system perfectly. Yet some approaches are better than others, because they deal more directly with the sources of rising expenditures and declining insurance coverage. Successful reforms must create incentives for consumers, insurers, and providers to cut costs and share the cost of care for the chronically ill.

Experience in other countries and in the United States suggests that health care costs cannot be controlled, even with waiting lines and limits on the use of medical treatments, unless the consumption of services is limited through incentives, such as deductibles and copayments, that encourage people to regulate the way they use health care services. Alternatively, insurers can monitor the use of care through coordinated care arrangements. Failure to control the overconsumption of services that results from insurance will make it impossible to control health care costs.

Even if overall costs can be controlled, expenditures for health care are likely to remain higher for those in poor health than for healthy people. One approach to this problem, community rating, creates a single premium level for everyone. In a competitive insurance market, however, community rating conflicts with the incentives of both insurers and healthy people. Insurers will try to discourage unhealthy people from enrolling in their insurance plans, leaving the chronically ill without insurance. Alternatively, healthy people will opt out of the insurance market or select plans with high deductibles and copayments, so that the premiums paid by those remaining in more comprehensive plans are very high. Another response to differences in health risk is the use of health risk adjusters, which provide insurers with incentives to insure those in poor health.

Because providers know more about medical treatment than do patients, a successful reform must give providers financial incentives to recommend only those treatments whose benefits exceed their costs. Financing arrangements that pay doctors and hospitals a fixed amount regardless of how many services they provide reduce the incentive for providers to recommend unnecessary services. An important additional step toward achieving this goal is to make it easier for patients to evaluate health care providers. Informed patients will be better able to identify providers that offer high-quality health care at a reasonable price.

Reforms that give consumers, insurers, and providers appropriate incentives are likely to be the most effective way of controlling costs, improving access to insurance, and giving Americans the quality of health care that they want. Without these incentives, health care costs will continue to climb and the number of uninsured will only grow larger.

CHAPTER 5

Markets and Regulatory Reform

THE U.S. ECONOMY RELIES primarily on the market system to determine what products are produced, in what quantity, and at what price. The market system is the most effective way of allocating resources to meet the needs and wants of households and families. The market system provides firms with strong incentives to produce the goods that consumers want at the lowest possible cost and to find innovative ways of meeting consumer demands. Firms that efficiently produce goods that consumers want will thrive; others will be driven out of business, and the resources they employ will be reallocated to more highly valued uses.

In deciding how much to buy at market prices, consumers register their opinions about the value of goods or services. In deciding how much to sell at market prices, producers reveal their information about how cheaply goods and services can be produced. Markets perform the complex job of sorting through this vast amount of information and opinion. The interaction between many producers and many consumers results in the production and consumption of an optimal quantity of each good—the best quantity from the standpoint of the economy as a whole. In order to produce more of one good, resources would have to be shifted away from producing other commodities, and the value of the lost production would be greater than the value gained by increased production of the first good.

Markets are flexible and accommodate change well. Changes in technology and consumer demands are quickly registered in the market, reordering the types, prices, and quantities of goods and services. The quest for profits encourages firms to develop new products and cheaper ways to produce existing products. A successful new product generates high profits, which provide an incentive to increase production of that product. Furthermore, markets can reduce the costs of adverse developments. A sudden shortage of a commodity will cause its market price to increase, encouraging consumers to conserve and producers to develop new sources of supply for the product.

The alternative to markets is to have central planners command production of what they think people should have, rather than what consumers want. As the experience of centrally planned

169

economies shows, government bureaucrats are rarely successful in matching quantity supplied and quantity demanded and can be quite inflexible in responding to change. In addition, people place a high value on the right to make free economic choices.

Some markets, however, do not operate according to the ideal. Some markets are necessarily served by a monopoly—a single seller that restricts output and sets prices higher than would occur in a more competitive market in order to maximize profits. In other markets, some people affected by the production or consumption of a good are not able to influence those choices. For example, firms and households may ignore the pollution problems they create or firms may not provide full information about the risks of using a product—information consumers may need to make the best decision. Market failures constitute a legitimate reason for governments to consider intervening in the private sector through such means as regulation. *There are costs associated with regulation, however. Attempts at regulation must be tempered by the understanding that the rules may be as imperfect as the market they are trying to improve; that is, governments as well as markets may fail.* A balanced approach to the limited amount of regulation that may be necessary in a market economy should be based on an understanding of costs and benefits and the use of market incentives to achieve the desired outcome.

REGULATORY REFORM

Since the mid-1970s, substantial progress has been made in reforming the way the Federal Government regulates industry. The result has been increased price competition and incentives for companies to introduce new products and services. For example, since the Airline Deregulation Act of 1978, the number of passengers flying annually has increased by 70 percent. Moreover, 43 percent of all trips are now flown in markets with three or more competitors, compared with only 24 percent in 1979 and the average fare per mile has declined 23 percent in real terms. In another example, the Securities and Exchange Commission eliminated fixed stock brokerage commissions in 1975, and in the following 6 years, rates for individual investors dropped by over 20 percent, while rates for institutional investors dropped almost 60 percent. Investors can now choose between discount brokers who simply make stock trades and brokers who provide complete investor services.

In some instances the benefits of regulatory reform efforts have not been fully realized because reform has not been completed. For example, the benefits of competition in the domestic airline industry have not been fully extended to international airline markets. Although the United States has negotiated some foreign aviation treaties that encourage competition, many of the agreements allow foreign governments to restrict seating capacity, the number of competitors, and price competition. In addition, U.S. air carriers continue to be immune from antitrust laws when using the International Air Transport Association as a forum for setting international air fares. The use of this forum can lead to higher prices and fewer services than would be available in a more competitive market. By eliminating the immunity enjoyed by U.S. carriers an impediment to competition would be removed.

While some important examples of regulatory reform over the past 17 years have been the result of congressional legislation, agencies of the Federal, State, and local government often have great discretion in deciding how to implement the laws. The President's regulatory reform initiative has encouraged Federal agencies to eliminate unnecessary regulations and to use market incentives to achieve regulatory goals at lower cost, rather than using "command-and-control" mechanisms that mandate particular technologies or set profit levels.

REGULATION AND GOVERNMENT FAILURE

While regulation based on a careful balancing of costs and benefits can sometimes improve market performance, policymakers often ignore the fact that the government is an imperfect regulator. There are three reasons to be cautious about government intervention as the solution to market failure.

First, regulators often lack accurate information about an industry and cannot always predict the effects of specific regulations. While the decision to regulate may be well-intentioned, the regulations themselves can have perverse and unintended consequences. For example, corporate average fuel economy standards have led manufacturers to produce lighter and therefore less crashworthy cars than they would have, resulting in an estimated several thousand additional highway deaths per year.

Second, the regulatory process tends to favor those groups or businesses that can most influence the process in their own interest, rather than in the interest of society as a whole. For example, Federal rules continue to restrict competition in various industries such as international ocean shipping and international aviation. Restraints on competition continue in part due to the fact that organized groups, such as those representing labor and firms in the industry, capture benefits from the rules that exceed the costs of participating in the process and therefore invest in maintaining those rules. Each individual consumer, who must make similar expenditures to participate in the regulatory process, has less of a stake and thus as a group consumers tend to underinvest in changing the rules.

171

Third, regulation does not always accommodate change well.
While regulation may be imposed to achieve economic and social
goals, it is administered as a legal process. It often takes years to
accommodate new technologies or new ways of doing business. For
example, amendments made to the Real Estate Settlement Procedures Act in 1983 were meant to respond to the real estate settlement industry's interest in providing one-stop shopping for settlement services. Yet the process of actually writing the regulation
that implemented the new laws took 9 years. During that period,
uncertainties about what the regulations would permit slowed the
development of innovative real estate settlement services. Regulatory inflexibility can also retard the introduction of new technologies, an issue discussed fully in the telecommunications section of
this chapter.

Often the process of developing a rule does not end at the regulatory agency. Because all legislation requires interpretation, disputes arise concerning how well the rule conforms to the legislation's intent. Also, because those who stand to lose from a change
in the regulatory structure can challenge a new rule, the regulatory process creates an incentive to litigate. Even after the courts
render a decision, the process may have to begin again at the regulatory agency. Extended litigation makes it harder for the regulatory process to respond to changes within an industry and imposes
costs over and above the expense of actually complying with a regulation.

A BALANCED REGULATORY POLICY

The Administration has sought to apply the lessons of imperfect
regulation in developing its regulatory policy. The central principles of this policy have been to deregulate markets that can be
competitive and to advocate only regulations meeting certain criteria: The benefits of any regulation should exceed the costs; the
rules should rely, to the extent possible, on market incentives to
achieve their goals; they should ensure that regulatory goals are
achieved at the lowest possible cost; and they should provide clarity
and certainty to the regulated community and be designed to minimize the potential for litigation. In January 1992 the President initiated a regulatory reform initiative asking Federal agencies to
focus on these principles.

Similar principles have been applied, although not nearly extensively enough, when developing new legislation. The Clean Air Act
Amendments of 1990 require major sulfur dioxide emissions reductions from electric utilities, but let markets arrange for those reductions at lowest cost. The use of "tradable allowances" will
achieve the pollution reduction goals at savings of billions of dollars over the cost of mandating rigid pollution controls. Similarly,

the Energy Policy Act of 1992 contains significant changes in Federal regulations governing electric utilities. By encouraging competition among firms that generate electricity for sale to local electric utilities, these changes aim at reducing the cost of electricity to consumers and promoting more efficient operation of electric utilities.

These central principles of regulatory policy have also been incorporated into proposals for legal reform. Wasteful litigation carries with it a very high cost for the U.S. economy. *The Administration's proposed legal reforms are designed to reduce the costs of litigation, while maintaining a fair system of dispute resolution.* The 1991 Agenda for Civil Justice Reform in America proposes to reduce litigation costs by employing alternative dispute resolution techniques and by modifying the incentives for litigation. Greater access to alternative dispute resolution mechanisms such as private mediation or arbitration will enable less complex legal matters to be resolved without resorting to the court process. To modify the incentives for litigation the proposals suggest, among other things:

- capping punitive damages at an amount equal to a plaintiff's actual damages;
- discouraging frivolous suits by adopting, in a limited set of Federal cases, a modified "English rule" in which the loser would pay the winner's legal expenses, up to a level equal to the loser's expenses;
- limiting the amount of free document requests, after which the requestor would have to pay the costs of providing the documents.

These proposals would reduce litigation costs by hastening the resolution of disputes and discouraging waste in litigation.

THE REGULATORY REFORM INITIATIVE

The President began a regulatory reform initiative in January 1992 that asked Federal agencies, within existing statutes, to eliminate unnecessary government regulations and to ensure that the remaining regulations meet the criteria described earlier. In all, the 24 Federal agencies actively participating in the initiative proposed or adopted hundreds of reforms covering a wide array of government regulatory activities.

Many of the reforms are designed to reduce the paperwork burden regulation imposes on businesses. For example, the Internal Revenue Service has simplified the rules governing payroll tax deposits by businesses. Under the old rules many employers were required to make deposits as often as twice a week, but not necessarily on the same 2 days each week. Under the new rules, large employers will deposit payroll taxes on fixed days of the week and more of the smaller employers are permitted to make monthly deposits.

Agencies have also streamlined the way they conduct their own business. For example, in April 1992 the Department of Justice and the Federal Trade Commission jointly issued Horizontal Merger Guidelines. For the first time, both agencies explicitly set forth the same standards for deciding whether certain mergers are anticompetitive. Joint guidelines should result in greater certainty about the standards applied in the more than 1,000 antitrust reviews of mergers conducted each year.

Finally, many agencies are working to promote competition by amending their existing regulations. For example, the Cable Communications Act of 1984 prevents local telephone companies from providing cable television service in their respective service areas. However, the act allows the Federal Communications Commission (FCC) to exempt telephone companies from this rule in rural areas, where competition from other sources is less likely to develop. In July 1992, as a part of its review of existing regulations under the regulatory reform initiative, the FCC proposed expanding the exemption from areas with fewer than 2,500 residents to those with fewer than 10,000 residents. If adopted, more rural residents would benefit from cable services provided by the telephone company in competition with existing television services. The FCC has also adopted new rules to increase competition in international communications and in local telephone markets.

MARKET INCENTIVES

A major objective of the regulatory reform initiative is to promote the use of regulations that utilize market incentives. The following sections describe three proposals of this type.

Performance Standards in Environmental Regulation

The Clean Air Act Amendments of 1990 require significant reductions in emissions that contribute to air pollution, but do not always dictate the precise methods that must be used to meet clean air standards. State and local governments will be able to determine how these standards are met in State Implementation Plans submitted to the Environmental Protection Agency (EPA) for approval.

The EPA has proposed allowing States to include in their plans the voluntary retirement of automobiles manufactured before the 1980 model year. Although these vehicles represent only 29 percent of registered vehicles, they cause 53 percent of hydrocarbon and 61 percent of carbon monoxide emissions, two contributors to air pollution. One cost-effective way of reducing these emissions is to replace aging vehicles with cars that emit fewer pollutants. Under the "cash-for-clunkers" program, a company that finds that a

174

planned expansion will increase its emissions over an existing EPA standard would have the option of offsetting this increase by purchasing and removing from the road "clunkers" operating in the same region as the plant.

For example, the cost to an industrial polluter of reducing emissions by some amount through conventional controls may be $1,000, but the owner of an old car that emits the same amount of pollution may be willing to sell the vehicle for $500. Under the EPA's proposal, the company could purchase the vehicle instead of directly reducing emissions from the plant. Estimates of emissions reduced would be based on a net reduction—for example, the difference between the emissions from the "clunker" and the emissions from the new car the seller is likely to purchase. *The EPA's "cash-for-clunkers" program expands the notion of performance standards by permitting standards to be met through alternative means, such as eliminating sources of pollution other than those directly controlled by the polluter.*

Incentive Regulation of Natural Gas Pipelines

Natural gas accounts for nearly one-half the energy consumed in American homes. Interstate natural gas pipelines transport gas across State lines, where it is sold to local gas distribution companies, electric utilities, and industrial users. The Federal Energy Regulatory Commission (FERC) is required by law to approve the prices interstate pipelines charge for transporting gas. Without regulation, a pipeline with a monopoly over gas delivery could raise prices above what they would be in a competitive market. Only when there is significant competition among pipelines to deliver gas would regulation be unnecessary.

While regulation may be necessary in cases where a pipeline does not face significant competition, the rules can be designed to create incentives to reduce costs and implement innovations. As part of the regulatory reform initiative, the FERC issued a policy statement on incentive rate regulation in October 1992. Along with outlining the essential elements of an incentive regulation policy, the policy statement sets guidelines for natural gas pipelines (as well as oil pipelines and electric utilities) that want to make specific incentive rate proposals to the FERC.

Under current practices, pipelines are regulated according to the traditional cost-of-service method. Pipelines provide the FERC with information on the costs they incur delivering gas, including the cost of building the pipeline facility. The FERC then determines the rates that can be charged to cover those costs, including a return on invested capital.

The limits placed on profits under cost-of-service regulation function as a substitute for the downward pressure on prices that exists in competitive markets. Unfortunately, cost-of-service regulation offers the regulated firm few rewards for cutting costs or using innovative techniques and sets few penalties for excessive spending. Any attempt to reduce costs will eventually be followed by a reduction in the rates the company can charge, reducing total revenues, and leaving the firm no better off. A service innovation that increases profits will also result in a reduction in rates to bring revenues in line with costs.

The distinguishing feature of incentive rate regulation is that, unlike cost-of-service regulation, it focuses on prices rather than profits. Once rates are no longer tied to the costs incurred, further cost-cutting efforts do not translate into dollar-for-dollar reductions in revenues. Incentive regulation allows regulated companies to retain a portion of their cost savings, giving them an incentive to produce efficiently and to innovate.

One challenge in implementing incentive rate regulation is determining the price standard. Price cap regulation establishes an initial level of rates and then links a regulated company's rate increases to changes in an index of prices. An index related to the pipeline company's own costs would be inappropriate because it would immediately reestablish a link between prices and costs. An appropriate index would be one over which the company has no control, such as the consumer price index or the producer price index. Prices could be allowed to rise each year by an amount equivalent to a change in the index, less a fixed percentage that reflects expected improvements in productivity.

The price cap method has been employed in the FCC's regulation of American Telephone and Telegraph's (AT&T) long-distance services. A problem with price cap regulation as a long-run approach is that it frequently uses current prices as the base rate to which the index is applied. As costs change over time, the continued use of the same index could lead to firms earning large profits or suffering large losses. This is not a critical problem in the case of AT&T, which is in a transition to full deregulation. Many pipelines, however, are unlikely to face competition in the near future.

An alternative to the price cap method is yardstick competition, which establishes a target against which a company's performance can be measured. If the company improves on the target, its profits increase; if it does not meet the target goals, its profits fall. One way to implement this idea is to set a pipeline's prices equal to the average costs of *other similar* pipelines. All pipelines would want to lower costs under this system. Any pipeline that did not would eventually find itself with prices targeted to industry costs that are lower than its own costs. Yardstick competition forces firms to compete on the basis of efficiency even though they do not compete directly in transporting natural gas. One critical task facing a regulator proposing to use yardstick competition will be in identifying comparable pipelines and adjusting for differences among them.

Peak/Off-Peak Pricing at Airports

Every day, consumers pay for services whose prices are dependant on the time of day or the season. A typical long-distance telephone call has a price of 23 cents per minute during business hours, when usage is high, but only 13 cents per minute late at night, when usage is low. Movie ticket prices are higher during evening hours, when demand for service is high, but are often lower at other hours. In both of these cases there is a fixed capacity for providing a service and patterns of usage that vary throughout the day. The prices reflect the high value placed on the service during periods of peak demand.

Airports are in a similar situation, because they also operate with a fixed capacity, in this case to handle takeoffs and landings. Approximately one-third of all delays are caused by demand that exceeds the capacity of air traffic control and runways during peak periods. As a result, the Nation's airport infrastructure is inefficiently used and some of the benefits of airline deregulation are lost. Constructing additional runways is a plausible long-term solution, but in the short term the existing system can be more efficiently used. Time-based fees, or "peak/off-peak" prices, used regularly by electric utilities and telephone companies, are not commonly used by airports. The Department of Transportation is considering guidelines for local airport authorities on the use of time-based takeoff and landing fees to reduce airport congestion.

Currently, the typical airport landing fee is based on the weight of the airplane using the runway. Basing fees on weight is aimed at approximating the airport's costs of servicing an airplane flight (including space used and wear-and-tear on the runway). However, such fees do nothing to alleviate airport congestion during periods of high demand. Instead, takeoff and landing fees should reflect all costs, including the costs of delay that one carrier imposes on another, so that those who value airport use most highly will use the airport at peak times.

By making congestion costs explicit, so that those placing the highest value on peak service will use the airport during peak hours, congestion would be reduced. *Without a peak/off-peak pricing system, passengers will continue to "pay" the costs of congestion, but it will be in the form of long waiting times and takeoff delays.* Similarly, publicly funded highways and streets that serve as low-cost or free roadways tend to be congested at peak use times. Peak/off-peak pricing could be used to solve road congestion problems as well.

SUMMARY

- A major goal of the President's regulatory reform initiative has been to encourage Federal agencies to eliminate unnecessary regulations and to use regulatory innovations such as incentive rate regulation.
- Regulations that incorporate market incentives can be used to reduce pollution at lower cost than command-and-control methods.
- Setting appropriate prices for the use of the Nation's transportation system will assure that these resources are being used efficiently.

TELECOMMUNICATIONS: REGULATORY REFORM AND INNOVATION

Telecommunications is a broad sector encompassing local and long-distance telephone services, satellite services, information services, broadcasting, cable television, program production, and manufacturing of associated equipment. Rapid technological change and regulatory reform in the industry have increased the variety and quality of entertainment, information, and communications services available to consumers and businesses. In the past, for example, many Americans could only receive 3 television channels; now access to 50 channels is not uncommon. The venerable national "phone company" monopoly is being transformed into a multiplicity of entrepreneurs and firms, and competition has developed in many markets for telecommunications services and equipment.

While some parts of the industry are vigorously competitive, others remain tightly regulated. There is legitimate concern that, without regulation, consumers in some markets will not be protected from monopoly pricing. Insufficient weight, however, has been placed on the costs of regulation; costs that not only include complying with regulation, but also the hidden costs of forgone product innovation. *The goal of the Administration has been to reform the regulatory structure for telecommunications so that consumers receive the benefits of new products and services but are protected in cases where markets are not competitive.*

TELECOMMUNICATIONS AND THE U.S. ECONOMY

The U.S. telecommunications industry comprises thousands of businesses and over 1 million workers. Telephone services alone, including long distance, local, and cellular, are provided by over 2,000 companies employing over 700,000 people—about the same number as the entire U.S. automobile manufacturing industry. In

178

1991, reported local telephone revenues were $86 billion and long-distance revenues were $55 billion. Interstate long-distance communications represents a particularly high-growth component, with the volume of calls more than doubling since 1984. A second major segment of the telecommunications industry, the mass media, includes approximately 1,500 broadcast television stations, 11,000 radio stations, and 76 national cable television networks. In 1991, these industries earned about $36 billion in advertising revenues.

One measure of performance in the telecommunications industry is productivity. Even with significant deregulation in the United States, the telephone services sectors in more heavily regulated France and Japan have the same labor productivity levels, measured by output per worker, as the United States. One possible reason is that the majority of U.S. telecommunications employees still work for the regulated local telephone monopolies. Competitive pressure to improve efficiency has, until recently, been absent in this sector because traditional rate-of-return regulation does not encourage cost-cutting measures that could improve labor productivity.

Where the United States does hold a lead is in capital productivity. A recent study estimates that 2.4 calls are made in the United States for each dollar invested in the network, but only 1.3 in Japan, 1.2 in the United Kingdom, and 0.6 in France and Germany. The United States' lead is due largely to a higher demand for telephone services and a correspondingly higher rate of network utilization. In part, competition among long-distance carriers and government pricing policies have stimulated demand by lowering long-distance rates so that they more closely reflect the actual costs of providing the service.

Some have called for large public expenditures on the U.S. telecommunications infrastructure to expand the use of technologies such as fiber optics. Yet it may be regulation that is discouraging firms from investing in new infrastructure. When regulatory barriers are removed, competition and the ability of firms to reap the rewards of their success provide sufficient incentives to invest in commercially viable telecommunications technologies. There are times, however, that firms are reluctant to invest because they cannot be assured of fully capturing all the benefits of their investments. It is often difficult or inefficient to prevent information on research or developing technologies from being used by other firms. In such cases the government may have an appropriate role to play in financing basic research and precommercial technologies, but only if the benefits of the project exceed the costs.

However, government investment in particular commercial technologies amounts to little more than an attempt to guess which products will be most in demand and then to determine the best ways of producing them. High-definition television (HDTV) provides a good example of this problem. The Japanese government determined the technology that would be used for HDTV in their country and financed its development. It now appears, however, that the government-chosen analog technology was inferior to other alternatives. Left to itself, U.S. industry has developed alternatives to Japanese HDTV using a digital technology that appears to be superior in quality. *Rather than having taxpayers invest in predetermined technologies, the government should create a more sensible regulatory environment to ensure continued productivity improvements and the development of advanced telecommunications technologies.*

GUIDELINES FOR REFORM IN TELECOMMUNICATIONS REGULATION

Today, technological innovations are making competition feasible in areas where it was previously considered infeasible. For example, one company has announced that it will soon have the technology to deliver movies over existing telephone wires. Similarly, cable television companies have the capability to provide customers with telephone service on their lines. The full benefits of these opportunities will be lost if the government maintains a regulatory structure that restricts competition and preserves artificial industry boundaries.

The Current Structure of Telecommunications Regulation

The U.S. telecommunications industry is governed by Federal, State, and local regulatory agencies, with the Federal courts playing a special role. The FCC, the principal Federal regulatory agency governing telecommunications, is responsible for regulating interstate and international long-distance telephone services, managing non-Federal U.S. radio spectrum use, enforcing the rules applicable to the broadcasting industry, and establishing standards.

A complicating factor in the Federal regulatory structure is the 1982 court settlement of the Federal Government's antitrust case against AT&T. This settlement, or consent decree, governed the subsequent breakup of AT&T. Under the decree, AT&T was required to divest itself of its 22 local telephone companies, which were then formed into 7 independent companies known as Regional Bell Operating Companies (RBOCs), or "Baby Bells." Most importantly, the decree also placed limits on the products and services the RBOCs could produce. Although some of these restrictions have been lifted, applications for interpretations of and waivers from the remaining restrictions have made the Federal courts a virtual second Federal regulator.

State regulatory commissions are responsible for regulating intrastate telephone services, but they also share their authority with Federal regulators because the same equipment is often used to provide both interstate and intrastate service. For example, the same telephone company switch that handles calls from San Francisco to Los Angeles may handle calls from San Francisco to Phoenix as well. But the first call is regulated by the State government and the second by the FCC. A system of rules and joint boards has been developed to help separate the Federal and State roles. The role of local government, on the other hand, has generally focused on franchising cable television service. The local government's role in cable television rate regulation will be expanded by new legislation, an issue discussed in detail below.

The Transition to Competition

One primary justification for limiting competition in the telecommunications industry has been the belief that certain markets are served by "natural monopolies," or single suppliers that can meet consumer needs more efficiently than multiple suppliers, often with appropriate regulation of prices and the number of competitors. A classic example is the costly duplication of facilities that would result from having competing electric utilities within the same geographic area. Based on the natural monopoly rationale, cable television services and local telephone services are provided by a single company in most communities.

But monopoly franchising and rate regulation can also have drawbacks. Protecting a monopoly may prevent potential competitors from implementing technologies that do not share the cost characteristics of a natural monopoly. For many years, regulators considered long-distance telephone service a natural monopoly, but the development of microwave technology allowed the provision of long-distance telephone service on a much smaller scale than had been previously possible. Almost 500 firms now provide long-distance services, ranging from those that serve a variety of customers on a national scale to those that target specialized business markets or operate on a much more limited geographic basis. New transmission technologies may achieve similar results in other markets that have been characterized as natural monopolies, such as cable television and local telephone service. In fact, government regulation, and not economic factors, may be the real bar to competition in those markets.

Competition drives firms to innovate and provide new services. In many telecommunications markets, competition is superior to continuing rate regulation and monopoly franchises, because competition can lower prices and increase the diversity of available services.

181

Protecting Consumers in the Transition

Markets in which competition has been precluded by government regulation cannot become competitive overnight. For example, providing local telephone service requires significant capital expenditures for new companies. Immediate deregulation of rates would allow a monopolist to increase rates without fear of an immediate response from a competitor. As a result, where changing technology and removal of governmental regulation make it possible for a regulated monopoly market to evolve into a competitive market, consumers must be protected from temporary price increases during the transition to competition. As part of the transition, incentive regulation is being used to encourage regulated companies to operate more efficiently.

In many areas, regulation has been used to enforce a system of cross-subsidies that keep prices low for certain classes of users, such as residential and rural telephone subscribers (Box 5-1). During a transition period—or longer if the subsidies are justified—these cross-subsidies should be replaced by direct subsidies.

When deregulatory policies create partially deregulated firms or allow regulated firms to enter unregulated markets, additional safeguards may be necessary to protect consumers and competition. For example, telephone companies in States that use cost-of-service regulation to determine rates may inappropriately transfer costs, or "cross-subsidize," from the unregulated to the regulated sector, artificially inflating prices for telephone service, and under some circumstances, reducing competition in the unregulated markets. In such cases, safeguards are necessary to ensure that customers are not subsidizing company activities in unregulated markets. Safeguards are also necessary to ensure that telephone companies do not design or misuse the network in ways that discriminate against companies selling related but unregulated services.

REFORMING TELECOMMUNICATIONS REGULATION

The transition from regulation to competition in telecommunications began over 20 years ago. Technological change, actions taken by the FCC, and the breakup of AT&T in 1984 have allowed many new firms to enter the telecommunications industry. For example, in 1970 AT&T's manufacturing subsidiary, Western Electric, provided almost all of the company's equipment needs and the equipment used by its customers. FCC and court decisions to allow customers to use non-AT&T equipment and the separation of the RBOCs from the manufacturing subsidiary, coupled with rapid advances in electronics, created a competitive market for equipment. For instance, AT&T's U.S. market share of sales for private branch exchanges (telephone exchange equipment for use within businesses) fell from 80 percent in 1970 to 28 percent in 1989.

Box 5-1.—If Deregulation Is So Great, Why Has My Phone Bill Gone Up?

When a telephone call is made across the country, a local phone company starts the call, a different local company completes the call, and a long-distance company carries the call between the two areas. Thus, the local phone network plays two roles: It provides phone service in a local area and access to long-distance service. Before 1984, AT&T, with its virtual monopoly over long-distance and local telephone service, carried nearly all phone calls. To determine the price of a long-distance call, Federal and State regulators had to allocate some of the costs of the local network to long-distance usage. With a higher share of the costs attributed to long-distance calling, long-distance prices would be higher and local service prices lower.

Political pressures resulted in a shift of costs to the long-distance operations of the telephone network, so that local rates were kept artificially low. This regulatory shift of costs resulted in prices that led to an inefficient use of the network. The cost of providing a customer access to a long-distance company is a *fixed cost*, unrelated to the number of long-distance minutes that are used. However, these fixed costs were reflected in the per-minute charge for service, a price that should only reflect the extra, or *marginal cost*, of providing the service. The higher long-distance rates resulting from this policy caused users to reduce long-distance calling and prompted the entry of other companies.

Realizing the problems arising from this pricing policy, the FCC began reform in the late 1970s. Instead of including the costs of access in long-distance prices, some access costs are now recovered through a fixed monthly *subscriber line charge* added to the local telephone bill. The FCC has been gradually shifting access costs for residential customers to the subscriber line charge since 1983. The monthly price for local telephone service increased 3.1 percent annually between 1983 and 1989 in real terms. For some, this increase has meant higher phone bills. But interstate long-distance prices *declined* 9.8 percent annually in the same period as a result of increased competition, the repricing of access, and technological improvements.

Many current regulations may continue to inhibit competition in the telecommunications industry, however. Even with safeguards in place, the RBOCs are limited in their ability to enter unregulated markets. Moreover, as discussed below, the cumbersome process

183

by which the government manages the electromagnetic spectrum continues to slow the development of new technologies that could lead to greater competition in local telephone markets. Competition in local telephone markets could make regulatory safeguards unnecessary. Competition would make it unprofitable for telephone companies to discriminate against customers wanting to connect with a local network, because dissatisfied customers could simply switch to alternative networks. Similarly, competition would undermine attempts by one firm to use one business to cross-subsidize another.

The government decides not only which services the local telephone companies can provide but also which services cable operators and broadcasters can provide. For example, three television broadcast networks—CBS, NBC, and ABC—have not been allowed to participate fully in the development, ownership, and syndication of programming for broadcast and cable television since 1970. At that time, the networks' over 90 percent share of the prime-time viewing audience created concern that the networks had excessive bargaining power over program producers, especially small independent producers. These financial interest and syndication rules are unnecessarily restrictive, given that the share of prime-time viewing the major networks command has fallen to 62 percent and that there are now a multiplicity of alternative broadcast outlets for program producers. Furthermore, an increasing fraction of program production is being done by a small number of large firms. Therefore, the rules should be eased to allow greater participation by networks to promote competition, while assuring that legitimately small independent producers are not subject to anticompetitive conduct. The FCC modified the rules slightly in 1991. A Federal Appeals Court, however, has questioned the manner in which the modified rules were devised and has sent the matter back to the FCC. The future of the rules remains uncertain.

While the goal of regulation has been to protect consumers, barring businesses from entering new markets may be reducing the incentive of firms to invest in new telecommunications technologies. Furthermore, policymaking in telecommunications is stymied because businesses protected from competition can use the political process to prevent entry by new competitors, while at the same time demanding freedom to enter other markets. To break this deadlock, protect consumers, and promote competition, reform of the current telecommunications regulatory policy is necessary.

Managing the Electromagnetic Spectrum

The electromagnetic spectrum is the foundation of many telecommunications services. Radio and television broadcasters, cellular telephone services, police and fire communications, air traffic control, and taxi dispatchers all rely on the spectrum. Because the range of frequencies within which these services can be provided is limited, spectrum is a very valuable resource. The FCC, which is responsible for managing the portion of the spectrum not used by the Federal Government, determines which services will be allowed to use a given spectrum band (known as "allocating" the spectrum), and who will be assigned licenses for their use.

While the FCC has a legitimate role in defining the terms under which spectrum is used in order to prevent users from interfering with each other, it is not well-suited to judge whether, for example, paging systems have a higher social value than taxi dispatching. The current administrative process for determining how bands are used is slow and inflexible, constraining the introduction of new technologies and the development of competitive markets. Cellular telephone technology illustrates this problem. The spectrum allocation process began in 1968, yet the first commercial cellular license was not assigned until 1982. Also, the number of licenses is fixed, limiting competition to two cellular franchises in each local market.

Currently, the FCC typically assigns licenses to use a given service either after comparative hearings or by lottery. Comparative hearings are time-consuming, trial-like procedures. Companies that place value on a license will naturally want the FCC to assign it to them. The result is large expenditures by applicants to acquire the license and a long delay before the license is assigned. The lottery system is also cumbersome, involving large numbers of applicants attempting to "win" a license. When an assignment is made, the chosen licensee often does not provide the service. Instead, licenses are frequently sold after the initial assignment. *Since licenses are often sold to other users, the FCC could hold an auction for licenses, eliminating the current cumbersome process and generating revenue for the U.S. Treasury.* The bidder attaching the greatest value to the spectrum license would receive it, and the step of holding lotteries or comparative hearings would be eliminated.

To permit more efficient use of the spectrum the FCC could allow the licenses it auctions not only to be resold, but also to be reassigned by the licenseholder for a different use. This approach would offer licensees the maximum flexibility in using the spectrum, subject only to prohibitions on interfering with other spectrum users. Flexibility in the use of the spectrum would also encourage users to develop technologies that conserve the amount of the spectrum used.

Removing Artificial Barriers to Innovation

Like the spectrum management system, the consent decree governing the breakup of AT&T limits innovation and competition in telecommunications markets. Among other things, the 1982 decree contained provisions that prevented the RBOCS from manufacturing telecommunications equipment, providing information services, and providing most long-distance services. The problems of cross-subsidization and discriminatory use of a monopoly network were two important reasons for initially limiting participation of the RBOCs in unregulated markets.

In 1991 a Federal court struck down the provision in the decree that barred the RBOCs from providing information services, allowing these companies to begin offering services such as message and database services. Previously forced to act as conduits for other providers of information services, the RBOCs can now provide these services themselves. Because these companies have developed expertise in communications networks and can take advantage of the efficiencies, or "economies of scope," that make it cheaper to provide multiple services over a single network than to have many specialized networks, they will increase competition for information services.

The benefits of having competing services will be reduced, however, if the RBOCs limit competition by engaging in cross-subsidization or by denying other firms access to the local telephone network. These problems must be continuously monitored by Federal and State regulatory agencies. To reduce the concern about cross-subsidization and discrimination, the FCC has adopted rules governing cost allocation and rules that attempt to assure open access to various components of the local telephone network on a timely and nondiscriminatory basis. If problems arise, these rules may have to be strengthened even further. The rules will continue to be necessary until competition is fully developed in local telephone markets.

The RBOCs are still barred from manufacturing telephone equipment, a category the courts have interpreted as including related research and development. The ban effectively prevents seven of the largest U.S. telecommunications companies from developing innovative technologies and otherwise competing in this market. Supporters of the ban fear that the RBOCs will attempt either to transfer manufacturing costs to the regulated sector or to engage in "self-dealing" by selling equipment to their affiliated telephone companies at inflated prices, raising the costs of regulated telephone service and reducing competition in equipment manufacturing.

The FCC and many States have begun using incentive regulation that should help to alleviate these problems by making it more difficult for the RBOCs to pass added costs on to telephone ratepayers. Also, a competitive market for telecommunications equipment should provide competitors and regulators with adequate information on the market value of equipment, to allow them to monitor the self-dealing problem.

While the consent decree prevents the RBOCs from participating in cer▪in businesses, the Cable Communications Policy Act of 1984 and related FCC regulations prevent local telephone companies from operating cable television systems (except in certain rural communities). This ban remains in place, even though virtually all communities with cable television have only one franchised operator, and average rates for the most popular basic cable service have increased 36.5 percent, in real terms, since 1986 when the act effectively barred regulation in most communities. Although this increase may be due in part to the growing number of channels available, it may also reflect the presence of market power.

The solution pursued in the Cable Television Consumer Protection and Competition Act of 1992 is to allow local governments to regulate prices for basic cable television service in almost all communities. Regulating prices, however, does not solve the underlying problem, which is a lack of competition. This approach also overestimates the ability of regulatory authorities to establish rates that approximate competitive prices. The danger is that in the attempt to regulate prices they will simultaneously diminish the variety and quality of cable programming.

The preferred alternative is to promote competition that lowers prices and provides alternative sources of television programming. Having already invested in some of the fixed plant necessary to provide video services, telephone companies are the most likely competitors for incumbent cable operators. The FCC's "video dialtone" policy, adopted in July 1992, allows local telephone companies to act as conduits for carrying television and other video services by other companies. *Legislation is needed, however, to remove the provisions in the 1984 Cable Act that prevent telephone companies from actually becoming full participants in providing programming.* Such legislation may create an incentive for telephone companies to construct the infrastructure necessary for combining telephone and video services. Whether there is a demand for the services that such an infrastructure can provide will not be known until the barriers to competition are removed.

Competition in Local Telephone Services

State regulators have begun to approve competition from alternative local service providers that typically provide private fiber optic links between long-distance telephone companies and large businesses. In 1989, the New York Public Service Commission ordered New York Telephone to interconnect with alternative local service providers. The FCC recently modified its rules to allow these providers to interconnect their private lines with the interstate facilities of local telephone companies. The policy of expanded interconnection increases the possibility of competition for large customers. It recognizes that residential customers may be served by a regulated monopoly for the near future, but is laying the groundwork for competition even in residential markets.

Technological changes suggest that competition can develop in the local telecommunications market. Many businesses have already switched to private networks for intracompany calls. Expanding wireless technologies, such as that for cellular telephone service, do not necessarily have the characteristics of a natural monopoly and represent potential competition for local telephone companies. Competition for local telephone service would be further enhanced if cable television companies were permitted to provide telephone service.

An important factor affecting competition in the future is the policy of "universal service"—access for all residential users to a basic level of telephone service at affordable rates. This policy has been motivated by both equity concerns and the understanding that each telephone user benefits from being connected to as many people as possible. To make telephone service universal, basic services are often priced lower than the cost of providing the service. Other services, such as touchtone or call waiting, are priced somewhat higher than costs to compensate for losses on the underpriced basic services. Residential customers are usually the recipients of these "subsidized" services.

One problem with this system of cross-subsidies is that companies—even those less efficient than the regulated incumbent—may be able to undercut the regulated price and still earn a profit. If the regulated monopolist cannot adjust its prices in response to this competition, the inefficient companies will remain in business. This pricing policy could ultimately cause many of the monopoly's customers to switch to the new entrants, meaning that rates for some of the subsidized services would have to be increased.

If regulated carriers are not permitted to respond to competition, they may find that their rates do not cover the costs of providing service to their remaining customers—most likely small businesses and residential customers. Restricting competition is not the answer to the problem, however. The best way to avoid the perverse results cross-subsidies can create is to give the regulated companies greater freedom to respond to competitive entry. Doing so will discourage entry by inefficient competitors and only efficient competitors will survive. Any perceived need for subsidies can be achieved directly—for example, by charging all interconnecting companies a fee that supports universal service and targeting the subsidy to the groups that need it.

Competition in Long-Distance Services

In a series of decisions that began in the 1970s, the FCC and the courts have opened the long-distance markets to competition. Chart 5-1 shows that since its breakup in 1984, AT&T's market share of long-distance calling minutes has fallen from 84 percent to 60 percent. The FCC estimates that some 480 firms currently provide interstate long-distance services, while over 90 percent of all telephone customers now have equal access to multiple long-distance providers. Customers have shown a willingness to respond to competitive service offerings: Approximately 15 percent of all residential customers switched to a new long-distance carrier in 1991.

Chart 5-1 **AT&T's Market Share**
AT&T's market share has declined significantly since the breakup in 1984.

Percent of long-distance telephone calling minutes

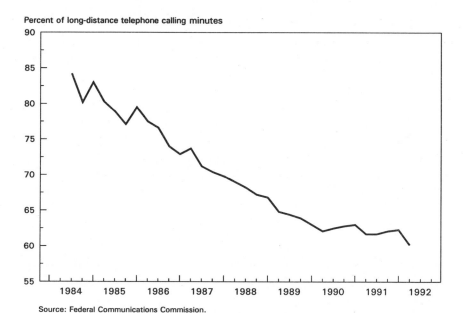

Source: Federal Communications Commission.

Except for AT&T, the FCC does not regulate the rates of interstate long-distance companies. To promote the efficiency of rate regulation while still protecting consumers, the FCC introduced price cap regulation for AT&T in 1989 and for the interstate services of local telephone companies in 1991. Several States have also introduced incentive regulation for intrastate services. In 1991, increasing competition led the FCC to eliminate price cap regulation for AT&T's large business services.

Price cap regulation is still in place for AT&T's residential, small business, and 800 number services. For these services AT&T must give the FCC at least 45 days notice before it can offer new services or prices. The ability of most long-distance customers to easily switch among long-distance companies that provide similar geographic coverage and service quality suggests that the FCC should

189

consider relaxing the constraints of price cap regulation on AT&T. However, some form of regulation would still be appropriate for communities that do not have a competitive long-distance market.

SUMMARY

- Government policies that protect consumers while allowing firms to compete in new lines of business will promote an advanced telecommunications infrastructure.
- The current system for allocating the electromagnetic spectrum hampers the development and implementation of new technologies that could create competition for existing monopoly service providers such as cable television and local telephone service.
- Because competition in long-distance telephone service is increasing, some of the remaining regulations governing AT&T could be relaxed.

REGULATING FINANCIAL MARKETS AND SERVICES

Well-functioning financial markets are essential to a modern market economy. New and expanding business enterprises need capital to make investments and create jobs, and they rely on the futures, options, and foreign exchange markets to control unwanted risks. Families and businesses buy insurance to shield themselves from catastrophic losses. Well-developed mortgage markets foster widespread homeownership.

Like the telecommunications markets, financial markets are subject to a wide variety of government regulations, including some that are unnecessary, outmoded, and overly rigid. *U.S. financial markets are the largest and most developed in the world, and their continued success depends on the government's ability to remove unnecessary regulatory impediments while at the same time protecting investors and maintaining market integrity.*

THE CHANGING FINANCIAL SCENE

The last 20 years have witnessed an explosion in the scope and complexity of financial markets. The traditional roles of banks and savings and loans (S&Ls) are in transition, and new institutions and services have multiplied. Several important developments have contributed to these changes. First, technological progress in electronic communications has lowered information costs and made financial services more available. A familiar example is the spread of automatic teller machines, which freed depositors from the constraints of limited geographical access and short banking hours. Increased computerization also has accommodated large increases in trading volume in the securities markets. Second, conceptual advances in finance have provided tools to assess the risk and value of financial instruments such as options and futures contracts, contributing to the rapid growth of these securities markets. Perhaps most important, the view of the government's role in financial markets has changed significantly since the 1970s. Regulatory reform has allowed the development of new services that are now available to the public. These changes have contributed to and in some cases were motivated by the globalization of these markets. Globalization has lowered the cost of raising capital for U.S. businesses by providing foreign sources of capital and has provided Americans with the opportunity to make valuable investments abroad.

These developments have not been universally welcomed. Some observers fear these innovations, perhaps because they know little about them or are uncomfortable with the colorful vocabulary used to describe new financial products. Skeptics associate what they view as the increased volatility of financial markets with some of these changes. After several highly publicized cases of fraud, other critics questioned the integrity of some markets. Still others are less concerned with the risks inherent in new products than with the possibility that an overly broad Federal safety net—including Federal deposit insurance—could encourage excessive risk-taking that would be difficult to monitor and regulate. In an effort to keep pace with innovation, public and private regulatory mechanisms have been put into place to identify problems as they arise and to correct them promptly. Most observers would agree that, in general, the innovations have been beneficial.

THE VALUE OF FINANCIAL SERVICES

Despite their seeming complexity, most financial instruments and institutions can be understood in terms of three basic functions. First, people use financial markets to reallocate money over time. For instance, instruments such as savings accounts, individual retirement accounts (IRAs), stocks, bonds, mutual funds, and pension funds allow households to save for retirement. At the same time, these instruments channel funds to businesses and households that borrow to make investments.

Second, people use financial contracts to share and reduce risk. An insurance policy is perhaps the most familiar example, but most new financial instruments can be used for risk management as well. One extremely effective way to reduce risk is through diversification. The return on a diversified stock portfolio is much less risky than the return on the stock of an individual company, because in a portfolio, gains from profitable firms offset losses from others that fail. Mutual funds are institutions that allow small investors to pool cash to purchase a diversified portfolio, balancing risk and return with tools once available only to large institutional investors or wealthy individuals.

Other contracts can also reduce risk. For instance, a U.S. manufacturer selling cars in France runs the risk of losing money if the franc falls against the dollar, and a French farmer selling cheese in the United States faces the opposite risk. In each case, the exchange-rate risk can be eliminated by writing a contract with a financial intermediary such as a bank or a trader in a brokerage firm, specifying the exchange rate that will be used in the future. Popular contracts of this type include futures, forwards, and swaps (all of which are agreements to make specified payments on specified dates). The growth of active futures, forward, and swap markets has significantly lowered the cost of risk-management.

The third function of financial markets is to provide liquidity. An asset is liquid if it can be bought or sold quickly, at a predictable price, and with low transactions costs. For instance, a savings account is very liquid because it can be turned into cash almost instantly, while a house is illiquid because it takes time to sell and its price is hard to predict. By offering standardized contracts with well-understood risks, returns, and legal status, and by providing information to the market, financial intermediaries enhance liquidity, lowering transactions costs for investors and borrowers alike.

Because participants in financial markets can invent, develop, and market new financial instruments, the macroeconomy has become better able to adapt to constantly changing conditions and weather external shocks. Even in an economic expansion, particular industries and geographic regions experience significant economic disruptions. For instance, the collapse of energy prices in 1986 hurt U.S. energy producers, and the sharp rise of the dollar in the early 1980s hurt our manufacturing industries. Episodes such as these would have had a more severe impact in the absence of active forward, futures, and swap markets in agricultural products, oil, interest rates, and foreign exchange.

THE CHANGING ROLE OF GOVERNMENT

As financial markets have evolved, so has the nature of the government's involvement with them. The history of government intervention in financial markets contains many useful lessons that can help in determining when intervention is appropriate and in understanding the problems that poorly designed intervention can cause.

Much of the regulatory structure governing the financial sector dates from the 1930s. The disruptive waves of bank failures throughout the 1800s and the early years of this century, as well as the Great Depression, convinced legislators that economic stability depends on the stability of the financial system. Actions such as the creation of the Federal Deposit Insurance Corporation (FDIC) and the passage of the Glass-Steagall Act, which mandates the legal separation of investment and commercial banking, date from this period. Although the framers of this regulatory structure initially expressed some doubts, until the late 1970s calm prevailed in the financial markets, and the regulatory system was widely considered a success.

High and volatile interest rates in the United States in the late 1970s began to expose some of the system's underlying weaknesses. The heavy losses suffered by the S&L industry set the stage for the recent string of failures. Commercial banks fared somewhat better, but even they were adversely affected as depositors withdrew their funds to seek higher market returns. Banks were prohibited from paying the market interest rate by Regulation Q of the Federal Reserve, which set a 5-percent interest rate ceiling for savings accounts. Some obvious impediments to the effective operations of financial institutions were removed by the regulatory reforms of the early 1980s, when interest rate ceilings were phased out and S&Ls were given more freedom in their choice of investments. These changes, however, did little to address many fundamental problems in the regulatory structure. In fact, careless or uneven deregulation sometimes exacerbated these problems and added to the losses from S&L insolvencies.

The Government's Role in Financial Markets

The growth of financial services has been accompanied by a steady increase in government involvement in many of the new activities. Is the large and expanding role of the Federal Government in these markets beneficial? To evaluate this important and complex issue, it is useful to start with another, more basic question: What current or potential market failures require government intervention to be corrected? Most observers agree that regulation should have a role in two areas.

First, government institutions help to maintain the stability of the financial system. Financial markets act as the circulatory system of the economy, creating vital connections between seemingly unrelated enterprises. When this system breaks down, even healthy sectors of the economy may suffer. The Great Depression is the most compelling example of this phenomenon, when a sharp contraction of credit and a fall in asset prices preceded a 30-percent drop in aggregate output and an unemployment rate that reached 25 percent.

Institutions such as the FDIC and the Federal Reserve System limit the damage a financial crisis can cause by providing an emergency source of liquidity and by preventing financial panics from spreading. For example, during the October 1987 stock market crash, the Federal Reserve provided the banking system with additional reserves. Banks used these reserves to make emergency loans that saved a number of financial firms from bankruptcy. Some have credited these measures with preventing more widespread repercussions from the crash.

A second role for regulation is to improve the day-to-day operation of financial markets, both by providing prudent oversight to prevent fraud and abuse, and by facilitating truthful disclosure of information. For example, the Securities and Exchange Commission (SEC) requires corporations financed with publicly traded stocks or bonds to disclose relevant financial information.

Challenges for Regulatory Reform

The dynamism of the financial marketplace presents a special challenge to regulators. When a rule becomes particularly onerous, someone is likely to invent a way to avoid it, often with unfortunate and unexpected consequences. For instance, in the late 1970s market interest rates rose well above the Regulation Q ceiling, and depositors moved their money into newly created high-yielding mutual funds. The drop in deposit levels ultimately hurt small businesses that depended on banks for loans not readily available elsewhere. Ironically, one of the original reasons for imposing interest rate ceilings had been to lower the cost of bank-intermediated financing. The lesson here is that effective regulation must be flexible and oriented toward creating incentives that will help and not hinder efficient resource allocation. Rigid regulations can cripple the market's ability to provide valuable services and almost inevitably result in an unproductive game of regulatory catch-up.

In designing effective policies, regulators must also take into account the globalization of the financial services industry. Large U.S. banks now have operations on every continent, while domestic banks face competition at home from U.S. branches of foreign banks. Many stocks that once traded exclusively in New York are now also traded in London and Tokyo. Securities change hands around the clock and around the world via new electronic trading systems.

As markets become more international, they also become extremely competitive and mobile. Policymakers worldwide have become increasingly aware that they must work together to create a fair and open environment, maintain stability, and ensure accountability. Because today's markets are highly mobile, countries that unilaterally impose costly regulations risk driving businesses to other, less regulated countries. For example, some have suggested imposing a heavy tax on stock or futures market transactions to discourage frequent trading and as a source of additional revenue. Such a policy, however, would have the unfortunate consequences of reducing market liquidity in the short run, and losing U.S. jobs and tax revenues in the long run as transactions shifted overseas.

Finally, one unfortunate consequence of the piecemeal process of financial regulation and reform has been that responsibility for regulating the financial markets is spread across a large number of Federal regulatory agencies. The Federal Reserve Board, Treasury Department, Office of Thrift Supervision, Commodity Futures Trading Commission, FDIC, and SEC often find themselves with overlapping jurisdictions, especially as banks increase their participation in the securities markets and new financial instruments fall across what were once distinct categories. In some cases, conflicts between agencies have actually prevented viable financial products from reaching the public. *Better coordination in designing and implementing regulatory policy could significantly reduce the unnecessary burden imposed by inconsistent rules and reporting requirements.*

CURRENT ISSUES IN REGULATORY REFORM

Recent regulatory developments affecting banks, S&Ls, and insurance markets have begun to address some of these issues, but further reform is needed to ensure a safe and efficient financial system.

Lessons From the S&L Debacle

Since 1980, regulators have shut down almost 1,200 insolvent S&Ls with assets of over $500 billion, and additional insolvent S&Ls are expected to be resolved over the next few years. The Administration estimates that this wave of S&L failures will ultimately cost taxpayers between $100 billion and $160 billion (in nominal dollars). Because of deposit insurance, however, no insured depositor has lost a dime. Furthermore, in the last half century deposit insurance has contributed to the relative stability of U.S. financial markets.

Understanding the underlying causes of these failures can reduce the probability of future losses of this magnitude. The troubles began when the high interest rates of the inflationary 1970s substantially reduced the value of the long-term, fixed-rate mortgages that were the primary assets of the S&Ls. As interest rates rose, the cost of the short-term deposits used to finance mortgages increased, but the mortgage payments remained constant. By 1981, the total value of S&L liabilities exceeded the total value of assets; S&Ls as a group were technically bankrupt.

Although regulators and the Congress were aware of the problems, they chose to allow many insolvent S&Ls to continue operating. Ordinarily, when a private company nears bankruptcy, its operations are severely limited because investors refuse to provide further financing. With deposit insurance, however, depositors have little incentive to withdraw their funds, and no natural market mechanism limits the activities of an insolvent S&L. In fact, regulations restricting investment to traditional mortgage lending were relaxed to make the S&Ls more competitive with commercial banks. With nothing to lose, many S&Ls used their insured deposits to gamble on high-risk investments in areas outside their scope of expertise. If these investments paid off, the financial health of the S&Ls would be restored. If they failed, the deposit insurer would pay the costs.

This episode provides several important lessons. First, deposit insurance can encourage excessive risk-taking by depository institutions, leading not only to enormous liabilities for the taxpayer, but to real economic losses to society through the inefficient use of private capital. For example, an insured lender has a greater incentive than an uninsured lender to provide financing for a very risky and economically unjustifiable venture. As long as the government provides deposit insurance, some regulation will be necessary to counterbalance this incentive. A second lesson concerns the workings of the regulatory system. Perhaps the most disquieting aspect of the S&L affair was the long delay before action was taken to close insolvent institutions.

Although most insolvent S&Ls have now been closed or merged with healthy institutions, a number of problems remain. The Resolution Trust Corporation (RTC), the Federal agency in charge of resolving insolvent S&Ls, is paying off depositors and recovering as much money as possible in liquidating remaining assets. The RTC can perform these activities only if it has the money to pay off depositors. As of this writing, the RTC has exhausted its funds. As a result, insolvent institutions continue to operate and to lose money. The Administration has urged prompt action, but until the Congress appropriates more funding, these avoidable costs will continue to mount.

Although they are less at risk than they were in the past, healthy S&Ls could still suffer substantial losses if interest rates rise, because these institutions hold a large portion of their portfolios in long-term mortgages or mortgage-backed securities financed with short-term deposits. A rapid increase in interest rates would raise funding costs, but the income from the mortgages would remain largely fixed. For the most part, this situation appears to be an indirect consequence of regulation and not the result of market forces. Partly to correct this bias, S&L regulators have recently proposed new interest rate risk-based capital requirements which are discussed below.

Developments In Commercial Banking

A variety of difficulties have also weakened commercial banks (Chapter 3 has a discussion of recent developments in banking).

The unusually large number of bank failures in recent years has left the bank insurance fund without enough money to cover anticipated future losses. Taxpayers are unlikely to be called on to make up the deficiency directly. Deposit insurance premiums have increased, however, and these increases are likely to be passed on to depositors through lower rates or higher service fees. To cover near-term costs, the FDIC is authorized to borrow up to $70 billion from the Treasury. This debt is expected to be repaid with future deposit insurance premiums.

The Impact of Recent Regulations

In December 1991 the Congress passed the Federal Deposit Insurance Corporation Improvement Act. This act is the most recent major legislative attempt to reform the rules governing depository institutions. Its primary goal is to decrease future deposit insurance losses by tightening supervisory standards and increasing insurance premium rates and capital requirements for riskier institutions. By authorizing new borrowing from the Treasury, it also provides some of the much-needed funding to finish closing insolvent banks and S&Ls.

In 1988, bank regulators around the world agreed, under the Basle Accord, to set capital standards based on the default risk of a bank's assets. Conceptually, bank capital is the difference between the value of a bank's assets and its liabilities. With deposit insurance, bank capital provides a buffer against losses to the FDIC, so it is appropriate that the capital requirement reflects a bank's risk.

For such a rule to provide the appropriate incentives, however, it must set a capital standard that reflects all types of risk. The current risk-based capital requirement primarily focuses on default risk. As a result, banks have an incentive to shift away from investing in commercial loans toward investing in Treasury securities, reducing one type of risk but incurring another: interest rate risk. If interests rates rise, the value of long-term Treasury securities will decline relative to the value of the deposits financing them, eroding bank capital. To correct this requires modifying risk-based capital standards to take into account interest rate and other types of risk.

The FDIC Improvement Act's "prompt closure" rule, which requires that the FDIC and other bank regulators restrict a bank's activities if its capital falls below specified levels, addresses the problem of lax regulation of weak institutions. For the most severely undercapitalized banks, the law generally requires closure or conservatorship within 90 days. The purpose of this regulation is to avoid the long delays and speculative losses that have added billions of dollars to the cost of the thrift crisis. The drawback is that because bank capital is often poorly measured, some healthy institutions may be unfairly constrained, and some insolvent institutions may be allowed to continue to operate.

Bank supervisors rely heavily on accounting data to determine the strength of individual banks. The need for reliable data has increased with regulations such as the prompt closure rule. Yet discrepancies between true and reported asset values continue to occur because the reported, or book, value of an asset does not necessarily reflect current market conditions. For instance, a bad loan can remain on the books for some time before a bank must recognize the loss. Conversely, a bank's assets may have appreciated, but regulators often do not take the increases into account.

Some observers have proposed adopting a system of market value accounting that would allow banks to report market values instead of (or in addition to) book values. Although market value accounting would increase the quality of some information available to regulators, it is difficult to determine the market value for infrequently traded assets such as some types of commercial loans. Many bankers believe that using a combination of market and book values can be more misleading than simply using book value. As debate on this issue continues, regulators appear to be moving toward a system that places increasing emphasis on market values but still relies primarily on book values.

Proposals for Further Bank Reform

The FDIC Improvement Act failed to address many of the fundamental problems in the current regulatory structure. In 1991 the Administration proposed a broader set of regulatory reforms to significantly improve the efficiency of our financial system. Since the 1991 *Report* described these proposals in detail, they are reviewed here only briefly.

The Administration supports the removal of branch banking regulations that limit interstate banking. Although such rules were originally intended to reduce the potential market power of large banks, they have had the opposite effect, decreasing competition between banks in local markets and increasing the cost of bank services. Interstate banking would make banks safer because they could more easily diversify their risks geographically and lower costs by avoiding legal barriers to efficient operation.

Currently, the FDIC insures deposits up to $100,000, and wealthy individuals can obtain virtually unlimited insurance by splitting deposits among many separate accounts. Capping the maximum insurance coverage for a single individual would reduce the government's liability and still provide ample protection for the savings of small depositors. An added benefit would be that large depositors would have the incentive to monitor the investment policies of their depository institutions.

The Administration supports a number of reforms that would allow banks to provide a wider range of financial services. Banks are currently limited in their ability to engage in such activities as selling insurance and underwriting new stock and bond issues—services that are complementary to traditional banking activities. Allowing banks greater freedom to participate in these activities could increase competition for such services and lower costs to the public.

Unfortunately, the recent legislative efforts to reform bank regulations—the FDIC Improvement Act and the Financial Institutions Reform, Recovery, and Enforcement Act of 1989 (FIRREA)—may have created as many new problems as they have solved. (The 1991 *Report* has a discussion of FIRREA.) These laws burdened banks with costly and unnecessary paper work, and generally created a regulatory atmosphere that exacerbated the shortage of commercial credit during the recent recession and recovery. The Administration has proposed legislation to repeal several of the supervisory provisions that impose unreasonably high compliance costs on banks and do little to improve the soundness of the system.

Government-Sponsored Enterprises

With little public fanfare, the mortgage market has undergone an enormous structural change. In 1975 S&Ls financed 46 percent of single-family mortgages. By 1991 this share had shrunk to 16 percent. Much of the private market has shifted to two government-sponsored enterprises (GSEs), the Federal National Mortgage Association (Fannie Mae) and the Federal Home Loan Mortgage Corporation (Freddie Mac) (Chart 5-2).

Fannie Mae and Freddie Mac are shareholder-owned corporations chartered by the Congress to provide a secondary, or resale market for residential mortgages. Homebuyers still apply for mortgages from traditional lenders—S&Ls, banks, and mortgage banks—that make and often service the loans. The GSEs buy mortgages from the initiating lenders and retain some of the mortgages in their own portfolios. Through a process known as securitization, the GSEs also gather mortgages into diversified pools. They issue securities backed by these mortgage pools and sell the securities to investors such as banks, insurance companies, and pension and mutual funds. Interest and principal payments from the pool of mortgages are passed through to investors as they arrive, and the GSE promises to provide payment in the event of a default on an underlying mortgage. Securitization enhances the liquidity of mortgages, lowering the cost of mortgage financing for homebuyers.

Although GSE charters state that the securities they issue are not obligations of the Federal Government, the GSEs receive significant government benefits including exemption from State and local income taxes and certain registration requirements, as well as

Chart 5-2   Single-Family Mortgage Debt Outstanding
The principal source of single-family mortgages has shifted from savings and loans to government-sponsored enterprises.

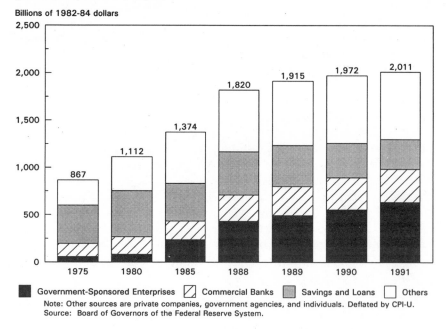

Billions of 1982-84 dollars

Government-Sponsored Enterprises ▮   Commercial Banks ▨   Savings and Loans ▨   Others □
Note: Other sources are private companies, government agencies, and individuals. Deflated by CPI-U.
Source: Board of Governors of the Federal Reserve System.

a contingent line of credit from the Treasury that authorizes discretionary emergency loans of up to $2.25 billion. Furthermore, the fact that yields on GSE securities are only slightly higher than those on Treasury securities with similar maturities suggests that investors believe that the Federal Government would step in and make the payments if the GSEs cannot meet their obligations.

In general, although the GSEs and the Federal Government may have eliminated the default risk for the purchaser of an insured security, they cannot eliminate the risk inherent in the investment activity being funded. The percentage of bad loans may actually increase when loans are insured and resold because the incentive to monitor the mortgage borrower is reduced. While the S&Ls suffered the consequences of their lending decisions, the GSEs resell mortgages originated by institutions that ultimately have a smaller stake in whether the loans are repaid, although they do have an interest in retaining the right to sell loans to the GSEs.

The phenomenal growth in GSE lending in recent years has made it appear likely that the government would honor the guarantee implicit in GSE securities rather than risk a crisis in the mortgage market. As a result, some have argued that potential losses from these guarantees should be recognized in the budget (Chapter 6). These GSEs have been very profitable in the last few years. For instance, Fannie Mae had a net income of $1.4 billion in 1991. But Fannie Mae lost over $350 million between 1981 and 1985, and a large drop in housing prices could trigger much greater losses.

Until recently GSEs have been lightly regulated in comparison with banks and S&Ls. This fact is somewhat surprising given the central role GSEs play in the housing market, the significant implicit subsidies provided by their status, and the potentially enormous liability the government faces if a GSE fails. Recognizing the need for protection, the Congress passed a bill in October 1992 that sets capital standards for GSEs and establishes a regulator who is appointed by the President and located in the Department of Housing and Urban Development.

As it does with banks and S&Ls, higher capital reduces the government's potential liabilities and increases the incentive for GSEs to control risk. The new GSE capital standards are structured similarly to those for banks and S&Ls; they are risk-based and mandate prompt closure if capital falls below specified levels. They are significantly lower than those for banks and S&Ls, however, for several reasons. First, mortgage loans have a lower default rate than the commercial loans that make up a significant part of bank portfolios. Second, GSE capital is based partially on market value, providing a reliable estimate of an institution's strength. Finally, because the GSEs resell most mortgages rather than keeping them on their balance sheets, private investors bear a larger portion of any interest rate risk, although the GSEs retain the default risk. Whether these new standards will adequately protect the taxpayer from GSE losses, however, remains to be seen.

The private sector successfully securitizes many other types of loans, including credit card receivables, automobile loans, and some types of mortgages and commercial credit. A larger role for private sector securitization would reduce government liability and further enhance market liquidity. Until 1992, one impediment to further private securitization of assets such as small business loans was the securities law itself, which required compliance with the outmoded restrictions of the 1940 Investment Company Act. The SEC recently adopted new regulations to facilitate private securitization, while still ensuring adequate investor protection.

Insurance Markets

Insurance allows people to reduce their exposure to many types of risk by spreading losses across a larger group. Government insurance programs have been developed in part because some risks are difficult to predict and catastrophic in size. The nature of the losses may make it difficult for the private market to develop actuarially sound premium rates or sufficient reserves to credibly insure such risks. Political considerations dictate the provision of other types of insurance that in principle could be provided by the private sector.

As in the credit markets, the government is increasingly taking a direct role in providing insurance. In fact, the Federal Government has become the Nation's largest underwriter of risk. Government insurance programs affect the economy in three main ways: They reduce and redistribute risk, reallocate wealth, and change the incentives of the insured.

When insurance is underpriced relative to its long-term cost, those who are protected receive a subsidy. Federal insurance programs have suffered substantial losses over the last decade (Chapter 6). Although some insurance losses were due to unforeseen and perhaps unavoidable events such as the droughts that struck the Nation's farms in 1983, 1988, and 1989, many can be attributed to inaccurate risk assessments.

The Federal Government often undermines its insurance programs by providing disaster assistance with similar benefits, but at little or no cost to the individual. This subsidy weakens incentives to avoid risk or to buy insurance, putting the government under increased pressure to provide assistance after the next disaster. A good example of this phenomenon is the experience of the Federal crop insurance program (Box 5–2).

Insurance also reduces incentives for people to make cost-effective choices. For example, offering subsidized insurance rates for flood protection can encourage people to retain homes on flood plains. Well-designed insurance programs must provide incentives that encourage prudent behavior, and the cost of misallocated resources due to distorted incentives should be part of any cost-benefit analysis of government insurance programs.

Is there a further role for the private sector in providing insurance? As private financial markets continue to expand, private insurers may be able to handle liabilities that were once considered too large. For example, futures contracts related to health, homeowners, and catastrophic insurance have been developed that will allow insurers to shift risk to other private entities such as banks, mutual funds, and individual investors. Innovative combinations of private and public insurance could also improve efficiency. For instance, it has been suggested that private insurers could set premium rates and cover a portion of deposit insurance, limiting the government's liability to losses that exceed the private coverage level. To explore this idea, the FDIC Improvement Act requires the FDIC to test private reinsurance and report the results in 1993.

Box 5-2.—Federal Crop Insurance and Disaster Assistance

Crop insurance protects farmers against losses from low crop yields caused by bad weather, pests, or disease. Since 1938, the Federal Government has offered farmers subsidized crop insurance. Between 1981 and 1990, the Federal Crop Insurance Corporation paid out $2.5 billion more than it collected in premiums.

The Federal Crop Insurance Act of 1980 set out to establish crop insurance as the primary source of disaster risk management for farmers. But despite subsidized rates, many farmers do not participate in the program. In recent years, less than one-half of the eligible acreage was covered by Federal crop insurance.

Disaster assistance has undermined the effectiveness of the crop insurance program. Based on their experience, many farmers believe that whenever a widespread natural disaster occurs the government will provide emergency disaster assistance to all affected. In a recent survey, 41 percent of farmers who did not purchase crop insurance said that they did not do so because they believe that the government would bail them out in the event of a disaster. Conversely, low participation in the crop insurance program makes it all the more likely that the Congress will face political pressure to enact disaster legislation whenever a widespread disaster occurs.

SUMMARY

- The growth of financial services has lowered the cost of risk management and expanded investment opportunities.
- The increasing flexibility and international mobility of financial markets necessitates a regulatory framework that focuses on incentives and avoids rigid rules.
- Progress has been made in reforming the regulation of depository institutions, but impediments to efficient operation remain. Further reform is needed to ensure a safe and competitive financial system.

OWNERSHIP AND PRICING OF NATURAL RESOURCES

In the United States, the government owns a substantial share of the Nation's resources. The Federal Government owns about one-third of the total land in the United States, including 29 percent of forestlands and 43 percent of rangeland. State and local governments and American Indian Nations own another 8 percent of U.S. lands. Over 10 percent of the U.S. population receives water from Federal projects. The land and water bring with them other important natural resources, including wildlife and minerals.

The principles of regulatory reform—allowing markets to work where possible, and harnessing the power of market incentives to accomplish regulatory objectives—should also be applied to issues of government ownership and pricing of resources. Some resources such as Federal rangelands and industrial timber stands are indistinguishable from adjacent privately owned lands and have no special features warranting public stewardship. In addition, the U.S. Government often sets the price for using resources below the market price, sometimes even below the direct cost of providing them. These low prices can lead to overconsumption, distorted economic priorities, damage to the environment, and lost revenue.

WHY DOES THE GOVERNMENT OWN AND MANAGE RESOURCES?

Most goods and services in our economy are private property, traded in markets that determine prices and quantities. As has been noted, markets efficiently allocate commodities to serve the best interests of all. Government ownership of land and other natural resources in the United States is, in large part, a residual effect of policies adopted in the last century to encourage settlement of sparsely populated western territory. In many cases, there is no economic reason for the government to own these resources.

However, for some resources, there may be a market failure that does provide an underlying reason for government activity. There are two interrelated ways in which private markets for natural resources and the right to use them may fail.

First, a private market may fail to produce the right amount of a public good. Public goods are goods that can be used or enjoyed by one person without detracting from the use or enjoyment of others. For example, suppose Farmer Jones paves the road into town. The neighbors can use the road without affecting its usefulness to Jones, and, therefore, the road meets the definition of a public good. While roads are not a natural resource, this example illustrates how a private market may fail: The neighboring farmers have an incentive to wait, hoping someone else will incur the costs of paving the road that all of them can use. Some natural resources have the character of public goods; one person can enjoy the beauty of a forest without detracting from another person's use of it. On the other hand, grazing land and timberland are not public goods: Timber harvested by one person is then not available to anyone else. In fact, it is not uncommon for grazing land and timberland to be privately owned.

Second, in many cases, markets fail to reflect external costs or benefits of using a resource. External costs and benefits, or externalities, affect individuals who are not parties to the economic transaction. For example, logging on a hillside may cause soil erosion, imposing a cost on the people living at the bottom of the hill. The cost to these people is not taken into account in the private market for trees and lumber. Often, people are excluded from an economic transaction affecting them because of the high costs of negotiating and enforcing a settlement.

External costs and benefits are often a consequence of the failure to establish property rights for natural resources. An example is a communal grazing field. Anyone can bring cows to graze, but no single farmer owns the field. Because every farmer can use the field for free, farmers tend to bring more and more cows until the field becomes congested. Each farmer using the field is creating an external cost to the other farmers. Unless property rights have been assigned stating which parties "own" the rights to the land or the rights to graze on the land, the private market will not allocate the pasture in a way that maximizes the joint benefits of all users.

ESTABLISHING MARKETS FOR THE RIGHT TO USE RESOURCES

Establishing private markets for the right to use a resource often requires government action. The establishment and enforcement of property rights is quintessentially in the realm of government. During the 18th and 19th centuries, the U.S. Government established property rights for lands on the western frontier and then sold or gave away those rights to homesteaders.

The most direct way for the government to address certain failures in markets for natural resources is to sanction legally valid private property rights and allow owners to limit or sell access to resources. For example, the common grazing field could be given or sold into private hands and access limited by a fence. Private property rights give owners the incentive to stop the resource from being overused and to manage it in a way that maintains or increases its value. Private timber companies in the United States replant their lands to maintain forested areas. On the other hand, timber companies in some developing countries hold only short-term logging concessions on government-owned land and have little incentive to replant or otherwise sustain forest resources.

Not all natural resources lend themselves to ordinary boundaries and fences. It is difficult to assign ownership of the atmosphere as a storage space for waste products. One way to address this problem is to have the government create a special kind of property right—the right to use the resource—and then to allow holders of the right to sell it like any other property.

A familiar example of a government-issued right to use a re-source is a deer hunting license that permits the licenseholder to hunt and kill a specified number of deer. However, hunting licenses cannot be traded or transferred. If a hunter wishes to kill more deer than the license allows, he or she cannot legally buy the licenses from other hunters and in that way gain the right to kill more deer.

Making permits tradable (allowing them to be bought and sold) is critical to ensure that the resource is used in an economically efficient way. People who attach a low value to using the resource will sell their right to use it to those who attach a relatively high value to use of the resource. The 1990 Clean Air Act Amendments, for example, use tradable permits in order to lower the cost of reducing pollution. The law sets yearly caps on sulfur dioxide emissions from electric utilities. Over time, the caps will be lowered, so that by the year 2000 these emissions will be about one-half of their 1990 levels. Plants receive permits each year for the amount of sulfur dioxide that may legally be released. Since the cost of limiting emissions may be much higher at some facilities than at others, it is not economical to force each plant to reduce emissions by the same amount. To deal with this, the law allows the permits to be bought and sold. Plants that would find it expensive to reduce emissions may be willing to pay a high price for the permits. Plants that can reduce emissions relatively cheaply may be willing to sell their permits. In this way, the market for permits reallocates them so that those plants able to reduce pollution inexpensively will reduce pollution the most. This system of tradable permits is expected to save the economy an estimated $1 billion per year, or about 15 to 25 percent of the cost of reducing pollution without tradable permits. Box 5-3 describes another example.

PRICING OF GOVERNMENT-OWNED NATURAL RESOURCES

Where privatizing a resource is not feasible, another solution to the problem of market failure is for the government itself to hold the resource on behalf of the public. Government ownership of a resource is most appropriate when the resource has the character of a public good (Box 5-4). Goods and services typically provided by the government include armed forces and public fire departments. The U.S. Government has purchased or created national parks such as the Grand Canyon. These are public goods that can be used and enjoyed by many people at the same time. As noted earlier, the private market may fail to provide the optimal quantity of public goods as potential users wait for others to make the investment. To an increasing extent, the government has adopted this prescription. Under this Administration, funds for State land and

Box 5-3.—Government Creates a Market for Fishing Rights

There is no practical way to establish ownership rights of ocean fish stocks. Traditionally, fish have been free for the taking—a common pool resource. Theory teaches that such underpricing leads to overconsumption. In the halibut fisheries off Alaska, fishing fleets caught so many halibut that the survival of the stock was threatened. No single fishing boat had an incentive to harvest fewer fish since the impact on its own future catch would be minimal and others would only increase their take. This is an example of what is known as "the tragedy of the commons."

Officials tried limiting the length of the fishing season. But this effort only encouraged new capital investment such as larger and faster boats with more effective (and expensive) fishing equipment. In order to control the number of fish caught, the season was shortened in some areas from 4 months to 2 days by the early 1990s. Most of the halibut caught had to be frozen rather than marketed fresh, and halibut caught out of season had to be discarded.

In late 1992, the Federal Government proposed a new approach: assigning each fisherman a permit to catch a certain number of fish. The total number of fish for which permits are issued will reflect scientific estimates of the number of fish that can be caught without endangering the survival of the species. Also, the permits will be transferable—they can be bought and sold. By making the permits transferable, the system in effect creates a market where one did not exist previously. The proposed system will encourage the most profitable and efficient boats to operate at full capacity by buying permits from less successful boats, ensuring a fishing fleet that uses labor and equipment efficiently. Moreover, the transferable permits system establishes a market price for the opportunity to fish—a price that better reflects the true social cost of using this common resource.

water conservation were tripled, and 20 new national park units and 57 new national wildlife refuges have been added or proposed.

The fact that the government owns certain resources does not automatically guarantee that they will be allocated and used in the best possible way. Prices charged for use of a resource significantly affect the economic efficiency of that use. The appropriate price is one where marginal social cost is equal to marginal social benefit. Marginal costs are the expenses involved in providing an incremental unit of a resource, marginal benefits are the gains associated

Box 5-4.—Forests as a Public Good

Government ownership of natural resources is sometimes intended to help produce the public goods that private ownership has failed to provide. A prime example is the recent reform of government stewardship of forests. Many private forests are harvested by logging companies through clearcutting, which involves removing every tree on a plot of land and then replanting the land with seedlings. While clearcutting can be the least costly way to produce timber for industrial uses, it does detract from the scenic value of forestlands.

In 1992 the Administration adopted a new "ecosystem approach" for managing these federally owned forests which phases out clearcutting as a standard timber harvest practice. Instead, trees in Federal forests will be selectively harvested in order to preserve the scenic value of the forests. The Forest Service expects that the new policy will reduce clearcutting on Federal lands by as much as 70 percent from 1988 levels while reducing the volume of logs cut by only 10 percent or less. This policy exemplifies the appropriate role of government, not as an owner of commercial timberland, but as a protector of forests as a public good.

with that additional unit. Social costs and benefits reflect the economic impact on all members of society and include externalities as well as direct economic effects. Box 5-5 discusses some difficulties in measuring social costs and benefits.

Chronic Underpricing

The rights to use government-owned natural resources are often sold at prices that fail to incorporate the full costs to society and sometimes at prices that do not even cover management expenses (Box 5-6). Nineteenth-century government policies set prices low to encourage settlement and development of the West. Powerful local constituencies have helped keep them low.

Timber from Federal forests has been sold at prices even lower than the government's cost of providing the timber—and without incorporating possible externalities such as environmental damage. Likewise, rights to graze on Federal lands are sold at prices that fail to cover administrative costs.

Drawbacks of Underpricing

Whether or not it was warranted in the past, underpricing the right to use natural resources today can create budgetary, economic, and environmental problems. On the first point, the budgetary consequences are readily apparent: When the government sells nat-

Box 5-5.—Measuring the Value of Nonmarket Goods

Since a public good is not traded on a competitive market, the market cannot assign it a price based on its value. Measuring the benefits public goods provide is problematic. One method is to infer the value of public goods from actual markets or observable economic behavior. For example, to estimate the value people put on scenic beauty, economists may measure the effect of scenic beauty on actual real estate prices. The value that people put on a park may be reflected in the amount of time and money that they spend to visit and use it.

The contingent valuation method (CVM) uses public opinion surveys. A polltaker asks people to estimate the amount they would be willing to pay to maintain or create a certain public good or the amount they would require to compensate for its loss. Advocates of the CVM argue that it can generate reliable estimates of value in cases where it is impossible to make inferences from actual markets or behavior, and in principle, it takes into account the fact that some people value a good more highly than others do.

However, the CVM also has generated considerable criticism. For example, those surveyed do not actually have to pay the amount they report, a factor that can lead to overstatements. Responses are sensitive to the way questions are posed. (In one case, the estimated value of protection from oil spills changed by a factor of 300 when polltakers asked additional questions before eliciting this value.) CVM results can be inconsistent. (For example, one CVM study showed that people were willing to pay more money to clean up small oilspills than to clean up both small and large spills.) In many cases CVM results cannot be verified except by another CVM study.

These problems are exacerbated when the CVM is used to estimate the value of goods that are abstract, symbolic, or difficult to comprehend. One study showed that if the CVM were used to estimate the value of saving whooping cranes from extinction, resulting estimates might be as high as $37 billion per year (more than the Federal Government spends each year on education and Head Start programs). Finally, even if all the problems of the CVM could be resolved, care must be taken to ensure that it is not used to analyze policy in a one-sided way. For example, a proposed program to protect whooping cranes might put people out of work. The $37 billion figure could be cited by those who claim that the benefits of the program exceed its costs. But opponents of that view could undertake a CVM study of their own asking people how much they would be willing to pay to protect these jobs.

Box 5-6.—Reform of California Water

One highly publicized example of government underpricing of natural resources has been California water. Forty-year contracts signed in the 1940s and 1950s guaranteed California farmers water from Federal projects at prices of about $3 per acre-foot, even though the government's current cost to supply that water is often about ten times that amount. Cities and industries that need water cannot obtain it from farmers because archaic legal restrictions block the development of water markets.

The Reclamation Projects Authorization and Adjustment Act of 1992 was signed by the President, despite his concern over certain aspects of the bill, in large part because it encouraged more market-oriented pricing of Federal water in California. The act allows those receiving water from the Federal Central Valley Project to pay low subsidized prices for the first 90 percent but increases the price for the last 10 percent, so that the price for the final units used will more closely reflect the full costs of providing the water.

The act also allows recipients of Federal water to sell their water rights. In this way, water can be shifted from relatively low-value agricultural use to relatively high-value municipal or industrial use. The high value of water to urban users is indicated by the fact that, in 1991, the California State Water Bank sold nearly 400,000 acre-feet of State water to cities and industrial users at a price of $175 per acre-foot.

ural resources below their market value, the taxpayer is subsidizing those uses. Under the 1872 Mining Law, mining companies are able to buy land from the Federal Government for $2.50-$5.00 per acre and then resell the land at market prices. In one extreme example, the government sold 17,000 acres of land for $42,500. Weeks later, these lands were resold to major oil companies for $37 million.

Second, underpricing diverts resources from uses that would benefit society the most to less valuable tasks. In California, cities and industries are often willing to pay substantially more than farmers for water, demonstrating the high value water can have. But low-priced Federal water is often used to grow crops such as alfalfa—a crop fed to dairy cattle—in effect subsidizing the production of milk which has been in oversupply and is already subsidized by Federal support programs. Letting farmers transfer water from low-value agricultural uses to high-value uses could generate substantial economic gains for farmers and nonfarmers alike.

Third, when underpricing leads to overuse, the environment may suffer. For example, if the government underprices grazing rights on federally owned land, overgrazing may lead to soil erosion. *Pricing the right to use government-owned natural resources to reflect actual social costs and benefits could help the environment as well as improve economic performance.*

REFORMING PUBLIC RESOURCE POLICY

Given the chronic problems of government ownership of natural resources, what practical steps can be taken toward developing a better system? As mentioned above, in some cases, government-owned natural resources can be "privatized"—given or sold to private individuals. Once in private hands, access to the resource would be priced by the market ensuring more efficient allocation and reducing overconsumption. From the standpoint of economic efficiency, the decision to give away the natural resource or to sell it is not important. Even if the government gives away the resource to someone who cannot use it efficiently, efficient users will make attractive offers to buy it from the initial recipients.

For the same reasons, the issue of who becomes the initial owner of the resource is also unimportant in terms of economic efficiency. However, it may be of critical importance in determining the political viability of privatization. If government-owned resources are sold rather than given away to those now using them, the present users may form a powerful group blocking privatization. On the other hand, sales bring in government revenues which could be used to pursue other objectives.

In cases where using a natural resource involves significant externalities, however, putting it in the hands of private owners will not solve the problem of market failure, since the prices private owners charge would reflect private costs and benefits rather than social costs and benefits. But government ownership is not the only way to deal with externalities. The actions of private owners can be regulated by laws such as those that make people liable for damages if they cause hillside erosion. Externalities can also be incorporated in private market decisions through taxes and subsidies, fines and fees, or other government action.

When natural resources remain in government hands, prices charged for access to these resources ought to reflect, to the fullest extent possible, the actual costs and externalities associated with using the resource. This policy can be implemented in any of three ways. First, when the appropriate price can be calculated, the government can set the selling price at that level. Second, when the market price is unknown, the government can auction rights to use the resource, allowing the auction to determine the market price. Third, the government can give away or sell at low prices the right to use the resource, and allow that right to be bought and sold. In this last case, the market for transferable rights will set prices and dictate the appropriate use.

SUMMARY

- Markets for natural resources are sometimes characterized by imperfections, either when the resource is a public good or when the use of the resource involves externalities.
- Sometimes the market imperfection can be eliminated by assigning property rights. One way to define these property rights is by creating tradable permits to use the resource.
- When the government retains ownership of a resource, access to that resource should be priced to reflect social costs and benefits.

RISKS TO HEALTH, SAFETY, AND THE ENVIRONMENT

Life involves risks as well as opportunities. Disease, crime, and car accidents are well-known risks; every week seems to bring claims of new kinds of risks, such as food contamination, toxic substances, and global climate change. Yet creating a truly zero-risk society would be impossible. And it would be undesirable, not only because such a goal would be prohibitively costly but also because people often decide that some risks are worth taking—such as testing new technologies, using the fastest mode of travel to save time, or even playing school sports.

Nevertheless, the risk of premature death and injury has in fact declined steadily over the long term as society has become richer and more technically advanced. In the short term, many risks can be reduced, but only at a cost; for example, cars built to withstand crashes will cost more than similar cars lacking such reinforcements. People often decide that avoiding risk is worth the cost: they buy insurance, join health clubs, install car alarms, and take detours to avoid dark alleys.

Amidst the myriad public choices about risk, the government often acts to reduce risks. It tests and sets safety standards for foods, drugs, automobiles, factories, and chemicals. It also plays an active role in providing information about risk, and in regulating behavior that may impose risks on others or on the environment.

RISK IN PERSPECTIVE

People commonly believe that contemporary life presents more risks than the "simpler" times of the past. Certainly some types of new technological risks exist today that did not in earlier eras. But it bears recalling that in the "good old days" standards of living were lower, nutrition and health care were poorer, workdays were longer and more dangerous, and food and water supplies were less safe and reliable than they are today.

In fact the risk of premature death and injury is lower in modern industrial society than in earlier and less technologically advanced societies. Average life expectancy at birth, the most salient indicator of overall risk, has improved in the United States from 47 years in 1900 to 75 years in 1990. In most poorer, less industrialized countries life expectancy is increasing but is only about 55 years. Other indicators of risk are also improving: The life expectancy of an American at age 65 increased by 45 percent between 1900 and 1990. American infant mortality rates fell 81 percent between 1940 and 1990 to under 1 percent of live births; in low-income countries the infant mortality rate is as high as 10 percent. Since 1945, a person's risk of being killed on the job has fallen by more than 70 percent. In 1900, infectious diseases (mainly tuberculosis, pneumonia, diarrhea, and enteritis) were the leading causes of death in the United States, accounting for 30 percent of all fatalities in that year; today they cause about 5 percent, although the growing crisis of AIDS (acquired immune deficiency syndrome)—and associated resurgence of pneumonia and tuberculosis—is cause for national and international concern. Today cancer, heart disease, and strokes are the leading causes of death in the United States, together accounting for about two-thirds of all fatalities.

To be sure, the risk to Americans of certain new types of accidents has increased over time; after all, no Americans died in airplane crashes in 1900. But even new types of risk have been reduced as technology and operations have improved. A person's risk of dying in an automobile accident has declined over 30 percent since 1970. Furthermore, the increasing ability of science to detect ever-smaller potential risks may cause people to perceive an increase in risk.

Health risks associated with environmental pollution have also declined. Between 1970 and 1989, air pollution decreased significantly: particulates fell 61 percent, sulfur oxides 26 percent, carbon monoxide 40 percent, and volatile organic compounds 31 percent. As lead was phased out of gasoline over this period, lead emissions dropped 96 percent. Industrial discharges of key water pollutants also declined over 90 percent between the mid-1970s and mid-1980s. Though difficult to quantify, the health benefits of reducing pollutant emissions can be significant. For example, substantial evidence suggests that elevated levels of lead in children's blood cause lasting neurological damage, impairing IQ, productivity, and quality of life and increasing expenses for remedial education and treatment.

Today cancer causes about a quarter of American fatalities, but experts estimate that environmental pollution accounts for only

1–5 percent of all cancer deaths. Occupational exposure is estimated to account for another 2–8 percent, and food additives (which in some cases actually protect against cancer) for −5 to 2 percent. Smoking and other behavioral factors make much larger contributions to cancer.

Cancer is a less common cause of death in poorer countries, where food spoilage, diseases borne by drinking water, and infant mortality take their toll long before cancer can develop. Similarly, within the United States, residents of low-income neighborhoods are more likely to face high rates of crime and infant mortality, and to have high levels of lead in their blood.

RISK IN THE MARKETPLACE

Every day, people make decisions about taking or avoiding risks. Like other aspects of the quality of goods and services, riskiness is a product feature that people evaluate when making transactions in the marketplace. People can choose products and jobs with varying characteristics, including riskiness. People buy child car seats, fire extinguishers, and reinforced locks. Today consumers are more interested than ever in automotive safety features such as airbags and antilock brakes, and manufacturers are responding to these market demands.

Market prices for goods and services thus reflect people's preferences about risk-taking, the information they have about risks, and the freedom they have to accept or avoid risks. When people are well informed and can make their own decisions about risk-taking, market prices will send signals that guide producers and consumers to provide and consume the socially desired amount of safety. When people do not have sufficient information and choice, social systems may develop that help people learn about and manage risk. Government policy is one such social risk-management system, but not the only one. Others include norms of behavior, insurance markets, and the system of tort (wrongful injury) liability operated by the courts.

Personal behavior probably has the most pervasive influence on the risks people face. People learn to drive defensively, look both ways before crossing the street, lock their doors, and wash their hands before eating. Many norms of behavior also help protect others in the community, such as covering one's mouth while coughing. Meanwhile, the risks that people willingly face—and could choose to avoid—are often much larger than the risks that people worry about being obliged to endure. Of those who regularly drive or ride in automobiles, about 2 out of every 10,000 die in car accidents each year, for a total of about 45,000 deaths annually. By comparison, for those who live near municipal solid waste landfills, the mortality risk is substantially less than 1 in 1,000,000 and may be far lower—a minute fraction of the risk of automobile travel, and a risk that shows up (if at all) only decades later in life.

In competitive labor markets, as Adam Smith pointed out in 1776, employers trying to attract workers will offer wage increases to offset undesirable job characteristics. Because most workers are less willing to take a more dangerous job, employers have to offer higher wages to attract workers to riskier jobs. The increase in wages paid to compensate for the added risk is called a "risk premium." *Studies show that workers in many occupations earn significant risk premiums.* Because workers vary in their aversion to bearing risk, the wage premium for a given amount of risk also varies. Evidence suggests that most workers accepting a job with an additional annual fatality risk of about 1 in 10,000 would earn some $300 to $700 (in 1990 dollars) more than they would in a similar job without the additional risk. Workers who are significantly less averse to bearing risk (such as those who seek jobs in especially risky occupations, like mining) tend to accept lower wage premiums for the same incremental increase in risk. *These risk premiums not only compensate workers for their willingness to bear risk, but also encourage employers to reduce risk.* An employer who can eliminate a risk at less than the cost of the premium the risk adds to wages has an incentive to invest in greater workplace safety. This incentive is significant: The extra wages that employers pay to compensate for risk currently total over $100 billion per year.

The fact that workers receive risk premiums for facing risk does not, of course, guarantee that the amount of these premiums represents the appropriate compensation or safety incentive. When people do not have enough information about risks, or when they cannot act freely on that information (such as when they cannot relocate to seek a new job), they may earn risk premiums that under- or overcompensate them for risk. Coal miners may be earning lower risk premiums because they are less mobile, not because they are more willing to accept risk. In situations where the perceived risk of an activity is less than the true risk—for instance, when a machine has an undisclosed defect or a substance is more toxic than believed—wage risk premiums probably do not fully compensate workers for the risk. Conversely, when the perceived risk of an activity is great but the true risk is small, market transactions may overcompensate for risk.

THE ROLE OF GOVERNMENT: PROVIDING INFORMATION AND REGULATING RISK

People's actions can create risks for others, yet in some circumstances the marketplace does not provide efficient price signals that encourage the socially desired amount of risk avoidance. Government can help people deal with risks by improving the way markets operate. When markets fail to offer people the information and choice needed to understand and avoid or accept risks, the government can intervene to assess and manage risks. But the government can fail, too, and its intervention is only justified where it does more good than harm—where its social benefits exceed its social costs.

First, the government can try to improve the information about risk available to people in the marketplace. Information about risks may be inadequate because market participants do not have an incentive to collect, distribute, or analyze it. Rules that government has developed to increase awareness of risks include those requiring labels on foods, electrical appliances, and other consumer products, as well as the Occupational Safety and Health Administration (OSHA) Hazard Communication Rule that requires employers to inform employees about chemical hazards in the workplace. But government efforts to mandate information can be expensive and confusing, or can omit important information; in some cases informational mandates can even discourage innovation of better products. Extensive requirements for food labeling, for example, could overload consumers with extra information that obscures the most important nutritional facts, and could even keep some healthier food products off the market. Reports on toxic materials released by factories, which are required by community right-to-know laws, often present only the total weight of each chemical discharged and do not differentiate chemicals by degree of toxicity, potentially misleading people about the risks posed.

Second, the government can regulate risk by managing and limiting the choices open to individuals. As noted earlier in this chapter, government intervention may be warranted when private transactions fail to take account of "external costs" imposed on society by pollution and other activities. Government regulation might also be warranted when the information on which a risk decision must be based is so complex that the people affected do not have the time to invest in understanding and acting upon it. Imagine trying to decide whether to board an airplane based on a risk information label posted on the fuselage. Hence the government evaluates the risks of complex machinery, medicines, and toxic substances, and sets safety standards for their production and use. Again, poorly chosen or designed government regulations can be expensive and can fail to reduce risk; they may even do more harm than good.

Risk Assessment

To provide accurate information to the public and to develop appropriate regulations, the government must first identify and evaluate risks. "Risk assessment" has become a widespread government function, performed by agencies such as the Food and Drug

Administration (FDA), the EPA, and OSHA. It plays a pivotal role both in government regulatory decisions and in choices made by individuals and businesses. Accurate risk assessment is a necessary element of setting intelligent priorities and taking effective action to improve people's health and safety.

Risk assessment is supposed to be a scientific, policy-neutral, reliable, and accurate method of obtaining information on risks. *Unfortunately, the scientific credibility of government risk assessment has been undermined by embedded policy judgments.* Faced with incomplete information and pressure to deliver simplified findings that support the goals of agency regulators, government risk assessors have developed methods that incorporate policy-based assumptions and methods. Instead of providing complete and accurate information, risk assessments present filtered estimates that are tilted toward particular results. These embedded policy choices bias government risk estimates away from true risk estimates, distorting decisions made by both the public and government agencies.

First, embedded policy judgments have encumbered the government's efforts to identify whether a substance or activity poses a risk. Government assessments of health risks have tended to focus almost exclusively on cancer, overemphasizing environmental cancer risks but overlooking other dangers, such as reproductive and neurological toxicity. Government risk assessors typically assume that if high-level exposure to a substance causes cancer, then any minimal exposure will pose a risk of cancer, even where available evidence does not show harm below low doses. And researchers are required to use a classification system that simplifies descriptions of test results, forcing important differences between the physiology of laboratory animals and that of human beings to be ignored. For example, gasoline vapors have been classified as a human carcinogen because male rats exposed to these vapors in the laboratory developed liver tumors, even though the researchers knew that the mechanism that triggered these tumors does not occur in humans.

Second, embedded policy choices also bias the government's assessment of the number of people actually exposed to a risk. Most risk assessments do not analyze real data about exposure to real people; instead, they hypothesize a "maximum exposed individual" who breathes or ingests the most concentrated emissions 24 hours a day for every day of a 70-year lifespan. Examples bordering on the absurd are not uncommon. To determine the potential risk of hazardous waste disposal sites, government risk assessors assume that hypothetical children will unerringly locate the most contaminated spot on the site, dig through a five-foot clay cap and two plastic liners to reach the most toxic dirt, and ingest 200 milligrams every day for 350 days a year (even in towns where the ground is frozen and snow-covered many months a year). Until recently, EPA risk assessors assumed that the level of pesticide residue on food was the maximum level permitted to be applied at the farm, even though the permitted level at the farm is hundreds to many thousands of times higher than the actual level of residue found at the supermarket.

The Impact of Skewed Risk Assessments on Decisions

Inaccurate and biased risk assessments do not help protect people. On the contrary, when skewed risk assessments are used to guide regulatory policy, they distort the government's effort to manage risks in ways that make regulation both more expensive and less protective. They lead to excessive regulation that imposes costs on society in lost use of products or the higher cost of substitutes. And they cause regulators to pay too much attention to low risks and not enough to high risks.

Even apart from biasing regulation, skewed risk assessments can have important negative consequences. Mixing policy with scientific risk assessment undercuts the credibility of risk estimates. Inconsistent risk assessment methods used by different agencies also erode their credibility. Reports implying that all chemicals pose high cancer risks can perpetuate exaggerated public fears. When reported risks are not put into the perspective of everyday experience, the public can be frightened away from substances that in fact pose very small risk.

Ironically, this fear may actually raise risks—increasing mortality and suffering—if inaccurate risk estimates mislead people into ignoring the risks or eschewing useful products. A particularly tragic example may have occurred recently in Peru when the government reduced the chlorination of its drinking water, apparently relying in part on a study reporting that chlorination of U.S. drinking water could increase the risk of cancer. Yet in Peru, waterborne disease may be far more important than minute cancer risks; the ensuing cholera outbreak killed nearly 4,000 people and afflicted almost 400,000 more.

Risk Management

If reliable information is available about the real risk posed by a given substance, what should the government do? In many cases the best answer is nothing, because the market will incorporate the information and provide appropriate incentives for safety. As noted above, government does have a role in addressing "externalities," as long as appropriate government action will do more good than harm.

The primary issue in shaping government risk management is the degree to which risk-causing activity should be restricted. Determining when the incremental cost of reducing risk begins to equal and then exceed the incremental benefit is often a difficult analytic task. With limited social resources to spend on reducing risk, weighing the costs and benefits of policy choices is not only inevitable: it is the daily challenge of good government. For example, experts have pointed out that if the entire U.S. national income were somehow devoted to preventing all of the 95,000 or so accident fatalities that are occurring every year, about $60 million could be spent per accident. Yet such a program would address only about 4 percent of the yearly death toll in America, with no funds left to address cancer or homicide, to say nothing of other social imperatives like food, housing, education, and national defense.

A frequent objection to cost-benefit analysis is that some benefits can be difficult to quantify. For example, it may be hard to measure in dollar terms the benefits of disease prevention or visibility across a national park. Some costs of regulation are also hard to quantify, such as the effect of a rule on future technological innovation. The solution to these difficulties, however, is not to give up on rational balancing of costs and benefits. It is often useful to produce a reliable estimate of the range within which costs and benefits fall, since the alternative is to make a subjective and unsubstantiated judgment. The real question is whether it makes sense to invest in improving our ability to measure costs and benefits—an investment which could end up costing society less than omitting important costs or benefits from regulatory decisions.

Federal agencies now routinely conduct cost-benefit analyses of policy proposals. Executive Order 12291, issued in 1981, requires agencies to analyze the costs and benefits of proposals for major regulations and to submit those analyses to an office of regulatory review, which examines the calculations and suggests possible alternative approaches.

Even with expert cost-benefit analysis, it is not easy to determine the proper level of government risk management. Yet we can be fairly sure that there are substantial problems with existing approaches. First, some laws prevent agencies from considering costs and benefits in making regulatory decisions. For example, parts of the 1977 Clean Air Act required companies to install equipment that reduced pollution by the maximum possible amount, no matter how small the benefits of the marginal reduction in pollution might be or how much the extra equipment might cost. The Delaney Clause of the Food, Drug, and Cosmetic Act requires the FDA to ban any food additive that is found to induce cancer in humans or animals, not matter how trivial the risk or how substantial the benefits of the substance; in 1992 a Federal court reaffirmed the rigidity of this rule. Moreover, the stringency of such

219

rules only increases as scientific ability to measure minute risks sharpens.

Second, some laws and rules set priorities that do not correspond to real risks. Money spent on programs that make little difference in risk is money no longer available for programs that are more effective in reducing risks. For example, hundreds of billions of dollars will be spent to clean up waste disposal sites, which experts have consistently ranked near the bottom of the environmental risks facing Americans, while much less money is dedicated to combating the greater risk of childhood exposure to lead in paint and soil in the inner city. Moreover, the costs of regulation can themselves increase health risks, by reducing the income of workers and consumers.

The costs and benefits of a risk management policy depend in part on the regulatory instrument or tool chosen to implement that policy. Given a defined goal for risk reduction, policy tools should be selected that minimize the cost of achieving that goal. On the other hand, given a fixed budget for reducing risk, policy tools should be selected that maximize the risk reduction achieved with those resources. These are the two sides of the cost-effectiveness of policy tools.

The "cost" side of cost-effectiveness has been heavily studied. The central conclusion is that *the cost of achieving a given regulatory goal can be significantly reduced by harnessing marketplace incentives to achieve that goal rather than by dictating specific conduct or technologies.* Risk management in the United States has often employed command-and-control regulations that compel businesses to install particular pollution control or workplace safety technologies. Today policymakers are increasingly using market-based regulatory tools, such as fees and tradable allowances, that focus on outcomes rather than methods. These tools set performance objectives and then allow industry the flexibility to achieve results at least cost, thus allocating control efforts to the least costly sources and providing an economic incentive to seek continuous improvements. Market-based tools have been applied to phase down lead in gasoline, phase out ozone-depleting chlorofluorocarbons, and limit urban air pollution. *Market-based incentive tools can achieve environmental goals at substantial cost savings compared to command-and-control tools.* Studies estimate these cost savings at 10 to 50 percent or more, even 90 percent in some cases.

The "effectiveness" side of cost-effectiveness has received less analytic attention, but is equally important. *Rules aimed at reducing risk can often miss their targets.* Increasingly critical attention is being paid to the standard assumption that regulations will successfully eliminate the problem they address, even in cases in which the regulated industry is in compliance. For example, studies show that even though employers comply with OSHA safety standards, injury rates are barely affected because OSHA's detailed standards for physical design of the workplace do not address the actual underlying causes of most injuries. In contrast, the workers' compensation insurance system simply charges employers insurance premiums tied to the safety record at the workplace. Because fewer injuries mean lower insurance payments, employers invest in safety improvements that address the causes of injury at each workplace. Although concerns about instances of abuse and mismanagement of workers' compensation have arisen recently, in general its incentive-based feature is estimated to have reduced workplace fatalities nationwide by some 20–30 percent.

The effectiveness of some regulations is undercut by "risk tradeoffs." Some regulations aimed at reducing a "target" risk inadvertently promote increases in "nontarget" risks.

- Because environmental laws focus on air, water, waste, and workplace pollution separately, in some cases they may only shift pollution from one of these "media" (such as air) to others (such as water or the workplace). Scrubbers to remove sulfur from air emissions, for example, generate sludge that must be disposed of in some other way.

- Ethylene dibromide (EDB), once a widely used pesticide, has been barred because regulators determined that it poses a small cancer risk. Yet this pesticide kills a mold on peanuts that harbors natural aflatoxins. The estimated human cancer risk from the aflatoxin in one peanut putter sandwich is about 75 times greater than a full day's dietary risk from EDB exposure. Focusing on the pesticide's risk alone, instead of on the net risk of the consumed food, may induce a net increase in overall cancer risk.

- Immediate removal of asbestos from schools to protect occupants many years in the future could stir up asbestos fibers that pose an increased risk to both the workers removing the material and the children occupying the school today.

A different type of "risk tradeoff" occurs when regulation aimed at one risk only causes consumers to switch to riskier products or activities.

- Rules requiring higher gas mileage in cars have saved fuel but encouraged consumers to purchase smaller, lighter vehicles that have higher fatality rates in crashes.

- Laws that place more restrictions on new facilities or products than on old ones create an incentive against innovation, encouraging people to keep existing high-risk plants and products in use longer, with a potential net increase in risk.

221

- Rules requiring parents to purchase separate airplane seats for infants could encourage the parents to travel by car instead, increasing the net risk of injury to the child.

IMPROVING GOVERNMENT EFFORTS TO ADDRESS RISK

By exaggerating some risks and using cumbersome regulatory tools, the current government approach to risk assessment and management provides far less protection of the public and the environment than it could for the resources it expends. The Administration has supported several efforts to improve risk assessment and management. The overriding goal is to save more lives and better protect the environment by improving our ability to identify the most important risks and to reduce them cost-effectively.

First, the Administration has sought to disentangle the scientific role of risk assessment from the policy role of risk management. In 1992 the EPA issued new "Risk Characterization" guidelines requiring that all assumptions and methods embedded in risk assessments be disclosed in full. These guidelines are a positive step toward credible and accurate risk assessment that should be forcefully implemented. Risk assessments need to examine not extreme hypothetical cases but the real physiological risks to which real people are exposed. In the case of pesticide residues on food, the EPA has begun to test real supermarket residue levels instead of assuming maximum permitted farm levels. Consideration should be given to creating an independent scientific office to review agency risk assessments, analogous to (but clearly separate from) the review of agency risk management proposals currently conducted by the Office of Management and Budget. Such a review process would improve interagency consistency as well as the accuracy, neutrality, and credibility of risk assessments.

Second, the Administration has emphasized the need to direct society's resources to their best uses. The Administration has insisted on cost-benefit review of regulations under Executive Order 12291, and is strengthening this process via the regulatory reform initiative discussed earlier. These efforts would be enhanced by automatic "sunset" provisions requiring that regulations be reviewed periodically to determine which have outlived their usefulness and can be removed. In 1992 the President extended the cost-benefit analysis requirement to proposals for legislation; surprisingly, agencies had not been routinely evaluating the costs and benefits of their legislative proposals, and the Congress still does not. And the Administration has worked to base legislation, regulations and the federal budget on the principle that priorities address major rather than minor risks.

Further, the problem of "risk tradeoffs" is not insoluble. *Broader and more thorough cost-benefit analyses, taking into account non-target risks, can help identify potential risk tradeoffs.* Cost-benefit analyses should also be performed by experts independent of the regulatory process who are not subject to pressure from affected constituencies. To address the problem of cross-media shifts in pollution, the EPA is now moving toward a more integrated multimedia regulatory approach that addresses air, water, and land pollution in concert. A potential solution to the problem of regulations that disproportionately burden new facilities and products is the use of new source offsets, such as the provisions in the EPA's urban air pollution rules, which allow new sources to operate as long as they obtain emissions reductions at existing plants equal to or larger than the new emissions they would contribute. *More generally, statutes and rules should direct agencies to prevent "unreasonable risk," rather than mandating reductions in narrow categories of risk or use of specific technological fixes.* By incorporating this principle, the Administration's 1992 policy on the oversight of biotechnology products will help ensure that biotechnology is used safely to produce better drugs, better pest control systems, and an improved food supply, without stifling a promising new technology.

SUMMARY

- Facing risks is inevitable, but reducing risk is costly. Some risks can be worth taking because of their significant benefits. Most risks are addressed by human behavior and by market functions such as insurance and compensating risk premiums.
- Government risk assessment activities need to be improved by disclosing embedded assumptions and incorporating more accurate risk assessment methods.
- The government should intervene to address risks when the benefits of government action exceed the costs. Government risk management policies should employ cost-effective incentive-based tools and should account for risk tradeoffs that may undermine the effectiveness of policy efforts.

CONCLUSION

Millions of complex economic decisions are made every day: How many soybeans should be produced, and how many ball bearings? How much labor and how much equipment should be used to produce these products? How much should a person be paid for a given job? The U.S. economy relies on the market system for answers to these questions. Markets constitute an extraordinarily effective system for processing information on consumer demand, the scarcity of resources, and methods of production. The market

223

system also allows people to make free economic choices. At times, however, markets may not perform well because of externalities, failures in the availability of information, or because they are inclined toward natural monopoly. While government intervention in such markets may be justified in these limited cases, government attempts to improve performance in these markets can create unintended consequences. Government regulation should be undertaken only when there is a strong presumption that the benefits from intervention exceed the costs, taking into account hidden costs such as forgone innovation. This analysis should be conducted with the understanding that regulation itself is imperfect and can reduce the ability of firms to respond to changing conditions, including new technologies. It is also important to recognize that government regulation of risk is only one among many risk management systems, including norms of behavior, insurance, the marketplace itself, and the tort system.

The President's regulatory reform initiative has established a governmentwide review of regulatory policy to ensure that existing regulations are necessary and cost-effective. Market incentives are now being used to achieve regulatory objectives such as pollution control and more efficient energy markets. Reform of telecommunications regulation is benefiting consumers by lowering prices for communications services and encouraging service innovations. Similarly, in the financial services sector, regulatory reform has been directed at reducing the cost of risk management and expanding investment opportunities while continuing to preserve investor protection and maintain market integrity. The government can also use market incentives to prevent the overconsumption of natural resources by establishing property rights and by considering all social costs when pricing government-owned resources.

CHAPTER 6

Economic Growth and Future Generations

STRONG AND SUSTAINED economic growth is the key to providing Americans with rising real incomes and the resources to meet their needs, desires, and aspirations. Sustained economic growth will also provide employment opportunities and offer people the dignity and self-respect that come with full participation in the economy.

Over the last century, Americans have achieved a remarkably high average standard of living. This achievement and the high average annual rates of growth needed to attain it must not be taken for granted. Cumulative increases in income are surprisingly sensitive to small differences in the long-term growth rate. For example, in 1870 per capita income in the United States was 15 percent below that of the United Kingdom. For the next 120 years, the average annual growth rate of real per capita income in the United Kingdom was 1.38 percent; in the United States it was 1.86 percent. As a result of this difference, per capita income in the United States is now 50 percent greater than it is in the United Kingdom. Such is the power of compounded growth.

As a consequence of America's economic record, each generation of Americans has started life with the prospect of achieving a higher standard of living than the preceding generation. Real national per capita income today is 15 times greater than it was in 1900. Real national private wealth, a partial measure of the Nation's productive capacity, stands at $70,000 per capita, more than twice what it was at the end of World War II. Increased human and physical capital, improved technology, and a strong market system allow the average worker of the 1990s to produce 6.5 times the real output of a worker in 1900. In the last two decades, however, productivity growth has slowed, raising questions about whether future generations will achieve the same advances in living standards.

Although economic growth is traditionally associated with rising levels of such measures of income and wealth, it is important to recognize its nonmonetary dimensions as well. Significant improvement in such indicators of well-being as health status, environmental quality, and life expectancy have also been recorded. Since 1945 the rate of occupational death has fallen by 70 percent. Changes in lifestyle and developments in health care have increased life expectancy by more than 20 years since 1920—an increase of 40 percent.

While improvements in average income levels do not ensure that all Americans are better off, a wealthier nation has more resources to care for its people and to provide them with opportunities for advancement. As average income has increased over the century, poverty has been reduced significantly. (The record of recent decades was examined in Chapter 4 of last year's *Report*.)

The condition of the Nation's productive resources, both tangible and intangible, will significantly affect living standards in the years ahead. Growth depends on the quantity and quality of the Nation's physical capital; the stock of natural and environmental resources; a military capable of providing for the Nation's defense; creative entrepreneurship; vigorous business, philanthropic, and government institutions; an educational system that prepares children for the challenges ahead; a legal system that protects property rights and resolves disputes in a cost-effective manner; and a national commitment to free enterprise and open world markets that captures the benefits from trade. While some of these factors are already laying a solid foundation for the future, others are badly in need of fundamental reform. America's elementary and secondary schools must be dramatically improved. The legal system needs to provide for more timely and affordable resolution of disputes. The financial system requires major changes to adapt to modern conditions. The tax system is overly complex and impedes economic progress. A central goal of the Administration has been to establish policies across the entire spectrum of economic affairs that address these problems and create an effective framework for continuing growth.

Some critics have expressed concern that economic growth can only be bought at the expense of the quality of the environment. In fact, economic growth has enabled America to devote increased resources to improving environmental quality. As discussed in Chapter 5, it is a myth that environmental regulation is "free" of any cost in terms of nonenvironmental goods and services. Another myth is that economic growth should be suppressed to preserve the world's stock of natural resources. Rather, well-functioning markets see to it that people have appropriate incentives to utilize and preserve such assets.

Current and prospective government policies will have a profound effect on the well-being of future generations. Many critics single out the Federal debt as the primary indicator of the stance of government policy toward future generations. While the Federal debt is an important component of the inheritance received by future generations—and the Administration has advocated significant spending cuts that would greatly reduce or eliminate the future deficits that increase the Federal debt—it is but one of the many channels through which government action will affect the future. Government policies that reduce or improve incentives for entrepreneurship, the quality of the Nation's legal system, the Nation's public infrastructure, and the quality of the educational system can be of even greater importance, yet they are not recorded in measures of the debt or deficit.

The debt and the deficit are imperfect measures, even in their narrow role of reflecting the government's financial liabilities. For example, they fail to account adequately for the future liabilities of government programs, such as future deposit insurance outlays. The debt, while suggestive of the intergenerational transfers caused by the government's financial liabilities, is often a far from precise measure.

Nevertheless, it is generally agreed that current government policies shift more of the financial burden to future generations than did the policies of the past. Government actions are needed to redress this imbalance, especially those encouraging economic growth so that future generations may be more productive.

In this chapter, the diverse resources that lay the foundation for growth are highlighted. The ways in which the financial liabilities of the Federal Government imbedded in its current policies can reduce future living standards are also stressed. Other chapters of this *Report* discuss reforms that could improve the prospects for future growth, as have previous *Reports*. Specific attention is given in this chapter to reforming the Nation's tax system to restore incentives for entrepreneurship, saving, and investment.

EVALUATING GROWTH

In view of the myriad advantages it offers, increased economic growth is obviously desirable. In particular, America needs to pursue every opportunity to obtain the gains that come from removing unnecessary obstacles to growth. Yet increasing future standards of living are often built upon sacrifices of present consumption in favor of investment, and in some instances the costs are borne by present generations and the benefits enjoyed by future generations. A policy that favors growth therefore often involves issues of intergenerational equity. Another problem that must be dealt with is finding ways to quantify standards of living, since the usual measures of income and wealth omit significant aspects of economic growth. A particularly important issue is the effect of economic growth on environmental amenities.

GROWTH AND INTERGENERATIONAL FAIRNESS

Productive investments in institutions, technology, and human and physical capital contribute to growth. The resources required for these investments are generally the result of reduced current consumption, obtained typically when people save and invest voluntarily out of a desire to increase their own or their children's income. Short-term growth can also be attained by forcing current generations to sacrifice so that future generations may be better off. Conversely, growth can be reduced when the capital stock is run down or when governments borrow from future generations to increase consumption today.

From an ethical or philosophical viewpoint, this intergenerational redistribution, which increases the well-being of one generation at the expense of another, may or may not be "just." Some argue that because future generations are not represented in the political process, government actions that reduce their well-being are inherently unfair. The national debt, a liability passed on to the future, is sometimes cited as indicative of a government financial policy that is "unjust" in this sense.

Future generations, however, benefit from many other private and governmental activities. They inherit stocks of private and public capital, technology, knowledge, and institutions. Government activities such as publicly supported schools and financial aid programs represent transfers from older to younger generations. And today's government-assisted scientific research often provides benefits to future generations, as well as current generations.

As a result of the growing stock of assets, Americans on average are likely to be better off in the future than they are today. If per capita income in the United States continues to grow at its historical rate, in 40 years the average American will have a real income that is twice the current level. Some might argue that as a result of this rising income, it is proper for the government to redistribute income from future generations to the current generation. This redistribution would not be unlike the redistribution government undertakes within a generation from the rich to the poor.

Others desire to increase the ability of future generations to achieve the same relative increases in living standards as have past generations. Few people, however, believe that ever-higher economic growth rates are worthwhile regardless of cost. Furthermore, even if such increases were desirable, sacrifice alone would not ensure rapid growth. In the 1930s, the Soviet Union directed massive amounts of resources away from consumption and into investment, but the investments were so poorly managed that this sacrifice went largely unrewarded. Indeed, the collapse of communism in Eastern Europe and the former Soviet Union is in large part the result of the failure of that economic system to raise living standards substantially.

Some long-standing government policies inadvertently create incentives that reduce the rate of saving and reduce growth. For example, compared with alternative forms of taxation, the current income tax system discourages saving in favor of current consumption. These policies impede the ability of current generations to save and invest and hamper efforts to improve living standards. Identifying and correcting such policies can result in improvements in the well-being of both current and future generations of Americans.

WHAT IS ECONOMIC GROWTH?

Quantifying economic growth ideally requires capturing many aspects of economic well-being, not just those reflected in statistical measures such as wages, gross domestic product (GDP), or the value of the physical capital stock. These statistics generally fail to include goods and activities that are not valued in the marketplace—for example, the expected future return on advances in knowledge, the quality of the environment, work in the home, or leisure time. Nor are activities in the "underground economy" captured.

Problems emerge even in measuring increases in marketed goods and services. Typically, measures of these quantities use an inflation-adjusted dollar volume of transactions. But separating the effect of inflation from the effect of changes in the quality of goods and services is difficult. For example, as discussed in Chapter 4, much of the increase in the price of health care since 1950 represents improvements in the quality of care, rather than true inflation. Furthermore, many goods and services were simply unavailable in 1950—for example, personal computers and automatic teller machines. One study estimates that the annual real growth rate in the U.S. economy may have been underestimated by as much as 1 percentage point since 1979, or about 50 percent of the reported growth in real GDP over this period, due to the failure to account fully for improvements in the quality of marketed goods and services.

Choosing a useful summary indicator presents another difficulty in measuring growth in living standards. Such an indicator can focus on growth in income or on growth in consumption, for example. Fundamentally, living standards depend on consumption, but consumption can grow over short periods independent of the income-producing capacity of a nation if the saving rate falls or if investment is insufficient to prevent the capital stock from diminishing.

As a result of the many possible differences between statistical indicators and actual living standards, changes in measures such as income, hourly compensation, or the value of the physical capital stock may understate or overstate actual changes in well-being. These problems have long been recognized, however, and measurement techniques continue to be improved.

To begin tracking the use of natural resources, for example, the Department of Commerce is developing supplementary accounts to the national income accounts. It is likely that building valuations of natural resource use into these measures of net output would change their reported levels only slightly in industrialized countries. For some developing countries, in contrast, where the sale of raw materials derived from natural resources tends to be a much larger share of output than in the United States, consideration of the depletion of environmental assets in net output could substantially reduce reported growth.

Simple comparisons are often made between the growth rates of different countries, but these calculations cannot be used to compare absolute levels of economic performance since a country may have a higher growth rate but a lower living standard. For instance, some economies that faced obstacles to growth two or three decades ago, such as South Korea, now have high growth rates, but their living standards remain far behind those of Western Europe and North America. Per capita growth rates indicate that living standards are rising, but these rates do not measure the level of living standards.

ECONOMIC GROWTH AND THE ENVIRONMENT

Economic growth should be properly understood to mean not just "more" but "better." Living standards rise not just because people consume more goods and services, but because the quality of those goods and services improves. This includes the services of a healthful environment. The innovations in technology that accompany economic growth allow resources to be used more efficiently and sometimes even decrease the actual amounts of resources consumed.

Nor need economic growth be associated with increased pollution. As incomes rise, people tend to increase their demand for the services of a beautiful and healthful environment. It is in poorer countries that daily survival depends on current consumption and preempts spending on long-term concerns, such as environmental goals. Evidence shows that as per capita incomes rise above a threshold (less than one-third of today's per capita GDP in the United States), levels of key air pollutants decline steadily. Similarly, disease carried by polluted drinking water—perhaps the greatest environmental threat to health worldwide—is lower in high-income areas. Rising national income is associated with a "demographic transition"—improved education, higher levels of labor force participation, and lower infant mortality—which historically has reduced desired family size and slowed population growth. In short, higher national incomes are associated with longer and healthier lives.

As this country has grown economically, it has devoted an increasing share of national income to environmental protection: 0.9 percent of GDP in 1972, 1.9 percent in 1987, and projected to increase to 2.6 percent by 2000. At the same time, the U.S. environment has become much cleaner: between 1970 and 1989, levels of particulates fell 61 percent, sulfur oxides 26 percent, carbon monoxide 40 percent, and organic air pollutants 31 percent. Emissions of lead and industrial water pollutants both fell over 90 percent. Regrettably, U.S. environmental regulation has too often relied on "command-and-control" rules that have raised the costs of achieving these gains (Chapter 5).

To characterize economic progress consistent with environmental concerns, some have advocated the concept of "sustainable development," yet a clear definition of this concept has been elusive. To some, "sustainable development" means that each generation should pass on to future generations an undiminished stock of natural resources. But such a definition fails to take into account the fact that each generation passes on many other valuable assets, notably advances in knowledge and technology. A reduction in the stock of one set of resources can easily be worthwhile—for future as well as present generations—if it generates more valuable increases in another set of resources. For example, future generations could benefit if part of a forest is harvested to build a school, yet they might be harmed if the school were built with the last remaining ancient forest.

A better definition of sustainable development is growth in which every generation passes on a stock of "net resources" no lower in per capita value than the stock it received—including natural and environmental resources as well as knowledge, technology, and physical and human capital (Box 6-1). Economic growth, properly understood, includes all of these resources.

SUMMARY

- Choices made by families, businesses, and the government affect economic growth and thus the amount of wealth transferred to future generations. While some decisions may reduce transfers to future generations, those generations are still likely to be significantly better off because of overall economic growth.

Box 6-1.—Global Climate Change and Future Generations

Could change on a global scale turn the world upside down? Some fear global climate change, others the suffering and conflict borne of poverty. In a world with limited resources, people must consider the cost (in terms of other valuable activities forgone) of reducing each risk.

The Intergovernmental Panel on Climate Change estimates that if the preindustrial level of greenhouse gases in the atmosphere is doubled by 2025, the Earth's surface would be expected to warm from 1.5°–4.5° C above today's average temperature by 2100. This scenario is far from certain, and scientists continue to study how much the climate may change, how quickly, and in what geographic patterns.

Taking into account the effects on agriculture, ecosystems, and other factors, economists have generated rough estimates of the damage that can be expected from such global climate change. Under the warming scenario laid out above, they estimate that global living standards in 2100 would be about 1 to 2 percent lower than otherwise expected. One study estimates that additional warming could raise this loss estimate to 6 percent or more by 2300.

This potential damage must be weighed against the costs of preventing global warming. Economists estimate that limiting greenhouse gas emissions enough to prevent the predicted warming—an action that would necessitate sharp emissions restrictions, especially painful in the developing world—would reduce world income by about 2 to 3 percent in 2100. Hence drastic restraint on emissions might cost future generations more (in deprivation) than it helps (in protection from warming).

Just as the predictions of physical science concerning climate change are uncertain, so are the economic estimates of losses stemming from global warming. These costs and uncertainties make policy decisions difficult. The best approach may be to take low-cost actions to limit emissions now and to pursue research aggressively. At current emissions rates, waiting 10 years to take more costly actions would raise predicted warming only slightly; but the advances in knowledge from research in that time could substantially reduce uncertainties and help identify the best response strategies. Thus, the United States has assembled a national action plan of low cost actions to limit emissions, and funds $1.4 billion annually in research on global change (more than the rest of the world combined).

- Sustained economic growth leads to substantial improvements in living standards over time.
- Growth, broadly defined, includes non-monetary concepts like the quality of leisure time and services from environmental and government assets, which are not yet fully reflected in the national income accounts.

THE PRODUCTIVE CAPACITY OF THE U.S. ECONOMY

The capacity of the U.S. economy to generate higher living standards encompasses the stocks of physical and human capital, technology, social and economic institutions, and natural resources. These economic resources, united by individuals willing to take entrepreneurial risks, operate together within a market economy to create innovative new products and processes to meet the demands of consumers and producers. Expanding America's productive capacity, in part by maintaining high output, is fundamental to long-term growth.

THE PHYSICAL CAPITAL STOCK

Perhaps the most commonly cited measure of the economy's productive capacity is the domestic stock of physical capital, which consists of equipment, buildings, inventories, and infrastructure located in the United States. Most of the domestic capital stock is privately owned, but a substantial portion is owned by Federal, State, and local governments. While the Federal government owns most defense-related capital, nearly 85 percent of nonmilitary government capital belongs to State and local governments, including airports, roads, and school facilities.

Since 1950, total physical capital per worker has grown at an annual rate of 1.6 percent (Chart 6-1). Growth in capital per worker is, over long periods of time, closely associated with labor productivity growth. From 1959 to 1973, for example, capital per worker grew by 2.0 percent per year, while estimated overall labor productivity (GDP per hour) grew by 2.8 percent annually. The end of the post-World War II period of very rapid labor productivity growth is often dated as 1973. From 1974 to 1991, capital per worker grew by 0.6 percent and productivity grew by 1.0 percent per year. While a variety of factors may be responsible for this reported slackening in productivity growth, including the difficulty of properly accounting for quality changes mentioned earlier, the slowdown in capital formation is likely to be an important factor.

The Nation's capital stock is augmented by the investments individuals, businesses, and governments make when, for example, they put in place new buildings and equipment. The capital stock

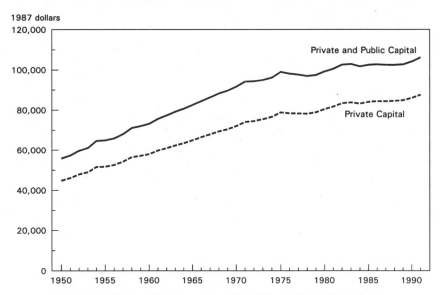

Note: Private and public capital stocks are net of depreciation. Public capital stock excludes military capital.
Sources: Department of Commerce and Department of Labor.

is increased during the year by such new investment—referred to as "gross" investment—and is diminished by wear-and-tear and obsolescence, or "capital consumption" (more popularly known as depreciation). Net investment—gross investment less depreciation—is the resulting change in the capital stock.

Although net investment measures the change in the capital stock, gross investment may have a separate effect that improves the quality of the capital stock. High rates of investment in physical capital may contribute to high rates of economic growth via "learning-by-doing" and "embodiment" effects. Learning-by-doing occurs when the process of investing in physical capital results in innovative techniques (such as new production processes) and products. The embodiment hypothesis states that new technology is generally incorporated into physical capital before it augments productivity. For example, the advance in the technology of recording music on compact discs requires new investment in compact disc players. Through these two effects, the rate of investment can compound the rate of technological change.

New capital investment is financed out of savings. Saving provides not only a source of funds for investment but assets for future consumption—for example, during retirement. Each year, families decide how much of their income to consume and how much to save, taking into account personal circumstances such as expected future wages and potential college expenses. Saving decisions are also influenced by government tax and transfer policies.

The domestic saving rate is simply the percentage of national income saved. It need not equal the domestic investment rate, although historically the two have been closely linked. Domestic investment may exceed domestic saving because of net foreign investment in the United States. Conversely, if U.S. saving used to finance investment overseas exceeds inflows of foreign investment from abroad, domestic investment will be less than domestic saving.

In an economy with well-functioning financial markets, households or firms that wish to save but have no productive investment opportunities of their own use banks and other financial intermediaries to invest their savings. Competition provides an incentive for intermediaries to invest in projects offering the highest rate of return for a given amount of risk.

MARKETABLE WEALTH

The physical capital stock is only one element of the Nation's productive capacity. Businesses also correctly regard as investment their expenditures on research and product development, advertising, specialized training for employees, and numerous other activities. The results of such forms of investment are sometimes called "intangible capital." Productive capacity also depends importantly on the manner in which the physical, intangible, and human capital are organized.

Under customary accounting practices, firms generally value their assets at "book" value, which is determined primarily by the purchase price of their assets less depreciation. The Department of Commerce values capital using what might be referred to as "adjusted book value," which reflects the current dollar cost of replacing existing assets. The Commerce Department measure of capital improves on standard book value by accounting for factors such as inflation, but it does share one shortcoming with book value in that it measures the cost of capital inputs rather than their anticipated productivity. This shortcoming is particularly important when major events, such as an unexpected and sustained increase in oil prices, render some past investment obsolete almost overnight.

An alternative measure of the productive capacity of assets is their market value. Market value reveals the earnings potential of a collection of assets as reflected in the prices investors would be willing to pay today to obtain them. The market value of a department store, for example, may be less than its book value (e.g., the

235

cost of its inventories on the shelves and its building less an allowance for depreciation) if a relocated highway has diminished its customer base. Conversely, the market value of a software company that develops a new word-processing program is likely to be much greater than the book value of the firm's tangible assets, which may consist only of a few computers. Market value also includes the value of intangible capital, much of which is omitted from conventional book value measures.

The market value of privately owned assets, or "private marketable wealth," reflects investors' current estimates of the value of these assets. It is forward looking, incorporating beliefs about the future demand for the products these assets will produce and the effects of current and future expected technological changes.

The Federal Reserve maintains statistics that allow calculation of an approximation to aggregate private marketable wealth of U.S. residents, using market prices for corporate stocks and land. Commerce Department adjusted book value data are used for noncorporate businesses, owner-occupied housing, and consumer durables, because current market prices for these assets are more difficult to obtain. Debt securities are valued at their issue value.

Chart 6-2 shows the growth of two measures of per capita private marketable wealth, derived from the Federal Reserve statistics: "household wealth" (the total wealth of U.S. residents, including wealth owned indirectly through pension plans, insurance policies, and the like) and "national private wealth" (household wealth less the value of net government debt). Because government debt can be viewed as a liability all Americans share, national private wealth may give a better measure of the net private wealth of Americans, although it ignores the value of government assets. By either measure, per capita wealth has increased significantly since 1960, reflecting both physical accumulation and technological gains.

The average annual rate of increase of real national private wealth per capita has been 1.8 percent since 1960. Fluctuations around this trend are the result of changes in both the rate of investment and the market's perception of asset values. Both measures indicate that marketable wealth declined significantly between 1989 and 1990, primarily due to falling land prices. By the end of 1991, however, private marketable wealth was again rising.

HUMAN CAPITAL

The stock of human capital is the total earnings capacity of the Nation's work force, given the available stock of physical capital, natural resources, and market institutions. Human capital in the United States has been estimated to exceed substantially the value of all other private wealth. Increases in human capital can also di-

236

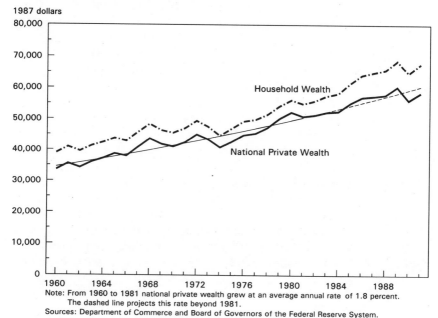

Chart 6-2 **Household and National Private Wealth Per Capita**

Household wealth is the value of all household assets less liabilities. National private wealth is household wealth less net government debt.

Note: From 1960 to 1981 national private wealth grew at an average annual rate of 1.8 percent. The dashed line projects this rate beyond 1981.

Sources: Department of Commerce and Board of Governors of the Federal Reserve System.

rectly increase growth in the economy in two ways—by providing more workers and by raising the knowledge and skills of the labor force.

The Size of the Labor Force

The American labor force has changed markedly over the past four decades in terms of size, composition, and skill level. The labor force has grown as the postwar baby boomers have matured and an increasing proportion of women have entered the workplace. (People who do unpaid work at home are not included in measures of the labor force.) In July 1992 more than 58 percent of working-age American women were participating in the labor market, compared with fewer than 34 percent in 1950. In addition, a growing number of immigrants have entered the labor force. The absolute increase in immigration during the 1980s was greater than it had been in any decade since the early 1900s; the annual rate of immigration, however, as a share of the total U.S. population, was only about one-fourth of 1 percent. These increases in the size of the labor force have led to increases in total output.

Experience, Education, and Earnings

The level of human capital depends not only on the size of the labor force but also on its education and experience. Improvements in the skills of the labor force directly raise productivity and living standards. Investing in human capital, like investing in physical capital, means spending money up front—in the form of tuition and earnings forgone during school or in training—in order to earn a return in the future (Box 6-2). Estimates suggest that an additional year of schooling increases wages by about 10 percent, on average. Additional years of on-the-job experience also yield higher future wages, although at a decreasing rate. The payoffs for education and on-the-job experience change over time. In the 1980s workers with high levels of education and experience earned even larger returns from these investments in human capital than they had previously.

Improvements in the skill level of the U.S. labor force over this century have been dramatic. In 1910 the typical American worker had completed only about 8 years of schooling and fewer than 5 percent of Americans had completed college. By 1990 the typical worker had completed almost 13 years of schooling, and more than one-fifth of all Americans aged 25–29 had completed 4 or more years of college.

These increases in education have generated returns in the form of higher wages. The average real hourly compensation of workers in the U.S. economy has increased about 70 percent since 1959, the earliest year for which the latest revision of these data are available. The rate of growth in real hourly compensation has slowed in recent decades, perhaps in part because of the rapid increase in the number of new entrants into the labor force caused by the baby boomers and the rising labor force participation rates of women. Real hourly compensation increased by only 4.2 percent between 1980 and 1991. (More detailed analysis of these changes in earnings was provided in Chapter 3 of the 1992 *Report.*)

TECHNOLOGY

Technological change is a very important factor in explaining economic growth. Developments in one field often revolutionize production processes in others. For example, advances in computer engineering have enabled the world's automobile manufacturers to transform their production processes with robotics. In the not-too-distant future, advances in chemical engineering may lead to other breakthroughs in the automobile industry, such as new batteries capable of powering electric cars. The production process itself has shifted from large inventories to just-in-time delivery systems. The process of producing a car today is quite different from that of 30 years ago, let alone that used in the first decade of this century.

Box 6–2.—Gary Becker

Gary Becker, winner of the 1992 Nobel Memorial Prize for economics, has devoted much of his career to the study of the labor force. His research has covered a wide variety of subjects and includes pioneering work on the economic returns to investment in human capital, the differences in earnings attributable to racial discrimination, and the determinants of fertility. He has also examined other aspects of human behavior, including the economics of crime and punishment, divorce, and addictive behavior. His application of economic analysis to such nontraditional areas has led to the establishment of entirely new fields of economic research that both Becker and the many scholars who have followed his lead continue to pursue.

Becker has made fundamental contributions to the theory of human capital. In his 1964 book, *Human Capital*, he developed a theory of on-the-job training that helps explain why earnings rise with experience. He drew a distinction between "general" skills that workers can take with them when they leave a particular job and skills useful only in a specialized setting. He argues that employers will provide workers with training in general skills only if the workers pay for that training themselves.

To pay for these skills, workers would have to accept lower-than-normal wages in their early years on a job. Once they had completed their training, however, their wages would rise to reflect their new skills. From then on, they would receive wages greater than those of workers who did not have their training.

Becker also argues that schooling is just a special form of general training. Students in school pay tuition and forgo earning wages while investing in general skills. After they complete school, they receive higher wages than those who did not attend. Becker estimated a return on college education between 1938 and 1961 that was over three times the rate of return on an investment in corporate bonds.

Private and government investments in research and development (R&D) increase the stock of technological knowledge. The growth in private R&D spending has slowed considerably since the mid-1980s. Federal civilian R&D spending has increased over this period, although government spending for defense-related research has declined somewhat. These R&D expenditures provide only a rough indication of the value of the technologies that emerge from them. Because much of the stock of technological knowledge is embodied in human, organizational, and physical capital, it is difficult to value it separately.

ORGANIZATIONAL CAPITAL AND MARKET INSTITUTIONS

The growth rate of an economy depends also on the way its human and physical capital is organized. In an economy characterized by a set of well-functioning markets, investors have an incentive to direct funds to their most valued use. In contrast, in the absence of markets, there are no prices to signal where investment returns are greatest.

Government can assist the functioning of markets by creating a legal system that protects property rights. In economies with ill-defined property rights, investors are often unwilling to make long-term investments because they may not be able to reap the rewards of their investments. Market performance is also enhanced by a regulatory system that regulates only when necessary and allows businesses to respond in a cost-efficient manner to changing conditions and emerging opportunities (Chapter 5). A tax system that does not hinder entrepreneurship or impede the ability of families to work and save provides a setting conducive to economic growth.

NATURAL RESOURCES

This country has great wealth in the form of environmental and natural resources. These natural resources—air, water, land, minerals, and living organisms—provide a variety of services that enrich society. Some, such as oil reserves, can be valued using market prices. Others provide valuable services that may not be fully reflected in market prices. For example, a forested area may do more than provide a source of timber for construction; it may anchor land against erosion and flooding, filter rain water bound for rivers, improve soil fertility, and harbor valuable wild plants and animals. Managing forests to maintain a flow of these goods and services can be more valuable than maximizing the production of timber or clearing the land for other uses, although these other actions could seem more profitable if the unpriced services were ignored. Prudent stewardship of the Nation's natural resources will increase wealth today and for future generations, and can reduce the environmental liabilities left to the future (Box 6–3).

Box 6–3.—Superfund Wastes as an Environmental Liability

American industrial activity in the postwar period left significant residual wastes in local disposal sites. In 1978 residents of Love Canal, New York, discovered wastes near their children's playground, prompting enactment of the 1980 "Superfund" law requiring cleanup of all such sites. Cleanups, which require 10 to 15 years per site are slated to continue well after the year 2000.

The risks to health and environment posed by these waste disposal sites are an example of an environmental liability left by previous generations for present and future generations. The Superfund law responds by imposing a financial liability (cleanup costs) today and in the future to reduce this environmental liability. Whether this response makes sense depends on the cost of the cleanup relative to the benefits of reducing these environmental risks.

Today there are about 1,250 sites on the Superfund national priority list, and another 1,000 or more may be added over the next decade. Experts estimate that at current cleanup standards, the total cost for cleaning up 2,000–3,000 sites over the next three decades may amount to $100-$160 billion or more in present value (1992 dollars).

However, the benefits of cleaning up these sites may be lower than originally believed. The Environmental Protection Agency's Science Advisory Board has ranked waste disposal sites among the lowest of major environmental risks. Yet communities tend to fear waste sites and demand top-notch cleanups, in some cases so clean that children could eat the most toxic dirt on the site, even 5 feet below the surface, year round, and suffer no ill effects. Such cleanups involve excavation of contaminated soil and incineration (in someone else's backyard), even though capping and containing wastes on site could often provide the same health protection at substantially lower cost.

While waste sites may represent a significant environmental liability, the cleanup cost liability created by Superfund may be larger still, and is only increased by the high litigation costs of the Superfund process. The costs of cleanup represent financial resources that a community could have spent reducing other environmental risks to the next generation, such as lead poisoning in the inner city, or increasing other economic assets, such as better schools, for the next generation.

LIMITS TO GROWTH?

Some believe that economic growth is ultimately constrained by finite natural resources. This view traces its roots at least as far back as Thomas Malthus, who wrote in 1798 that the population has a natural tendency to grow faster than food production, and hence is constrained by starvation, pestilence, and war. The "limits-to-growth" hypothesis gained new popularity in the 1970s and again in the 1990s, with attendant forecasts of disaster.

The limits-to-growth view, however, neglects the fact that markets induce adjustment to scarcity. When goods, services, or raw materials become scarce, their prices rise, motivating investment in more efficient ways of obtaining and using them or in developing substitutes. Rising energy prices encourage conservation. Rising prices for land encourage improvements in agricultural techniques that increase the output of food per acre. Indeed, contrary to the Malthusian view, world cereal production has actually grown faster than the global population.

Yet when markets do not operate well—or at all—valuable resources can be consumed too rapidly or simply exhausted. Inadequate property rights in water or forest resources, for example, may result in their value to the future being neglected. In such cases, establishing reliable property rights or, where markets are seriously deficient, establishing appropriate fees or regulations that are targeted at the problem constitute the economically sensible approach, rather than misguided attempts to limit economic growth. (See Chapter 5 of the *Report* for a discussion of market-oriented regulatory approaches.)

SUMMARY

- Physical, human, and organizational capital, and the technology that has been incorporated in each of them, determine the Nation's productive capacity and are key contributors to economic growth.
- Total (private plus government-owned) physical capital per worker in the United States has been on a long upward trend, but the rate of increase has slowed since the early 1970s. This slackening of growth is associated with a slowdown in the rate of growth of worker productivity.
- The impact of organizational and technological improvements is captured in part by the marketable private wealth of U.S. residents, a measure of productive capacity that incorporates investors' expectations of the future profitability of businesses. Real national private wealth has shown sustained growth over the post-World War II period, averaging 1.8 percent annually from 1960 to 1991.

- Increases in the skill level of American workers have been another important contributor to growth in the standard of living.
- Properly understood, economic growth is not rigidly constrained by natural resource limits.

BUDGET DEFICITS AND FUTURE GENERATIONS

Americans have become increasingly concerned that the Federal Government is passing on to future generations large and growing liabilities that will reduce their standard of living below what it might otherwise have been. Of the many government activities that may affect future living standards, considerable attention has focused on the Federal debt and the large and persistent Federal budget deficits. Much of this concern is correctly placed: The debt and deficit can affect intergenerational equity and, under certain conditions, can adversely affect the economy's productive capacity. During the last 2 years, the Administration has recommended significant controls on spending that, if enacted, would reduce projected Federal budget deficits to a level roughly half that of fiscal 1992 within several years.

However, the Federal debt and Federal budget deficit represent only two of many factors that will affect future living standards. They are an incomplete measure of the legacy being passed to the future because they deal only with Federal liabilities, but ignore the surpluses traditionally run by State and local governments, private assets, the assets of the Federal, State, and local governments, and the benefits received from economic and social institutions, such as a sound monetary system, international markets open to free trade, and the Nation's educational system. Taking these factors into account can markedly affect any assessment of how much future generations will inherit. For instance, one recent study finds that between 1970 and 1985, the tangible assets of the Federal Government were 20 to 80 percent greater in value than the Federal debt held by the public.

Even in accounting for the Federal Government's liabilities, the debt and the deficit are narrow and imprecise measures. The deficit reported by the government reflects almost entirely current cash outlays and receipts, ignoring the future costs of current commitments. Further, the reported deficit fails to account for the effects of inflation in reducing the burden of outstanding debt and the effects of government spending on productive investments that will generate income or reduce outlays in future years.

Because the Federal debt and the deficit are imperfect measures of the liabilities passed on to the future by government action, it is important to understand what they do and do not reveal. This section examines how the traditional measure of the deficit can be enhanced by taking into consideration the effects of inflation, government investment, future government commitments, and more directly assessing the intergenerational effects of these financial liabilities through generational accounts.

DEFICITS AND THE ECONOMY: SOME BASICS

The government collects revenues from households and corporations through taxes and fees, and spends money on various programs. *The government runs a deficit when it spends more in any given year than it collects in revenues.* In fiscal 1992 the Federal Government ran a deficit of $290 billion. It took in $1.1 trillion (equal to 18.6 percent of GDP) from individual and corporate income taxes, social insurance taxes and contributions, and several other sources, and spent $1.4 trillion (23.5 percent of GDP) on transfer payments, purchases of goods and services, and interest payments.

The deficit is the difference between two very large numbers— total spending and total receipts—each of which significantly influences the economy. For example, attempting to balance the budget, either by raising taxes that seriously distort economic decisions or by cutting productive government investment spending, clearly would have a damaging effect on the economy. The Administration has sought to reorient spending programs toward investment in the future, and has advocated tax reforms to reduce impediments to enterprise and productive investment.

Alternative Deficit Concepts

The deficit is measured in a number of ways. Each method conveys different information about the gap between government spending and revenues.

The Unified Deficit. The difference between all Federal cash outlays and cash receipts is called the unified deficit, and is the measure of the deficit typically referred to in public discussions. *To obtain funds in excess of its revenues, the government must borrow from the public an amount equal to the unified deficit,* which is usually the most prominent concern about deficits. Chart 6-3 shows the unified deficit of the Federal Government from 1950 to 1992, together with projections through 1996. To account for the increasing size of the economy, the deficits are shown as a percentage of GDP. Relatively large deficits developed in the 1970s and have persisted for two decades. In recent years, the unified deficit has been significantly reduced by the large surplus of Social Security tax revenues in excess of payments made to beneficiaries. In 1992, for instance, a $62 billion Social Security surplus reduced the deficit by that amount.

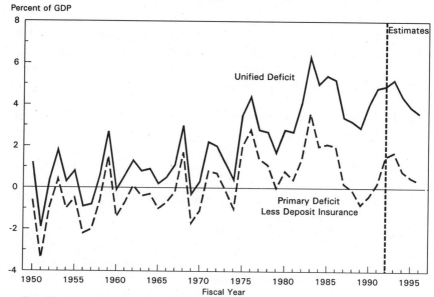

Chart 6-3 **Unified Deficit and Primary Deficit Less Deposit Insurance Payments**
The primary deficit less deposit insurance payments measures whether spending on current programs is covered by current revenues.

Percent of GDP

Fiscal Year

Note: The primary deficit is the unified deficit less net interest.
Sources: Department of Commerce and Office of Management and Budget.

Primary Deficits. The debt held by the public is the accumulation of previous unified deficits. Interest payments on this debt are a current obligation that results from past decisions to borrow from the public. To examine the extent to which current actions, as opposed to past policies, are responsible for the development of the debt, analysts look at a measure called the primary deficit—the unified deficit less net interest on the debt.

Since 1989, the Federal Government has made large payments for deposit insurance to resolve the problems in the savings and loan industry. Like interest on the debt, deposit insurance outlays represent payments for liabilities incurred in the past, so they have also been subtracted from the government's expenditures to derive the series shown in Chart 6-3, which is the primary deficit less deposit insurance payments. According to this measure, the Federal Government's current actions led to surpluses in 19 of the 25 years from 1950 to 1974, but led to deficits in 14 of the 19 years since 1974. Notice also that the government can run a unified deficit and a surplus in the primary budget (net of deposit insurance) at the same time, as it did from 1988 to 1990.

If the government runs a surplus in the primary budget, then current revenues pay for all of the government's current programs and some of the interest on the debt. However, with a primary deficit, the government must borrow to finance all the net interest *and* some portion of its current programs as well.

Structural or Cyclically Adjusted Deficits. Deficits usually increase during business slowdowns, in part because of the so-called automatic stabilizers built into fiscal policy. (Automatic stabilizers are discussed in Chapter 3 of this *Report.*) For example, deficits grew during the economic slowdowns of 1974–75, 1982–83, and 1990–92. In fact, economists agree almost unanimously that deficits *should* increase during and immediately after recessions. Tax revenues decrease when people's earnings drop, while government spending increases as more demands are made on unemployment insurance and other "safety net" programs. Both the reduced receipts and increased outlays partially offset the decline in private spending, helping to make recessions shorter and shallower than they would be otherwise.

The portion of the unified deficit attributable to fluctuations in overall business activity is called the cyclical deficit. Removing this cyclical component results in the cyclically adjusted or structural deficit. By abstracting from imbalances caused by short-term business conditions, the structural deficit can reveal whether a more fundamental imbalance exists between revenues and outlays.

How Big Is the Debt?

The debt held by the public is the sum total of all the outstanding Treasury bills, notes, and bonds, U.S. savings bonds, and other financial obligations of the Federal Government that the Treasury sells to the public. The debt held by the public does not include the $1 trillion in debt held in government trust funds. This debt is owed by the government to itself, so economists generally use the debt held by the public as the economically meaningful measure of the national debt. At the end of 1992, the debt held by the public was just over $3 trillion.

To put this sum into perspective, the debt held by the public is 52 percent of the size of GDP, about average for the industrialized countries in the Organization for Economic Cooperation and Development. The debt is slightly more than twice as large as the government's annual outlays.

The debt-to-GDP ratio fell steadily from 1950 to 1974, but has been increasing steadily since 1982 (Chart 6–4). Projections for the immediate future show the debt-to-GDP ratio increasing slightly. If uncontrolled, growth in entitlement programs, particularly medicare and medicaid, is projected to significantly increase the debt-to-GDP ratio after the turn of the century.

Chart 6-4 Debt Held by the Public as Percent of GDP

Primary budget surpluses and strong growth allowed the debt-to-GDP ratio to fall until 1974, but primary budget deficits have caused it to rise since then.

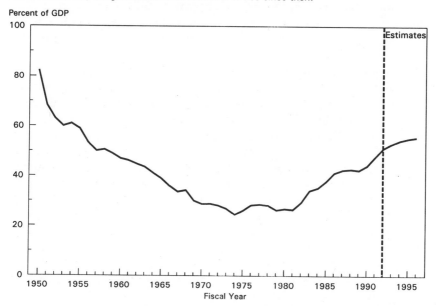

Sources: Department of Commerce and Office of Management and Budget.

If GDP grows faster than the debt, the debt-to-GDP ratio falls, as it did from 1950 to 1974, even though the Federal Government ran a unified deficit for 20 of those 25 years. In 19 of those years, however, the government ran a primary surplus, so current (non-interest) spending was covered by current revenues (Chart 6-3). At the same time, GDP grew faster than interest accumulated on the existing debt, indicating that the government's ability to service the debt grew more rapidly than the cost of debt service. This illustrates the fact that *balancing the budget, in the sense of achieving a zero unified deficit, is not necessarily a prerequisite to reducing the debt-to-GDP ratio.*

How Deficits Can Affect the Economy

Beginning in the 1970s, the Federal Government has been running large unified deficits, regardless of the state of the economy. Such deficit financing can have adverse economic consequences, encouraging consumption at the expense of saving and slowing capital formation.

The question, "What are the economic effects of deficit financing?" can only be answered clearly by comparing deficit financing to some other policy. To examine the implications of deficit financ-

247

ing versus the alternative of raising current taxes, the current level and composition of government spending will be taken as given and fixed.

Because the focus here is on the effect of running deficits from a long-run perspective, questions of the short-run impact of changing policies will be neglected. The general subject of short-run macroeconomic policy has been extensively treated elsewhere in this and previous *Reports*.

To begin exploring the economic effects of deficit financing relative to current taxation, two further simplifying assumptions are helpful: First, the portion of after-tax income that households save in aggregate is largely unaffected by the government's choice between deficit financing and current taxation. Second, the economy is closed to international capital flows, so that investment in the United States is financed entirely by domestic savings. The conclusions of the analysis are sensitive to these assumptions, and alternatives are discussed below.

For example, the government could finance the last $10 billion of its spending by borrowing and running a $10 billion deficit, or it could increase taxes by $10 billion. Under the above assumptions, if the government runs a $10 billion deficit and borrows from the public, this $10 billion of private saving is no longer available to finance the private investments of firms and households.

Alternatively, the government could obtain $10 billion by raising taxes, which would reduce aggregate after-tax income by $10 billion. Households would pay the additional $10 billion in taxes by reducing both current consumption and saving. Because the tax increase, unlike a deficit, absorbs consumption as well as saving, more saving is available to finance private investment.

In this scenario, using deficit financing to support government spending depresses investment more than a tax increase would, causing the Nation's capital stock to increase less than it would if tax revenues had increased. Over time, small reductions in investment rates can leave workers with substantially less capital, reducing productivity and wage growth. However, the economy is not closed to foreign investment and households can change their saving behavior in response to government policy, partially offsetting the adverse consequences of deficit financing on capital formation.

International Capital Flows. International capital markets are becoming increasingly integrated as discussed in Chapter 7. When government borrowing or tax increases reduce the supply of available domestic savings, interest rates in the United States tend to rise. Foreign investors take advantage of the higher yields by investing in U.S. assets, either directly, as when a foreign automobile company builds an assembly plant in the United States, or indirectly, by buying debt issued by the government, or the debt or equity of U.S. firms.

Foreign investment in the United States tends to reduce the effect of the deficit (or a current tax increase) on private domestic investment and the capital stock. Evidence of the importance of this mechanism is provided by national income and product account (NIPA) data, which show a net inflow of foreign capital during most of the 1980s (Chart 6-5). Whether the government chooses deficit or tax finance, foreign investment in the United States adds to the domestic capital stock. American workers are more productive and earn higher wages when foreign capital augments domestic saving.

Chart 6-5   **Net Foreign Investment as Percent of GDP**

Net inflows of foreign capital to the United States between 1982 and 1990 permitted both lower interest rates and more investment than otherwise would have been possible.

Percent of GDP

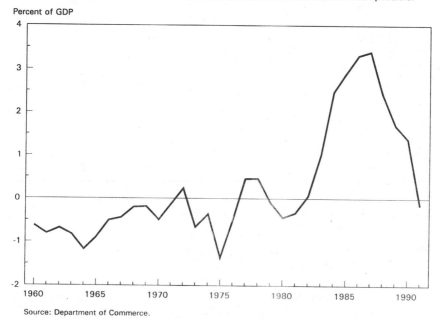

Source: Department of Commerce.

Even with foreign capital inflows, however, future generations are still relatively worse off with deficit than with tax financing if the deficit absorbs more saving than a tax increase would have. With deficit financing, foreigners will own more of the U.S. capital stock than with tax financing, and future generations will have to make larger payments to foreign investors (or, equivalently, will enjoy lower payments from foreign debtors).

249

The Influence of Deficits on Private Saving. The conclusion that national saving falls more with debt financing than it would with a tax increase rests on the assumption that people maintain higher consumption levels under deficit financing. Some economists have argued, however, that taxpayers tend to save a large part, or even all, of the amount by which current taxes are reduced by the choice of deficit finance. Such behavior would occur, for example, if families were to make provision for the future debt service burden on themselves and their children that is implied when the government chooses debt financing. To the extent that such provision is made, the effect of deficit rather than tax financing on national private wealth accumulation (household wealth less government debt) is reduced or eliminated, and future generations inherit approximately the same amount of wealth under either policy.

NIPA data for the period of high deficits during the 1980s suggest, however, that private saving did not increase to offset the deficit. In fact, deficits increased from an average of 1.6 percent of GDP between 1959 and 1981 to an average of 4.4 percent of GDP between 1982 and 1992, but net private saving—gross private saving less depreciation—actually fell as a percent of GDP from an average of 7.8 percent to an average of 3.0 percent over the same periods.

The statistics on national private wealth accumulation appear to present a somewhat different story. Unlike the NIPA statistics, this measure of wealth incorporates increases in the value of shares of corporate stock and land into aggregate saving, reflecting the idea that households assess their economic positions using the market value of their wealth. Since real national private wealth per capita (defined as total household wealth less the Federal debt) continued to grow throughout most of the 1980s, consistent with the trend prior to 1981 (Chart 6-2), one might conclude that the large Federal deficits of the period did not affect the path of wealth accumulation.

Both the simple NIPA and national private wealth statistics, however, can be misleading when viewed in isolation. More detailed studies that account for a number of other factors affecting saving conclude that large deficits may induce somewhat higher private saving. This increased saving, however, does not offset the increased deficits dollar for dollar—national saving declines. Many economists are concerned that the national saving rate is too low, in part due to Federal deficits, and endorse adopting policies to increase the U.S. saving rate.

CORRECTING DEFICITS FOR INFLATION AND GOVERNMENT INVESTMENT

Two improvements to the standard deficit measures have frequently been proposed: correcting for inflation and taking into account government investment activities. These additions result in a more precise measure of the net liabilities incurred by the government each year, although they do not reflect the future costs of new commitments.

Correcting for Inflation

The unified deficit measures the change in the outstanding Federal debt over the course of a year. Because the Federal debt is an obligation to repay fixed dollar amounts in the future, its real value is eroded by inflation (see Chapter 3). The debt burden passed to the future is better measured in real, or inflation-adjusted, terms.

In effect, inflation produces a hidden reduction in the deficit because it reduces the value of the outstanding debt. A concept corresponding to the real debt would be the real deficit—that is, the increase in the real debt during the year. (Note that this is *not* simply the budget deficit expressed in real dollars.) These inflation adjustments would have had a large effect in some years, eliminating more than half of the measured deficit in 1989, for example.

Some have argued that because inflation has reduced or sometimes eliminated real deficits, the need for fiscal restraint in inflationary times has been exaggerated. Most would agree, however, that it would be a mistake to increase government spending or cut taxes for this reason, since this would only add to inflationary pressures.

Government Investment

Like business investments, government investments add to the Nation's capital stock. The text of the Federal budget draws attention to some of the government's investment activities, such as road construction and R&D, but it does not systematically distinguish between investment and consumption expenditures. Separating capital and current expenses is not always easy, however, and for that reason the distinction can be subject to political controversy since special interests may have a stake in whether expenditures are labeled as consumption or investment. The current cash flow accounts, on the other hand, require less in the way of arguable judgments. Several studies show that correcting recent deficits for government investments would have resulted in relatively small changes because of offsetting adjustments for the depreciation of the government's capital assets.

THE FEDERAL DEBT AND FUTURE BUDGETARY PROBLEMS

Starting in the 1970s, budget deficits started to reflect large imbalances between government spending and tax revenues, and have added significantly to the Federal debt. But servicing that debt is only one way in which present and past budgetary choices affect the future budgetary picture. People also expect to receive future payments from a variety of ongoing government programs, such as Social Security and medicare, and they expect the government to continue providing services such as national defense.

Of course, expected future benefits from government programs differ in legal status from the promised future principal and interest payments on government debt. The Congress can change spending programs, such as Social Security, without repudiating explicit promises, but it is legally bound to meet debt service obligations. In fact, however, the government can effectively repudiate a portion of the debt by increasing the inflation rate to reduce the debt's real value, although the adverse reaction of financial markets to such a policy serves as a strong deterrent. Despite these varying degrees of commitment, people reasonably expect a variety of future government benefits.

People not only expect the government to make future payments, they also expect it to collect future revenues. The existing revenue systems, including the personal and corporate income tax and the payroll-based contributions to Social Security and medicare, can be counted on to produce very substantial future cash flows.

Federal Debt as an Indicator of Future Fiscal Challenges

The Federal debt measures the effects of past discrepancies between spending and revenues, but it does not reveal the gap between future spending and revenues. A tax system that generates large revenue increases as income grows, coupled with the anticipation of vigorous economic growth, could result in future surpluses if present policies remain unchanged. Conversely, present policies might imply rapid growth in outlays in the future without specification of how they will be financed.

Because the current Federal debt is the same whether future surpluses or deficits are expected, explicit projections of anticipated future revenues and expenditures are required. In general, the government's spending programs and tax receipts depend on the interaction between existing laws and policies, and the level of economic activity. Combining projections of future laws and policies with projections of economic performance provides an estimate of future government outlays and revenues.

Such projections, in combination with the current level of the Federal debt, would indicate the extent of the future fiscal challenges. A large Federal debt, for example, would be much less worrisome if future projections revealed large budget surpluses. To the extent that projections suggest a future budgetary gap, at some point outlays will have to be reduced or revenues increased. Clearly, enhanced economic growth is the most desirable way to close the gap between expenditures and revenues.

Long-Run Fiscal Projections

Assessing the future budgetary challenge requires making explicit projections of the likely course of policy. The Office of Management and Budget's January 1993 Long-Run Budget Projections show that, through 2030, the government's revenues should remain fairly constant at between 18.5 and 19 percent of GDP (Chart 6-6). Spending is projected to decline from 23.9 percent of GDP in 1993 to 21.2 percent of GDP by 2003, after which it is expected to increase sharply, reaching 31.2 percent of GDP by 2030. These revenue and outlay projections show future deficits, which are projected to fall from 5.4 percent of GDP in 1993 to 2.6 percent of GDP in 2004, and then to rise to 12.1 percent of GDP in 2030.

Chart 6-6 **Long-Run Budget Projections as Percent of GDP**
The Administration's proposal to cap the growth of mandatory spending programs, except Social Security, would balance the budget by 2001 and generate surpluses thereafter.

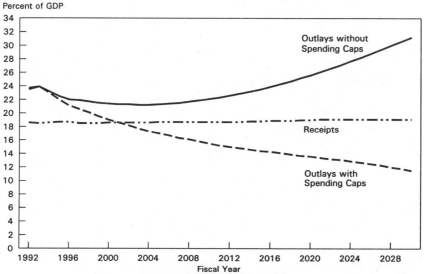

Note: Estimates employ the extended middle path of the Administration's economic forecast. Outlays without caps assume continuation of current services. Outlays with caps assume success in limiting mandatory spending growth to inflation plus beneficiary population growth.
Sources: Council of Economic Advisers and Office of Management and Budget.

The growth in projected total expenditures reflects the explosive growth of so-called "mandatory" spending for three programs—medicare, medicaid, and Social Security—and also the growing

253

annual interest payments on the debt. Combined, medicare and medicaid are projected to grow 6 percentage points faster than inflation from 1992 to 2030. Social Security is projected to grow 3 percentage points faster than inflation. And the rapid accumulation of deficits causes interest payments on the debt to grow 4 percentage points faster than inflation.

To restrain the growth in medicare and medicaid expenses, the Administration proposed the Comprehensive Market-Based Health Care Reforms, discussed in Chapter 4, in combination with a proposal to control mandatory spending. The mandatory spending caps would restrict the growth rate of all mandatory spending programs, including medicare and medicaid, but excluding Social Security, to the percentage increase in the beneficiary population plus an adjustment for inflation, and some spending increases in the first 2 years to facilitate the transition.

Over the 10 years from 1993–2002, the proposed spending caps would reduce projected outlays by a cumulative $1.6 trillion in 1992 dollars (Chart 6–6). The caps would achieve most of these savings by limiting growth in medicare and medicaid spending, and, by reducing deficits, it would also limit the growth in net interest payments. Limiting mandatory spending along these lines would close the projected budgetary gap just after the turn of the century and generate large projected surpluses thereafter.

ACCOUNTING FOR INTERGENERATIONAL TRANSFERS

For many, the most important implication of a deficit is that it may signal a shift of fiscal burdens to future generations. The government influences intergenerational distribution in many ways, sometimes directly, as when local governments construct schools, and sometimes indirectly, as when government social spending programs weaken the stability of families or when tax rules are redesigned to reduce obstacles to innovation. Some programs, such as Social Security, have both direct and indirect consequences. Social Security may directly transfer resources across generations via its tax and benefit policies (Box 6–4), and indirectly influence future well-being through its influence on private saving decisions.

Intergenerational Transfers and the Deficit

Even when considered in terms of the more narrowly defined financial implications of government policies, the deficit can be a misleading measure of intergenerational burden shifting, as the following examples illustrate.

Accounting for a Spending Increase. A policy change that does not affect the budget deficit can still shift large fiscal burdens across generations. For example, a decision to expand medicare benefits to include extended home care services could be financed by an increase in the medicare payroll tax. The budget deficit and

Box 6-4.—Intergenerational Redistribution From Social Security

Under the current method of financing retirement benefits, taxes on workers today are sufficient to pay the benefits of current retirees and to fund a portion of the benefits that will be paid to future retirees. As a result of the maturing of the Social Security system, as well as legislated changes, nearly all researchers conclude that future retirees will have paid much more for a similar level of benefits than current and past retirees.

Chart 6-7 compares the benefits a single wage earner can expect to receive in the first year he or she becomes eligible for full benefits with the accrued value of the combined employer-employee payroll taxes paid over the worker's life. The chart assumes both that the worker earned the average wage each year and that none of the benefits are subject to income tax. As shown in the chart, a retiree in 1972 received about 30 percent of the accrued value of past payroll tax payments in the first year of retirement. Such benefits will continue throughout the worker's life. The corresponding figure for a single worker retiring in 1992 is less than 10 percent. By 2012, benefits received in the first year will represent only about 5 percent of past taxes.

the government debt would be unaffected, but today's senior citizens would receive a significant benefit paid for by younger Americans and future generations. An alternative method of financing increased medicare benefits might be to require upper-income medicare beneficiaries to pay a larger percentage of their own expenses. Such a policy also would not affect the budget deficit, but it would have dramatically different implications for younger Americans and future generations.

Borrowing to Finance Investments for the Future. In some instances, current spending benefits future generations because it finances a valuable investment. Some have argued that the defense buildup of the 1980s should be credited not only with accelerating the end of the Cold War and making the world a safer place, but also with significantly reducing needed outlays on national defense for many years into the future. Similarly, investments such as the construction of the interstate highway system provide future benefits that should be taken into account along with any associated increase in national debt.

These examples point to two distinct problems with using current deficits to assess the effect of policy on intergenerational dis-

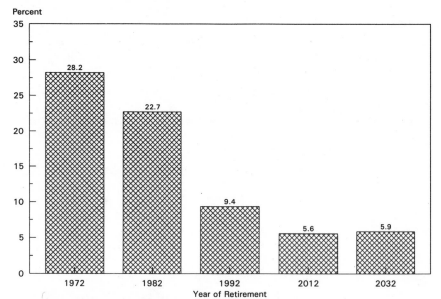

Chart 6-7 **Social Security Benefits as Percent of Payroll Taxes**
Retirement benefits for single workers as a fraction of the accrued value of their lifetime payroll taxes have declined over time.

Percent

Year of Retirement

Note: Data show first-year benefits as percent of accrued taxes paid.
Source: Social Security Administration.

tribution. *Even if the government balanced its budget every year, policy changes could still cause substantial resource transfers across generations. Conversely, if the government finances an investment by borrowing, the benefits future generations receive from the investment may more than offset the added debt burden.*

Generational Accounts

To address the issue of the government's direct influence on the distribution of wealth between generations, researchers have begun to develop "generational accounts" for the United States and other countries. Generational accounts attempt to estimate the likely present value of all taxes paid to all levels of government, less all transfer payments received (from programs such as Social Security, medicare, medicaid, and aid to families with dependent children) from all levels of government, by each generation over its lifetime. The accounts combine the existing debt with projections of the course of future policy to provide an estimate of the burden projected to be placed on existing and future generations by government fiscal policy. The *Budget of the United States Government for Fiscal Year 1993* included for the first time a set of generational accounts for the United States. The *Budget Baselines of January 1993* includes an updated and improved analysis.

To assess the long-term budgetary problem, generational accounts have been used to address the following hypothetical question: How much would the net tax rate (tax payments less transfers as a percentage of lifetime earnings) need to be raised on future generations to close the projected budgetary gap, under the strong assumptions that today's generations share none of the increased burden and existing spending programs remain unchanged? The best estimate is that the net tax rate must be more than doubled for future generations.

Maintaining a constant net tax rate might be considered a rough standard of "fiscal neutrality" across the generations. This exercise, which projects an increase in the fiscal burden on future generations relative to their earning power, supports the prevailing sense that existing policies are placing a growing burden on future generations and gives some idea of the magnitude of the effect.

The *Budget Baselines of January 1993* also includes a discussion of the way certain policy alternatives would affect the estimates. One option is a modified version of the President's proposal to cap mandatory spending that does not produce the large surpluses evident in Chart 6-6. By reducing the growth of transfers, this proposal would raise the net tax rate of existing generations, and comes very close to restoring fiscal neutrality.

Estimates based on generational accounts are inherently subject to a wide margin of error. The analysis depends on a great many assumptions about future policy changes, demography, interest rates, and growth rates, among other things. Additionally, this newly developed approach does not yet take into account the potential effects of different policy choices on the assumed growth rate, so-called dynamic feedback effects, which are clearly of considerable importance.

In using generational accounts, care should be taken to consider a range of alternative assumptions about key factors, rather than relying too heavily on specific estimates. In the case discussed above, varying the key assumptions about interest rates and growth rates within reasonable ranges does not change the qualitative conclusion that *future generations will inherit a large burden if current policies remain unchanged.*

A second general guideline is that generational accounting analysis is likely to be most useful when comparing one specific policy with another. Comparing the effect of adopting mandatory spending caps, for example, with the existing mandatory spending programs indicates how achieving the President's proposed goals would reduce significantly the tendency to pass fiscal burdens to future generations.

Because generational accounts attempt to answer important questions about the effect of fiscal policy on current and future generations, further development of this approach, as well as wider understanding of its strengths and weaknesses, should be very much encouraged.

SUMMARY

- The $3 trillion debt held by the public is a financial obligation that the government has promised to pay in the future. It is one of many long-term obligations of the government.
- The debt and deficits are only one part of the legacy left to the future. They neglect Federal Government assets; Federal, State and local government assets and liabilities; and, most importantly, private assets that will be transferred to future generations.
- A sustained policy of running deficits when the economy is performing relatively well can decrease investment in favor of consumption, which slows capital formation and wealth accumulation.
- Long-run budget projections show deficits declining relative to GDP for about a decade, after which entitlement spending is expected to increase much faster than revenues, threatening resumed increases in the debt-to-GDP ratio.
- The national debt is a proxy for the Federal financial liabilities passed to future generations, but to get a more accurate picture requires taking into account factors such as inflation, government assets, and other government commitments that do not have specified funding sources.
- Generational accounts combine the existing debt with projections of current services to conclude that existing fiscal policies tend to place a larger burden on future generations of Americans than on existing generations.

HIGHLIGHTING THE COST OF GOVERNMENT RETIREMENT AND INSURANCE PROGRAMS

Significant long-term commitments arise from a variety of government programs such as pensions through Social Security and pension guarantee programs, and insurance outlays from deposit and disability insurance. The generational accounts and long-run fiscal projections reflect the liabilities from these programs, but it is useful to examine more closely those programs that will contribute most heavily to the financial burden passed to future generations if current policies continue.

Estimating the size of the liabilities arising from these programs requires a forward-looking measure of program commitments. Currently the Federal budget recognizes payments and receipts for many of these programs only in the year they are made or arrive. For instance, under the current budgetary system, if the government commits itself to pay out $50 million this year and $100 million next year for a certain program and receives $50 million in receipts for this program in both years, it reports a balanced budget this year, simply overlooking next year's anticipated $50 million shortfall. "Accrual accounting" provides an alternative method of calculating liabilities that would reflect projected future shortfalls in the current year. More precisely, the accrual account would show a deficit equal to the amount that would have to be invested today to yield $50 million next year (the "present value" of $50 million).

Accrual accounting procedures have the advantage that they direct attention to fiscal problems as they are developing. For example, in fiscal 1982 the Federal Deposit Insurance Corporation took in $1.4 billion more in deposit insurance premiums than it paid out in payments to depositors, and the unified deficit was $1.4 billion lower in that year as a result. However, one study finds that the projected future losses on developing country loans alone would have resulted in an estimated $10 billion increase in the 1982 unified deficit on an accrual basis, alerting policymakers to the growing deposit insurance liabilities in a much more timely manner.

Progress has been made toward including forward-looking estimates of liabilities in the Budget. An accrual method was adopted for Federal direct lending and credit programs under the Federal Credit Reform Act of 1990. Provision is now made in the budget appropriation process for future losses from new government loans by taking into account the probability that borrowers will default. The Administration also proposed budgeting for government insurance programs on an accrual basis starting in 1993, but this reform was not adopted by the Congress.

In recent years, the Administration also has highlighted the current and expected future costs of Social Security and other retiree annuity and health care programs by presenting projections of future receipts and outlays in text tables in the Federal Budget. These projections assume that currently mandated benefits and earmarked receipts will continue at their present levels. The estimates provide useful information about potential future imbalances, but unlike Federal direct credit and loan guarantee programs, which are treated on an accrual basis, these estimates do not affect the budget appropriations process.

THE SOCIAL SECURITY SYSTEM

The Federal Government has an implicit commitment to workers contributing to Social Security to provide retirement and disability benefits and some hospitalization costs in old age. The specific benefits that workers will receive depend on the Social Security rules in effect at the time benefits are paid. Because the benefits will not be paid until the future, they are not reflected in the current budget or deficit.

The Social Security program has three major components: old age and survivors insurance (OASI), which primarily finances retirement benefits; disability insurance (DI), which makes payments to disabled workers and their families; and hospital insurance (HI), which finances inpatient hospital and other related care for those age 65 and over and the long-term disabled. Tax payments (or "contributions") and benefit payments flow through separate Social Security trust funds for each of these programs (Box 6–5).

Will Social Security Reserves Cover Baby-Boom Retirees?

Until recently, the OASI program operated under a pay-as-you-go method. The retirement benefits of older workers were covered by current workers, who, in their turn, expected to have their retirement benefits covered by future younger workers. As the program matured, this system allowed most retirees to receive benefits that far exceeded the accumulated value of their contributions. Over the past 20 years, the Social Security taxes from approximately 3.7 workers have been used to pay benefits for one OASI beneficiary. Estimates project that by 2030, there will be only 2.3 workers for each beneficiary.

In the early 1980s, the Federal Government recognized that pay-as-you-go funding for OASI would require large future tax increases or large benefit cuts to maintain parity between annual contributions and annual benefit payments. As a result, the government modified the pay-as-you-go policy. Currently, the OASI trust fund collects contributions in excess of current benefit payments and is expected to continue to do so for the next several decades.

The other Social Security trust funds have more immediate cash-flow problems. Because the DI trust fund is expected to be depleted as early as 1997, the trustees have recommended prompt legislation to strengthen the financing of this program. Similar problems with the HI program have led to recommendations that the Congress take appropriate action to control health care costs through specific legislation or as part of more comprehensive health care reform. (See Chapter 4 of this *Report* for a discussion of health care reform.)

Social Security and Saving

Some researchers have suggested that the Social Security program reduces private saving for retirement. Because American workers know that Social Security will provide them with retire-

Box 6–5.—Trust Funds

Many government receipts are from taxes earmarked for specific purposes rather than for general revenues. Some of these dedicated tax receipts are deposited into trust funds which may build up surpluses until they are drawn down by expenditures. For example, the Social Security payroll tax is deposited into three trust funds: the old age survivors insurance trust fund, the disability insurance trust fund, and the hospital insurance trust fund (medicare, part A). Other programs also operate through trust funds. By law, most trust account surpluses must be invested in government securities.

The trust fund device is a source of much confusion in public debate. Occasionally, some have mistakenly viewed the existence of reserves, or an increase in reserves, as an indication that the program financed through the trust fund is financially solvent. Others take the surplus to mean that there are additional resources available to fund other government spending. A positive balance, however, does not indicate that the underlying program is necessarily financially solvent in the long-run. Rather, the programs are required to maintain a positive balance in order to ensure that dedicated revenues are sufficient to meet the payments as they arise. With strict pay-as-you-go financing, dedicated revenues and expenditure levels are adjusted to maintain a small surplus.

For example, in the case of the Social Security trust funds, projecting the exhaustion of reserves does not imply the end of Social Security. Instead, it indicates that adjustments will have to be made, including decreasing projected benefits, increasing Social Security taxes, or using revenues from other sources. Conversely, a current surplus does not indicate that all future payments can be financed from reserves.

In all, there are more than 150 trust funds that held just over $1 trillion in government bonds at the end of fiscal 1992. When these are added to the $3 trillion of government bonds held by the public, the result is a $4 trillion Gross Federal Debt—a number often quoted in the press. For the reasons discussed in this chapter, however, economists and public policy analysts appropriately focus on the debt held by the public.

ment income, their incentive to accumulate private savings may be reduced.

Currently available private saving vehicles offer an incomplete substitute for the type of retirement benefits Social Security provides. In particular, most forms of private saving offer incomplete protection against inflation, while Social Security retirement benefits are indexed for inflation. If the government issued bonds indexed for inflation, private savings plans might be more able to offer inflation-adjusted annuities, allowing a larger share of secure retirement income to be provided by private sources.

GOVERNMENT INSURANCE AND CREDIT PROGRAMS

The Federal Government is the Nation's largest provider of credit and underwriter of risk. Two-fifths of all outstanding private and local government credit has been assisted by the Federal Government. In 1991, 82 percent of the credit for housing was federally assisted. Most credit for agriculture and education is also federally aided. Failures and defaults in these programs, which result in substantial liabilities for the government, have been occurring with increasing frequency.

The government provides insurance for a wide range of activities. By far the largest insurance commitment is held by the Federal Deposit Insurance Corporation (FDIC), which covers deposits up to $100,000 at commercial banks and S&Ls. Other forms of direct government insurance include pension fund insurance, veteran's life insurance, crop insurance, flood insurance, political risk insurance against such losses as expropriation and war damage in foreign countries, and aviation and maritime war risk insurance.

The beneficiaries of these programs cover some of the costs through insurance premiums. However, if premiums are set too low, the government transfers resources from the taxpaying public to the insured group. The difference between the premium payments and the expected losses to the government represents a subsidy to the insured group.

Federal insurance programs have lost substantial sums in the last decade. Estimates of the total bill for the S&L cleanup range from $110 billion to $160 billion in present value (1992 dollars). Indemnity payments made to farmers by the Federal Crop Insurance Corporation exceeded insurance premiums by $2.5 billion over the period 1981–90. High future payouts are also anticipated for programs such as the Pension Benefits Guarantee Corporation (Box 6–6).

As discussed above, the cash outlays of insurance programs do not provide a clear and timely measure of the actual program costs. Insurance programs commit the government to future outlays that are not delimited or estimated when the Congress authorizes the insurance, and the costs are not recorded when they accrue. Instead, the budget records them when they are paid— months, years, or in the case of pension guarantees, even decades later. To correct these problems, the Administration proposed shift-

Box 6–6.—The Growing Liabilities of the Pension Benefit Guarantee Corporation

When Pan American World Airlines entered into bankruptcy proceedings in January 1991, among its debts was the money required to fund pension benefits for its workers. Pan Am's pension commitments exceeded the funds the company had accumulated for benefit payments by over $900 million. The Federal Government, which guaranteed the pensions, suffered a loss estimated at between $500 million and $700 million when the plan was terminated. Unfortunately, Pan Am's experience is representative of a growing number of companies with underfunded pension plans that expose taxpayers to significant losses.

The Federal Government insures many of the pensions of the Nation's work force through the Pension Benefit Guarantee Corporation (PBGC), a Federal agency established in 1974. Private corporations are required to pay a per-participant fee in exchange for the PBGC's guarantee on defined-benefit pension plans—those which promise retirees specific monthly payments. The PBGC insures approximately $900 billion in benefits for 40 million workers. The vast majority of these funds are solvent: The 85,000 insured pension funds have over $1 trillion in assets. Thus, taken as a group, these funds have a surplus.

However, the PBGC, which ran a $2.3 billion deficit in 1991, faces financial difficulty. Costs of future payments are projected to be $40 billion (in present value), offset by expected premiums of only $10 billion (in present value). These projections suggest that the PBGC will be unable to fund this $30 billion shortfall, and a future taxpayer bailout will be necessary if the program is not modified.

The Administration proposed a number of measures to reform the current pension insurance system, including shifting the budget treatment of insurance programs to an accrual basis. The PBGC's position in bankruptcy proceedings would be clarified to allow it better access to a company's assets when it defaults on pension obligations. Further, the PBGC would not be required to guarantee future benefit increases unless a plan is fully funded. Efforts would be made to require companies with underfunded plans to increase funding more quickly, without seriously affecting their operations. Without these changes, troubled companies can continue to promise overly generous benefits knowing that they will not be responsible for repayment if they go out of business.

ing the budgetary treatment of insurance and pension guarantee programs to an accrual basis.

Accounting for these unfunded future liabilities can produce startling results. The Office of Management and Budget estimates that for the PBGC, what appear to be 6 years of small cash surpluses starting in 1993 become 6 years of deficits totaling $18 billion when the anticipated future payments resulting from current commitments are taken into account. For Federal deposit insurance programs over the same period, on a cash basis receipts from the sale of closed banks' assets are expected to lead to future cash inflows, but on an accrual basis deficits appear in most years. Taken together, the total deficit between 1993 and 1998 would be over $78 billion larger if these two programs were budgeted for on an accrual basis.

Measuring the Cost of Implicit Guarantees

The large and rapidly growing government-sponsored enterprises (GSEs) facilitate the provision of various types of credit, including home mortgages, student loans, and agricultural loans. GSEs are privately funded businesses, chartered by the government, that make loans or repackage and sell them. Many investors believe that the GSEs have an implicit guarantee that the government will back these securities in the event of a GSE bankruptcy (see Chapter 5 for a discussion of the housing GSEs). Although the government has no legally binding obligation to make such payments, in the one instance of a GSE insolvency, in 1987, the government stepped in to protect investors by authorizing $4 billion for the ailing Farm Credit System.

Currently the budget does not formally account for potential liabilities arising from the GSEs. This asymmetry in the treatment of GSEs and other government credit programs has been justified by the "private" nature of these enterprises and the fact that currently these enterprises are quite profitable. The high probability of government intervention in the event that circumstances change and a default occurs, however, suggests that neglecting to account for these potentially large obligations could be a costly mistake.

SUMMARY

- Significant long-term commitments are being passed to future generations through a number of government programs. The Federal budget does not report the cost of the commitments entailed in many of these programs until the year payments are actually made.
- The Social Security disability insurance and hospital insurance trust funds are not sufficient to maintain benefit payments at currently legislated levels without reforms to these programs.

The DI trust fund is projected to be depleted by 1997 and the HI trust fund by 2002 if reforms are not implemented.

- Accrual accounting for government insurance programs incorporates the anticipated future costs of commitments made today, providing a long-term view of the true financial implications of these programs.

STRENGTHENING THE FRAMEWORK FOR GROWTH

Current and future generations of Americans have the capacity to achieve great prosperity, but serious attention must be paid to the Nation's institutions in order to ensure this result. Although the real productive capacity of the economy has grown substantially since the end of World War II, productivity growth has slowed significantly in the past two decades. This has raised concerns that the rates of saving and investment are not sufficient to maintain the historic high rate of growth in living standards. The Nation's work force is highly educated, but many people now fear that America's schools are not providing children with the skills they need to compete in the future. The Nation possesses unmatched technological strength, but recent declines in the rate of private R&D investment could reverse this historic advantage. Our Nation is the leader in demonstrating the strengths of a market economy, but unnecessarily costly and inflexible regulatory and legal systems and an overly complex and inefficient tax system have reduced the benefits that the market system could provide. The government's fiscal policies, unless brought under control, will reduce the inheritance that future generations will receive.

While the government is not the most important factor in economic growth, it can affect growth positively by providing an environment conducive to market enterprise. Conversely, it can inhibit growth through burdensome tax and regulatory policies. Efficient, well-functioning markets are essential in order to channel labor, capital, and entrepreneurial effort into their most productive uses.

The Administration's economic policy has aimed at promoting growth through broad-based policies designed to improve the functioning of the market system. The Administration has strongly opposed policies designed to subsidize select industries on the grounds that such policies substitute government intervention for the free-market incentives that motivate private businesses to earn profits, workers to seek rewarding employment, and consumers to choose the most desirable and cost-effective products. The energy of the private sector is misdirected when businesses find it easier and more profitable to appeal to the government for special assistance than to improve their performance in the marketplace.

265

GOVERNMENTAL POLICIES TO PROMOTE GROWTH

Government activities that facilitate well-functioning markets range from maintaining a sound monetary system to providing a legal system that supports contracts and private property. These activities are addressed elsewhere in this and previous *Reports*. The ability of government to undertake these activities in a capable manner is critical to promoting growth rather than hindering it. As discussed in Chapter 5, the regulatory system can play an important role in promoting or interfering with the efficient allocation of resources. An open world trading and investment system is also vital to economic growth. The policies of this Administration have been designed to promote the efficient worldwide allocation of resources, as discussed in Chapter 7.

Policies designed to enhance the skills and productivity of the labor force are critical to ensuring that the rising living standards made possible by economic growth are spread throughout the economy. The Administration has supported increased funding for Head Start, a program aimed at developing skills required for learning at an early age; promoting school choice for elementary and secondary education; better access to higher education; and improved job training for labor market entrants and displaced workers.

Crime, drugs, joblessness, and welfare dependency are sapping the strength of America's inner cities. Stemming and reversing these conditions will directly add to America's productive capacity and allow our citizens to share in its benefits. The Administration has actively supported enterprise zone legislation that would offer a variety of tax incentives to stimulate job creation in distressed communities and has supported other reforms to reduce the negative effects of the welfare system on the incentive to work and to save, as well as home ownership opportunities for public housing tenants (these reforms are discussed in Chapter 4 of the 1992 *Report*).

One vital test of a well-functioning market system is its ability to encourage and sustain new and innovative firms. The United States has a tremendous number of successful startup firms. The government must ensure that regulations do not inhibit these developing new businesses, and that the tax system encourages entrepreneurship, saving, and investment. The President's Regulatory Reform Initiative was undertaken to guard against regulations that create more burdens than benefits, particularly for small businesses.

The Federal Government also promotes technological advancement by funding R&D. Additional support for R&D investment is provided through the Tax Code. Historically, investment in R&D has resulted in very high rates of return. Private industry, however, is unable to capture the full benefit of some types of R&D activities because the knowledge gained is quickly disseminated. Consequently, these activities frequently confer significant benefits to the public at large. In these cases, provided the expected benefits of the activities exceed their costs, government support can contribute to economic growth.

Sound policies to protect the environment and manage natural resources can also strengthen the framework for growth, provided their benefits exceed their costs. Careful cost-benefit analysis should be the basis for determining whether an environmental policy will add or subtract to economic growth and future well-being.

TAX STRUCTURE TO PROMOTE GROWTH

A nation's tax system comprises a set of rules that can have important implications for saving, investment, labor supply, occupational choice, innovation, and entrepreneurial endeavors. Eliminating or improving tax rules that impede these essential activities increases the well-being of current and future generations.

Impediments to Growth

The U.S. income tax system has been modified significantly over the past decade, but still contains a number of obstacles that impede economic growth. The current tax system shares one weakness of all *income* tax systems: it taxes the return to saving—interest, dividends, and capital gains. As a result, people who save pay a tax penalty for saving rather than consuming. For example, a worker who saves regularly pays the same tax on wage, salary, and professional income as an individual paid the same amount who spends everything he earns. In the future, however, the worker who saves must also pay tax on the interest earned on the savings and in the end pays more taxes than the nonsaver, even though both have the same initial earnings. If this double tax on saving reduces savings levels, as most believe it does, then the capital stock grows more slowly. In turn, this acts as a drag on the growth of output and real wages.

Corporate income distributed to shareholders in the form of dividends is also taxed twice, once under the corporate tax and a second time under the personal income tax, while income in the noncorporate sector is taxed only once. This double taxation of corporate income is likely to reduce investment by corporations. The corporate tax also creates financing distortions because corporate debt and equity are treated differently. This disparity affects corporate decisions to raise additional funds through new share issues, retained earnings, or issuance of new debt. Corporate income paid as interest to bondholders is taxable only to the bondholder. Because debt is not burdened with the double tax on corporate

267

income, firms may be encouraged to issue excessive debt that can increase their vulnerability to economic downturns and adversely affect investment decisions.

Because of the economic costs of the corporate tax, some have suggested integrating it with the individual income tax. In December 1992 the Department of the Treasury proposed a sweeping reform of the tax system (*Restructuring the U.S. Tax System for the 21st Century: An Option for Fundamental Reform*) which, among other reforms, eliminates the double taxation of corporate income. Under the Treasury proposal, corporate income distributed as dividends would not be subject to tax at the shareholder level. Shareholders would also be able to reduce their capital gains tax liability by treating retained earnings as additions to the amount they originally paid for their shares.

The present income tax also misallocates capital across the economy, because income earned by different assets is taxed at different rates. This misallocation results in less output from the capital stock than could otherwise be produced. In principle, this misallocation could be eliminated by providing depreciation deductions that reflect the expected decline in the value of business assets. In practice, however, it is quite difficult to measure the rate at which assets depreciate, and in order to prevent excessive complexity, the Tax Code must provide general rules for depreciation that may not adequately distinguish between different types of assets. As a result, the annual deduction provided under the income tax for the cost of a van used by a delivery service is the same if it is driven 1 mile or 100,000 miles. The formula for calculating the van's depreciation deduction is the same for a computer (whether laptop or mainframe) even though the rates at which these assets lose economic value can be very different. While it may be nearly impossible to provide a formula in the Tax Code that correctly accounts for the depreciation of an asset, the inability to account properly for depreciation means that the tax system favors investments in some assets and discourages investment in others. Because investors ultimately seek the investments with the highest after-tax yields, relatively greater investment occurs in assets favored under the Tax Code and too little investment occurs in disfavored investments.

CONSUMPTION TAXES

In recent years, consumption taxes have been discussed as a partial or total replacement for the income tax. The recent Treasury proposal, for example, would partially replace the current income tax with a type of consumption tax. Consumption taxes can take various forms. Under some, tax liability is tied directly to a person's level of consumption. Under others, tax liability may be assessed only on wage, salary, and business income. Despite differences in form, these taxes share one common principle: either they tax income only when it is consumed, so that the tax on income saved is deferred, or they impose no tax on the return to saving. Proponents argue that consumption taxes distribute the tax burden more fairly than income taxes, that they permit vast simplification of tax rules, and that, partly as a result of this simplification, they would lead to a much more efficient allocation of the Nation's resources.

Personal Consumption Taxes

Income taxes in the United States are generally thought to be progressive, while consumption taxes commonly employed, such as State sales taxes and the value-added taxes used by many foreign countries, may not be. *However, consumption taxes can be designed to achieve any desired level of progressivity.*

The individual income tax is progressive because it ties the tax rate to income: The more a person earns, the higher the tax rate. In the same way, a consumption tax is progressive if it is based, at least in part, on total household consumption. A consumption tax of this form is frequently called a personal consumption tax.

One type of personal consumption tax, the consumed income tax, permits taxpayers to deduct net saving from taxable income. In its pure form, this tax would extend the present income tax treatment of pension saving and deductible individual retirement accounts (IRAs) to all forms of saving, with no restrictions on the amount that can be saved and no requirement that the money be used only for retirement. Since the difference between income and saving is consumption, this method effectively taxes households on total annual consumption. The pure form of the consumed income tax would not tax businesses (including corporations) directly, although employers would typically be required to withhold taxes in the same way as they do now.

Unlike sales and value-added taxes that tax consumption proportionately, the consumed income tax can tax high levels of consumption at higher rates, achieving any desired level of progressivity. The double tax on saving under the income tax is eliminated, because income saved is taxed only once—in the year it is consumed. A consumed income tax in its pure form would treat borrowed funds in the same way it would a withdrawal from an IRA and subject the amount to tax. Subsequent repayment of interest and principal would be considered saving and would therefore be deductible. Some versions of consumed income taxes allow the taxpayer to exclude from the tax calculation both the initial borrowing and subsequent repayment.

An alternative method of addressing progressivity through a consumption tax is a two-tiered cash-flow tax that levies taxes at both the individual and the business level. At the individual level, only wages and other compensation are taxed according to a progressive rate schedule. At the business level, both corporate and noncorporate enterprises are taxed at a flat rate on their gross receipts after deducting costs such as materials, capital goods, and labor. Borrowing, lending, and interest paid and received are entirely omitted from the tax calculation at both the business and individual level—a major simplification. By not subjecting business income to a second tax at the individual level, the double taxation of corporate income under the current tax system is eliminated; the business level tax is in place of a direct tax on the owners.

Improved Economic Efficiency Under Consumption Taxes

Advocates of consumption taxes believe that they result in a more efficient allocation of resources than income taxes. With consumption taxes, the government essentially becomes a silent partner in every business, sharing in the costs of the business in the same proportion to which it shares in the earnings. Thus, consumption taxes do not distort relative incentives among alternative investment projects. The market can ensure that investments with the highest expected pretax returns are undertaken, the same as would occur in the absence of taxes.

In contrast, under an income tax, the government shares in the returns of investment projects, but not in the costs of the funds invested. As a result, the income tax creates a bias against investment, favoring current consumption over future consumption.

In addition to the distortion an income tax creates in favor of consumption at the expense of investment, any income tax that is reasonable to administer also is likely to affect the allocation of investment across diverse assets. This occurs when the income tax fails to provide depreciation deductions that accurately correspond to the actual decline in the value of assets. Investment patterns are distorted as investors seek out projects that receive relatively favorable tax treatment and avoid those receiving less favorable treatment. Projects may be attractive only because of the favorable depreciation deductions offered. Other projects that offer higher pretax but lower after-tax returns may be passed over. Because the pretax return measures a project's entire yield, including both the return the investor keeps after taxes are paid and the tax revenues the government collects, projects with the highest pretax returns offer the greatest benefit to the economy as a whole. *Allowing investment to move to its most productive use generates the maximum economic output.* A consumption tax can help allocate investment more efficiently across different activities. A consumption tax also treats debt and equity equally, avoiding the distortions the income tax creates in the choice of the source of financing.

Both forms of consumption taxes provide capital gains income with more favorable treatment than it receives under the current income tax. Under the consumed income tax, income earned on savings is taxed only when it is actually used for consumption, permitting the tax-free rollover of reinvested capital gains. The two-tiered cash-flow tax does not tax capital gains at all at the personal level; at the business level, the government shares in all earnings of the business to the same degree that it shares in the costs of the business.

The income tax affects saving behavior in two ways: It reduces the reward to saving (a substitution effect), which can be thought of as reducing the incentive to save; the tax also reduces lifetime income, and this loss in income can also affect saving (an income effect).

In many cases, however, consumption taxes result in higher rates of saving than an income tax. A consumption tax that generates the same revenue as an income tax can have a similar income effect to that of the income tax, but without the *saving-reducing* substitution effect. It is possible, in theory, for this positive saving response not to occur if labor supply declines under the consumption tax and by enough to offset the substitution effect. Although some people incorrectly believe that the labor supply must fall under a consumption tax, there is no reason to expect such an effect. While the tax rate on income consumed presently may have to be higher than it is under the income tax, those choosing between working more and working less face two tradeoffs: the amount of *present* consumption affordable by working more *and* the amount of *future* consumption affordable by working more. The first tradeoff is likely to be worsened under a consumption tax, but the second tradeoff is improved. The net effect on labor incentives is ambiguous.

The efficiency effects of consumption taxation can be summarized as promoting the efficient allocation of assets in production and reducing the distortion in favor of present consumption relative to future consumption, while its effects on work incentives are ambiguous. Under a range of parameters, researchers find that a consumption tax generates net efficiency gains compared with the present tax system. The advantages of a consumption tax could, of course, be weakened in practice, depending on the extent to which it was complicated by special exemptions and deductions added through the political process.

Improved Fairness and Simplicity

Fairness is inherently difficult to define, but a personal consumption tax can be considered fairer than the income tax for several reasons. First, it does not treat people differently on the basis of when they choose to consume the income they earn. In addition,

271

consumption may be a better measure of people's living standards than current income. When making decisions on major purchases, families may try to estimate their likely earnings and expenses at least several years in advance. As a result, consumption reflects, in part, expected income over an extended period. Consumption may thus provide a more accurate measure of the family's "permanent income" than annual income, which often fluctuates from year to year, depending on personal circumstances. Others believe consumption taxes are fairer because they base tax liability on what people take out of the economy rather than on what they produce. To the extent that it is desirable to have those who consume more pay higher rates of tax, consumption taxes can be made progressive.

Finally, the consumption taxes outlined here could potentially be much simpler than the current income tax. Tax filing under the two-tiered cash-flow tax could be particularly easy for individuals. Tax liability could be determined by subtracting personal exemptions and a standard deduction from compensation and applying the rate structure. Business returns too could be very simple under this form of taxation. Multiyear accounts for depreciation would be eliminated, since all investments are deducted the year they are made. Because tax considerations would be removed from the investment process, business investments could be evaluated more simply.

The abundance of exclusions, adjustments, deductions, and credits under the current income tax creates complexity, increases paperwork, and interferes with economic decisions. One estimate suggests that Americans spend $75 billion annually in direct costs and lost time associated with complying with the U.S. tax system. Reducing the needless complexity of the current tax system can only help the economy.

IMPROVING THE INCOME TAX

Although replacing the income tax with some form of consumption tax has received much support, the current tax system can be reformed to eliminate or reduce aspects that inhibit growth. Among these modifications are cutting the tax rate on saving and entrepreneurship, in particular by reducing capital gains taxes, depreciation reform, and eliminating the double taxation of corporate earnings by integrating the corporate and individual income tax systems. The 1992 Treasury proposal for fundamental reform of the tax system embraces a number of changes to reduce the tax rate on saving.

Removing the Tax Penalty on Saving

Reducing the tax rate on saving would make the income tax more like a consumption tax. As discussed above, many forms of retirement saving already receive the kind of treatment accorded to all saving under a consumption tax. Reducing capital gains tax rates would also increase the return to saving and encourage entrepreneurial activity. Much of the return from the startup of new ventures lies in the increasing value of a business, which is taxed as capital gain. Furthermore, because capital gains are taxed only when an asset is sold, high capital gains tax rates discourage such sales. Investors are locked into current investments, including entrepreneurs who might be willing to sell previously successful startup enterprises to fund new ventures. As a result, the capital gains tax is likely to raise little revenue relative to the costs it imposes on the economy. Further, capital gains are overstated due to inflation. Modification of the income tax system to provide for the indexation of capital gains income for inflation would be a worthwhile reform in itself (Box 6–7). Adjusting debt for inflation might also reduce incentives for excessive debt financing.

Reducing Biases in Business Taxation

In a vibrant economy, business activity takes many forms. It is conducted by corporations, partnerships, and people working on their own. *But however business is conducted, all business income is ultimately earned by people and all taxes are ultimately paid by people, whether in their role as workers, consumers, or investors.*

The tax system should not hinder the diversity of business activity. In many cases, individuals and small businesses are best suited to foster entrepreneurial innovation—for example, small firms now comprise more than 90 percent of high-technology businesses. In other cases, large corporations may be the most efficient means of conducting business.

The U.S. tax system can influence business activity in many ways. Small businesses may face enormous difficulty in complying with complex tax rules, such as those governing pension benefits. The cost of complying with tax rules is in many cases a fixed cost that exacts a higher share of revenues from small businesses than from large businesses. The asymmetric treatment of profitable and unprofitable firms under the Tax Code, which limits the ability of firms with operating losses to receive tax refunds or carry these losses forward with interest, may deter investment and, in particular, limit entrepreneurial activity and new business formation, since new businesses often incur losses in their initial startup phase.

Integrating the corporate and individual income tax systems could eliminate many of these distortions. Other reforms of business taxation that could be implemented immediately include providing depreciation deductions at replacement cost to reflect the effect of inflation and repealing the alternative minimum tax (Box 6–8).

Box 6-7.—Inflation and Capital Gains

The fact that capital gains are overstated due to inflation is one reason that they were taxed at a lower rate than other income prior to the 1986 Tax Reform Act. The effect of inflation can also be accounted for directly by indexing for inflation the purchase price of an asset that is used to calculate capital gains. Currently inflation adjustments are provided elsewhere in the Tax Code—for instance, personal exemptions, standard deductions, and tax brackets are all indexed for inflation.

The overstatement of income earned from capital gains that results from inflation can be explained through the following example. Consider an investor who bought a share of stock for $100 in 1980 and who sold the stock for $175 in 1992. Under current law, the investor is taxed on a nominal capital gain of $75, the difference between the sale price and the purchase price. An investor in the 28-percent tax bracket would pay $21 in taxes on this gain.

Because of inflation since 1980, it would take roughly $170 in 1992 to purchase the same quantity of consumer goods that $100 bought in 1980. As a result, the additional purchasing power the investor has earned from this investment is only $5, the difference between the sale price and the inflation-adjusted purchase price of the stock.

Under current law, the investor in the 28-percent tax bracket pays $21 in taxes on a $5 real capital gain, an effective tax rate of over 400 percent. If only real capital gains were taxed, the investor would pay $1.40 in taxes on the $5 of real capital gain earned on this investment.

Investment tax credits (ITCs) for equipment have traditionally been used to stimulate the economy and reduce the cost of capital. By reducing the after-tax cost of equipment, the ITC, like accelerated depreciation allowances, can be an important incentive for businesses to increase investment. While not a necessary outcome, traditionally the incentives the ITC has provided were uneven, diminishing its effectiveness in promoting investment in those sectors of the economy where investment returns may be greatest. For example, all new equipment but only certain special types of structures have traditionally qualified for the ITC, and short-lived equipment has been favored relative to long-lived equipment. This disparity in the stimulus for different types of investment has resulted in an inefficient allocation of investment. While reducing the cost of acquiring investment goods is highly desirable for economic growth, tax incentives should be designed to be unbiased so

Box 6-8.—The Corporate Alternative Minimum Tax

The 1986 Tax Reform Act implemented a more extensive minimum tax on corporations. The alternative minimum tax was developed in response to findings that showed a number of large corporations had paid little or no tax during certain periods of the early 1980s. The minimum tax makes it more likely that corporations that otherwise would have low income tax liabilities relative to their "book profits" will pay increased amounts of tax. Although some believe that the minimum tax improves fairness, there are two basic reasons why they do not.

First, low tax liability is not an indication of high after-tax rates of profit. The 1-year accounting period on which the tax system is based may penalize firms with low income tax liabilities due to temporarily large investment or research outlays relative to their book profits.

Second, corporate taxes are ultimately paid by people. Higher corporate tax payments under the alternative minimum tax are not directly related to any measure of a person's ability to pay the tax. For example, many low- and middle-income families own corporate stock indirectly through pension funds and thus also share in the burden of corporate taxes.

The recession of 1990–91 demonstrates another adverse feature of the minimum tax. The structure of the alternative minimum tax suggests that minimum tax payments increase during recessions, an undesirable feature of any tax system. Recent data indicate that among the largest firms, approximately one-third more firms paid minimum tax in 1990 than in 1989. Minimum tax revenues in 1990 from corporations were $4.6 billion more than in 1989, rising to $8.1 billion. Increased tax collections during recessions reduce the spending power of the private sector and can deepen and prolong recessions. While the rise in the minimum tax paid in 1990 is only about 5 percent of total corporate tax revenues, the procyclical feature of this tax reduces the "automatic stabilizer" property of the income tax.

as not to alter the relative profitability of investments in different sectors of the economy. Capital cost recovery and investment credits can be designed to achieve the desired investment stimulus without distorting the allocation of investment across sectors as has been the case historically.

SUMMARY

- The government should direct its tax, regulatory, and spending policies toward providing an environment conducive to market enterprise.
- Consumption taxes are likely to increase the amount of saving and the amount and efficiency of investment relative to the current income tax.
- Consumption taxes can be designed to achieve any level of progressivity. Consumption taxes are likely to be fairer and simpler than income taxes.
- Individuals ultimately bear the burden of corporate taxes. Integrating the individual and corporate income tax systems can do away with wasteful distortions of investment, organizational, and financial decisions.

CONCLUSION

It would be difficult to overstate the importance of economic growth to future standards of living. Small increases in the growth rate of the economy compound over many years into dramatic differences in the standard of living. Economic growth, broadly defined, includes the many factors affecting living standards, such as the amount and quality of leisure time, as well as income.

Economic growth cannot be taken for granted. It results from the interaction of labor, capital, and technology within the institutions of the economic system. It requires the effort of the labor force, the willingness of entrepreneurs to take calculated risks on promising endeavors, the imagination of scientists and engineers to develop new products, and the managerial talent to bring them to market.

The market system has a tremendous capacity to organize the productive resources of an economy in a way that will satisfy the needs and desires of the Nation's people, permitting them to generate the rising living standards that are manifested as economic growth.

Government participation in the market can either contribute to or detract from economic growth. In certain cases when markets do not work well, the government may be able to intervene to improve the allocation of resources. Whenever possible, government intervention should attempt a targeted correction of the market mechanism, allowing people and firms the greatest possible latitude to generate economic growth.

The government undertakes many activities that affect economic growth indirectly. It maintains the legal system that guarantees private property rights and supports the economic system. It provides a social safety net for its citizens. The taxes it uses to raise revenue can encourage or discourage saving, investment, and capital formation relative to consumption. Its investment in productive infrastructure provides public goods that can enhance market activity for all. It can promote growth by funding research and development when the nature of the research will not permit private firms to appropriate the full returns and when the benefits of the research exceed the costs. To the extent that these policies are carried out properly or improperly, the government affects the living standards of present and future generations.

Much of the discussion about the government's impact on future generations tends to be limited to the impact of the Federal Government's deficit and the consequent debt. Both the deficit and the debt are incomplete and imperfect measures of the legacy future generations will inherit. They are incomplete because they neglect the many assets, public and private, future generations of Americans will receive. They are imperfect because they often do not accurately measure the financial liabilities of the Federal Government.

While the existing debt and projected budget deficits are incomplete and imperfect measures, they serve as proxies for these liabilities. Considering the debt and deficits together with the many broad concerns discussed in this chapter suggests that, on balance, government policy has changed in recent decades to a position that is less favorable to future generations. Moving to redress that imbalance should be an important national priority in coming years.

Consistent with the concern for future generations, however, this should be done with mechanisms that encourage rather than discourage economic growth. Indeed, it is possible to reduce the deficit substantially and immediately in ways that will cause much more harm than good for the country. In contrast, the Administration has advocated controlling the growth of mandatory spending to reduce budget deficits and removing tax obstacles to entrepreneurship, saving, and investment, and hence economic growth. The Administration worked to guarantee the benefits of an open trading system to all Americans. In the past year, the Administration's regulatory reforms made an important start in rationalizing the regulatory system. The Administration proposed fundamental reforms for our elementary and secondary education systems that would harness the power of parents choosing schools to encourage schools to improve their performance through competition. Proposed reforms of the legal system would accelerate the resolution of disputes and discourage wasteful litigation. These policies, and others like them, are needed to ensure that future generations will continue to enjoy an improved standard of living.

CHAPTER 7

Whither International Trade and Finance?

THROUGHOUT HISTORY, international trade and finance have been powerful engines of growth for the United States and the world. International trade has benefited all countries; one country does not capture the benefits of open trade at the expense of its trading partners. A key part of the Administration's economic policy has been to work toward more open trade and investment relationships through such initiatives as the North American Free Trade Agreement (NAFTA) and the Uruguay Round of multilateral trade talks under the General Agreement on Tariffs and Trade (GATT). Successful negotiations on NAFTA were completed in 1992, and progress has been made toward an agreement on the long-lasting and complex Uruguay Round. In the area of international finance, the Administration implemented the Brady Plan, which worked to make it easier for developing countries to service commercial bank debt, and the Enterprise for the Americas Initiative (EAI), which supports investment and growth in the Western Hemisphere.

International trade—the voluntary exchange of goods or services across national boundaries—increases the well-being of all participants by promoting economic efficiency in a variety of ways. International trade allows each country to concentrate on its most efficient activities. Trade gives firms access to the large international market, allowing them to increase output and lower their average cost by taking advantage of scale economies. Access to world markets for raw materials, capital goods, and technology improves productivity. Foreign competition forces domestic monopolies or oligopolies to lower prices, and imported goods provide consumers with greater choice. Finally, a liberal trade regime can provide a better climate for investment and innovation, raising the rate of economic growth.

An expansion in opportunities for international trade has effects similar to those of technological improvements: For the same amount of inputs and resources, more output will be produced. On the other hand, like technological change, more open international trade may require economic adjustments. Just as the invention of the transistor shifted production away from vacuum tubes, in-

279

creased trade causes shifts in resources away from production of commodities that compete with imports and toward production of commodities exported from the country.

Open trade may be especially beneficial to the growth of the developing economies and the former Communist nations that have smaller, less competitive markets and a greater need for investment and capital goods embodying modern technology. By creating new competition, providing domestic producers with access to large international markets, and improving the environment for investment, international trade can make a far greater contribution than direct aid to economic development.

In general, international trade has grown much faster than world production during the last 300 years. Most recently, between 1965 and 1990, inflation-adjusted merchandise exports grew by 439 percent, while world production rose 136 percent. The increase in world trade is, in part, the result of GATT, which was created after World War II to reduce tariffs and remove other nontariff barriers to international trade. In seven rounds of GATT-sponsored multilateral trade negotiations (the Uruguay Round is the eighth), countries have lowered tariff barriers and agreed on codes of conduct for nontariff barriers. Trade among GATT members now accounts for over 80 percent of world trade.

An important counterpart to an integrated global trade system is a well-functioning international financial system for the transfer of bonds, equities, short-term securities, and other assets among nations. The international flow of capital takes various forms: Direct foreign investment is the establishment of a business in a foreign country; portfolio investment is the purchase of financial assets such as corporate bonds or government securities; and direct lending is a similar form of capital inflow where a borrower promises to repay a foreign lender.

The international financial system serves several important functions. It provides traders with access to foreign exchange and credit, expanding the scope for commercial transactions, and allows nations to finance trade imbalances through private capital flows, government borrowing and lending, or changes in reserves. Second, the system of international finance encourages capital to move to countries where it is more productive. Capital inflows can finance domestic investment, and therefore enable a country to invest more than it saves; as a consequence, the country imports more goods and services than it exports (that is, it runs a trade deficit). Finally, international finance allows investors to diversify their portfolios, and thus reduce the risk of losses due to poor economic performance or political upheaval in individual countries.

Trade in currencies represents another facet of international finance. Because international trade typically involves two or more currencies, a smoothly functioning foreign exchange (or currency) market—the market where currencies are exchanged for one another—is important for efficiency in the international markets for goods, services, and assets. An exchange rate—the price of one currency in terms of another—influences both international capital flows and international trade by affecting the domestic prices of foreign commodities and assets. Between the end of World War II and the early 1970s, exchange rates were pegged—that is, maintained at particular values—in line with an agreement made shortly before the end of World War II, commonly called the Bretton Woods Agreement. Subsequently, exchange-rate regimes with varying degrees of flexibility have evolved. How, and under what circumstances, exchange rates should be allowed to change has become an important issue, especially within the European Community (EC), which reestablished pegged rates among most of its national currencies in the late 1970s. The reluctance to realign exchange rates within the pegged rate system in the face of major disturbances has played a role in the current sluggish growth and recession in a number of countries in Europe. This has adversely affected the EC's trading partners by reducing demand for their exports.

Since World War II, the growth of international trade has been complemented by the rapid expansion of international capital flows. As economies grow and become more integrated with the world economy, they develop occasional trade surpluses or deficits that are financed through capital flows. For example, in the wake of World War II, Europe's reconstruction needs far exceeded its available savings, leading to large trade deficits for Europe and, conversely, substantial U.S. trade surpluses coupled with capital flows from the United States to Europe. Likewise, in the 1960s and 1970s, capital scarcity in many developing countries was reflected in trade deficits and higher expected rates of return to investment that attracted capital from industrialized countries.

In fact, the growth of international capital movements has dwarfed the growth in trade. The stock of international bank loans, for example, has grown from 5 percent of gross domestic product (GDP) of countries in the Organization for Economic Cooperation and Development (OECD) in 1973 to about 20 percent of OECD GDP in 1991. Gross sales and purchases of U.S. long-term securities by foreigners grew from $144 billion in 1978 to $5.6 trillion in 1991, far outstripping the growth of world output and trade over this period. Average daily turnover in U.S. markets for foreign currencies is estimated at about $192 billion in 1992, more than a tenfold increase from $18 billion in 1980.

The growth in international finance is the result not only of the increase in international trade but also of improvements in technology, financial innovations, and changes in regulatory environments. Technological improvements in communications and computers have made international financial transactions faster, easier, and cheaper, and now provide investors with up-to-the-minute information on financial activity throughout the world. Improved technology has also spurred development of new financial products that require extensive processing of information to construct and price accurately.

The regulatory environment affecting international capital flows has become less restrictive since World War II. During the 1950s, for example, European countries removed laws restricting the exchange of domestic for foreign currency. By the end of 1992, members of the EC had removed almost all their capital controls. The liberalization of restrictions on capital flows provided significant impetus to the development of an integrated global financial market.

As an important example, the removal of external capital restrictions in Europe, along with other U.S. and European tax and regulatory policies, contributed to the creation in the 1950s and 1960s of the Eurodollar markets in which banks outside the United States accept deposits and make loans denominated in dollars. The Eurodollar markets have developed into "Eurocurrency" markets with transactions in other currencies in addition to dollars, and have expanded throughout much of the globe. After the oil shocks of the 1970s, the Eurodollar markets played an important role in taking deposits from oil-producing countries running trade surpluses and lending those funds to oil-consuming nations requiring financing for their trade deficits.

THE EVOLUTION OF EXCHANGE-RATE ARRANGEMENTS

The past half century has been marked by a number of experiments with different exchange-rate arrangements. Under the Bretton Woods system, designed at the end of World War II, currencies of participating nations were pegged to the dollar and only occasionally adjusted. Since this system was abandoned in the early 1970s, the exchange rates of the major industrialized countries have generally "floated" against each other in response to market forces. However, a number of European countries revived the pegged exchange-rate system when they created the European Monetary System (EMS) in 1979. Many developing countries peg their currencies to the dollar or other stable currencies, and this is considered a viable option for some of the economies of Eastern Europe and the former Soviet Union as well.

At the heart of the widespread experimentation with different exchange-rate arrangements is the fact that no one arrangement—be it a pegged-or a floating-rate system—is appropriate to all countries at all times and under all circumstances. Exchange-rate arrangements may be classified according to how rigidly they fix exchange rates between currencies (Box 7-1). At one extreme, several countries (or for that matter, regions within a country) share a single currency, so that there is no actual exchange rate to change. At the other extreme lies a system with freely floating exchange rates, in which currency values are determined exclusively by supply and demand. Pegged exchange rates represent an intermediate case: Governments maintain exchange rates at desired levels, but occasionally change those levels as circumstances change.

Box 7-1.—Exchange-rate arrangements

Single currency arrangements. Two or more countries form a "currency union" to share a single currency. Because there is only one currency, there is no exchange rate between participating nations.

Pegged exchange rates. Governments buy or sell currencies in order to maintain the value of their own currency within a specified band around the pegged rate. The pegged rate itself occasionally can be changed in response to changing circumstances.

Floating exchange rates. With a freely floating exchange rate, governments do not enter the foreign exchange markets to influence exchange rates, which are determined exclusively by market forces. In practice, governments occasionally intervene in foreign exchange markets to buy or sell currencies in order to influence their value; this is known as a "dirty float."

Different exchange-rate arrangements offer different benefits. A pegged exchange rate, if held for extended periods, can reduce the risks of exchange-rate changes to businesses conducting international trade. It can also exert pressure on governments to keep inflation low in order to maintain the value of their currencies. On the other hand, pegging the exchange rate may prevent a country's monetary authorities from responding flexibly to major shifts in economic conditions, and in that regard floating rates or more readily adjusted pegged rates may provide for more appropriate responses. For example, if world demand for one of a country's principal export products drops sharply, perhaps because a cheaper substitute has been developed, it may be helpful to let the value of that country's currency fall in international markets; this will make the country's other products cheaper to foreigners, helping to maintain demand for its goods and reducing the downward pressure on income and employment that a reduction in exports could cause.

Hence, countries choosing an exchange-rate arrangement face a tradeoff between the stability offered by fixed exchange-rate systems and the greater freedom to set domestic monetary policies that is offered by more flexible exchange-rate arrangements. When the international environment is relatively stable and rates of inflation are similar among countries, pegged exchange-rate systems may work smoothly while inducing governments to control inflation. Conversely, major disturbances such as escalating oil prices, or widely divergent inflation rates among countries, may call for more flexible exchange-rate arrangements that can permit smooth adjustment to these developments.

In practice, the distinction between the stability of one system and the flexibility of the other can be exaggerated. Even in floating-rate systems, central banks often intervene in foreign exchange markets in order to moderate fluctuations in currency values, although such interventions usually have very little impact, and then only for brief durations, unless accompanied by fundamental shifts in monetary policies. Conversely, the risk of exchange-rate fluctuations to importers and exporters could be greater in a pegged-rate system that experiences occasional large and unpredicted devaluations than in a floating-rate system where exchange rates move continuously but by small amounts. Moreover, private markets have developed means of helping traders "hedge" (protect against) such risks. An exporter expecting to receive British pounds in one year can contract now, at a specified "forward" exchange rate, to buy dollars for pounds next year, thereby guaranteeing the dollar value of future receipts. In fact, since World War II, international trade has grown vigorously under both pegged and flexible exchange rates.

Nevertheless, the choice of an exchange-rate arrangement can substantially affect the performance of the economy and, in fact, exchange-rate issues have been very important over the past year. In Europe, the EMS came under severe strain as its members struggled to keep pace with high German interest rates, exacerbating the economic slowdown and prompting Italy and the United Kingdom to float their currencies. Argentina entered the second year of a disinflation program that is based on a pegged exchange rate and reduced budget deficits. The major industrialized countries pledged $6 billion to help Russia stabilize the ruble once appropriate policies are in place.

These developments may have important implications for our own living standards and national security. Slower growth in Europe has reduced demand for U.S. exports and slowed our own recovery. Strong growth in various Latin American economies, on the other hand, in part based on the stabilization of their currencies, is contributing to their emergence as key trading partners for the United States. Economic stabilization and growth in the former Soviet Union is indispensable to achieving peace and democracy in that part of the world. An understanding of how and why exchange-rate arrangements have evolved since the creation of the Bretton Woods system may shed light on the exchange-rate choices confronting these economies today.

PEGGED EXCHANGE RATES UNDER THE BRETTON WOODS SYSTEM

The primary objective of the Bretton Woods system was to ensure a stable financial setting for international trade. When the designers of the system met in Bretton Woods, New Hampshire, in 1944, they were eager to avoid repeating the experience of the 1930s. The abandonment at that time of the gold standard, which had fixed the values of national currencies in terms of gold and therefore in terms of one another, was followed by marked swings in exchange rates and a sharp decline in international trade. While increases in tariffs and falling incomes were primarily responsible for the reduction in trade, the chaotic conditions of the interwar period, including the Great Depression, convinced participants at the Bretton Woods Conference of the need to limit market-driven fluctuations in the value of currencies.

At the same time, the Bretton Woods participants recognized that a system of permanently fixed exchange rates, such as the gold standard, could establish too strong a link between domestic economic activity and external developments. In a fixed exchange-rate system, governments or central banks must finance surpluses or deficits in their balance of payments (the difference between international sales and purchases of goods, services, and assets) by buying or selling international reserve currencies or gold. Whenever a central bank buys assets, whether domestic bonds or foreign currencies, it increases the domestic money supply; conversely, the domestic money supply falls when the central bank sells reserves of foreign exchange. These changes in the money supply, in turn, tend automatically to reduce existing payments imbalances. For example, countries with deficits sell reserves, leading to a decline in the money supply, a contraction in aggregate demand and imports, and thereby an automatic reduction in the balance of payments deficit. The opposite occurs when countries with surpluses buy foreign exchange.

Depending on the initial state of the economy, these adjustments may either improve or worsen the domestic situation. For example, in a booming economy with inflationary pressures, the reduction in

285

the money stock associated with a payments deficit should restrain demand and reduce inflation. If the economy is already weak, however, a payments deficit will lead to further contraction and increases in unemployment. The contraction may become even more pronounced if the country is in danger of running out of international reserves; in this case, it may take strong action to suppress domestic demand further in order to reduce its external deficit and retain the reserves needed to protect its exchange rate.

By contrast, with freely floating exchange rates, the authorities are not committed to a specific rate, and can focus on domestic objectives when setting monetary and fiscal policies. Balance of payments pressures lead to changes in exchange rates that, by changing the prices of exports and imports, lead to a reduction of payments imbalances with less need for domestic adjustment.

As a compromise between fixed and floating exchange-rate systems, the Bretton Woods system provided for an "adjustable peg." Under this system, each country would peg the price of its currency in terms of the dollar. When temporary balance of payments deficits occurred, countries with limited reserves would be able to borrow from the International Monetary Fund to alleviate the need to contract aggregate demand sharply, giving them time to adjust domestic policies more gradually. In the event of "fundamental disequilibrium" in the balance of payments—a phrase never precisely defined but clearly referring to a situation in which countries are unable to adjust their payments imbalances without severely disturbing the domestic economy—countries were allowed to change their official exchange rates. The United States, in turn, linked the dollar to gold at $35 per ounce.

Economic Performance Under the Bretton Woods System

For most of its quarter-century of existence (1946–71), the Bretton Woods system was relatively successful in securing its twin goals of strong growth in international trade and stable exchange rates. In fact, exchange rates were even more stable than had been anticipated. National authorities, desiring to avoid the loss of prestige and increased speculative pressures associated with devaluations, were increasingly reluctant to change their official parities. After some changes in parities in the late 1940s, exchange rates remained, with a few exceptions, largely unchanged until 1967 (Chart 7–1).

The Bretton Woods era was also marked by a steady growth in output and, after a postwar burst of inflation, by relatively stable prices. Inflation in the seven major industrial economies averaged 3.5 percent between 1950 and 1970, compared with 7.4 percent between 1970 and 1991 (Table 7–1). Annual growth in output averaged 5.4 percent and 2.9 percent, respectively, during the two periods. Some observers attribute the favorable performance of the in-

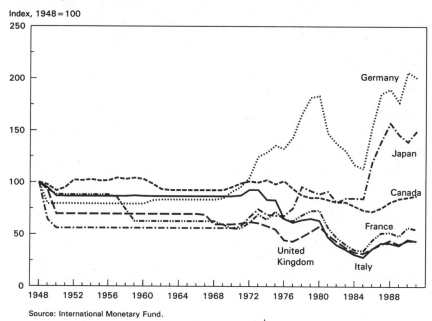

Chart 7-1   Exchange Rates of Major Industrialized Countries in Terms of the Dollar
Exchange rates were considerably more stable during the Bretton Woods era than they have been in the past two decades.

Index, 1948 = 100

Source: International Monetary Fund.

dustrial economies in the 1950s and 1960s to the pegged exchange-rate system, which may have exerted pressure to pursue responsible macroeconomic policies, moderating the cycles of inflation and recession that became more pronounced after 1971. However, others contend that the successful economic performances of the Bretton Woods period should not be attributed to pegged exchange rates and that the relative stability of prices and of output growth during this period is what enabled exchange rates to remain stable.

TABLE 7-1.—*Output Growth and Inflation in the G7 Countries*

Country	Output Growth		Inflation	
	1950–70	1970–91	1950–70	1970–91
United States	2.8	2.1	2.4	6.2
Japan	9.2	4.4	4.9	5.5
West Germany	6.3	2.5	2.2	3.8
Canada	4.9	3.5	2.5	6.9
United Kingdom	3.6	2.4	3.7	10.0
France	5.3	2.7	4.9	7.8
Italy	5.7	3.0	3.5	11.7
Average	5.4	2.9	3.5	7.4

Note.—Output growth is the average annual growth of GDP/GNP in constant 1985 units of each domestic currency. Inflation is the average annual growth of the CPI.

Source: International Monetary Fund.

287

The Breakdown of the Bretton Woods System

As the Bretton Woods era progressed, tensions within the exchange-rate system became more pronounced, in part because of the increasing international integration of capital markets. At the beginning of the Bretton Woods era, most countries had controls on the purchase and sale of foreign exchange and on capital flows. Over time, these controls were lifted, and by 1958 most European countries had liberalized transactions in foreign exchange for trade in goods and services. While most countries retained capital controls through the 1960s and beyond, advances in telecommunications and institutional developments such as the Eurodollar market made these controls increasingly easy to evade.

As a result of increased capital mobility, balance of payments deficits that raised the prospect of a currency devaluation tended to trigger speculative capital outflows, forcing governments to take severe restrictive actions or even to devalue their currencies. This tendency substantially limited economic policy choices, since even a moderate shift in a country's balance of payments could lead to a crisis that would be difficult to resolve. Since governments tended to resist devaluations (or in some cases, revaluations) until they had no alternatives, purchases of foreign currency offered near-certain profits to speculators. Strong capital outflows forced the devaluations of the British pound in 1967 and the French franc in 1969. Ironically, growing capital mobility not only increasingly restricted domestic economic policy but also reinforced tendencies to keep exchange rates unchanged. Governments declined to make corrective adjustments in their parities in order to bolster confidence in their currencies.

A second source of heightened tension under the Bretton Woods system was concern about the dollar's role in the international monetary system. During the Bretton Woods period, the dollar became the prime reserve currency, that is, it was used by other countries as a medium of payment for international transactions and as a reserve asset in case of future balance of payments deficits. On the one hand, the dollar's status as a reserve currency meant that the United States could run balance of payments deficits without having to tighten its domestic policies (sometimes referred to as "deficits without tears"), since the countries that were running balance of payments surpluses were willing to accumulate U.S. dollars.

On the other hand, the willingness of other countries to hold dollars as a reserve currency depended in part on their confidence that the dollar would retain its value in terms of gold. Persistent U.S. balance of payments deficits, reflecting capital outflows in excess of U.S. trade surpluses, caused foreign dollar claims on the United States to grow significantly larger than U.S. holdings of gold during the Bretton Woods period, increasingly throwing into question the ability of the United States to maintain the official price of gold at $35 per ounce. In March 1968, faced with declines in its stock of gold, the United States participated in an international arrangement that allowed the price of gold to float in private markets, although the price was held at $35 per ounce for transactions with foreign central banks. These banks, however, became increasingly reluctant to continue accumulating dollars whose price in terms of gold was declining in private markets.

Reinforcing these concerns was the asymmetrical nature of exchange-rate adjustments under Bretton Woods. Countries running balance of payments deficits often had to devalue when international reserves threatened to run out, while surplus countries generally faced no analogous pressure to revalue. Since changes in exchange rates were made vis-a-vis the dollar, this led to a bias toward devaluation for the system as a whole that caused the dollar itself to become overvalued.

In 1971, record levels of U.S. private capital outflows occurred in response to both expansionary monetary policy aimed at spurring recovery from the 1970 recession, a policy that heightened fears of rising inflation, and further concerns about the dollar provoked by the first U.S. trade deficit in the postwar period. The threat of a depletion of its stock of gold prompted the United States to suspend the convertibility of dollars into gold in August 1971, in the process eliminating a key feature of the Bretton Woods system and encouraging those countries that had not already floated their currencies to do so. An attempt to reconstruct the global pegged exchange-rate system, marked by the Smithsonian Agreement of December 1971, was abandoned by March 1973 in response to continued balance of payments difficulties among a number of participating countries.

THE DOLLAR IN THE FLOATING-RATE ERA

In the 1970s and 1980s exchange rates fluctuated more widely than they had during the Bretton Woods period of the 1950s and 1960s (Table 7-2). Inflation and production in the United States also became more variable since the breakdown of the Bretton Woods system, and this occurred in other industrialized countries as well.

As noted earlier, observers disagree on whether the end of the pegged exchange-rate system was itself responsible for the increased economic volatility. During the 1970s, the world experienced a number of economic shocks, most notably the oil price increases of 1973–74 and 1979–80. These shocks tended to affect each country differently, prompting a variety of policy responses and partially explaining the increased volatility of exchange rates. Moreover, the changes in exchange rates helped economies adjust

TABLE 7-2.—*The Increasing Variability of U.S. Exchange Rates, Output and Inflation*

	Ratio of Variability: 1971–91/1950–70[1]
Exchange rate[2]...	13.00
Output[3]	2.58
Inflation[4]..	2.25

[1] Ratio of statistical variance of the indicator during the 1971–91 period to its variance during the 1950–70 period.
[2] Monthly deutsche mark/dollar rate.
[3] Deviation from quarterly trend of real GDP (or GNP) in billions of 1982 dollars.
[4] Twelve-month growth rate of the monthly, seasonally adjusted CPI.
Sources: Department of Commerce, Bureau of Economic Analysis; Department of Labor; and International Monetary Fund.

to the shocks (Box 7-2); had exchange rates not been allowed to adjust, many countries would have had to respond to balance of payments difficulties by more sharply reducing aggregate demand.

Box 7-2.—Floating Exchange Rates

Under a floating exchange-rate system, governments allow the market to set the prices of currencies. A central virtue of floating exchange rates is that currency prices eventually adjust to correct international payments imbalances, reducing the need for domestic economic adjustment.

When there are tendencies toward a U.S. balance of payments deficit, the receipts of foreign exchange (from the sale of goods and services abroad or from capital inflows) are less than the demand for foreign exchange (to buy foreign goods and services or to invest abroad). As a result, the prices of foreign currencies rise (or equivalently, the dollar depreciates), making foreign products more expensive at home and U.S. products cheaper abroad. Imports fall, exports rise, and the supply and demand for foreign exchange move into balance. An incipient balance of payments surplus—when the supply of foreign exchange exceeds the demand at the current exchange rate—will have the opposite effect, increasing the dollar's value, depressing exports, and again restoring balance.

However, the fluctuations in currency values in the post-Bretton Woods era reflected divergent economic policies and performances as well as international economic shocks. Inflation rates for the United States, Japan, and Germany diverged considerably in the late 1970s, when U.S. policies focused on supporting recovery from the mid-1970s recession and U.S. inflation rose in relation to that of the other two countries (Chart 7-2). The higher inflationary pressures in the United States meant that any attempt to have fixed the value of the dollar during this period would have significantly increased balance of payments difficulties for the United

States, although a pegged exchange-rate system might have provided greater incentives to pursue disinflationary policies.

Chart 7-2   **Inflation Rates in Japan, Germany, and the United States**
Inflation in the three largest industrial economies diverged substantially in the 1970s.

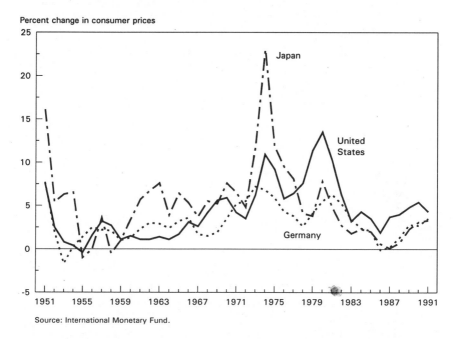

Percent change in consumer prices

Source: International Monetary Fund.

The connection between international differences in macroeconomic policies and the value of the dollar is illustrated in Chart 7–3, which uses the case of the United States and Germany as an example. Chart 7–3 compares the difference between U.S. and German real short-term interest rates, one measure of the relative tightness of monetary policy in the two countries, with the real (price-adjusted) value of the dollar against the deutsche mark (DM). (Real exchange rates and real interest rates are explained in Box 7–3.) When U.S. interest rates have been significantly higher than foreign rates, capital has tended to flow to the United States, raising the value of the dollar; conversely, when U.S. interest rates have been significantly below foreign rates, capital has tended to flow abroad, depressing the dollar. As noted above, the depreciation of the dollar in the late 1970s reflected, among other factors, our expansionary monetary policy, which increased inflation and lowered real interest rates relative to other countries, depressed confidence in the dollar, and led to substantial capital outflows.

The reversal of the dollar's decline in 1980 and its unprecedented appreciation through the middle of the decade primarily reflected

291

Chart 7-3 **Exchange Rate and Interest Rate Differences: United States and Germany**
During the floating rate era, the difference in interest rates between the United States
and Germany has been an important determinant of the DM/$ exchange rate.

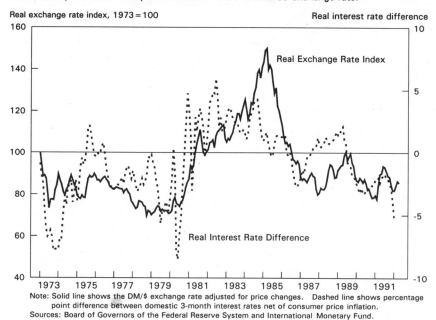

Real exchange rate index, 1973 = 100   Real interest rate difference

Note: Solid line shows the DM/$ exchange rate adjusted for price changes. Dashed line shows percentage
point difference between domestic 3-month interest rates net of consumer price inflation.
Sources: Board of Governors of the Federal Reserve System and International Monetary Fund.

major changes in U.S. macroeconomic policy, as well as substantial differences in economic performance among the United States and its major trading partners. In late 1979, in its determination to restrain the soaring rate of inflation, the Federal Reserve initiated policies that led to a substantial rise in U.S. short-term interest rates. In 1981–83 a reduction in tax rates and growing expenditures boosted the fiscal deficit, reinforcing the rise in U.S. interest rates. The improved environment for business associated with lower tax rates and an expanding economy, as well as the reduced attractiveness of investment in regions such as Latin America, encouraged foreign investment in the United States. Finally, foreign investors may have regarded the United States as a safe haven from political and economic turbulence abroad. These considerations prompted substantial inflows of capital, pushing up the value of the dollar in international currency markets.

The dollar's sustained rise contributed to a substantial widening of the U.S. trade deficit and corresponding surpluses in other countries. Concern over the sustainability of these imbalances began to outweigh factors attracting capital flows into the United States, and the dollar began to decline in early 1985. Also, U.S. monetary

Box 7-3.—Real Exchange Rates and Real Interest Rates

When rates of inflation differ across countries, it is the *real exchange rate* rather than the *nominal (that is, actual) exchange rate* that matters most to the balance of payments. The real exchange rate takes into account changes in price levels. For example, if Japanese prices doubled while U.S. prices remained unchanged, then for a given nominal yen/dollar exchange rate, the real exchange rate—which measures the purchasing power of the dollar in terms of Japanese goods—would drop by half. A real exchange-rate appreciation signifies that a country's goods and services are becoming more expensive compared with foreign products; a real exchange-rate depreciation indicates that a country's products are becoming cheaper compared with foreign products. When a country's inflation rate differs from inflation rates abroad, its competitive position generally will be stable if its nominal exchange rate adjusts by enough to keep its real exchange rate stable.

Exchange-rate movements are often determined primarily by capital movements, especially in the short run. Capital tends to flow from countries with low real interest rates to those with high real interest rates. The real interest rate is (approximately) the nominal interest rate less the expected rate of inflation. When differences in nominal interest rates merely reflect differences in expected inflation rates—that is, when real interest rates are the same across countries—capital flows are unlikely to occur in response, since exchange rates are likely to change in the future to compensate for different rates of inflation.

An inflow of capital into a country with a high real interest rate will create demand for the domestic currency, causing it to appreciate. Conversely, the currency of a country with a low real interest rate will depreciate as capital migrates out of that country. As a result, monetary and fiscal policies that affect real interest rate differentials will cause movements in the exchange rate (Chart 7-3).

policy had begun to ease in 1984, while attempts to reduce inflation abroad had strengthened, narrowing the gap between U.S. and foreign interest rates. Against this background, in September 1985, the G-5 countries (the United States, Germany, France, Japan, and the United Kingdom) reached the Plaza Accord, agreeing to coordinate policies more closely to lower the dollar's value further. With the dollar still falling in February 1987, six major industrial countries (the G-5 plus Canada) reached agreement, in the Louvre

Accord, to strengthen policy coordination and stabilize the dollar, although it continued to decline until the end of the year. The downward correction of the dollar and stronger growth in the other major countries led to a narrowing of the U.S. trade deficit from its peak of $160 billion in 1987 to $73 billion in 1991.

The widening U.S. trade deficit of the 1980s cannot be attributed solely to the effects of floating exchange rates. Underlying both the appreciation of the dollar and the increase in the trade deficit was the widening gap between saving and investment in the United States. U.S. gross investment averaged 17 percent of GDP in the 1980s, about the same as in the 1970s. However, the gross national saving rate declined from 17 percent in the 1970s to 15.4 percent in the 1980s, reflecting both reductions in household savings rates and the growing Federal deficit. The reduction in national saving meant that a greater share of U.S. investment had to be financed with resources from abroad. Therefore, the trade deficit would have widened with either pegged or floating exchange rates.

THE MOVEMENT TOWARD A SINGLE CURRENCY IN EUROPE

In the Maastricht Treaty of 1991, the members of the European Community agreed to replace their national currencies with a single currency by the year 2000, thereby superseding the present system of pegged exchange rates under the EMS and permanently ruling out exchange-rate changes. Ironically, events in 1992, including the (at least temporary) withdrawal of a number of countries from the exchange rate mechanism of the EMS, underscored the shortcomings of a pegged exchange-rate system in the face of economic disturbances and provided an example of the pressures that can build up if exchange rates are not realigned in a timely way.

Progress toward a single European currency is viewed as complementary to the increasing integration of the European market for goods and services. In 1985, the member states of the EC agreed to remove almost all remaining barriers to the free movement of goods, capital, services, and people by the end of 1992, a step often referred to as "EC 92." A single European currency is expected to reinforce this integration by eliminating both the transactions costs of dealing in different currencies and concerns about exchange-rate fluctuations that could interfere with cross-border business planning. In addition, the move to a single currency is expected to lower interest rates and thereby promote growth in some member countries by eliminating the risk to lenders that the currency might be devalued against others in the system.

Many observers, however, believe that the primary economic benefit of European integration lies in the elimination of barriers to trade. There is uncertainty as to how much additional benefit will be yielded by the permanent fixing of exchange rates implied by a single currency. By comparison, NAFTA is designed to achieve the benefits of regional free trade, but a currency union among the United States, Mexico, and Canada is not believed to be necessary to achieve these gains.

The European Monetary System

The EMS was created in March 1979, partially as a reaction to the increased exchange-rate volatility that followed the end of the Bretton Woods system. Under the exchange rate mechanism of the EMS, most member countries are required to maintain their exchange rates within 2¼ percent of "central rates" established between their currency and each of the other members' currencies. When an exchange rate between two members' currencies moves 2¼ percent away from its central rate—that is, to the edge of the exchange-rate band—the central banks of both countries are required to intervene to prevent the exchange rate from moving outside the band. Realignments of each country's central rate are permitted. In this sense, the exchange rate mechanism was designed to operate much like the adjustable peg of the Bretton Woods system.

It was initially intended that the central rates would be changed more frequently and in smaller increments than under Bretton Woods; rates would be changed before irresistible pressures built up. While realignments did take place relatively often in the first few years of the EMS, they later became less frequent. Between 1979 and 1987, there were 11 realignments, after which essentially no realignments took place until September 1992 (Chart 7-4).

The difference between the appreciating currencies of Germany and the Netherlands and the most swiftly depreciating currencies, such as those of France and Italy, is accounted for primarily by differences in their macroeconomic performance, particularly inflation (Chart 7-5). The countries with the highest inflation rates had to devalue their currencies frequently in the early years of the EMS in order to maintain the competitiveness of their exports and prevent increases in external deficits.

By the mid-1980s, differences in rates of inflation became smaller as the most inflationary nations brought their rates down toward those of Germany and the Netherlands. Some observers argue that the desire to avoid realignments, in particular because of the loss of credibility and national standing such realignments entailed, was important in leading policymakers in the countries with high inflation to implement strong disinflationary measures. These countries, notably France, concentrated on maintaining stable exchange rates with respect to the deutsche mark, since Germany had for historic reasons established an unwavering commitment to price stability; French inflation declined from over 10 percent at

Following an initial period of frequent realignments, exchange rates among the countries
of the EMS became more stable after the mid-1980s.

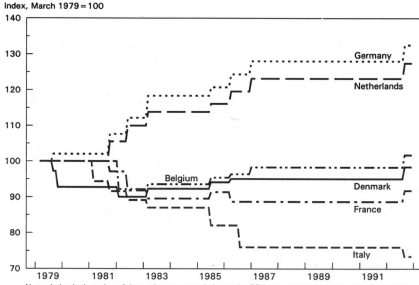

Index, March 1979 = 100

Note: Index is the value of domestic currency relative to the ECU (a weighted average of the currencies
of the EMS).

Source: Banque Nationale de Paris.

the start of the 1980s to under 3 percent in 1992. Increasingly, the
deutsche mark became the monetary anchor for the EMS.

To the extent that disinflationary policies can be linked to the
EMS, this highlights an important rationale for the pegged exchange-rate system: to exert anti-inflationary discipline over domestic policies. An alternative view is that the disinflationary policies of various countries were not motivated by the EMS itself but
were part of a more widespread movement to correct the inflationary excesses of the preceding decade. During the 1980s, inflation
declined in many countries that did not participate in the pegged-
rate system of the EMS, including the United Kingdom (which did
not join the exchange rate mechanism of the EMS until 1990) and
the United States. This fact suggests that the relative stability of
EMS parities in recent years could have been the result, as much
as the cause, of a convergence in rates of inflation. By implication,
future changes in national priorities concerning inflation and
growth, such as those that have occurred recently, would reduce
the viability of a pegged exchange-rate system unless the members
were willing to make more frequent adjustments to their pegs.

Chart 7-5   Inflation Rates in Selected EMS Countries
During the 1980s, inflation rates in EMS countries declined while differences in inflation rates across countries narrowed.

Percent change in consumer prices

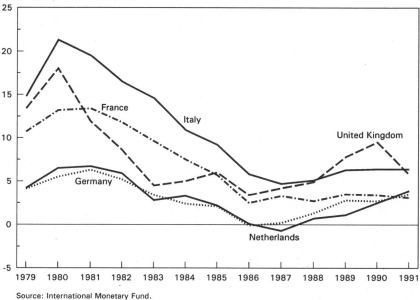

Source: International Monetary Fund.

The Maastricht Treaty on Economic and Monetary Union

The Maastricht Treaty of December 1991 is a blueprint for the replacement of the EMS by an Economic and Monetary Union (EMU) with a single currency and a European central bank overseeing a single monetary policy. Under the treaty, progress toward the EMU would take place in stages, with the final stage—when exchange rates are fixed irrevocably—to be initiated by 1999.

High standards for joining the EMU have been established, although there is still debate over how precisely these criteria will be applied. An entering country's inflation rate must not be more than 1.5 percentage points above the average of the three EC countries with the lowest inflation. Its interest rate on long-term government bonds cannot exceed those of the three members with the lowest inflation by more than 2 percentage points. The country's budget deficit must not exceed 3 percent of GDP, and outstanding government debt must not exceed 60 percent of GDP. For at least 2 years, the country's currency must have remained within its EMS band without realignment.

As of 1992, only three countries in the European Community appear to have met all these conditions: Denmark, France, and

Luxembourg. Three—Greece, Italy, and Portugal—met none. The difficulty of meeting these conditions suggests either that they may have to be relaxed, that it may be difficult to meet the 1999 target date, or that some countries may be admitted to the EMU only after they have had additional time to improve their economic performance. The chances of this last possibility, sometimes referred to as a "two-tier" or "two-speed" approach to monetary unification, may have increased because of the recent developments in European exchange markets and politics discussed below.

Recent Pitfalls in Progress Toward Monetary Unification

A development that potentially could slow progress toward the EMU is the partial collapse of the EMS in September 1992. A proximate cause of that event was the rise in interest rates and increased difficulty of supporting growth in Europe that accompanied the reunification of Germany in 1990, and that added to tensions within the EMS stemming from concerns over the declining competitiveness of some of its members' economies.

German reunification was a welcome development that helped to mark the end of the Cold War. However, the costs of raising productivity and providing a social "safety net" in the former East Germany sharply increased German government spending. The conversion in 1990 of most East German ostmarks into West German deutsche marks at a rate of 1-to-1 (a very favorable rate of exchange for the East Germans) further increased aggregate demand. An acceleration of German wage increases, largely reflecting attempts to reduce wage disparities between East and West Germany, added to inflationary pressures. In response to increased government expenditures and higher inflation, Germany tightened monetary policy rather than raising taxes enough to offset increased outlays. In consequence, the overall public sector budget deficit increased from 0.8 percent of gross national product, or output, in 1989 to over 6 percent in 1992, while the rise in interest rates that had begun in 1988 continued through 1992 (Chart 7-6).

In order to maintain their exchange rates within their prescribed bands, the other EMS countries were forced to increase their interest rates as well. Countries such as the United Kingdom, where interest rates and inflation had been declining, were prevented from further reducing interest rates. This tightening of monetary policy exacerbated the already existing slowdown in growth. In the United Kingdom, where output had declined to a level more than 4 percent below its previous peak and the unemployment rate had climbed above 10 percent by mid-1992, increasing pressure developed to either realign the pound or drop out of the EMS so that interest rates could be lowered. High interest rates were also weakening Italy's prospects of retaining its EMS parity by boosting in-

Germany's interest rates have increased since 1988, leading other EMS countries to increase their interest rates or to lower them less than they might have otherwise.

Percent per year

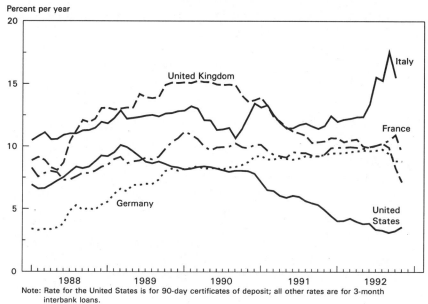

Note: Rate for the United States is for 90-day certificates of deposit; all other rates are for 3-month interbank loans.
Source: Board of Governors of the Federal Reserve System.

terest payments on its large public debt, thereby increasing its fiscal deficit and posing the threat of higher inflation in the future.

Even without the difficulties posed by Germany's tighter monetary policy, Italy and the United Kingdom had been considered more likely to devalue than many other EMS members. Italy had maintained its nominal exchange rate essentially unchanged since 1987 but its inflation rate persistently exceeded the EMS average. Inflation in the United Kingdom also had exceeded the EMS average; additionally, there was concern that when the United Kingdom entered the EMS's exchange rate mechanism in 1990, it had pegged the pound at too high a level.

As the pressure of matching Germany's interest rates increased the cost of maintaining their nominal parities, both Italy and the United Kingdom began to experience massive capital outflows, eventually prompting them to float their currencies and suspend their participation, at least temporarily, in the exchange rate mechanism of the EMS in September 1992. In addition, selling pressure against the currencies of Ireland, Portugal, and Spain led these countries to re-impose temporarily limited exchange controls that in most cases had been dismantled previously under EC 92

299

goals. A subsequent episode of speculative pressure prompted the devaluation of the Portuguese and Spanish currencies within the framework of the EMS.

Recent pressure on exchange rates within the EMS has been heightened by a second major development in the past half year, the failure to achieve strong popular support for the Maastricht Treaty. In June 1992, Danish voters rejected ratification of the treaty. In September 1992, a French referendum endorsed the treaty by just 51 percent of the vote. These revelations of popular discontent with the Maastricht Treaty have raised concerns that the treaty may have to be revised or its implementation delayed.

PEGS TO THE DOLLAR AMONG DEVELOPING COUNTRIES

At present, about 27 countries as diverse as Argentina, Hong Kong, and Sudan unilaterally peg their currencies to the dollar. A number of developing countries also link their exchange rates to the currencies of other industrialized nations, particularly France. Notwithstanding the difficulties of maintaining a pegged exchange-rate arrangement, pegs may help to stabilize the economy if combined with appropriate macroeconomic policies.

Pegs to the dollar or other stable currencies offer two important benefits. First, the prices of many developing countries' traded goods are determined mainly in the markets of industrialized countries such as the United States, and so by pegging to the dollar or the currencies of other industrialized nations, these countries can stabilize the domestic currency prices of their exports and imports. This is probably the most important reason why some of the Asian newly industrializing economies have linked their currencies (with varying degrees of flexibility) to the dollar. Additionally, linking to the dollar could help to stabilize trade flows with the United States, their principal trading partner.

Second, and perhaps more important in recent decades, many countries with high inflation have pegged to the dollar in order to exert restraint on domestic policies and reduce inflation. At 3 to 4 percent annually, the U.S. inflation rate is well below inflation rates in the developing world. By making the commitment to stabilize their exchange rates against the dollar, governments hope to convince their citizens that they are willing to adopt the responsible monetary policies necessary to achieve low inflation. Pegging the exchange rate may thereby reduce inflationary expectations, leading to lower interest rates, reduced wage demands, a lessening of the loss of output as a result of disinflation, and a moderation of price pressures. In the 1980s various countries successfully augmented the initial phases of their disinflation programs with pegged exchange rates, including Israel in 1985 and Mexico in 1988.

However, the histories of countries with high inflation are replete with examples of failed disinflation programs based on pegged exchange rates. Typically, such programs fail because the government neglects to reduce budget deficits and continues to print money to finance them. These policies lead to continued inflation and an overvalued currency, causing a deterioration in the balance of payments and prompting capital outflows in anticipation of a subsequent devaluation. The authorities are then forced to devalue their currency, abandoning the linch-pin of the disinflation program. While exchange-rate policies may usefully support a disinflation program, the exchange-rate system is not a substitute for appropriate monetary and fiscal policies. In addition, to encourage economic growth as well as reduce inflation, responsible macroeconomic policies should be complemented with reforms aimed at strengthening the market system, including the removal of price controls, the privatization of state-owned enterprises and elimination of public monopolies, and the reduction of barriers to external trade.

Some countries have experimented with means of strengthening the discipline over domestic policies that pegged exchange rates provide. A currency board arrangement ties the domestic monetary base (bank deposits at the central bank plus currency in circulation), a primary determinant of the money supply, to the foreign exchange holdings of the monetary authority. The monetary base responds mechanically to the balance of payments, since the currency board purchases all foreign exchange offered to it at the official price and sells foreign exchange to all who demand it at that price. This automatically keeps the exchange rate fixed and prevents the government from issuing domestic currency to finance its budget deficit. In Hong Kong, which has linked its money supply to the dollar since 1983, inflation has averaged 7.7 percent annually. Argentina developed a slightly different mechanism, passing a law in 1991 fixing its currency against the dollar and requiring the central bank to hold international reserves at least equal to the monetary base (Box 7–4). This law limits the central bank's ability to finance the fiscal deficit, much as a currency board would, and has led to substantial declines in inflation.

Even when disinflation programs based upon pegged exchange rates succeed, factors such as wage contracts or slow-to-adjust expectations may slow inflation's decline and prevent it from falling quickly to international levels. As a result, currencies often become overvalued during disinflation programs, and countries adopting pegged exchange rates then face the challenge of devaluing their currencies later without reigniting inflationary expectations. For example, Israel and Mexico, as noted above, both initiated relatively successful disinflation programs based on pegged exchange rates

Box 7-4.—Pegged Exchange Rates and Disinflation in Argentina

Between 1982 and 1990, inflation in Argentina averaged almost 1,000 percent annually. Three major disinflation programs based on a pegged exchange rate, announced in 1985, 1988, and 1989, all failed to achieve a lasting reduction in inflation. In each case, continued budget deficits and monetary growth forced a devaluation that set the stage for further inflation. Inflation peaked at 197 percent per month in July 1989.

After March 1990, the government reduced the fiscal deficit while allowing the exchange rate to float. The exchange rate remained relatively stable, even though monthly inflation remained above 10 percent for most of the remainder of 1990. In March 1991, following another plunge in the value of the domestic currency, Argentina passed a law fixing the exchange rate against the dollar and requiring the central bank to hold international reserves exceeding, at that exchange rate, the value of the domestic monetary base. This meant that the central bank would have sufficient reserves to support the exchange rate, even if the entire domestic monetary base were exchanged for dollars. The law prevents the central bank from financing fiscal deficits on an extended basis, since that would cause money growth to exceed the growth of the central bank's international reserves.

So far, the "Convertibility Program," as the 1991 initiative was labeled, has been successful. Annual inflation has declined below 20 percent, its lowest level since the early 1970s, while interest rates on deposits, a key indicator of inflationary expectations, have declined to around 10 percent. The interest rate is well below the rate of inflation, but, as asset holders apparently consider a devaluation of the currency to be unlikely in the near future, they are willing to accept rates of return on deposits roughly comparable to those available in international financial markets. The success of the Convertibility Program shows how a pegged exchange rate can help to lower inflationary expectations and accelerate the process of disinflation. However, the program was credible only because it was preceded by nearly a year of budget tightening and because, by requiring international reserves exceeding the monetary base, it made continued budget tightening a necessity. This aspect of the fixed exchange-rate program distinguishes it from its failed predecessors. However, Argentina's inflation remains above international levels, underscoring the continued vulnerability of the stabilization program and the need for continued responsible fiscal and monetary policies.

in the 1980s. Because their inflation rates subsequently remained above international levels, however, both countries have had to adopt more flexible exchange-rate policies. This underscores the need for continued monetary discipline, even after inflation has declined significantly.

EXCHANGE ARRANGEMENT OPTIONS FOR THE FORMER SOVIET UNION

The demise of the Communist regime at the end of 1991 marked the beginning of a new era of hope and opportunity for the people of the former Soviet Union. Over time, market-based reforms promise to raise the standard of living and increase the potential for growth. However, systems of taxation, budgeting, and monetary control that were designed for a command economy have not been adequate to ensure macroeconomic stability in the transition to a market economy. Budget deficits in many of the new independent states (NIS) of the former Soviet Union, as well as subsidies extended by the central bank to state-owned firms, have soared. With the lifting of price controls, inflation has climbed as money is printed to finance these outlays. The plummeting value of the ruble has reduced people's desire to use and hold it. In some instances, this has led to barter trade, contributing to sharp reductions in output and a collapse of trade among the new states of the former Soviet Union.

In developing their monetary and exchange-rate policies, the new states face two distinct but interrelated issues. First, how should the ruble's value be stabilized, in terms both of goods and of other currencies? Second, what type of monetary and exchange-rate arrangement among the states would best support stabilization and continued intra-NIS trade? Additionally, the new states face the challenge of complementing policies to stabilize macroeconomic conditions with structural reforms aimed at establishing and protecting private property rights, encouraging competition and market-determined prices, privatizing state-owned firms, and fostering private entrepreneurship.

Stabilizing the Ruble

Toward the end of 1992, inflation in Russia was running at over 25 percent per month, largely due to the printing of money to cover government outlays and credit extended by the central bank to deficit-ridden industrial firms. As a result, the ruble's value has diminished substantially; it took about 140 rubles to buy one dollar in July 1992, when exchange rates for various transactions were combined into a single floating rate, while it took over 400 rubles to buy a dollar at the end of the year. At the time the single exchange rate was established, the ruble's market value was expected to fluctuate initially because of the unstable macroeconomic situa-

303

tion but then stabilize as economic reforms progressed, at which time the government planned to peg the exchange rate to the dollar or another "hard" (stable) foreign currency. At the end of 1992, economic reforms had not progressed sufficiently for the exchange rate to be pegged.

To help support the ruble when macroeconomic conditions improve, the G–7 countries announced in April 1992 the creation of a $6 billion currency stabilization fund, conditional on an economic reform program for Russia supported by the International Monetary Fund. Like the $1 billion 1989 stabilization fund for Poland, this fund would be used to support the ruble if its market price declined. The mere existence of this fund could stabilize the ruble by reducing the chances of devaluation and thus the incentive to speculate against it. In fact, the Polish stabilization fund was never drawn upon, although Poland devalued its currency in May 1991 and subsequently has adjusted its value regularly in order to maintain the country's competitiveness in the face of continued inflation.

Successfully stabilizing the ruble would increase the demand for domestic money, helping to reduce inflation; restore the currency's credibility as a medium of transaction, reviving business that had faltered when enterprises resorted to barter; and increase incentives to invest, promoting economic growth. However, pegging the ruble must be combined with appropriate domestic policies. The experience of various developing nations in the 1980s underscores the government's inability to peg the currency without cutting the budget deficit and reducing monetary growth. In the absence of such measures, an additional $6 billion in reserves could do no more than briefly delay a devaluation.

Options for a Monetary Arrangement for the NIS

The difficulties of stabilizing the ruble are compounded by the fact that it is the common currency of most of the new states of the former Soviet Union. While only Russia can create ruble banknotes, the central banks of the other states can create ruble bank deposits, thereby increasing the overall money supply. Additionally, some states—most notably Ukraine before it adopted its separate currency—have issued their own coupons which act as a substitute for ruble banknotes, partially in response to a shortage of such notes; in the first half of 1992, shipments of ruble banknotes from Russia to the other states were insufficient to keep up with increases in the demand for banknotes. Even if Russia were to substantially reduce government spending and subsidies to state enterprises and stop printing money to finance these outlays, money creation by other states could lead to continued inflation. Since each state enjoys the direct benefits of its monetary creation, while the inflationary costs are spread throughout the NIS, the individual states have strong incentives to create rubles.

The deterioration of trade between the states is another pressing concern. The Communist regime created monopolies for many products throughout the former Soviet Union and located them in the different republics, so the new states are highly dependent on trade with each other. To monitor and control trade imbalances between Russia and the other states, at the start of 1992 Russia required all intra-NIS payments to be channeled through special "correspondent" accounts at the Russian central bank. Processing payments through these accounts has been extremely slow, impeding trade flows and further reducing production and sales throughout the NIS. Moreover, Russia has sought to limit the impact of monetary creation outside Russia by explicitly limiting the credit it will extend to other states through the correspondent accounts.

Various options for an intra-NIS exchange and monetary system that would address these problems have been considered.

Ruble zone. All members would continue to use the Russian ruble as their currency. The central banks of the individual states would agree on rules to limit monetary creation.

A ruble zone, like Europe's EMU, would have most of the features (both positive and negative) of a single-currency system. Ideally, it would both support intra-NIS trade by providing a common credible currency and, through its rules on ruble creation, restrain the states' monetary policies and lead to lower inflation. However, in the absence of a stable and credible ruble, some states may believe that they can do better by adopting their own currencies. Moreover, the lack of political cohesion among these states, as well as their difficult economic circumstances, means that the individual states are more likely than are the EMU members to break the zone's monetary rules or even depart from the zone entirely in order to pursue their own policies. In fact, the Baltic states and Ukraine adopted their own currencies in 1992, dropping out of the de facto ruble zone that has existed since the breakup of the Soviet Union.

Ruble area. In a ruble area, each state would create its own currency and have its own independent central bank (as various states already are doing) but would conduct intra-NIS trade in rubles. This system would be less constraining and possibly more sustainable than a ruble zone, since member states could adjust their exchange rates and follow independent monetary policies. However, unless Russia can sharply reduce its inflation rate and stabilize the ruble exchange rate against Western currencies, the other states may be unwilling to use the ruble.

Payments union. An alternative to using the ruble for intra-NIS transactions would be to use a hard currency such as the dollar or deutsche mark. Because intra-NIS trade accounts for such a high proportion of economic activity in the NIS, however, each state would need to maintain hard currency reserves in considerable excess of their current holdings. One way to economize on the use of hard currencies would be to create a payments union.

In a payments union, gross payments flows between countries are recorded and net payments calculated; at regular intervals, countries settle their accounts, in whole or in part, in hard currencies. An arrangement of this type, the European Payments Union, was instrumental in supporting intra-European trade after World War II, when initially dollars and other reserve assets were scarce. Additionally, the European Payments Union helped to foster reductions in trade barriers within postwar Europe, and such an institution could play a similar role in the NIS.

THE FUTURE OF EXCHANGE-RATE RELATIONS

International exchange-rate arrangements continue to evolve. Because there are serious tradeoffs between the stability offered by pegged exchange-rate systems and the freedom to respond to shocks offered by more flexible currency arrangements, the most appropriate arrangement may vary over time and across countries. Nonetheless, there are strong advocates for a single global exchange-rate system. Some observers tie many of the current economic difficulties among industrial countries to marked swings in currency values, and advocate a return to a global pegged-rate system, as in the Bretton Woods era, to enhance policy coordination among the industrial countries and foster a more stable international economic environment. Conversely, others argue that slow growth and increased unemployment in Europe have been exacerbated by the commitment to maintaining parities within the EMS, and advocate floating exchange rates free of government intervention.

In fact, implementing a global exchange-rate system would entail serious difficulties. The United States, Germany, and Japan, with their different macroeconomic circumstances and priorities, may find little room for agreement on the common policies needed to sustain a pegged exchange-rate system. Conversely, a global system of floating rates would be unsatisfactory for many of the smaller countries, which would want to continue pegging their currencies to those of the major economies, either to stabilize their trade flows or to help maintain responsible domestic policies.

Under these circumstances, a number of regional exchange-rate blocs could evolve around a few major currencies, which would then float or otherwise move against each other. In the foreseeable future, the dollar will be the most important international currency, but other currencies may become the center of regional blocs. A single European currency might become the basis of a Europe-centered bloc, while it is possible that the yen could perform a similar role in East Asia.

The development of such currency blocs might occur most naturally in the context of regional trading arrangements. This is most obviously the case in Europe, where the EMU is scheduled to follow the elimination of trade barriers and other obstacles to a single market that is taking place under EC 92. The development of a bloc of nations with currencies linked to the dollar may develop as NAFTA is extended to additional countries in the Western Hemisphere. If trading/currency blocs develop, however, it is essential that they remain outward looking, focusing on the elimination of internal barriers to the movement of goods and capital rather than on raising barriers to the rest of the world.

As regional economic arrangements develop rapidly in Europe and in the Western Hemisphere, it may be time for a systematic evaluation of the options for different exchange-rate arrangements.

SUMMARY

- Pegged exchange-rate arrangements can stabilize the environment for trade and provide incentives to avoid inflationary policies. However, pegged rates can also constrain domestic policies that could offset economic shocks and are likely to be unsustainable when national policies diverge.
- The Bretton Woods system, designed as a compromise between fixed and flexible exchange-rate systems, allowed pegged rates to be adjusted if external pressures became too great. However, the reluctance to adjust either official parities or domestic policies to maintain those parities made the Bretton Woods system increasingly vulnerable to increased capital mobility and divergences in national priorities, leading to its breakdown in the early 1970s.
- The EMS revived pegged exchange rates among a number of European countries in 1979. Recent developments, including German unification, have imposed great strains on the EMS, contributing to a slowdown in output and prompting Italy and the United Kingdom to float their currencies, raising concerns about future progress toward monetary unification.
- By exerting pressure to pursue responsible domestic policies, pegging to stable currencies like the dollar has helped some developing countries reduce their inflation rates. Such an arrangement may also be useful in the former Soviet Union, but it will be effective only if combined with fiscal and monetary restraint.

- Exchange-rate arrangements continue to evolve, and regional currency blocs built around the dollar, a single European currency, and perhaps the yen may develop.

THE CHANGING ROLE OF THE INTERNATIONAL MONETARY FUND

The International Monetary Fund (IMF) was envisaged by its creators at Bretton Woods as the institutional linch-pin of the international monetary system. In recent decades, however, its role in lending to the industrialized countries has diminished substantially, while its relationship with many developing countries has evolved considerably beyond temporary balance of payments financing. This evolution reflects important changes in the international financial system itself.

THE IMF IN THE BRETTON WOODS ERA AND AFTERWARDS

The IMF initially was intended to serve three functions in the Bretton Woods system: overseeing the system of pegged exchange rates, providing temporary financial assistance to countries with balance of payments problems (conditional on their adjusting domestic policies appropriately), and working to eliminate restrictions on transactions in foreign exchange that could limit the growth of international trade. It soon became apparent, however, that the IMF would not be as powerful as might initially have been intended. The resources provided by the United States under the Marshall Plan immediately after World War II largely dwarfed those available from the IMF, reducing the new institution's leverage over national policies. Subsequently, U.S. payments deficits continued to increase global liquidity and reduce dependence on the IMF for funding.

The move to floating exchange rates in the 1970s further reduced the need to draw on IMF resources, since governments no longer had to defend pegged exchange rates. The floating-rate system also transformed what initially had been envisaged as one of the IMF's key functions, the oversight of currency parities, although the IMF Articles of Agreement were amended in 1978 to authorize the institution to "exercise firm surveillance over the exchange-rate policies of members." Finally, the growing international integration of capital markets provided the industrialized countries with alternatives to the IMF. In particular, after the oil price increases of the 1970s, additional funds became available in the Eurodollar markets as the oil-exporting countries invested their surplus dollars. The last IMF loans to major industrial countries in support of adjustment programs were made to Italy and the United Kingdom in 1976.

Conversely, the oil shocks increased the financing needs of the oil-importing developing countries. While some of these countries were able to obtain commercial bank loans, this source of funding evaporated with the debt crisis of the early 1980s, when excessive accumulations of debt and rising global interest rates made it difficult for developing countries to repay their existing loans. In the 1970s and 1980s, the developing countries came to depend increasingly on the IMF for financing. The proportion of IMF credit outstanding extended to developing countries rose from an average of 58 percent in the 1950s to 65 percent in the 1970s and 100 percent in the 1980s.

LONG-TERM FINANCING, THE IMF, AND THE WORLD BANK

With the shift in focus from developed to developing countries have come other changes in the role of the IMF. First, the IMF has evolved from a type of credit union whose members took turns as temporary borrowers and lenders to a financial intermediary between developed and developing countries. A second and related development is that the current recipients of IMF loans typically do not suffer from purely transitory payments imbalances, but from longer term payments difficulties associated with sustained structural imbalances and poor macroeconomic policies. As a result, some countries have undergone prolonged sequences of IMF programs, many of them never fully implemented. Increasingly, observers have recognized that solving the payments problems of some countries may require long-term programs of structural adjustment such as those supported by the IMF's Extended Fund Facility, which was created in 1974.

The Extended Fund Facility, and particularly the structural adjustment facilities developed for low-income countries in the 1980s, is similar in time frame and objectives to the Structural Adjustment Loan program initiated by the World Bank in 1980. The World Bank, created along with the IMF at the 1944 Bretton Woods Conference, is an investment bank that traditionally has sustained much longer financing relationships with its members than has the IMF. The World Bank initially focused on financing specific projects such as roads, dams, power stations, agriculture, and education, but its activities subsequently evolved to include support for broader programs of structural reform such as the Structural Adjustment Loan program. As a result, the activities of the World Bank and the IMF increasingly have begun to parallel each other.

The ongoing efforts to assist the former Communist economies provide a good example of the convergence of roles between the IMF and the World Bank. While many of these economies certainly require financial assistance to meet their balance of payments deficits, their major problems are long term and linked to the need to develop strong market-oriented economies and credible macroeconomic policies. The IMF is an important conduit of technical assistance in the areas of macroeconomic analysis and exchange-rate policy, although its advice has at times been quite controversial. At the same time, the World Bank has been active in assisting these countries to privatize state-owned enterprises, restructure their financial sectors, and liberalize prices.

Despite the increasing similarity of their activities, the institutions clearly differ in their areas of focus: The IMF has a comparative advantage in macroeconomic policy analysis, and the World Bank is better qualified to provide assistance in the design of specific projects and sectoral reform programs. Because progress toward macroeconomic stabilization and microeconomic reforms are mutually dependent, close coordination between the IMF and World Bank is essential. Discussions on the division of responsibility between the IMF and the World Bank led in 1989 to an agreement reaffirming the IMF''s focus on macroeconomic and balance of payments issues and the World Bank's primary role in microeconomic and structural issues. It also strengthened the process of collaboration and coordination between the two institutions. However, the evolution of the roles of the IMF and the World Bank will continue to be important to the world economy in the coming years.

SUMMARY

- The move to flexible exchange rates in the 1970s and the increasing integration of global capital markets has reduced the IMF''s role in providing financing for the industrialized nations. The focus of the IMF has shifted toward providing technical assistance and recurrent financing to the developing countries, bringing its activities closer to those of the World Bank.

THE NORTH AMERICAN FREE TRADE AGREEMENT

The United States, Canada, and Mexico reached an agreement on NAFTA in August 1992. NAFTA will create a free-trade area with more than 360 million consumers and over $6 trillion in annual output, linking the United States to its first- and third-largest trading partners (Box 7-5). NAFTA will stimulate growth, promote investment in North America, enhance the ability of North

American producers to compete, and raise the standard of living of all three countries. NAFTA will also speed up technological progress and provide innovating companies with a larger market. Many economic studies show that NAFTA will lead to higher wages, lower prices, and higher economic growth rates.

NAFTA will also reinforce the market reforms already under way in Mexico. In recent years, Mexico has opened its markets and implemented sweeping economic reforms. In 1986 Mexico joined GATT and began unilaterally to lower its tariffs and other trade barriers. In mid-1985, for example, the production-weighted tariff in Mexico was 23.5 percent, but by 1988 it was only 11 percent. Mexico's reforms have raised its economic growth rate, making it an important export market for the United States. As economic opportunities in Mexico improve, Mexican workers have fewer incentives to migrate to the United States.

A stable and prosperous Mexico is important to the United States, from both an economic and a geopolitical standpoint. The United States shares a border roughly 2,000 miles long with Mexico. In addition, the United States and Mexico are linked by centuries-old ties of family and culture. NAFTA will help the two countries forge a lasting relationship based on open trade and cooperation.

Existing duties on most goods will be either eliminated when the agreement enters into effect or phased out in 5 or 10 years (for certain sensitive items, up to 15 years). Approximately 60 percent of U.S. industrial and agricultural exports to Mexico will be eligible for duty-free treatment within 5 years. NAFTA will also eliminate quotas along with import licenses unless they are essential for such purposes as protecting human health.

In addition to dismantling trade barriers in industrial goods, NAFTA also includes agreements in services, investment, intellectual property rights, agriculture, and the strengthening of trade rules. There are also side agreements on labor provisions and protection of the environment.

TRADE IN SERVICES AND INVESTMENT

Under NAFTA, the three countries extend both national treatment and most-favored-nation treatment in services to each other. Each NAFTA country must treat service providers from other NAFTA countries no less favorably than it treats its own service providers and no less favorably than it treats service providers from non-NAFTA countries. In addition, a NAFTA country may not require that a service provider of another NAFTA country establish or maintain a residence as a condition for providing the service.

Box 7–5.—Free-Trade Areas and Customs Unions

In a free-trade area such as NAFTA, substantially all barriers to trade among the member countries are eliminated, while each participant maintains its own individual trade barriers with nonmembers. In contrast, a customs union such as the European Community not only eliminates internal barriers among members, but also establishes a common external tariff on imports from nonmembers.

Producers from outside a free-trade area have an incentive to ship products through the low-tariff member and then reship it duty free to a high-tariff member. The problem of transshipment arises whenever tariffs with nonmembers differ among members in a free-trade area.

The standard method of dealing with the transshipment problem is to confine duty-free benefits to products originating within the free-trade area. This practice requires that rules of origin be established to determine those products that fall into this category. NAFTA bases its general rules on changes in tariff classification. A product is classified as originating within North America if imported parts or materials have been transformed enough to shift the product to a different tariff classification. There are also specific rules of origin for products such as textiles, automobiles, and computers.

The transshipment problem does not arise in a customs union, since all members have the same external tariff. Under NAFTA, the external tariff will be the same for some products, likewise eliminating the transshipment problem. For example, the external tariffs of the member countries will eventually be harmonized and set at zero for certain computer products.

NAFTA eliminates discriminatory restrictions on U.S. sales to and investments in the Mexican telecommunications market. Specifically, NAFTA gives U.S. providers of voice mail and packet-switched services nondiscriminatory access to the Mexican public telephone network and eliminates all investment restrictions in this sector by July 1995.

In financial services, Mexico's closed markets will be opened, allowing U.S. and Canadian banks and securities firms to establish wholly owned subsidiaries. In insurance, firms with existing joint ventures will be permitted to obtain 100 percent ownership by 1996, and new entrants can obtain a majority stake in Mexican firms by 1998. By the year 2000, most equity and market share restrictions will be eliminated.

For investment, NAFTA will in most cases require that investors of the parties be treated the same as domestic investors. For all industries, the agreement will eliminate a variety of performance requirements such as minimum export levels and preferences for domestic sourcing. NAFTA investors will be able to convert local currency into foreign currency at the prevailing market exchange rate for transactions associated with an investment. Each NAFTA country will ensure that such foreign currency may be freely transferred among NAFTA countries. No NAFTA country may directly or indirectly expropriate the investments of NAFTA investors, except for a public purpose and in accordance with law.

INTELLECTUAL PROPERTY RIGHTS

NAFTA protects inventions by requiring each country to provide product and process patents for virtually all types of inventions, including pharmaceuticals and agricultural chemicals. Copyrights of computer programs and databases, as well as rental rights for computer programs and sound recordings are also protected—sound recordings for at least 50 years. Service marks and trade secrets are also covered, along with integrated circuits both directly and as components of other products.

AGRICULTURAL TRADE

Over a period of 15 years, NAFTA will virtually eliminate barriers to trade in agricultural commodities between the United States and Mexico. About 50 percent of the agricultural trade between the two countries will be free of all trade barriers as soon as the agreement takes effect. For remaining products, the phaseout will take between 5 and 15 years. For most tariffs imposed by the United States, the phaseout will simply involve an annual reduction in the tariff rate.

The phaseout for remaining nontariff barriers such as quotas is more complicated. Initially, they will be replaced by tariff-rate quotas that allow products to be imported in limited quantities at a low (or zero) tariff rate and impose high tariffs for quantities above the limit. The tariff-rate quotas will be phased out over a 10- to 15-year period by increasing the quantity limit and/or reducing the tariff applied to imports above the limit.

Liberalization of agricultural trade between the United States and Canada continues as agreed to in the United States-Canada Free-Trade Agreement, under which existing tariffs on all agricultural commodities will be eliminated by 1998, while nontariff barriers for dairy products, poultry, eggs, and sugar will remain. In a separate agreement under NAFTA, Canada and Mexico agree to eliminate tariffs on bilateral agricultural trade between the two countries, exempting dairy products, poultry, eggs, and sugar. The

313

three NAFTA countries also agree to move toward domestic agricultural policies that are more conducive to free international trade and to work toward eliminating export subsidies for agricultural products.

NAFTA is expected to lead to substantial increases in agricultural trade between the United States and Mexico. For example, as a direct result of NAFTA, U.S. wheat and corn exports to Mexico are expected to grow by about 40 and 50 percent, respectively, and Mexican exports of some fresh vegetables to the United States are expected to increase.

SAFEGUARDS AND OTHER TRADE RULES

During the transition period, if increases in imports from a partner country cause or threaten to cause serious injury to a domestic industry, a NAFTA country may take a safeguard action that either temporarily suspends the agreed duty elimination or re-establishes the pre-NAFTA duty. If a NAFTA country undertakes a global or multilateral safeguard action, each NAFTA partner must be excluded unless its exports account for a substantial share of the total imports and they contribute importantly to the serious injury or the threat of serious injury.

In reviewing antidumping and countervailing duty determinations, binational panels will substitute for domestic judicial review. Under antidumping laws, duties may be imposed when a foreign firm is found to be dumping—exporting its product at a price that is below either the selling price in its home market or the cost of production. Countervailing duty law allows the imposition of duties on imports that are subsidized by foreign governments. Both the importing and the exporting countries can request a review. A panel must apply the domestic law of the importing country in reviewing the disputed determination. NAFTA preserves the right of each country to retain its own antidumping and countervailing duty laws. The panel's decisions will be binding.

Dispute resolution can involve several stages. First, a country may request consultations. If the consultations fail, it may call a meeting of the Trade Commission, which will include Ministers designated by each country. If the issue remains unresolved, a panel is convened to make findings of facts and determinations according to NAFTA. Upon receiving the panel's reports, the disputing countries are to agree on the resolution of the dispute. If a panel finds that a complaint is justified but the countries cannot reach an agreement, the complaining country may suspend equivalent benefits.

THE ENVIRONMENT AND LABOR

The three countries are committed to implementing the agreement in a manner consistent with environmental protection. The agreement requires that international environmental agreements regarding endangered species, ozone-depleting substances, and hazardous wastes take precedence over NAFTA provisions. NAFTA countries recognize that it is inappropriate to encourage investment by relaxing domestic health, safety, or environmental measures.

The agreement affirms the right of each country to choose what it considers appropriate measures to protect human, animal, or plant life, health and the environment. In February 1992, the Governments of the United States and Mexico announced the integrated U.S.-Mexico Environmental Border Plan, a multiyear program to improve protection of human health and natural ecosystems along the border. The United States and Mexico will spend well over $1 billion during the next several years to implement the plan's first stage. In September 1992 a new U.S.-Mexico bilateral agreement on environmental cooperation was initialed. The agreement establishes a joint committee which will meet at least annually to oversee joint work programs and to assess environmental issues, which may include enforcement, pesticides, waste management, responses to chemical emergencies, and pollution.

In the area of labor adjustment assistance, the Administration announced in August 1992 a new comprehensive worker adjustment program—Advancing Skills through Education and Training Services. This program will nearly triple the resources now available for all worker adjustment by providing $2 billion annually, of which at least $335 million is specifically reserved for workers affected by NAFTA.

The U.S. and Mexican labor ministries have been implementing a 1991 memorandum of understanding addressing issues ranging from worker rights to child labor. In September 1992 the United States and Mexico signed a new agreement establishing a Consultative Commission chaired by the U.S. and Mexican Secretaries of Labor that will provide a permanent forum for promoting the rights and interests of workers in both countries. It will manage new and ongoing cooperative labor activities directed at enhancing workplace health and safety and enforcement, among other things.

OTHER REGIONAL AND BILATERAL TRADE DEVELOPMENTS

In addition to NAFTA, there have been several important recent developments in trade, including the Enterprise for the Americas Initiative (EAI), the market access agreement with China, and the Airbus accord.

Enterprise for the Americas Initiative

The agreement for a free-trade area in North America is only the beginning. The EAI, proposed by the Administration in June 1990, addresses trade, debt, and investment issues in a comprehensive manner. The trade and investment aspects of EAI aim to open up markets and increase investment flows throughout the hemisphere. The ultimate objective is to create a free-trade area stretching from Alaska to Argentina. The United States has signed trade and investment framework agreements with a majority of countries in Latin America and the Caribbean, which establish principles governing mutual commercial relationships. They also set up trade and investment councils, which provide an important mechanism for discussing trade and investment liberalization, and protecting intellectual property rights.

Market Access Agreement With China

The market access agreement with China signed in October 1992 will provide greater export opportunities for the United States. China has committed to removing import restrictions, such as import licensing requirements and quotas, from hundreds of products. This agreement commits China to substantially liberalize its import administration and to make reforms that would lay the foundations for a more prosperous China and a closer trade relationship between the two countries.

Among many commitments in the agreement, China's decision to make its trade regime transparent is of long-term importance and it moves China toward compliance with GATT rules. No later than October 10, 1993, China will, among other things, publish regularly and promptly all relevant trade laws and regulations. China has also agreed to remove 75 percent of all nontariff import restrictions within 2 years. In addition, China will reduce tariffs on many of the 90 categories of commodities for which tariffs have been raised since 1988.

The Airbus Agreement

In July 1992, the United States and the European Community signed a bilateral agreement limiting government subsidies and other forms of support for large civilian aircraft programs. This agreement is a step forward in limiting trade conflicts in an important industry. It prohibits all future production subsidies. Funds advanced by governments for aircraft development will be limited to 33 percent of total development costs. The agreement also establishes terms and conditions for repayment of development funds advanced by governments. Efforts are now underway to negotiate a multilateral agreement limiting aircraft subsidies.

SUMMARY

- The Administration has successfully negotiated an agreement with Mexico and Canada that will open up markets for trade and investment in North America.
- NAFTA will eliminate most barriers to trade among Canada, Mexico, and the United States; open markets in banking, insurance, and telecommunication among them; ensure nondiscriminatory treatment for NAFTA investors within the three countries; protect intellectual property rights among NAFTA countries; and provide dispute settlement mechanisms. There are also side agreements on environmental protection and labor provisions.
- NAFTA will reinforce the market-based economic reforms under way in Mexico. As the Mexican economy grows, it will continue to provide the United States with a valuable market for exports. The EAI addresses trade, debt, and investment issues throughout the hemisphere.
- The market access agreement with China will provide U.S. firms with increased access to the growing Chinese market and move China toward compliance with GATT rules. The Airbus agreement provides limits on subsidies to the civilian aircraft industry in the United States and the European Community.

THE URUGUAY ROUND

The Uruguay Round of multilateral trade talks aims not only to lower tariffs on merchandise trade but also to integrate into GATT areas of trade and investment that have not been subject to effective GATT disciplines. These areas include agriculture, textiles, trade in services, investment, and intellectual property rights. The Uruguay Round has also made progress in reforming GATT rules, especially safeguards and other trade rules and dispute settlement procedures. A breakthrough in the agricultural negotiations in November 1992 has improved prospects for a successful completion of the round, but some issues remain to be settled.

The potential rewards for success in the Uruguay Round negotiations are great, as are the potential costs of failure. Failure to conclude the Uruguay Round successfully would not only deny us the benefits of faster growth, it could also lead to a backsliding toward greater barriers to, and contraction in, international trade, and a resulting drag on living standards in the United States and around the world.

AGRICULTURE

Throughout the Uruguay Round negotiations, the most difficult issue has been agriculture. The Uruguay Round agenda for agricul-

317

ture includes transforming nontariff trade barriers into tariffs as well as reducing tariffs, domestic support of agriculture, and export subsidies. Agreement has been difficult to reach on all of these issues, especially on how much to reduce domestic support of agriculture and subsidies of agricultural exports. The lengthy and contentious negotiations on agriculture illustrate how domestic political interests may conflict with trade liberalization. Box 7-6 describes another such example.

Virtually every developed country in the world subsidizes agricultural products. In 1986, at the beginning of the Uruguay Round, government programs accounted for almost 80 percent of the value of agricultural products in Japan, over 40 percent in the EC, and over 30 percent in the United States. (The 1988 *Report* discusses this in more detail.)

These subsidies interfere with world trade by increasing the degree to which countries are self-sufficient in food production. In many instances, the subsidy raises domestic prices for farm products above world prices and necessitates quotas or tariffs to keep out lower-priced imported agricultural products. The subsidies can even increase domestic production to such an extent that the country builds up surpluses that are disposed of on world markets. Countries whose agricultural production costs are relatively high can compete against countries whose production costs are low only by directly or indirectly subsidizing exports. Because this practice limits export markets for countries whose production costs are at or near world price levels, some of these countries may react by adopting subsidies of their own.

The Uruguay Round negotiations began with the general intention of liberalizing agricultural trade. The initial U.S. proposal in 1987 was that all subsidies—direct and indirect, domestic and export—that distort agricultural trade should be gradually but totally eliminated over a 10-year period. This proposal was not accepted by other countries however, and negotiations continued for several years without a successful resolution. In 1991, the GATT Director General attempted to move the negotiations forward by proposing a draft text that continued to serve as the basis for negotiations throughout 1992. The current draft negotiating text, often referred to as the "Dunkel Text," called for reductions in (but not elimination of) internal agricultural supports and export subsidies. In addition, all nontariff barriers would be converted to tariffs and old and new tariffs would be reduced by an average of 36 percent. Finally, countries would be required to open their agricultural markets to international competition, so that exporting countries would have at least a minimum level of access to a country's market. Although the current draft negotiating text is less ambitious than the United States and some other countries had hoped

Box 7-6.—The Oilseeds Dispute

In December 1987, U.S. farmers complained that exports of soybeans and other oilseeds to the EC were being unfairly restricted by a program that encouraged the production of oilseeds in the EC. In the 1960–61 Dillon Round of GATT negotiations, the EC had agreed to make a concession to oilseeds exporters by setting its oilseeds tariff at zero. At that time individual EC countries had no widespread system of supports for domestic oilseed production. By the early 1980s, the EC had adopted an oilseeds support program that increased domestic supply, reduced growth in demand for imported oilseeds, and, according to international trade law, "impaired the value of the concession."

The U.S. Government instituted an investigation to determine the validity of this complaint. As the investigation proceeded, the United States asked GATT to establish an expert panel and issue an opinion. In December 1989, the expert panel agreed that the U.S. complaint was justified and recommended that the EC end or modify its oilseeds program to remove the impairment. In October 1991, the EC approved substantial modifications in the oilseeds program. However, the GATT panel studied the modifications and found, in March 1992, that they were not sufficient to bring the EC into conformity with its GATT obligations.

In accordance with Section 301 of the Trade Act of 1974, the U.S. Government threatened to impose tariffs on $1 billion worth of imports from the EC if the EC did not take appropriate actions. Intense negotiations between the United States and the EC continued throughout the summer and fall of 1992, but no solution could be found that would fully compensate U.S. oilseed farmers for their lost market.

On November 5, the United States announced that it would impose a 200 percent tariff on over $300 million of EC exports, primarily white wine, starting on December 5. The United States deliberately announced a retaliation for only part of the damage caused to its trade by the EC policies in order to leave the door open for further negotiations while making clear its intention to insist on its rights under GATT.

Later in November, the United States and the EC reached an agreement in principle resolving the oilseeds dispute. Among other things, the EC agreed to reduce the area on which oilseeds will be grown by reducing program payments if plantings exceed specified area limits. With the agreement in place, the U.S. withdrew its threat to retaliate.

for, it nevertheless represents a significant step. For the first time domestic agricultural policies would be submitted to effective GATT discipline and support levels and export subsidies would be reduced.

In the meantime, some countries have taken steps to reduce their agricultural subsidies, largely because the subsidies are becoming so costly. The United States moved toward a more market-oriented agricultural policy with the 1985 and 1990 farm bills and budget legislation. Government outlays for agricultural support fell from almost $26 billion in 1986 to about $10 billion in 1991. The changes brought about by these laws put the internal support targets of the current draft negotiating text within easy reach for the United States.

In the EC, however, the cost of agricultural subsidies continued to escalate (Table 7-3). In the spring of 1992 the EC adopted a new set of internal agricultural policies, called Common Agricultural Policy (CAP) reform, which represented a major departure from previous policy. The old method of supporting crop farmers by keeping farm prices above world levels was phased down, and a new method of directly subsidizing farm incomes was adopted. CAP reform represents significant progress, but still falls short of the standards in the current draft GATT negotiating text.

TABLE 7-3.—*Common Agricultural Policy Expenditures, EC agricultural trade, and EC self-sufficiency for selected commodities: 1975-1990*

[Millions of dollars]

	1975	1980	1985	1990
Total expenditures[1] [2]	5,612	15,739	15,125	33,676
per capita (dollars)	22	60	55	103
Export subsidies[2] [3]	1,457	7,922	5,125	9,830
EC agricultural exports[4]	11,648	27,580	25,067	44,800
EC agricultural imports[4]	29,684	51,258	39,874	71,200
Degree of self–sufficiency[5]				
Wheat	101	117	124	127
Beef	99	104	106	100
Fresh vegetables	95	99	107	106

[1] Data for 1975 and 1980 refer to EC–9; for 1985 to EC–10; for 1990 to EC–12.
[2] CAP spending refers to Guarantee Section expenditures.
[3] Export subsidies are expenditures for export refunds.
[4] Trade data are for EC–12 and exclude intra–EC trade.
[5] Self–sufficiency is the ratio of domestic consumption to production. For 1975 and 1980, values refer to marketing years ending in those years. Values for 1985 are from marketing year 1985/86, except for beef which is from 1986/87. The 1990 values for wheat, beef and vegetables are from 1989/90, 1989, and 1987/88 respectively.

Sources: Department of Agriculture and Commission of the European Communities.

In November 1992 the United States and the EC reached an agreement on the major elements that had blocked progress in the multilateral negotiations in Geneva. Under the agricultural agreement, aggregate internal subsidies would be reduced by 20 percent, and export subsidies would be reduced by 36 percent in value and 21 percent in volume over 6 years. To complete the Uruguay Round, this agreement between the United States and the EC must be agreed to by other parties to the negotiations, and multilateral agreements on remaining agricultural and nonagricultural issues must be reached.

TEXTILES AND OTHER IMPORTANT ISSUES

For decades, international trade in textiles and apparel products has effectively been exempted from GATT rules. Instead, agreements have been established under the Multi-Fiber Arrangement to limit textile and apparel exports from developing to developed countries. These limits cost American consumers an estimated $11 billion in 1987. Under the current draft negotiating text for GATT, 51 percent of the volume of textile products covered by the Multi-Fiber Arrangement would be free of quotas in 10 years. After 10 years, quotas would be eliminated and textiles would be reintegrated into general GATT rules. All countries, including developing countries, would cut their trade barriers in textiles significantly.

A successful Uruguay Round will also yield GATT rules governing trade and investment in services such as telecommunication and financial services. Negotiations have led to agreements on some trade-related investment measures. For example, the current text prohibits requirements that foreign firms use a predetermined amount of locally produced goods. A successful round could also provide protection for intellectual property rights such as patents, copyrights, and trademarks.

The current draft negotiating text prohibits voluntary export restraints and other similar measures often used as safeguards outside GATT rules. It sets specific time limits on the dispute settlement panels and provides for automatic adoption of their reports. (Further details of the current draft negotiating text may be found in the 1992 *Report*).

SUMMARY

- The Uruguay Round aims at extending and tightening multilateral trade and investment rules in areas such as agriculture, textiles, services, investment, and intellectual property rights. Substantial progress has been made, but final agreement has not been reached.
- The most difficult area in the Uruguay Round has been agriculture. Negotiations continue in order to multilateralize the U.S.-E.C. breakthrough in agriculture and other areas.

REGIONAL INTEGRATION AND MULTILATERALISM

Regional integration such as NAFTA can further promote free trade. The administration's objective is to expand open and transparent trade worldwide. Government policies should be aimed at opening rather than closing markets. Multilateral, regional, and bilateral trade agreements are instruments to realize such an objective. Multilateral integration is the most important, with regional integration and bilateral agreements fulfilling a complementary role. GATT permits the creation of free-trade areas and customs unions under two main conditions. Trade barriers must be eliminated on substantially all trade within the region. In addition, regional integration must not result in duties and regulations for outside countries that are more restrictive than original barriers. These conditions make it more likely that regional integrations will have an overall liberalizing impact, and will not promote trade within the region at the expense of trade with outside countries.

Regional integration and multilateral efforts to reduce worldwide trade barriers have often gone hand in hand. For example, despite controversies, the integration of the European Community in the 1950s and the 1960s was accompanied by the Dillon Rounds and the Kennedy Rounds of multilateral liberalization. Furthermore, for countries that are left out of the regional groupings, there may be added incentives to accelerate the process of multilateral liberalization to ensure that the benefits of freer trade will not be confined to members of regional agreements. Regional integration can also help countries identify issues that are outside the scope of GATT and later resolve them in a multilateral setting. For instance, the issues of extending and strengthening GATT rules to services, investment, and intellectual property rights have been successfully negotiated in NAFTA, providing useful experience for negotiating the same topics in the Uruguay Round.

Though economic integration consistent with GATT will generally promote greater well-being for all participants, some economic objections can be raised against regional trade arrangements. Primary among these is trade diversion, which occurs when member countries switch from importing from a low-cost nonmember country to importing from a higher cost member country because the countries outside the area do not benefit from the tariff cuts among the members. Trade diversion distorts the trading pattern and hurts countries outside the trading area.

The amount of trade diversion can be minimized if regional integration brings together countries that are already trading intensively with each other such as Canada, Mexico, and the United States through NAFTA and the European economies through the European Community.

SUMMARY

- Regional integration promotes trade within the free-trade area. Trade may be diverted away from efficient producers in nonmember countries. Regional free-trade associations can minimize potential risks by remaining within GATT guidelines. The risk of trade diversion is less when a free-trade area is made up of countries that already trade intensively with each other.

TRADE POLICY AGENDA FOR THE FUTURE

The ratification of NAFTA and the satisfactory conclusion of the Uruguay Round are the two immediate trade priorities. Next will be the successful implementation of NAFTA and the round. While GATT has contributed significantly to a more open and harmonious world trading system, new areas in trade will arise as the world economy evolves. The international community will face several important trade issues in the not-too-distant future.

INTERNATIONAL TRADE AND COMPETITION POLICY

Within nations, governments have antitrust laws to enforce competition and prevent predatory practices by large firms. When more than one country is involved, however, policies promoting competition become more complex. Faced with unfair competition from abroad, firms generally do not have the option of antitrust actions, and often turn to antidumping actions instead. Some critics have observed that—unlike domestic antitrust enforcement which generally lowers prices—antidumping actions raise prices. One solution is to make competition policies more compatible among nations, and enforceable across borders.

NAFTA contains provisions that the three countries will cooperate on issues of competition law enforcement and other antitrust issues. It also imposes rules on federal monopolies and on any designated privately owned monopoly. Each country must ensure that the monopolies do not engage in anticompetitive practices, including dealings with an enterprise with common ownership operating in a different country. A trilateral committee will be set up to consider the relationship between competition laws and trade in the NAFTA countries.

Competition policy in the EC is a special case. Firms in member states of the EC cannot initiate antidumping actions against firms from other member states, because competition policy is a community-wide issue. Antidumping actions can only be taken against firms from nonmember countries.

Given the increasing linkages between international trade and antitrust policies, there probably will be more attention paid to this area. Multilateral efforts can resolve potential frictions and help achieve economic efficiency and trade liberalization supported by nondiscriminatory, transparent trade and competition rules.

TRADE RULES FOR HIGH-TECHNOLOGY INDUSTRIES

Increasingly, trade disputes involve government support for high-technology industries. Some have expressed concern that unless the United States provides preferential treatment, subsidies, and/or trade restrictions to help high-technology industries, some of these industries may not survive domestically. Economists generally doubt the merits of government intervention in industries unless market failures are clearly identified. If there are market failures they are likely to occur at the early stage of research and development. At the generic and pre-competitive stage of research and development, the fruits of research may be hard to capture. But even when the benefits of research cannot be fully appropriated by the market, this does not mean that the government should automatically step in. The economic benefits of government-sponsored research must also be weighed against their costs. The role of government-sponsored research in our economy must be considered in light of two standards: Appropriability and the balance of costs and benefits.

If the U.S. Government had a policy of choosing specific technology for massive government subsidy in the past quarter century, it is quite possible that we would have supported the supersonic passenger airplane and the development of a high-definition television technology that soon proved to be obsolete. Neither of these projects—which attracted strong support at the time—would have represented a good investment. For example, the development of high-definition television has already cost the Japanese government more than $700 million, with little prospect of recovering the investment. As for the supersonic aircraft, the British and the French Governments paid for the development of the Concorde. The results have been a commercial disaster. Concordes are extremely expensive to run and only a few Concordes have been sold. It is sometimes argued that the chances of failure can be lessened by having choices made by a governmental technical group, divorced from political pressures. There is no reason to believe, however, that a governmental group would be better at making correct choices than private individuals putting their own capital at risk. Moreover, it is naive to believe that the spending of large sums by the government can be kept free of the political process. Nor is it self-evident that this would be desirable in a democratic system.

In spite of the difficulties in picking "winners," a number of governments are likely to continue active participation in research and development activities, which could lead to an international competitive race to subsidize high technology. To limit this danger, bilateral and multilateral mechanisms may be needed to identify what types of support may be legitimate. In the aircraft industry, for example, the United States and the EC recently agreed to limit development subsidies and prohibit future production subsidies. This agreement demonstrates how nations can cooperate on questions of government support.

TRADE AND THE ENVIRONMENT

Trade and environmental issues have become intertwined in recent years. Some accuse GATT of being hostile to the environment, while others argue that some environmental policies are only disguised protectionism. Generally, economists view international trade as an effective means of promoting economic growth and a higher standard of living. By improving the allocation of resources and access to the world market, trade will provide more resources and better technology to clean up the environment. In addition, as nations grow richer through open trade and the overall quality of life improves, people will prefer and demand a cleaner and better environment.

From an economic standpoint, environmental problems may require government action when prices do not reflect environmental costs. But, even if these environmental problems exist, trade restraints are usually not the best policy. If the environmental problem is limited to one country, domestic policies should be employed. Where pollution or other environmental problems spill across borders, however, international rules and cooperation will be necessary.

There are three main international environmental conventions that affect trade. The Montreal Protocol seeks to reverse the depletion of the upper atmosphere ozone layer caused by the release of chlorofluorocarbons and other chemicals. The protocol establishes binding commitments to reduce the production and consumption of controlled substances according to a strict time schedule. The protocol also requires certain types of trade restrictions imposed against nonparties to support its objectives. The Convention on Trade in Endangered Species of Fauna and Flora aims to protect endangered species of wildlife by restricting and monitoring their trade. The Basel Convention controls the transboundary movement of hazardous wastes from one party to another. Both exporting and importing countries are obligated to prohibit a transboundary movement if there is reason to believe that the wastes will not be managed in an environmentally sound manner.

Founders of GATT could not have foreseen the present importance of environmental problems. Clarification of environmental policies, perhaps through GATT, may be desirable to ameliorate environmental problems without unnecessary disruption of trade.

SUMMARY

- The international community may soon have to confront several emerging trade issues, including the relationship between trade and competition policy, a code of conduct for government support of high-technology industries, and the clarification of trade and environmental issues.

CONCLUSION

Open trade provides important economic benefits: more vigorous competition; greater incentives for innovation; a larger variety of goods; and a more efficient allocation of resources. This implies that trade will lead to a higher standard of living and higher economic growth. International trade is mutually beneficial—it benefits all countries involved. International trade has grown rapidly since World War II, in part because of the success of GATT in removing trade barriers. The benefits of freer trade can be obtained by regional as well as multilateral agreements. In 1992, the three North American countries successfully completed negotiations for NAFTA, which will remove most trade and investment barriers among the three signatories and strengthen ongoing Mexican market reforms. On the multilateral front, though progress has been made in the complex Uruguay Round, no final agreement has been reached.

Freer capital flows provide strong support for the continued growth of global trade and output by facilitating trade, allocating capital to its most efficient uses, and enabling people to diversify their portfolios. Flows of international capital promise to play an important role in supporting investment and growth in many developing and former Communist countries that are reforming their economies.

Several exchange-rate arrangements have been used since the Bretton Woods Conference almost 50 years ago. The Bretton Woods system allowed the pegged rate to be adjusted when external pressures on a currency became too intense. But it was abandoned because of the reluctance to adjust official parities or to adjust domestic policies to defend these parities, the inability of the United States to adjust its exchange rate, and greater capital mobility. More recently, the EMS revived the pegged exchange-rate system among many European countries. But events of the past year have strained that system as EMS member countries were forced to match increases in German interest rates, contributing to an economic slowdown and leading Italy and the United Kingdom to float their currencies. Some developing countries have sought to lower inflation by pegging their currencies to a stable currency, but a pegged exchange-rate policy must be combined with reasonable domestic fiscal and monetary policies.

As the world economy evolves, international institutions such as GATT and the IMF face new challenges. Following the collapse of the Bretton Woods system, the primary focus of the IMF has shifted toward providing technical assistance and recurrent financing to the developing countries and the transitional economies of Eastern Europe and the former Soviet Union. With GATT, there are several emerging trade issues to be confronted including the relationship between trade and competition policy, government support in high-technology industries, and international trade and the environment.

Appendix A
REPORT TO THE PRESIDENT ON THE ACTIVITIES OF THE COUNCIL OF ECONOMIC ADVISERS DURING 1992

LETTER OF TRANSMITTAL

COUNCIL OF ECONOMIC ADVISERS,
Washington, D.C., December 31, 1992

MR. PRESIDENT:

The Council of Economic Advisers submits this report on its activities during the calendar year 1992 in accordance with the requirements of the Congress, as set forth in section 10(d) of the Employment Act of 1946 as amended by the Full Employment and Balanced Growth Act of 1978.

Sincerely,

Michael J. Boskin, *Chairman*
David F. Bradford, *Member*
Paul Wonnacott, *Member*

Council Members and their Dates of Service

Name	Position	Oath of office date	Separation date
Edwin G. Nourse.....................	Chairman..............................	August 9, 1946............................	November 1, 1949.
Leon H. Keyserling.......................	Vice Chairman............................	August 9, 1946............................	
	Acting Chairman	November 2, 1949......................	
	Chairman..............................	May 10, 1950	January 20, 1953.
John D. Clark	Member..................................	August 9, 1946............................	
	Vice Chairman............................	May 10, 1950	February 11, 1953.
Roy Blough................................	Member..................................	June 29, 1950............................	August 20, 1952.
Robert C. Turner	Member..................................	September 8, 1952......................	January 20, 1953.
Arthur F. Burns............................	Chairman..............................	March 19, 1953..........................	December 1, 1956.
Neil H. Jacoby............................	Member..................................	September 15, 1953......................	February 9, 1955.
Walter W. Stewart	Member..................................	December 2, 1953	April 29, 1955.
Raymond J. Saulnier	Member..................................	April 4, 1955............................	
	Chairman..............................	December 3, 1956	January 20, 1961.
Joseph S. Davis............................	Member..................................	May 2, 1955............................	October 31, 1958.
Paul W. McCracken......................	Member..................................	December 3, 1956	January 31, 1959.
Karl Brandt................................	Member..................................	November 1, 1958........................	January 20, 1961.
Henry C. Wallich	Member..................................	May 7, 1959............................	January 20, 1961.
Walter W. Heller	Chairman..............................	January 29, 1961........................	November 15, 1964.
James Tobin................................	Member..................................	January 29, 1961........................	July 31, 1962.
Kermit Gordon..........................	Member..................................	January 29, 1961........................	December 27, 1962.
Gardner Ackley...........................	Member..................................	August 3, 1962............................	
	Chairman..............................	November 16, 1964	February 15, 1968.
John P. Lewis...............................	Member..................................	May 17, 1963	August 31, 1964.
Otto Eckstein............................	Member..................................	September 2, 1964......................	February 1, 1966.
Arthur M. Okun............................	Member..................................	November 16, 1964	
	Chairman..............................	February 15, 1968	January 20, 1969.
James S. Duesenberry	Member..................................	February 2, 1966........................	June 30, 1968.
Merton J. Peck............................	Member..................................	February 15, 1968	January 20, 1969.
Warren L. Smith..........................	Member..................................	July 1, 1968............................	January 20, 1969.
Paul W. McCracken......................	Chairman..............................	February 4, 1969........................	December 31, 1971.
Hendrik S. Houthakker.................	Member..................................	February 4, 1969........................	July 15, 1971.
Herbert Stein	Member..................................	February 4, 1969........................	
	Chairman..............................	January 1, 1972........................	August 31, 1974.
Ezra Solomon	Member..................................	September 9, 1971......................	March 26, 1973.
Marina v.N. Whitman....................	Member..................................	March 13, 1972..........................	August 15, 1973.
Gary L. Seevers	Member..................................	July 23, 1973............................	April 15, 1975.
William J. Fellner........................	Member..................................	October 31, 1973........................	February 25, 1975.
Alan Greenspan	Chairman..............................	September 4, 1974......................	January 20, 1977.
Paul W. MacAvoy........................	Member..................................	June 13, 1975............................	November 15, 1976.
Burton G. Malkiel........................	Member..................................	July 22, 1975............................	January 20, 1977.
Charles L. Schultze......................	Chairman..............................	January 22, 1977........................	January 20, 1981.
William D. Nordhaus	Member..................................	March 18, 1977..........................	February 4, 1979.
Lyle E. Gramley	Member..................................	March 18, 1977..........................	May 27, 1980.
George C. Eads...........................	Member..................................	June 6, 1979............................	January 20, 1981.
Stephen M. Goldfeld	Member..................................	August 20, 1980..........................	January 20, 1981.
Murray L. Weidenbaum..................	Chairman..............................	February 27, 1981	August 25, 1982.
William A. Niskanen	Member..................................	June 12, 1981............................	March 30, 1985.
Jerry L. Jordan	Member..................................	July 14, 1981............................	July 31, 1982.
Martin Feldstein..........................	Chairman..............................	October 14, 1982	July 10, 1984.
William Poole	Member..................................	December 10, 1982......................	January 20, 1985.
Beryl W. Sprinkel	Chairman..............................	April 18, 1985	January 20, 1989.
Thomas Gale Moore	Member..................................	July 1, 1985............................	May 1, 1989.
Michael L. Mussa	Member..................................	August 18, 1986..........................	September 19, 1988.
Michael J. Boskin.........................	Chairman..............................	February 2, 1989.	
John B. Taylor..............................	Member..................................	June 9, 1989............................	August 2, 1991
Richard L. Schmalensee.................	Member..................................	October 3, 1989	June 21, 1991
David F. Bradford.........................	Member..................................	November 13, 1991	
Paul Wonnacott...........................	Member..................................	November 13, 1991	

Report to the President on the Activities of the Council of Economic Advisers During 1992

ORGANIZATION AND STAFF OF THE COUNCIL

The Council of Economic Advisers was established by the Employment Act of 1946 to provide economic analysis and advice to the President and thus to assist in the development and implementation of national economic policies. The Council also advises the President on other matters affecting the health and performance of the Nation's economy.

Michael J. Boskin, David F. Bradford, and Paul Wonnacott, who comprised the Council at the end of 1991, continued to serve as Council Members in 1992, with Dr. Boskin continuing to serve as Chairman. Dr. Boskin is on a leave of absence from Stanford University where he is the Burnet C. and Mildred Finley Wohlford Professor of Economics. Dr. Bradford is on a leave of absence from Princeton University where he is a Professor of Economics and Public Affairs. Dr. Wonnacott came to the Council from the University of Maryland where he was a Professor of Economics.

Throughout 1992 the Council stressed the importance of maximizing sustainable economic growth to raise American living standards, setting ambitious but realistic long-term economic goals, and removing barriers to market forces. In addition, the Council argued at every opportunity for the enactment of the Administration's proposals to accelerate the economic recovery and spur long-term growth. These included proposals to reduce certain taxes on a temporary basis to accelerate the economic recovery as well as proposals to slow the growth of mandatory spending to reduce the budget deficit.

This year's *Economic Report* follows the previous three *Economic Reports* of this Administration in outlining the fiscal, monetary, regulatory, and trade policy principles that guided the Administration throughout 1992, and in indicating how the consistent application of these principles would contribute to stronger economic growth and improved standards of living.

In the Council's view, the Nation faces serious challenges and cannot take economic growth for granted. Abiding by sound economic policy principles in the formulation of the full range of Federal policies is essential to ensuring strong, sustainable growth.

The Administration's policies were designed to support sustained increases in the standard of living by raising the Nation's long-run productivity growth. Such policies included a pro-growth fiscal policy to reduce disincentives for entrepreneurship, saving, and investment, and spending control to reduce the multiyear structural budget deficit; a trade policy to promote growth through opening markets worldwide; and a regulatory policy that avoided unnecessary burdens on business and consumers. The Administration also supported a monetary policy designed to promote real growth while maintaining low and stable inflation.

MACROECONOMIC POLICIES

Throughout the year the Council emphasized the need to enact a set of temporary tax reductions to increase employment and output in the economy without increasing the Federal budget deficit in the future. Such a stimulus could have accelerated the pace of the recovery and would have helped to ensure against a return to slower growth as occurred in 1991. The Council pressed for temporary tax stimulus within a framework of credible and systematic fiscal and monetary policies to sustain maximum economic growth.

The Council briefed the President and participated in regular discussions on macroeconomic policy issues with the Department of the Treasury, the Office of Management and Budget (OMB), and other members of the President's economic team. The Council also regularly exchanged information and met with members of the Federal Reserve Board on monetary policy issues and the economic outlook.

The Council, the Department of the Treasury, and OMB—the "Troika"—continued to produce the Administration's economic forecasts and projections. The Council chairs the Troika's forecasting group. Dr. Wonnacott, in close collaboration with Dr. Boskin and Council Senior Economists, was responsible for much of the work of the Troika. Of the two official forecasts released each year, one is published at the start of the year and is used in formulating the President's budget, and one is published as part of the July mid-session budget review. In preparing its forecasts, the Troika continued the practice, initiated in the first year of the Administration, of indicating that the forecasts and resulting budget calculations bear a considerable degree of uncertainty.

The Council continued to work to improve the general understanding of economics and the quality of economic information through a comprehensive series of memoranda and briefing papers on economic events for the President and the White House Senior Staff, occasional briefings for the White House press corps on major economic news, and meetings with outside economists, forecasters, financial analysts, and business executives. The Chairman and the other Council Members appeared before numerous other organizations to explain the Administration's economic principles, policies, and outlook.

Dr. Boskin continued to chair the Working Group on the Quality of Economic Statistics, an assembly of the major Federal statistical agencies. The Council worked closely with the Working Group throughout 1992 in implementing a list of 25 recommendations the President had previously approved for improving the quality and timeliness of economic statistics.

The Council was one of the leading participants in the formulation of the Administration's economic policies through various Cabinet and sub-Cabinet working groups. In testimony before the Congress and in meetings with business and other groups the Chairman and the Council Members stressed the importance of enacting a set of stimulative, temporary tax reductions while slowing spending to reduce the long-term structural Federal budget deficit, shifting the composition of Federal spending toward investment in productive infrastructure and research and development, and reducing the disincentives in the tax system to entrepreneurship, innovation, saving, and capital formation.

INTERNATIONAL ECONOMIC POLICIES

International economic issues remained a very high priority at the Council during 1992. The Chairman and the Council Members stressed the benefits of free trade and open markets for goods, services, and investment in numerous meetings with outside groups and they emphasized the risk to world economic growth posed by rising protectionism. The Council participated in formulating Administration policy on the Uruguay Round of the General Agreement on Tariffs and Trade, the North American Free Trade Agreement, and many other issues pertaining to international trade policy. The Council also participated in formulating the Administration positions on legislation in the international arena.

The Council continued to be involved in Administration policies for advancing economic reform in Eastern Europe and the former Soviet Union, meeting with numerous officials from these countries throughout the course of the year.

Dr. Boskin traveled to Paris as part of the U.S. delegation to the Organization of Economic Cooperation and Development (OECD) Ministerial Meeting. He also served as Chairman of the OECD Economic Policy Committee. Dr. Boskin continued to chair the Administration's working group on economic reform in the former Soviet Union and continued to be a coordinator for the Administration's assistance programs for the Commonwealth of Independent States.

Dr. Wonnacott led the U.S. delegation to assess U.S. economic policy. He was also a member of the U.S. delegation to the OECD

Working Party 3 on macroeconomic policy coordination. Dr. Bradford headed the U.S. delegation to the OECD Working Party 1 meetings on microeconomic and structural issues.

The Council provided the President and the White House Senior Staff with regular briefings and analytical materials on international developments and participated in preparations for the Economic Summit in Munich.

The Council also participated in discussions on a wide range of issues—including developing country debt, macroeconomic policy coordination, and various export promotion proposals—with other members of the Administration, the Federal Reserve, the World Bank, the International Monetary Fund, and representatives of other countries. The Council Members and the Council Senior Staff conducted numerous briefings on the U.S. economy for visiting officials and scholars.

MICROECONOMIC POLICIES

The Administration considered and proposed action this year on a wide range of microeconomic issues. In its work in this area, the Council repeatedly stressed that government regulation must pass careful cost-benefit tests and that where regulation is appropriate, it should be formulated to allow workers and firms maximum flexibility, as well as to provide incentives to meet social goals in the least costly manner. The Council was instrumental in ensuring that legislative initiatives were designed to achieve reforms in as cost-effective a manner as possible. The Council emphasized the principles of promoting flexibility, enhancing incentives, and placing maximum reliance on the private sector in a wide range of policy areas.

The Council was also instrumental in the President's decision in January 1992 to establish a 90-day Regulatory Moratorium. During the moratorium Federal agencies issued only those new regulations deemed essential to preserving the health and maintaining the safety of the American people. Also during the moratorium all agencies were encouraged to reexamine the regulations which were already in place and for which they were responsible, with the goal of rescinding those regulations that were no longer necessary and modifying those regulations where the purpose could be achieved at a lower cost to American businesses and individuals.

The Council worked with the Office of the White House Counsel and the Council on Competitiveness within the Office of the Vice President to assist the various agencies in implementing the President's regulatory review policies. The Council was particularly concerned that the proposed regulatory changes achieve the goals of the underlying legislation at reduced cost to the American economy, and that the agency's claims of cost savings were credible and supportable.

At the end of the first 90 days the Regulatory Moratorium was extended for another 120 days, after which it was extended for an additional year.

In addition to the Moratorium, the Administration established new criteria for performing cost-benefit analysis and new requirements for reviewing legislative proposals. The President asked all agencies to perform cost-benefit analyses of legislative proposals under active consideration by the Congress or to be proposed by the agencies.

As a member of the Environmental Policy Review Group, Dr. Bradford dealt with a wide range of environmental issues, including climate change policy, Western water reforms, the Wisconsin Electric Power Company ruling on modifications at power plants, and the development of appropriate contingent valuation methods. He participated in a variety of working groups on income distribution, financial institution reform and regulation, tax policy, telecommunications, energy markets, and science and technology policy. He also chaired the newly created interagency Committee on Economic Research on Natural Resources and the Environment.

Dr. Bradford was instrumental in the development of the Administration's health care proposals, particularly the small market reform and health risk adjuster proposals.

PUBLIC INFORMATION

The Chairman and the Council Members regularly testify before the Congress, make public speeches, participate in radio and television news programs, and hold news briefings. In addition, the Council produces two publications a year for the public.

The *Economic Report of the President* is the principal medium through which the Council informs the public of its work and its views. It is an important vehicle for presenting the Administration's domestic and international economic policies. Annual distribution of the *Economic Report* in recent years has averaged about 45,000 copies. The Council assumes primary responsibility for the monthly *Economic Indicators*, which is issued by the Joint Economic Committee of the Congress and has a distribution of approximately 10,000.

THE COUNCIL AND THE STAFF

The Chairman is responsible for communicating the Council's views on economic developments to the President through personal discussions and written reports. The Chairman also represents the Council at Cabinet meetings, meetings of the National Security Council on issues of economic importance, daily White House senior staff meetings, budget team meetings with the President, and at many other formal and informal meetings with the President and senior White House staff, as well as with other senior government officials. The Chairman guides the work of the Council and exercises ultimate responsibility for directing the work of the professional staff.

Members of the Council are involved in the full range of issues within the Council's purview, and are responsible for the daily supervision of the work of the professional staff. Members represent the Council at a wide variety of interagency and international meetings and assume major responsibility for selecting issues for Council attention.

The small size of the Council permits the Chairman and Members to work as a team on most policy issues. There continued to be, however, an informal division of subject matter. Dr. Bradford was primarily responsible for microeconomic and sectoral analysis and regulatory issues. Dr. Wonnacott was primarily responsible for domestic and international macroeconomic analysis and economic projections.

PROFESSIONAL STAFF

The professional staff of the Council consists of the Special Assistant, the Staff Assistant to the Chairman, the Senior Statistician, 11 senior staff economists, 1 staff economist, 7 junior staff economists, and 1 research assistant. The professional staff and their respective areas of concentration at the end of 1992 were:

Special Assistant to the Chairman

J.D. Foster

Staff Assistant to the Chairman

Shelley A. Slomowitz

Senior Staff Economists

K.C. Fung	International Trade
Sherry Glied	Health and Labor
Andrew S. Joskow	Regulation, Energy, and Industrial Organization
Steven B. Kamin	International Finance
John H. Kitchen	Macroeconomics and Forecasting
Michael M. Knetter	Macroeconomics, Monetary Policy, and Quality of Statistics
Howard D. Leathers	Agriculture, International Trade, and Natural Resources
Deborah J. Lucas	Financial Markets and Monetary Policy
Andrew B. Lyon	Public Finance

338

| Raymond L. Squitieri .... | Energy and Environment |
| Jonathan B. Wiener .... | Environment, Natural Resources, and Health and Safety |

Senior Statistician

Catherine H. Furlong

Staff Economist

| Kevin Berner .... | Public Finance |

Junior Staff Economists

Christopher J. Acito	Macroeconomics and Finance
Lucy P. Allen	Regulation and Microeconomics
Sherif Lotfi	International Macroeconomics and Finance
Joshua B. Michael..................	Macroeconomics and Quality of Statistics
Kimberly J. O'Neill	Health and Public Finance
Natalie J. Tawil......................	Environment and International Trade
Darryl S. Wills.......................	Labor and Agriculture

Research Assistant

| Bret M. Dickey .... | Macroeconomics and Forecasting |

Mrs. Furlong manages the Statistical Office assisted by Susan P. Clements, Linda A. Reilly, Margaret L. Snyder, and Brian A. Amorosi. The Statistical Office maintains and updates the Council's statistical information system, overseeing the publication of the *Economic Indicators*, the statistical appendix to the *Economic Report*, and the verification of statistics in memoranda, testimony, and speeches.

Emily Chalmers provided editorial assistance in the preparation of the 1993 *Economic Report*.

Two former staff members returned to assist in the preparation of the 1993 *Report*: Dorothy Bagovich (statistician) and Lissa J. Rideout (student assistant).

SUPPORTING STAFF

The Administrative Office, which provides general support for the Council's activities, consists of Elizabeth A. Kaminski, Administrative Officer, and Catherine Fibich, Administrative Assistant.

The secretaries for the Council of Economic Advisers during 1992 were Alice H. Williams and Sandra F. Daigle (secretaries to the Chairman), Lisa D. Branch and Francine P. Obermiller (secretaries to the Members). The secretaries for the Council's staff were Mary E. Jones, Rosalind V. Rasin, Mary A. Thomas, and Janet J. Twyman.

Mark H. Fithian, Ian B. Goldberg, and Jennifer Howard served as student assistants during the year. Janet L. Fitzgerald and Mary

Elizabeth Pignone served as research assistants during the summer.

DEPARTURES

Harry G. Broadman, who served as Special Assistant to the Chairman and Senior Staff Economist, resigned in February 1992 to accept an appointment as Assistant U.S. Trade Representative.

The Council's senior staff economists in most cases are on leave of absence from faculty positions at academic institutions or from other government agencies or research institutions. Their tenure with the Council is usually limited to 1 or 2 years. Most of the senior staff economists who resigned during the year returned to their previous affiliations. They are Randall W. Eberts (Federal Reserve Bank of Cleveland), Joseph W. Glauber (U.S. Department of Agriculture), Spencer D. Krane (Board of Governors of the Federal Reserve System), Catherine L. Mann (Board of Governors of the Federal Reserve System), and Robert W. Staiger (Stanford University). Others went on to new positions: They are David S. Bizer (Securities and Exchange Commission) and William G. Gale (The Brookings Institution). Junior staff economists generally are graduate students who spend 1 year with the Council and then return to complete their dissertations. Those who returned to their graduate studies in 1992 are: Jeffrey S. Gray (University of Pennsylvania), John A. Higgins (Columbia University), Thomas N. Hubbard (Stanford University), Philip I. Levy (Stanford University), and Derek H. Utter (University of Pennsylvania). Nancy L. Maritato (National Academy of Sciences) and Michael G. Williams (Securities and Exchange Commission) went to new positions.

Appendix B
STATISTICAL TABLES RELATING TO INCOME, EMPLOYMENT, AND PRODUCTION

CONTENTS

NATIONAL INCOME OR EXPENDITURE:

POPULATION, EMPLOYMENT, WAGES, AND PRODUCTIVITY:

344

MONEY STOCK, CREDIT, AND FINANCE:

GOVERNMENT FINANCE:

CORPORATE PROFITS AND FINANCE:

General Notes

Detail in these tables may not add to totals because of rounding.
Unless otherwise noted, all dollar figures are in current dollars.
Symbols used:

ᵖ Preliminary.

——Not available (also, not applicable).

Data in these tables reflect revisions made by the source agencies from January 1992 through early January 1993.

Historical data for the national income and product accounts (NIPA) tables for 1929–58 were not available in time for inclusion in these tables. A Supplementary Table (Table B–111) has been added that contains data for selected NIPA series for those years. See *Survey of Current Business,* December 1992.

TABLE B–1.—*Gross domestic product, 1959–92*

[Billions of dollars, except as noted; quarterly data at seasonally adjusted annual rates]

Year or quarter	Gross domestic product	Personal consumption expenditures				Gross private domestic investment						Change in business inventories
						Total	Fixed investment					
								Nonresidential				
		Total	Durable goods	Non-durable goods	Services		Total	Total	Structures	Producers' durable equipment	Residential	
1959	494.2	318.1	42.8	148.5	126.8	78.8	74.6	46.5	18.1	28.3	28.1	4.2
1960	513.4	332.4	43.5	153.1	135.9	78.7	75.5	49.2	19.6	29.7	26.3	3.2
1961	531.8	343.5	41.9	157.4	144.1	77.9	75.0	48.6	19.7	28.9	26.4	2.9
1962	571.6	364.4	47.0	163.8	153.6	87.9	81.8	52.8	20.8	32.1	29.0	6.1
1963	603.1	384.2	51.8	169.4	163.1	93.4	87.7	55.6	21.2	34.4	32.1	5.7
1964	648.0	412.5	56.8	179.7	175.9	101.7	96.7	62.4	23.7	38.7	34.3	5.0
1965	702.7	444.6	63.5	191.9	189.2	118.0	108.3	74.1	28.3	45.8	34.2	9.7
1966	769.8	481.6	68.5	208.5	204.6	130.4	116.7	84.4	31.3	53.0	32.3	13.8
1967	814.3	509.3	70.6	216.9	221.7	128.0	117.6	85.2	31.5	53.7	32.4	10.5
1968	889.3	559.1	81.0	235.0	243.1	139.9	130.8	92.1	33.6	58.5	38.7	9.1
1969	959.5	603.7	86.2	252.2	265.3	155.2	145.5	102.9	37.7	65.2	42.6	9.7
1970	1,010.7	646.5	85.3	270.4	290.8	150.3	148.1	106.7	40.3	66.4	41.4	2.3
1971	1,097.2	700.3	97.2	283.3	319.8	175.5	167.5	111.7	42.7	69.1	55.8	8.0
1972	1,207.0	767.8	110.7	305.2	351.9	205.6	195.7	126.1	47.2	78.9	69.7	9.9
1973	1,349.6	848.1	124.1	339.6	384.5	243.1	225.4	150.0	55.0	95.1	75.3	17.7
1974	1,458.6	927.7	123.0	380.8	423.9	245.8	231.5	165.6	61.2	104.3	66.0	14.3
1975	1,585.9	1,024.9	134.3	416.0	474.5	226.0	231.7	169.0	61.4	107.6	62.7	−5.7
1976	1,768.4	1,143.1	160.0	451.8	531.2	286.4	269.6	187.2	65.9	121.2	82.5	16.7
1977	1,974.1	1,271.5	182.6	490.4	598.4	358.3	333.5	223.2	74.6	148.7	110.3	24.7
1978	2,232.7	1,421.2	202.3	541.5	677.4	434.0	406.1	274.5	93.9	180.6	131.6	27.9
1979	2,488.6	1,583.7	214.2	613.3	756.2	480.2	467.5	326.4	118.4	208.1	141.0	12.8
1980	2,708.0	1,748.1	212.5	682.9	852.7	467.6	477.1	353.8	137.5	216.4	123.3	−9.5
1981	3,030.6	1,926.2	228.5	744.2	953.5	558.0	532.5	410.0	169.1	240.9	122.5	25.4
1982	3,149.6	2,059.2	236.5	772.3	1,050.4	503.4	519.3	413.7	178.8	234.9	105.7	−15.9
1983	3,405.0	2,257.5	275.0	817.8	1,164.7	546.7	552.2	400.2	153.1	247.1	152.0	−5.5
1984	3,777.2	2,460.3	317.9	873.0	1,269.4	718.9	647.8	468.9	175.6	293.3	178.9	71.1
1985	4,038.7	2,667.4	352.9	919.4	1,395.1	714.5	689.9	504.0	193.4	310.6	185.9	24.6
1986	4,268.6	2,850.6	389.6	952.2	1,508.8	717.6	709.0	492.4	174.0	318.4	216.6	8.6
1987	4,539.9	3,052.2	403.7	1,011.1	1,637.4	749.3	723.0	497.8	171.3	326.5	225.2	26.3
1988	4,900.4	3,296.1	437.1	1,073.8	1,785.2	793.6	777.4	545.4	182.0	363.4	232.0	16.2
1989	5,250.8	3,523.1	459.4	1,149.5	1,914.2	832.3	798.9	568.1	193.3	374.8	230.9	33.3
1990	5,522.2	3,748.4	464.3	1,224.5	2,059.7	799.5	793.2	577.6	201.1	376.5	215.6	6.3
1991	5,677.5	3,887.7	446.1	1,251.5	2,190.1	721.1	731.3	541.1	180.1	360.9	190.3	−10.2
1982: IV	3,195.1	2,128.7	246.9	787.3	1,094.6	464.2	510.5	397.7	168.9	228.8	112.8	−46.3
1983: IV	3,547.3	2,346.8	297.7	839.8	1,209.3	614.8	594.6	426.9	154.6	272.3	167.7	20.2
1984: IV	3,869.1	2,526.4	328.2	887.8	1,310.4	722.8	671.8	491.5	184.1	307.3	180.4	51.0
1985: IV	4,140.5	2,739.8	354.4	939.5	1,446.0	737.0	704.4	511.3	195.4	315.9	193.1	32.6
1986: IV	4,336.6	2,923.1	406.8	963.7	1,552.6	697.1	715.9	491.7	168.4	323.3	224.2	−18.8
1987: IV	4,683.0	3,124.6	408.8	1,029.4	1,686.4	800.2	740.9	514.3	180.0	334.3	226.5	59.3
1988: IV	5,044.6	3,398.2	452.9	1,105.8	1,839.5	814.8	797.5	560.2	186.8	373.4	237.3	17.3
1989: I	5,150.0	3,440.8	450.8	1,121.1	1,868.8	843.9	800.2	563.4	190.2	373.3	236.8	43.7
II	5,229.5	3,499.1	457.6	1,146.5	1,895.1	840.3	800.5	568.4	189.6	378.8	232.1	39.8
III	5,278.9	3,553.3	470.8	1,157.1	1,925.4	819.6	800.0	571.5	195.5	376.1	228.5	19.6
IV	5,344.8	3,599.1	458.3	1,173.5	1,967.3	825.2	795.0	568.8	198.0	370.8	226.2	30.2
1990: I	5,445.2	3,672.4	478.0	1,199.3	1,995.0	820.3	812.2	580.1	202.4	377.6	232.1	8.1
II	5,522.6	3,715.3	463.5	1,208.7	2,043.1	833.0	795.3	572.1	201.5	370.6	223.1	37.7
III	5,559.6	3,787.8	463.0	1,235.3	2,089.6	805.7	795.3	585.2	204.1	381.0	210.1	10.4
IV	5,561.3	3,818.2	452.7	1,254.5	2,111.1	739.0	770.0	572.9	196.3	376.6	197.1	−31.0
1991: I	5,585.8	3,821.7	439.5	1,245.0	2,137.2	705.4	733.9	551.4	190.0	361.4	182.6	−28.5
II	5,657.6	3,871.9	441.4	1,254.2	2,176.3	710.2	732.0	545.8	185.2	360.6	186.2	−21.8
III	5,713.1	3,914.2	453.0	1,255.3	2,205.9	732.8	732.6	538.4	175.6	362.8	194.2	.2
IV	5,753.3	3,942.9	450.4	1,251.4	2,241.1	736.1	726.9	528.7	169.7	358.9	198.2	9.2
1992: I	5,840.2	4,022.8	469.4	1,274.1	2,279.3	722.4	738.2	531.0	170.1	360.8	207.2	−15.8
II	5,902.2	4,057.1	470.6	1,277.5	2,309.0	773.2	765.1	550.3	170.3	380.0	214.8	8.1
III	5,978.5	4,108.7	482.5	1,292.8	2,333.3	781.6	766.6	549.6	166.1	383.5	217.0	15.0

See next page for continuation of table.

[Billions of dollars, except as noted; quarterly data at seasonally adjusted annual rates]

Year or quarter	Net exports of goods and services [1]			Government purchases					Final sales of domestic product	Gross domestic purchases [2]	Addendum: Gross national product [3]	Percent change from preceding period	
	Net exports	Exports	Imports	Total	Federal			State and local				Gross domestic product	Gross domestic purchases [2]
					Total	National defense	Non-defense						
1959	−1.7	20.6	22.3	99.0	57.1	46.4	10.8	41.8	490.0	495.8	497.0	8.7	9.1
1960	2.4	25.3	22.8	99.8	55.3	45.3	10.0	44.5	510.1	510.9	516.6	3.9	3.0
1961	3.4	26.0	22.7	107.0	58.6	47.9	10.6	48.4	528.9	528.4	535.4	3.6	3.4
1962	2.4	27.4	25.0	116.8	65.4	52.1	13.3	51.4	565.5	569.2	575.8	7.5	7.7
1963	3.3	29.4	26.1	122.3	66.4	51.5	14.9	55.8	597.5	599.8	607.7	5.5	5.4
1964	5.5	33.6	28.1	128.3	67.5	50.4	17.0	60.9	643.0	642.5	653.0	7.4	7.1
1965	3.9	35.4	31.5	136.3	69.5	51.0	18.5	66.8	693.0	698.8	708.1	8.4	8.8
1966	1.9	38.9	37.1	155.9	81.3	62.0	19.3	74.6	756.0	767.9	774.9	9.5	9.9
1967	1.4	41.4	39.9	175.6	92.8	73.4	19.4	82.7	803.8	812.9	819.8	5.8	5.9
1968	−1.3	45.3	46.6	191.5	99.2	79.1	20.0	92.3	880.2	890.6	895.5	9.2	9.6
1969	−1.2	49.3	50.5	201.8	100.5	78.9	21.6	101.3	949.8	960.7	965.6	7.9	7.9
1970	1.2	57.0	55.8	212.7	100.1	76.8	23.3	112.6	1,008.4	1,009.5	1,017.1	5.3	5.1
1971	−3.0	59.3	62.3	224.3	100.0	74.1	25.9	124.3	1,089.2	1,100.2	1,104.9	8.6	9.0
1972	−8.0	66.2	74.2	241.5	106.9	77.4	29.4	134.7	1,197.1	1,215.0	1,215.7	10.0	10.4
1973	.6	91.8	91.2	257.7	108.5	77.5	31.1	149.2	1,331.9	1,349.0	1,362.3	11.8	11.0
1974	−3.1	124.3	127.5	288.3	117.6	82.6	35.0	170.7	1,444.4	1,461.8	1,474.3	8.1	8.4
1975	13.6	136.3	122.7	321.4	129.4	89.6	39.8	192.0	1,591.5	1,572.3	1,599.1	8.7	7.6
1976	−2.3	148.9	151.1	341.3	135.8	93.4	42.4	205.5	1,751.7	1,770.7	1,785.5	11.5	12.6
1977	−23.7	158.8	182.4	368.0	147.9	100.9	47.0	220.1	1,949.4	1,997.8	1,994.6	11.6	12.8
1978	−26.1	186.1	212.3	403.6	162.2	108.9	53.3	241.4	2,204.8	2,258.8	2,254.5	13.1	13.1
1979	−23.8	228.9	252.7	448.5	179.3	121.9	57.5	269.2	2,475.9	2,512.5	2,520.8	11.5	11.2
1980	−14.7	279.2	293.9	507.1	209.1	142.7	66.4	298.0	2,717.5	2,722.8	2,742.1	8.8	8.4
1981	−14.7	303.0	317.7	561.1	240.8	167.5	73.3	320.3	3,005.2	3,045.3	3,063.8	11.9	11.8
1982	−20.6	282.6	303.2	607.6	266.6	193.8	72.7	341.1	3,165.5	3,170.2	3,179.8	3.9	4.1
1983	−51.4	276.7	328.1	652.3	292.0	214.4	77.5	360.3	3,410.6	3,456.5	3,434.4	8.1	9.0
1984	−102.7	302.4	405.1	700.8	310.9	233.1	77.8	389.9	3,706.1	3,879.9	3,801.5	10.9	12.2
1985	−115.6	302.1	417.6	772.3	344.3	258.6	85.7	428.1	4,014.1	4,154.3	4,053.6	6.9	7.1
1986	−132.5	319.2	451.7	833.0	367.8	276.7	91.1	465.3	4,260.0	4,401.2	4,277.7	5.7	5.9
1987	−143.1	364.0	507.1	881.5	384.9	292.1	92.9	496.6	4,513.7	4,683.0	4,544.5	6.4	6.4
1988	−108.0	444.2	552.2	918.7	387.0	295.6	91.4	531.7	4,884.2	5,008.4	4,908.2	7.9	6.9
1989	−79.7	508.0	587.7	975.2	401.6	299.9	101.7	573.6	5,217.5	5,330.5	5,266.8	7.2	6.4
1990	−68.9	557.0	625.9	1,043.2	426.4	314.0	112.4	616.8	5,515.9	5,591.1	5,542.9	5.2	4.9
1991	−21.8	598.2	620.0	1,090.5	447.3	323.8	123.6	643.2	5,687.7	5,699.3	5,694.9	2.8	1.9
1982: IV	−29.5	265.6	295.1	631.6	281.4	205.5	75.9	350.3	3,241.4	3,224.6	3,222.6		
1983: IV	−71.8	286.2	358.0	657.6	289.7	222.8	66.9	367.9	3,527.1	3,619.1	3,578.4		
1984: IV	−107.1	308.7	415.7	727.0	324.7	242.9	81.9	402.2	3,818.1	3,976.2	3,890.2		
1985: IV	−135.5	304.7	440.2	799.2	356.9	268.6	88.3	442.4	4,107.9	4,276.0	4,156.2		
1986: IV	−133.2	333.9	467.1	849.7	373.1	278.6	94.5	476.6	4,355.4	4,469.8	4,340.5		
1987: IV	−143.2	392.4	535.6	901.4	392.5	295.8	96.7	500.9	4,623.7	4,826.2	4,690.5		
1988: IV	−106.0	467.0	573.1	937.6	392.0	296.8	95.2	545.7	5,027.3	5,150.7	5,054.3		
1989: I	−85.1	489.7	574.9	950.4	392.3	293.5	98.7	558.1	5,106.2	5,235.1	5,164.0	8.6	6.7
II	−80.1	509.5	589.6	970.2	401.6	298.2	103.4	568.6	5,189.7	5,309.6	5,243.3	6.3	5.8
III	−79.7	509.0	588.7	985.6	407.3	305.3	101.9	578.4	5,259.3	5,358.6	5,294.7	3.8	3.7
IV	−73.9	523.8	597.7	994.5	405.1	302.5	102.6	589.3	5,314.6	5,418.7	5,365.0	5.1	4.6
1990: I	−72.1	541.2	613.3	1,024.7	420.3	311.6	108.7	604.3	5,437.1	5,517.4	5,464.1	7.7	7.5
II	−59.9	551.2	611.2	1,034.3	424.4	312.9	111.5	610.0	5,484.9	5,582.6	5,537.0	5.8	4.8
III	−76.3	555.9	632.2	1,042.4	422.6	308.4	114.3	619.7	5,549.2	5,635.9	5,577.8	2.7	3.9
IV	−67.2	579.7	646.9	1,071.3	438.3	323.2	115.0	633.0	5,592.3	5,628.5	5,592.7	.1	−.5
1991: I	−28.7	573.2	602.0	1,087.5	451.3	332.4	118.8	636.3	5,614.4	5,614.6	5,614.9	1.8	−1.0
II	−15.3	594.3	609.6	1,090.8	449.9	325.9	124.0	640.8	5,679.4	5,672.9	5,674.3	5.2	4.2
III	−27.1	602.3	629.5	1,093.3	447.2	321.9	125.3	646.0	5,712.9	5,740.3	5,726.4	4.0	4.8
IV	−16.0	622.9	638.9	1,090.3	440.8	314.7	126.1	649.5	5,744.2	5,769.3	5,764.1	2.8	2.0
1992: I	−8.1	628.1	636.2	1,103.1	445.0	313.6	131.4	658.0	5,855.9	5,848.3	5,859.8	6.2	5.6
II	−37.1	625.4	662.5	1,109.1	444.8	311.7	133.1	664.3	5,894.1	5,939.4	5,909.3	4.3	6.4
III	−36.0	639.0	675.0	1,124.2	455.2	319.6	135.7	669.0	5,963.5	6,014.5	5,992.0	5.3	5.2

[1] Excludes receipts and payments of factor income from or to rest of the world.
[2] Gross domestic product (GDP) less exports of goods and services plus imports of goods and services.
[3] GDP plus net receipts of factor income from rest of the world.

Source: Department of Commerce, Bureau of Economic Analysis.

TABLE B-2.—*Gross domestic product in 1987 dollars, 1959-92*

[Billions of 1987 dollars, except as noted; quarterly data at seasonally adjusted annual rates]

Year or quarter	Gross domestic product	Personal consumption expenditures				Gross private domestic investment						Change in business inventories
							Fixed investment					
								Nonresidential				
		Total	Durable goods	Non-durable goods	Services	Total	Total	Total	Structures	Producers' durable equipment	Residential	
1959	1,928.8	1,178.9	114.4	518.5	546.0	296.4	282.8	165.2	74.4	90.8	117.6	13.6
1960	1,970.8	1,210.8	115.4	526.9	568.5	290.8	282.7	173.3	80.8	92.5	109.4	8.1
1961	2,023.8	1,238.4	109.4	537.7	591.3	289.4	282.2	172.1	82.3	89.8	110.1	7.2
1962	2,128.1	1,293.3	120.2	553.0	620.0	321.2	305.6	185.0	86.1	98.9	120.6	15.6
1963	2,215.6	1,341.9	130.3	563.6	648.0	343.3	327.3	192.3	86.9	105.4	135.0	16.0
1964	2,340.6	1,417.2	140.7	588.2	688.3	371.8	356.2	214.0	95.9	118.1	142.1	15.7
1965	2,470.5	1,497.0	156.2	616.7	724.1	413.0	387.9	250.6	111.5	139.1	137.3	25.1
1966	2,616.2	1,573.8	166.0	647.6	760.2	438.0	401.3	276.7	119.1	157.6	124.5	36.7
1967	2,685.2	1,622.4	167.2	659.0	796.2	418.6	391.0	270.8	116.0	154.8	120.2	27.6
1968	2,796.9	1,707.5	184.5	686.0	837.0	440.1	416.5	280.1	117.4	162.7	136.4	23.6
1969	2,873.0	1,771.2	190.8	703.2	877.2	461.3	436.5	296.4	123.5	172.9	140.1	24.8
1970	2,873.9	1,813.5	183.7	717.2	912.5	429.7	423.8	292.0	123.3	168.7	131.8	5.9
1971	2,955.9	1,873.7	201.4	725.6	946.7	475.7	454.9	286.8	121.2	165.6	168.1	20.8
1972	3,107.1	1,978.4	225.2	755.8	997.4	532.2	509.6	311.6	124.8	186.8	198.0	22.5
1973	3,268.6	2,066.7	246.6	777.9	1,042.2	591.7	554.0	357.4	134.9	222.4	196.6	37.7
1974	3,248.1	2,053.8	227.2	759.8	1,066.8	543.0	512.0	356.5	132.3	224.2	155.6	30.9
1975	3,221.7	2,097.5	226.8	767.1	1,103.6	437.6	451.5	316.8	118.0	198.8	134.7	-13.9
1976	3,380.8	2,207.3	256.4	801.3	1,149.5	520.6	495.1	328.7	120.5	208.2	166.4	25.5
1977	3,533.3	2,296.6	280.0	819.8	1,196.8	600.4	566.2	364.3	126.1	238.2	201.9	34.3
1978	3,703.5	2,391.8	292.9	844.8	1,254.1	664.6	627.4	412.9	144.1	268.8	214.5	37.2
1979	3,796.8	2,448.4	289.0	862.8	1,296.5	669.7	656.1	448.8	163.3	285.5	207.4	13.6
1980	3,776.3	2,447.1	262.7	860.5	1,323.9	594.4	602.7	437.8	170.2	267.6	164.8	-8.3
1981	3,843.1	2,476.9	264.6	867.9	1,344.4	631.1	606.5	455.0	182.9	272.0	151.6	24.6
1982	3,760.3	2,503.7	262.5	872.2	1,368.9	540.5	558.0	433.9	181.3	252.6	124.1	-17.5
1983	3,906.6	2,619.4	297.7	900.3	1,421.4	599.5	595.1	420.8	160.3	260.5	174.2	4.4
1984	4,148.5	2,746.1	338.5	934.6	1,473.0	757.5	689.6	490.2	182.8	307.4	199.3	67.9
1985	4,279.8	2,865.8	370.1	958.7	1,537.0	745.9	723.8	521.8	197.4	324.4	202.0	22.1
1986	4,404.5	2,969.1	402.0	991.0	1,576.1	735.1	726.5	500.3	176.6	323.7	226.2	8.5
1987	4,539.9	3,052.2	403.7	1,011.1	1,637.4	749.3	723.0	497.8	171.3	326.5	225.2	26.3
1988	4,718.6	3,162.4	428.7	1,035.1	1,698.5	773.4	753.4	530.8	174.0	356.8	222.7	19.9
1989	4,838.0	3,223.3	440.7	1,051.6	1,731.0	784.0	754.2	540.0	177.6	362.5	214.2	29.8
1990	4,877.5	3,260.4	439.3	1,056.5	1,764.6	739.1	732.9	538.1	179.1	359.0	194.8	6.2
1991	4,821.0	3,240.8	414.7	1,042.4	1,783.7	661.1	670.4	500.2	157.6	342.6	170.2	-9.3
1982: IV	3,759.6	2,539.3	272.3	880.7	1,386.2	503.5	548.4	417.2	173.2	244.0	131.2	-44.9
1983: IV	4,012.1	2,678.2	319.1	915.2	1,443.9	669.5	640.2	449.6	162.6	287.0	190.6	29.3
1984: IV	4,194.2	2,784.8	347.7	942.9	1,494.2	756.4	708.4	509.6	189.5	320.1	198.8	47.9
1985: IV	4,333.5	2,895.3	369.6	968.7	1,557.1	763.1	732.9	525.5	198.3	327.2	207.4	30.2
1986: IV	4,427.1	3,012.5	415.7	1,000.9	1,595.8	705.9	725.9	495.5	170.4	325.0	230.5	-20.1
1987: IV	4,625.5	3,074.7	404.7	1,014.6	1,655.5	793.8	733.9	510.6	177.9	332.7	223.3	59.9
1988: IV	4,779.7	3,202.9	439.2	1,046.8	1,716.9	785.0	764.1	538.8	175.7	363.1	225.3	20.9
1989: I	4,817.6	3,203.6	435.2	1,048.1	1,720.3	802.9	761.7	539.5	177.0	362.4	222.2	41.2
II	4,839.0	3,212.2	440.2	1,047.0	1,725.1	794.5	757.5	542.2	174.7	367.5	215.4	36.9
III	4,839.0	3,235.3	450.6	1,052.6	1,732.2	769.0	753.1	541.8	178.8	363.0	211.2	16.0
IV	4,856.7	3,242.0	436.8	1,058.9	1,746.3	769.5	744.6	536.7	179.8	356.9	208.0	24.9
1990: I	4,890.8	3,259.5	453.5	1,058.3	1,747.7	763.0	755.4	544.8	182.0	362.8	210.7	7.5
II	4,902.7	3,260.1	439.2	1,057.1	1,763.7	770.2	737.4	535.6	180.1	355.5	201.8	32.8
III	4,882.6	3,273.9	437.7	1,059.1	1,777.1	743.1	732.0	542.9	181.2	361.7	189.1	11.2
IV	4,833.8	3,248.0	426.6	1,051.6	1,769.8	680.0	706.8	529.3	173.2	356.1	177.5	-26.8
1991: I	4,796.7	3,223.5	412.0	1,043.0	1,768.5	646.0	671.1	507.0	166.8	340.2	164.1	-25.1
II	4,817.1	3,239.3	411.3	1,046.3	1,781.8	649.5	669.8	503.0	162.2	340.8	166.9	-20.4
III	4,831.8	3,251.2	419.4	1,044.8	1,787.0	672.0	671.4	498.7	153.0	345.8	172.6	.6
IV	4,838.5	3,249.0	416.1	1,035.6	1,797.4	676.9	669.3	492.1	148.4	343.7	177.3	7.5
1992: I	4,873.7	3,289.3	432.3	1,049.6	1,807.3	668.9	681.4	495.8	149.4	346.4	185.6	-12.6
II	4,892.4	3,288.5	430.0	1,045.6	1,812.9	713.6	705.9	514.7	149.1	365.6	191.2	7.8
III	4,933.7	3,318.4	439.8	1,052.0	1,826.6	724.9	710.0	518.7	144.7	374.0	191.3	15.0

See next page for continuation of table.

TABLE B-2.—*Gross domestic product in 1987 dollars, 1959-92*—Continued

[Billions of 1987 dollars, except as noted; quarterly data at seasonally adjusted annual rates]

Year or quarter	Net exports of goods and services [1]			Government purchases					Final sales of domestic product	Gross domestic purchases [2]	Addendum: Gross national product [3]	Percent change from preceding period	
					Federal								
	Net exports	Exports	Imports	Total	Total	National defense	Non-defense	State and local				Gross domestic product	Gross domestic purchases [2]
1959	−21.8	73.8	95.6	475.3	265.7				209.6	1,915.2	1,950.6	1,939.6	5.5	5.8
1960	−7.6	88.4	96.1	476.9	259.0				217.9	1,962.7	1,978.5	1,982.8	2.2	1.4
1961	−5.5	89.9	95.3	501.5	270.1				231.4	2,016.6	2,029.3	2,037.1	2.7	2.6
1962	−10.5	95.0	105.5	524.2	287.3				236.9	2,112.5	2,138.6	2,143.3	5.2	5.4
1963	−5.8	101.8	107.7	536.3	285.7				250.6	2,199.6	2,221.4	2,231.8	4.1	3.9
1964	2.5	115.4	112.9	549.1	281.8				267.3	2,324.9	2,338.1	2,358.1	5.6	5.3
1965	−6.4	118.1	124.5	566.9	282.1				284.8	2,445.4	2,476.9	2,488.9	5.5	5.9
1966	−18.0	125.7	143.7	622.4	319.3				303.1	2,579.5	2,634.2	2,633.2	5.9	6.4
1967	−23.7	130.0	153.7	667.9	350.9				317.0	2,657.5	2,708.9	2,702.6	2.6	2.8
1968	−37.5	140.2	177.7	686.8	353.1				333.7	2,773.2	2,834.4	2,815.6	4.2	4.6
1969	−41.5	147.8	189.2	682.0	340.1				341.9	2,848.2	2,914.5	2,890.9	2.7	2.8
1970	−35.2	161.3	196.4	665.8	315.0				350.9	2,868.0	2,909.1	2,891.5	.0	−.2
1971	−45.9	161.9	207.8	652.4	290.8				361.6	2,935.2	3,001.8	2,975.9	2.9	3.2
1972	−56.5	173.7	230.2	653.0	284.4	209.6	74.8	368.6	3,084.5	3,163.6	3,128.8	5.1	5.4
1973	−34.1	210.3	244.4	642.2	265.3	191.3	74.1	378.9	3,230.9	3,302.7	3,298.6	5.2	4.4
1974	−4.1	234.4	238.4	655.4	262.6	185.8	76.8	392.9	3,217.2	3,252.2	3,282.4	−.6	−1.5
1975	23.1	232.9	209.8	663.5	262.7	184.9	77.8	400.8	3,235.6	3,198.6	3,247.6	−.8	−1.6
1976	−6.4	243.4	249.7	659.2	258.2	179.9	78.3	401.1	3,355.3	3,387.1	3,412.2	4.9	5.9
1977	−27.8	246.9	274.7	664.1	263.1	181.6	81.4	401.0	3,499.0	3,561.1	3,569.0	4.5	5.1
1978	−29.9	270.2	300.1	677.0	268.6	182.1	86.5	408.4	3,666.3	3,733.3	3,739.0	4.8	4.8
1979	−10.6	293.5	304.1	689.3	271.7	185.1	86.6	417.6	3,783.2	3,807.4	3,845.3	2.5	2.0
1980	30.7	320.5	289.9	704.2	284.8	194.2	90.6	419.4	3,784.6	3,745.7	3,823.4	−.5	−1.6
1981	22.0	326.1	304.1	713.2	295.8	206.4	89.4	417.4	3,818.6	3,821.2	3,884.4	1.8	2.0
1982	−7.4	296.7	304.1	723.6	306.0	221.4	84.7	417.6	3,777.8	3,767.7	3,796.1	−2.2	−1.4
1983	−56.1	285.9	342.1	743.8	320.8	234.2	86.6	423.0	3,902.2	3,962.8	3,939.6	3.9	5.2
1984	−122.0	305.7	427.7	766.9	331.0	245.8	85.1	436.0	4,080.6	4,270.5	4,174.5	6.2	7.8
1985	−145.3	309.2	454.6	813.4	355.2	265.6	89.5	458.2	4,257.6	4,425.1	4,295.0	3.2	3.6
1986	−155.1	329.6	484.7	855.4	373.0	280.6	92.4	482.4	4,395.9	4,559.6	4,413.5	2.9	3.0
1987	−143.1	364.0	507.1	881.5	384.9	292.1	92.9	496.6	4,513.7	4,683.0	4,544.5	3.1	2.7
1988	−104.0	421.6	525.7	886.8	377.3	287.0	90.2	509.6	4,698.6	4,822.6	4,726.3	3.9	3.0
1989	−73.7	471.8	545.4	904.4	376.1	281.4	94.8	528.3	4,808.3	4,911.7	4,852.7	2.5	1.8
1990	−51.8	510.0	561.8	929.9	383.6	283.3	100.3	546.3	4,871.3	4,929.3	4,895.9	.8	.4
1991	−21.8	539.4	561.2	941.0	388.3	282.8	105.5	552.7	4,830.3	4,842.8	4,836.4	−1.2	−1.8
1982: IV	−19.0	280.4	299.4	735.9	316.0	229.4	86.6	419.9	3,804.5	3,778.6	3,791.7		
1983: IV	−83.7	291.5	375.1	748.1	322.2	242.9	79.3	425.9	3,982.8	4,095.8	4,046.6		
1984: IV	−131.4	312.8	444.2	784.3	341.7	254.3	87.4	442.6	4,146.2	4,325.5	4,216.4		
1985: IV	−155.4	312.0	467.4	830.5	363.7	272.1	91.6	466.7	4,303.3	4,488.9	4,349.5		
1986: IV	−156.0	342.9	498.9	864.8	377.5	282.2	95.3	487.3	4,447.2	4,583.1	4,430.8		
1987: IV	−136.0	386.1	522.1	893.0	391.6	295.0	96.6	501.4	4,565.6	4,761.5	4,633.0		
1988: IV	−102.7	438.2	540.9	894.5	378.4	285.7	92.7	516.1	4,758.7	4,882.4	4,789.0		
1989: I	−79.8	454.5	534.3	890.8	370.1	276.7	93.4	520.7	4,776.3	4,897.3	4,830.7	3.2	1.2
II	−70.0	472.0	541.9	902.3	376.9	280.4	96.5	525.4	4,802.0	4,908.9	4,851.6	1.8	1.0
III	−77.5	472.9	550.5	912.2	381.5	286.9	94.5	530.7	4,823.0	4,916.5	4,853.4	.0	.6
IV	−67.4	487.7	555.0	912.6	376.1	281.5	94.7	536.5	4,831.8	4,924.1	4,875.1	1.5	.6
1990: I	−58.4	500.2	558.6	926.8	383.4	284.9	98.5	543.4	4,883.3	4,949.2	4,907.8	2.8	2.1
II	−56.9	508.7	565.6	929.4	385.4	285.1	100.3	544.0	4,870.0	4,959.7	4,915.5	1.0	.9
III	−59.3	508.4	567.7	924.8	378.3	277.3	101.0	546.5	4,871.4	4,941.9	4,898.9	−1.6	−1.4
IV	−32.7	522.6	555.3	938.5	387.3	285.8	101.5	551.2	4,860.6	4,866.5	4,861.4	−3.9	−6.0
1991: I	−17.9	515.9	533.8	945.1	394.1	291.8	102.2	551.0	4,821.8	4,814.6	4,822.0	−3.0	−4.2
II	−17.4	536.1	553.5	945.6	393.8	287.6	106.2	551.8	4,837.4	4,834.4	4,831.8	1.7	1.7
III	−31.6	544.2	575.8	940.2	387.2	280.6	106.6	553.0	4,831.2	4,863.4	4,843.7	1.2	2.4
IV	−20.5	561.4	581.8	933.1	378.2	271.0	107.2	554.9	4,830.9	4,858.9	4,848.2	.6	−.4
1992: I	−21.5	565.4	586.8	937.0	375.3	265.0	109.7	561.8	4,886.3	4,895.2	4,890.7	2.9	3.0
II	−43.9	563.4	607.3	934.2	372.7	262.1	110.6	561.5	4,884.6	4,936.3	4,899.1	1.5	3.4
III	−52.7	575.9	628.6	943.0	379.5	267.4	112.1	563.5	4,918.7	4,986.4	4,945.6	3.4	4.1

[1] Excludes receipts and payments of factor income from or to rest of the world.
[2] Gross domestic product (GDP) less exports of goods and services plus imports of goods and services.
[3] GDP plus net receipts of factor income from rest of the world.

Source: Department of Commerce, Bureau of Economic Analysis.

[Index numbers, 1987=100, except as noted; quarterly data seasonally adjusted]

Year or quarter	Gross domestic product	Personal consumption expenditures				Fixed investment Total	Nonresidential			Residential
		Total	Durable goods	Nondurable goods	Services		Total	Structures	Producers' durable equipment	
1959	25.6	27.0	37.4	28.6	23.2	26.4	28.1	24.4	31.2	23.9
1960	26.0	27.5	37.7	29.1	23.9	26.7	28.4	24.2	32.1	24.0
1961	26.3	27.7	38.3	29.3	24.4	26.6	28.2	24.0	32.2	24.0
1962	26.9	28.2	39.1	29.6	24.8	26.8	28.6	24.1	32.4	24.0
1963	27.2	28.6	39.7	30.1	25.2	26.8	28.9	24.4	32.6	23.8
1964	27.7	29.1	40.4	30.5	25.6	27.1	29.2	24.7	32.8	24.1
1965	28.4	29.7	40.6	31.1	26.1	27.9	29.6	25.4	32.9	24.9
1966	29.4	30.6	41.3	32.2	26.9	29.1	30.5	26.3	33.6	25.9
1967	30.3	31.4	42.3	32.9	27.8	30.1	31.5	27.2	34.7	26.9
1968	31.8	32.7	43.9	34.3	29.0	31.4	32.9	28.6	36.0	28.4
1969	33.4	34.1	45.2	35.9	30.2	33.3	34.7	30.5	37.7	30.4
1970	35.2	35.6	46.4	37.7	31.9	34.9	36.5	32.7	39.4	31.4
1971	37.1	37.4	48.3	39.0	33.8	36.8	39.0	35.2	41.7	33.2
1972	38.8	38.8	49.2	40.4	35.3	38.4	40.5	37.8	42.2	35.2
1973	41.3	41.0	50.3	43.7	36.9	40.7	42.0	40.7	42.7	38.3
1974	44.9	45.2	54.1	50.1	39.7	45.2	46.4	46.3	46.5	42.4
1975	49.2	48.9	59.2	54.2	43.0	51.3	53.3	52.0	54.1	46.6
1976	52.3	51.8	62.4	56.4	46.2	54.5	56.9	54.7	58.2	49.6
1977	55.9	55.4	65.2	59.8	50.0	58.9	61.3	59.2	62.4	54.6
1978	60.3	59.4	69.1	64.1	54.0	64.7	66.5	65.2	67.2	61.3
1979	65.5	64.7	74.1	71.1	58.3	71.2	72.7	72.5	72.9	68.0
1980	71.7	71.4	80.9	79.4	64.4	79.2	80.8	80.8	80.9	74.8
1981	78.9	77.8	86.4	85.7	70.9	87.8	90.1	92.5	88.5	80.9
1982	83.8	82.2	90.1	88.6	76.7	93.1	95.3	98.6	93.0	85.2
1983	87.2	86.2	92.4	90.8	81.9	92.8	95.1	95.5	94.8	87.3
1984	91.0	89.6	93.9	93.4	86.2	93.9	95.7	96.1	95.4	89.7
1985	94.4	93.1	95.4	95.9	90.8	95.3	96.6	98.0	95.7	92.0
1986	96.9	96.0	96.9	96.1	95.7	97.6	98.4	98.5	98.4	95.8
1987	100.0	100.0	100.0	100.0	100.0	100.0	100.0	100.0	100.0	100.0
1988	103.9	104.2	102.0	103.7	105.1	103.2	102.8	104.6	101.9	104.2
1989	108.5	109.3	104.2	109.3	110.6	105.9	105.2	108.9	103.4	107.8
1990	113.2	115.0	105.7	115.9	116.7	108.2	107.3	112.3	104.9	110.7
1991	117.8	120.0	107.6	120.1	122.8	109.1	108.2	114.3	105.4	111.8
1982: IV	85.0	83.8	90.6	89.4	79.0	93.1	95.3	97.5	93.8	86.0
1983: IV	88.4	87.6	93.3	91.8	83.7	92.9	95.0	95.1	94.9	88.0
1984: IV	92.3	90.7	94.4	94.2	87.7	94.8	96.4	97.2	96.0	90.7
1985: IV	95.5	94.6	95.9	97.0	92.9	96.1	97.3	98.5	96.5	93.1
1986: IV	98.0	97.0	97.8	96.3	97.3	98.6	99.2	98.8	99.5	97.3
1987: IV	101.2	101.6	101.0	101.5	101.9	101.0	100.7	101.2	100.5	101.5
1988: IV	105.5	106.1	103.1	105.6	107.1	104.4	104.0	106.3	102.8	105.3
1989: I	106.9	107.4	103.6	107.0	108.6	105.1	104.4	107.4	103.0	106.5
II	108.1	108.9	104.0	109.5	109.9	105.7	104.8	108.6	103.1	107.8
III	109.1	109.8	104.5	109.9	111.2	106.2	105.5	109.3	103.6	108.2
IV	110.1	111.0	104.9	110.8	112.7	106.8	106.0	110.1	103.9	108.8
1990: I	111.3	112.7	105.4	113.3	114.2	107.5	106.5	111.2	104.1	110.2
II	112.6	114.0	105.5	114.3	115.8	107.8	106.8	111.9	104.3	110.6
III	113.9	115.7	105.8	116.6	117.6	108.7	107.8	112.7	105.3	111.1
IV	115.0	117.6	106.1	119.3	119.3	108.9	108.2	113.3	105.7	111.0
1991: I	116.5	118.6	106.7	119.4	120.8	109.4	108.7	113.9	106.2	111.3
II	117.5	119.5	107.3	119.9	122.1	109.3	108.5	114.2	105.8	111.6
III	118.2	120.4	108.0	120.2	123.4	109.1	108.0	114.8	104.9	112.5
IV	118.9	121.4	108.3	120.8	124.7	108.6	107.4	114.4	104.5	111.8
1992: I	119.8	122.3	108.6	121.4	126.1	108.3	107.1	113.9	104.2	111.7
II	120.6	123.4	109.4	122.2	127.4	108.4	106.9	114.2	103.9	112.3
III	121.2	123.8	109.7	122.9	127.7	108.0	106.0	114.9	102.5	113.4

See next page for continuation of table.

TABLE B-3.—*Implicit price deflators for gross domestic product, 1959–92*—Continued

[Index numbers, 1987=100, except as noted; quarterly data seasonally adjusted]

Year or quarter	Exports and imports of goods and services [1]		Government purchases	Federal			State and local	Final sales of domestic product	Gross domestic purchases [2]	Percent change from preceding period, GDP implicit price deflator [3]
	Exports	Imports	Total	Total	National defense	Non-defense				
1959	28.0	23.4	20.8	21.5			19.9	25.6	25.4	2.8
1960	28.6	23.8	20.9	21.3			20.4	26.0	25.8	1.6
1961	29.0	23.8	21.3	21.7			20.9	26.2	26.0	1.2
1962	28.9	23.7	22.3	22.8			21.7	26.8	26.6	2.3
1963	28.9	24.3	22.8	23.3			22.3	27.2	27.0	1.1
1964	29.1	24.9	23.4	23.9			22.8	27.7	27.5	1.8
1965	30.0	25.3	24.0	24.6			23.5	28.3	28.2	2.5
1966	31.0	25.8	25.0	25.5			24.6	29.3	29.2	3.5
1967	31.8	26.0	26.3	26.5			26.1	30.2	30.0	3.1
1968	32.3	26.2	27.9	28.1			27.7	31.7	31.4	5.0
1969	33.3	26.7	29.6	29.6			29.6	33.3	33.0	5.0
1970	35.3	28.4	31.9	31.8			32.1	35.2	34.7	5.4
1971	36.6	30.0	34.4	34.4			34.4	37.1	36.7	5.4
1972	38.1	32.2	37.0	37.6	36.9	39.3	36.5	38.8	38.4	4.6
1973	43.6	37.3	40.0	40.9	40.5	41.9	39.4	41.2	40.8	6.4
1974	53.0	53.5	44.0	44.8	44.5	45.5	43.5	44.9	44.9	8.7
1975	58.5	58.5	48.4	49.3	48.5	51.2	47.9	49.2	49.2	9.6
1976	61.2	60.5	51.8	52.6	51.9	54.1	51.2	52.2	52.3	6.3
1977	64.3	66.4	55.4	56.2	55.6	57.7	54.9	55.7	56.1	6.9
1978	68.9	70.7	59.6	60.4	59.8	61.7	59.1	60.1	60.5	7.9
1979	78.0	83.1	65.1	66.0	65.8	66.4	64.5	65.4	66.0	8.6
1980	87.1	101.4	72.0	73.4	73.5	73.3	71.1	71.8	72.7	9.5
1981	92.9	104.5	78.7	81.4	81.1	82.1	76.7	78.7	79.7	10.0
1982	95.2	99.7	84.0	87.1	87.6	85.9	81.7	83.8	84.1	6.2
1983	96.8	95.9	87.7	91.0	91.6	89.5	85.2	87.4	87.2	4.1
1984	98.9	94.7	91.4	93.9	94.8	91.3	89.4	90.8	90.9	4.4
1985	97.7	91.9	95.0	96.3	97.3	95.7	93.4	94.3	93.9	3.7
1986	96.9	93.2	97.4	98.6	98.6	98.6	96.4	96.9	96.5	2.6
1987	100.0	100.0	100.0	100.0	100.0	100.0	100.0	100.0	100.0	3.2
1988	105.3	105.1	103.6	102.6	103.0	101.4	104.3	103.9	103.9	3.9
1989	107.7	107.8	107.8	106.8	106.6	107.3	108.6	108.5	108.5	4.4
1990	109.2	111.4	112.2	111.2	110.8	112.0	112.9	113.2	113.4	4.3
1991	110.9	110.5	115.9	115.2	114.5	117.1	116.4	117.8	117.7	4.1
1982: IV	94.7	98.5	85.8	89.0	89.6	87.7	83.4	85.2	85.3	
1983: IV	98.2	95.4	87.9	89.9	91.7	84.3	86.4	88.6	88.4	
1984: IV	98.7	93.6	92.7	95.0	95.5	93.7	90.9	92.1	91.9	
1985: IV	97.7	94.2	96.2	98.1	98.7	96.4	94.8	95.5	95.3	
1986: IV	97.4	93.6	98.3	98.8	98.7	99.2	97.8	97.9	97.5	
1987: IV	101.6	102.6	100.9	100.2	100.3	100.1	101.5	101.3	101.4	
1988: IV	106.6	106.0	104.8	103.6	103.9	102.6	105.7	105.6	105.5	
1989: I	107.8	107.6	106.7	106.0	106.1	105.8	107.2	106.9	106.9	5.4
II	107.9	108.8	107.5	106.6	106.4	107.1	108.2	108.1	108.2	4.6
III	107.6	106.9	108.1	106.8	106.4	107.8	109.0	109.0	109.0	3.8
IV	107.4	107.7	109.0	107.7	107.5	108.4	109.9	110.0	110.0	3.7
1990: I	108.2	109.8	110.6	109.6	109.4	110.4	111.2	111.3	111.5	4.4
II	108.4	108.0	111.3	110.1	109.7	111.2	112.1	112.6	112.6	4.8
III	109.3	111.4	112.7	111.7	111.2	113.2	113.4	113.9	114.0	4.7
IV	110.9	116.5	114.1	113.2	113.1	113.3	114.8	115.1	115.7	3.9
1991: I	111.1	112.8	115.1	114.5	113.9	116.2	115.5	116.4	116.6	5.3
II	110.9	110.6	115.4	114.3	113.3	116.8	116.1	117.4	117.3	3.5
III	110.7	109.3	116.3	115.5	114.7	117.6	116.8	118.3	118.0	2.4
IV	111.0	109.8	116.9	116.6	116.2	117.6	117.1	118.9	118.7	2.4
1992: I	111.1	108.4	117.7	118.6	118.1	119.8	117.1	119.8	119.5	3.1
II	111.0	110.0	118.7	119.3	118.9	120.3	118.3	120.7	120.3	2.7
III	111.0	107.4	119.2	120.0	119.5	121.0	118.7	121.2	120.6	2.0

[1] Excludes receipts and payments of factor income from or to rest of the world.
[2] Gross domestic product (GDP) less exports of goods and services plus imports of goods and services.
[3] Quarterly changes are at annual rates.

Note.—Separate deflators are not calculated for gross private domestic investment, change in business inventories, and net exports of goods and services.

Source: Department of Commerce, Bureau of Economic Analysis.

353

TABLE B-4.—*Changes in gross domestic product and personal consumption expenditures, and related implicit price deflators and fixed-weighted price indexes, 1960–92*

[Percent change from preceding period; quarterly data at seasonally adjusted annual rates]

Year or quarter	Gross domestic product				Personal consumption expenditures			
	Current dollars	Con-stant (1987) dollars	Implicit price deflator	Fixed-weight-ed price index (1987 weights)	Current dollars	Con-stant (1987) dollars	Implicit price deflator	Fixed-weight-ed price index (1987 weights)
1960	3.9	2.2	1.6		4.5	2.7	1.9	1.3
1961	3.6	2.7	1.2		3.3	2.3	.7	.8
1962	7.5	5.2	2.3		6.1	4.4	1.8	.6
1963	5.5	4.1	1.1		5.4	3.8	1.4	.9
1964	7.4	5.6	1.8		7.4	5.6	1.7	1.1
1965	8.4	5.5	2.5		7.8	5.6	2.1	1.0
1966	9.5	5.9	3.5		8.3	5.1	3.0	1.8
1967	5.8	2.6	3.1		5.8	3.1	2.6	2.6
1968	9.2	4.2	5.0		9.8	5.2	4.1	3.8
1969	7.9	2.7	5.0		8.0	3.7	4.3	3.8
1970	5.3	.0	5.4		7.1	2.4	4.4	4.4
1971	8.6	2.9	5.4		8.3	3.3	5.1	4,4
1972	10.0	5.1	4.6		9.6	5.6	3.7	3.3
1973	11.8	5.2	6.4		10.5	4.5	5.7	4.6
1974	8.1	−.6	8.7		9.4	−.6	10.2	9.3
1975	8.7	−.8	9.6		10.5	2.1	8.2	8.1
1976	11.5	4.9	6.3		11.5	5.2	5.9	5.6
1977	11.6	4.5	6.9		11.2	4.0	6.9	6.4
1978	13.1	4.8	7.9		11.8	4.1	7.2	7.0
1979	11.5	2.5	8.6		11.4	2.4	8.9	8.5
1980	8.8	−.5	9.5		10.4	−.1	10.4	10.3
1981	11.9	1.8	10.0		10.2	1.2	9.0	8.6
1982	3.9	−2.2	6.2		6.9	1.1	5.7	5.4
1983	8.1	3.9	4.1	3.9	9.6	4.6	4.9	4.3
1984	10.9	6.2	4.4	3.4	9.0	4.8	3.9	3.7
1985	6.9	3.2	3.7	3.5	8.4	4.4	3.9	3.8
1986	5.7	2.9	2.6	2.8	6.9	3.6	3.1	3.0
1987	6.4	3.1	3.2	3.1	7.1	2.8	4.2	4.1
1988	7.9	3.9	3.9	3.9	8.0	3.6	4.2	4.3
1989	7.2	2.5	4.4	4.4	6.9	1.9	4.9	4.9
1990	5.2	.8	4.3	4.5	6.4	1.2	5.2	5.3
1991	2.8	−1.2	4.1	4.0	3.7	−.6	4.3	4.4
1987: I	6.8	3.0	3.3	3.4	5.5	−.1	5.9	5.6
II	8.1	5.1	2.9	2.8	9.4	4.8	4.5	4.4
III	7.2	4.0	3.3	3.3	8.3	3.9	4.1	4.3
IV	9.9	5.9	3.6	3.6	4.4	−.1	4.5	4.5
1988: I	6.1	2.6	3.6	3.6	9.9	7.1	2.8	2.7
II	9.1	4.3	4.4	4.5	7.9	2.5	5.2	5.2
III	7.6	2.5	5.1	5.4	8.4	2.9	5.1	5.3
IV	8.1	3.9	3.9	3.7	8.9	4.1	4.7	4.6
1989: I	8.6	3.2	5.4	5.0	5.1	.1	5.0	5.2
II	6.3	1.8	4.6	4.7	7.0	1.1	5.7	5.9
III	3.8	0	3.8	3.7	6.3	2.9	3.3	3.5
IV	5.1	1.5	3.7	3.6	5.3	.8	4.4	4.3
1990: I	7.7	2.8	4.4	5.4	8.4	2.2	6.3	6.4
II	5.8	1.0	4.8	4.6	4.8	.1	4.7	4.4
III	2.7	−1.6	4.7	4.7	8.0	1.7	6.1	6.4
IV	.1	−3.9	3.9	4.1	3.2	−3.1	6.7	6.8
1991: I	1.8	−3.0	5.3	4.7	.4	−3.0	3.4	3.4
II	5.2	1.7	3.5	3.5	5.4	2.0	3.1	3.3
III	4.0	1.2	2.4	3.0	4.4	1.5	3.0	3.0
IV	2.8	.6	2.4	2.4	3.0	−.3	3.4	3.1
1992: I	6.2	2.9	3.1	3.6	8.4	5.1	3.0	3.5
II	4.3	1.5	2.7	2.9	3.5	−.1	3.6	3.5
III	5.3	3.4	2.0	2.1	5.2	3.7	1.3	2.6

Source: Department of Commerce, Bureau of Economic Analysis.

TABLE B–5.—*Selected per capita product and income series in current and 1987 dollars, 1959–92*

[Quarterly data at seasonally adjusted annual rates, except as noted]

Year or quarter	Current dollars							Constant (1987) dollars						Population (thousands) [1]
	Gross domestic product	Personal income	Disposable personal income	Personal consumption expenditures				Gross domestic product	Disposable personal income	Personal consumption expenditures				
				Total	Durable goods	Non-durable goods	Services			Total	Durable goods	Non-durable goods	Services	
1959	2,791	2,209	1,958	1,796	242	838	716	10,892	7,256	6,658	646	2,928	3,083	177,073
1960	2,840	2,264	1,994	1,839	240	847	752	10,903	7,264	6,698	638	2,915	3,145	180,760
1961	2,894	2,321	2,048	1,869	228	857	784	11,014	7,382	6,740	595	2,926	3,218	183,742
1962	3,063	2,430	2,137	1,953	252	878	823	11,405	7,583	6,931	644	2,964	3,323	186,590
1963	3,186	2,516	2,210	2,030	273	895	861	11,704	7,718	7,089	688	2,977	3,423	189,300
1964	3,376	2,661	2,369	2,149	296	936	917	12,195	8,140	7,384	733	3,065	3,586	191,927
1965	3,616	2,845	2,527	2,287	327	987	974	12,712	8,508	7,703	803	3,173	3,726	194,347
1966	3,915	3,061	2,699	2,450	348	1,060	1,041	13,307	8,822	8,005	844	3,294	3,867	196,599
1967	4,097	3,253	2,861	2,562	355	1,091	1,116	13,510	9,114	8,163	841	3,316	4,006	198,752
1968	4,430	3,536	3,077	2,785	404	1,171	1,211	13,932	9,399	8,506	919	3,417	4,169	200,745
1969	4,733	3,816	3,274	2,978	425	1,244	1,308	14,171	9,606	8,737	941	3,469	4,327	202,736
1970	4,928	4,052	3,521	3,152	416	1,318	1,418	14,013	9,875	8,842	896	3,497	4,449	205,089
1971	5,283	4,302	3,779	3,372	468	1,364	1,540	14,232	10,111	9,022	970	3,494	4,558	207,692
1972	5,750	4,671	4,042	3,658	528	1,454	1,676	14,801	10,414	9,425	1,073	3,601	4,751	209,924
1973	6,368	5,184	4,521	4,002	585	1,602	1,814	15,422	11,013	9,752	1,164	3,670	4,917	211,939
1974	6,819	5,637	4,893	4,337	575	1,780	1,982	15,185	10,832	9,602	1,062	3,552	4,988	213,898
1975	7,343	6,053	5,329	4,745	622	1,926	2,197	14,917	10,906	9,711	1,050	3,552	5,110	215,981
1976	8,109	6,632	5,796	5,241	734	2,072	2,436	15,502	11,192	10,121	1,176	3,674	5,271	218,086
1977	8,961	7,269	6,316	5,772	829	2,226	2,717	16,039	11,406	10,425	1,271	3,722	5,433	220,289
1978	10,029	8,121	7,042	6,384	909	2,432	3,043	16,635	11,851	10,744	1,316	3,795	5,633	222,629
1979	11,055	9,032	7,787	7,035	952	2,725	3,359	16,867	12,039	10,876	1,284	3,833	5,760	225,106
1980	11,892	9,948	8,576	7,677	933	2,999	3,745	16,584	12,005	10,746	1,154	3,779	5,814	227,715
1981	13,177	11,021	9,455	8,375	994	3,236	4,146	16,710	12,156	10,770	1,150	3,774	5,845	229,989
1982	13,564	11,589	9,989	8,868	1,018	3,326	4,523	16,194	12,146	10,782	1,131	3,756	5,895	232,201
1983	14,531	12,216	10,642	9,634	1,173	3,490	4,971	16,672	12,349	11,179	1,270	3,842	6,066	234,326
1984	15,978	13,345	11,673	10,408	1,345	3,693	5,370	17,549	13,029	11,617	1,432	3,953	6,231	236,393
1985	16,933	14,170	12,339	11,184	1,480	3,855	5,849	17,944	13,258	12,015	1,552	4,019	6,444	238,510
1986	17,735	14,917	13,010	11,843	1,619	3,956	6,269	18,299	13,552	12,336	1,670	4,118	6,548	240,691
1987	18,694	15,655	13,545	12,568	1,662	4,163	6,742	18,694	13,545	12,568	1,662	4,163	6,742	242,860
1988	19,994	16,630	14,477	13,448	1,783	4,381	7,284	19,252	13,890	12,903	1,749	4,223	6,930	245,093
1989	21,224	17,706	15,307	14,241	1,857	4,647	7,737	19,556	14,005	13,029	1,781	4,251	6,997	247,397
1990	22,092	18,660	16,174	14,996	1,857	4,899	8,240	19,513	14,068	13,044	1,757	4,227	7,059	249,961
1991	22,466	19,106	16,658	15,384	1,765	4,952	8,666	19,077	13,886	12,824	1,641	4,125	7,058	252,711
1982: IV	13,709	11,786	10,189	9,134	1,059	3,378	4,696	16,132	12,154	10,895	1,169	3,779	5,948	233,060
1983: IV	15,085	12,613	11,033	9,980	1,266	3,572	5,143	17,062	12,591	11,390	1,357	3,892	6,141	235,146
1984: IV	16,310	13,668	11,925	10,649	1,383	3,742	5,524	17,680	13,145	11,739	1,466	3,975	6,298	237,231
1985: IV	17,296	14,440	12,565	11,445	1,480	3,924	6,040	18,102	13,278	12,095	1,544	4,046	6,505	239,387
1986: IV	17,953	15,102	13,121	12,101	1,684	3,990	6,428	18,328	13,522	12,472	1,721	4,144	6,607	241,550
1987: IV	19,213	16,076	13,907	12,819	1,677	4,223	6,919	18,977	13,685	12,615	1,660	4,162	6,792	243,745
1988: IV	20,506	17,053	14,850	13,814	1,841	4,495	7,477	19,429	13,996	13,020	1,785	4,255	6,979	246,004
1989: I	20,893	17,466	15,133	13,959	1,829	4,548	7,582	19,545	14,090	12,997	1,766	4,252	6,979	246,488
II	21,170	17,639	15,214	14,165	1,852	4,641	7,672	19,589	13,967	13,003	1,782	4,238	6,983	247,026
III	21,312	17,720	15,322	14,345	1,901	4,671	7,773	19,536	13,951	13,061	1,819	4,249	6,993	247,701
IV	21,519	17,995	15,558	14,491	1,845	4,725	7,921	19,554	14,015	13,053	1,759	4,263	7,031	248,372
1990: I	21,874	18,365	15,917	14,752	1,920	4,818	8,014	19,647	14,128	13,094	1,822	4,252	7,021	248,931
II	22,130	18,595	16,092	14,887	1,857	4,843	8,187	19,646	14,120	13,063	1,760	4,236	7,067	249,558
III	22,211	18,748	16,242	15,133	1,850	4,935	8,348	19,507	14,038	13,080	1,749	4,231	7,100	250,303
IV	22,152	18,928	16,443	15,209	1,803	4,997	8,409	19,254	13,988	12,938	1,699	4,189	7,049	251,050
1991: I	22,194	18,884	16,433	15,184	1,746	4,947	8,491	19,058	13,861	12,808	1,637	4,144	7,027	251,687
II	22,422	19,050	16,604	15,345	1,749	4,971	8,625	19,090	13,891	12,838	1,630	4,147	7,061	252,329
III	22,577	19,151	16,706	15,468	1,790	4,961	8,717	19,094	13,876	12,848	1,658	4,129	7,062	253,053
IV	22,671	19,337	16,885	15,537	1,775	4,931	8,831	19,066	13,913	12,803	1,639	4,081	7,082	253,776
1992: I	22,958	19,578	17,143	15,814	1,845	5,008	8,960	19,159	14,017	12,930	1,700	4,126	7,104	254,388
II	23,141	19,717	17,297	15,907	1,845	5,009	9,053	19,182	14,021	12,893	1,686	4,099	7,108	255,054
III	23,373	19,790	17,332	16,063	1,887	5,054	9,122	19,288	13,998	12,973	1,719	4,113	7,141	255,786

[1] Population of the United States including Armed Forces overseas; includes Alaska and Hawaii beginning 1960. Annual data are averages of quarterly data. Quarterly data are averages for the period.

Source: Department of Commerce (Bureau of Economic Analysis and Bureau of the Census).

TABLE B–6.—*Gross domestic product by major type of product, 1959–92*

[Billions of dollars; quarterly data at seasonally adjusted annual rates]

Year or quarter	Gross domestic product	Final sales of domestic product	Change in business inventories	Goods [1] Total			Durable goods		Nondurable goods		Services [1]	Structures	Auto output
				Total	Final sales	Change in business inventories	Final sales	Change in business inventories	Final sales	Change in business inventories			
1959	494.2	490.0	4.2	250.8	246.6	4.2	91.1	3.1	155.5	1.1	181.7	61.7	19.4
1960	513.4	510.1	3.2	257.1	253.9	3.2	93.8	1.6	160.1	1.6	195.1	61.1	21.3
1961	531.8	528.9	2.9	260.4	257.4	2.9	93.1	−.1	164.3	3.0	208.6	62.8	17.8
1962	571.6	565.5	6.1	281.5	275.4	6.1	103.4	3.4	172.0	2.7	223.1	67.0	22.4
1963	603.1	597.5	5.7	293.2	287.5	5.7	110.0	2.7	177.5	3.0	238.1	71.9	25.1
1964	648.0	643.0	5.0	313.5	308.5	5.0	119.6	4.0	188.9	1.0	256.9	77.6	25.9
1965	702.7	693.0	9.7	342.9	333.2	9.7	132.4	6.7	200.8	3.0	276.0	83.8	31.1
1966	769.8	756.0	13.8	380.1	366.3	13.8	147.9	10.2	218.5	3.6	302.8	86.9	30.2
1967	814.3	803.8	10.5	395.1	384.6	10.5	154.5	5.5	230.2	5.0	330.7	88.5	27.8
1968	889.3	880.2	9.1	427.4	418.3	9.1	169.1	4.7	249.1	4.4	363.0	98.9	35.0
1969	959.5	949.8	9.7	456.6	446.8	9.7	180.1	6.4	266.8	3.3	395.8	107.1	34.7
1970	1,010.7	1,008.4	2.3	467.8	465.6	2.3	182.1	−.1	283.5	2.3	434.3	108.6	28.5
1971	1,097.2	1,089.2	8.0	493.0	485.0	8.0	189.4	2.8	295.5	5.2	477.0	127.2	38.9
1972	1,207.0	1,197.1	9.9	537.4	527.5	9.9	209.7	7.2	317.8	2.7	523.6	145.9	41.4
1973	1,349.6	1,331.9	17.7	616.6	598.9	17.7	242.0	15.0	356.9	2.8	571.0	161.9	45.9
1974	1,458.6	1,444.4	14.3	662.8	648.5	14.3	257.1	11.2	391.4	3.1	631.3	164.5	38.8
1975	1,585.9	1,591.5	−5.7	715.1	720.8	−5.7	288.8	−7.0	432.0	1.3	706.9	163.8	40.3
1976	1,768.4	1,751.7	16.7	798.8	782.0	16.7	323.6	10.3	458.4	6.4	782.2	187.5	55.1
1977	1,974.1	1,949.4	24.7	880.4	855.7	24.7	368.3	9.7	487.4	15.0	870.4	223.3	64.2
1978	2,232.7	2,204.8	27.9	989.1	961.2	27.9	416.9	20.3	544.3	7.6	975.5	268.1	67.9
1979	2,488.6	2,475.9	12.8	1,100.2	1,087.5	12.8	474.5	9.6	613.0	3.1	1,079.6	308.8	66.2
1980	2,708.0	2,717.5	−9.5	1,176.2	1,185.7	−9.5	502.1	−2.6	683.6	−6.8	1,215.4	316.4	59.2
1981	3,030.6	3,005.2	25.4	1,324.6	1,299.2	25.4	544.2	6.2	755.0	19.2	1,357.4	348.6	68.3
1982	3,149.6	3,165.5	−15.9	1,315.0	1,330.9	−15.9	541.6	−16.0	789.3	.1	1,494.2	340.4	65.3
1983	3,405.0	3,410.6	−5.5	1,407.3	1,412.8	−5.5	579.4	5.5	833.4	−11.0	1,636.3	361.5	88.3
1984	3,777.2	3,706.1	71.1	1,591.9	1,520.8	71.1	647.0	44.9	873.8	26.2	1,770.7	414.7	104.2
1985	4,038.7	4,014.1	24.6	1,652.6	1,628.0	24.6	704.8	8.6	923.2	16.0	1,939.0	447.1	115.8
1986	4,268.6	4,260.0	8.6	1,705.3	1,696.7	8.6	730.2	1.6	966.5	7.1	2,097.3	466.0	120.4
1987	4,539.9	4,513.7	26.3	1,794.5	1,768.2	26.3	753.5	21.6	1,014.7	4.7	2,267.2	478.2	118.9
1988	4,900.4	4,884.2	16.2	1,942.0	1,925.7	16.2	835.6	24.3	1,090.1	−8.1	2,460.9	497.5	129.1
1989	5,250.8	5,217.5	33.3	2,097.0	2,063.6	33.3	891.2	25.2	1,172.5	8.1	2,642.1	511.7	135.1
1990	5,522.2	5,515.9	6.3	2,166.4	2,160.0	6.3	920.6	−.9	1,239.5	7.2	2,846.4	509.4	129.7
1991	5,677.5	5,687.7	−10.2	2,182.5	2,192.7	−10.2	907.6	−19.2	1,285.1	9.0	3,030.2	464.7	119.7
1982: IV	3,195.1	3,241.4	−46.3	1,302.2	1,348.5	−46.3	550.6	−41.1	798.0	−5.2	1,553.3	339.5	63.2
1983: IV	3,547.3	3,527.1	20.2	1,483.0	1,462.8	20.2	620.5	25.5	842.3	−5.3	1,686.1	378.2	101.9
1984: IV	3,869.1	3,818.1	51.0	1,617.5	1,566.5	51.0	676.3	38.5	890.2	12.5	1,824.7	426.9	110.4
1985: IV	4,140.5	4,107.9	32.6	1,673.7	1,641.1	32.6	705.7	10.9	935.4	21.7	2,008.9	457.9	115.1
1986: IV	4,336.6	4,355.4	−18.8	1,714.5	1,733.3	−18.8	751.5	−11.9	981.8	−7.0	2,154.1	468.1	122.5
1987: IV	4,683.0	4,623.7	59.3	1,865.4	1,806.1	59.3	769.3	37.1	1,036.9	22.2	2,327.6	490.1	120.9
1988: IV	5,044.6	5,027.3	17.3	2,007.0	1,989.7	17.3	861.0	35.3	1,128.7	−18.0	2,528.5	509.1	136.1
1989: I	5,150.0	5,106.2	43.7	2,060.9	2,017.2	43.7	867.2	40.2	1,149.9	3.5	2,576.8	512.3	140.3
II	5,229.5	5,189.7	39.8	2,104.1	2,064.3	39.8	893.2	17.0	1,171.2	22.8	2,616.7	508.7	137.3
III	5,278.9	5,259.3	19.6	2,106.9	2,087.3	19.6	910.3	10.6	1,177.0	9.0	2,659.9	512.1	131.9
IV	5,344.8	5,314.6	30.2	2,115.9	2,085.7	30.2	893.9	33.0	1,191.8	−2.8	2,715.2	513.7	131.0
1990: I	5,445.2	5,437.1	8.1	2,151.6	2,143.5	8.1	936.1	−1.3	1,207.4	9.4	2,765.1	528.5	129.5
II	5,522.6	5,484.9	37.7	2,180.0	2,142.3	37.7	914.5	10.7	1,227.8	27.0	2,826.6	516.1	132.9
III	5,559.6	5,549.2	10.4	2,178.0	2,167.6	10.4	919.5	10.3	1,248.1	.2	2,875.6	506.0	139.0
IV	5,561.3	5,592.3	−31.0	2,155.8	2,186.8	−31.0	912.1	−23.1	1,274.6	−7.9	2,918.4	487.1	117.4
1991: I	5,585.8	5,614.4	−28.5	2,158.3	2,186.8	−28.5	897.3	−35.4	1,289.5	6.8	2,963.3	464.3	112.6
II	5,657.6	5,679.4	−21.8	2,179.1	2,200.9	−21.8	916.8	−26.5	1,284.1	4.8	3,013.8	464.7	118.8
III	5,713.1	5,712.9	.2	2,195.1	2,194.9	.2	910.8	−7.0	1,284.1	7.2	3,053.6	464.8	125.0
IV	5,753.3	5,744.2	9.2	2,197.6	2,188.4	9.2	905.7	−8.1	1,282.7	17.3	3,090.3	465.5	122.3
1992: I	5,840.2	5,855.9	−15.8	2,217.8	2,233.6	−15.8	923.6	−19.3	1,310.0	3.5	3,142.2	480.1	125.1
II	5,902.2	5,894.1	8.1	2,241.3	2,233.2	8.1	932.3	9.5	1,300.8	−1.4	3,173.4	487.6	135.0
III	5,978.5	5,963.5	15.0	2,273.4	2,258.4	15.0	943.8	2.7	1,314.6	12.3	3,217.8	487.3	135.0

[1] Exports and imports of certain goods, primarily military equipment purchased and sold by the Federal Government, are included in services.

Source: Department of Commerce, Bureau of Economic Analysis.

TABLE B-7.—*Gross domestic product by major type of product in 1987 dollars, 1959–92*

[Billions of 1987 dollars; quarterly data at seasonally adjusted annual rates]

Year or quarter	Gross domestic product	Final sales of domestic product	Change in business inventories	Goods [1] Total — Total	Goods [1] Total — Final sales	Goods [1] Total — Change in business inventories	Durable goods — Final sales	Durable goods — Change in business inventories	Nondurable goods — Final sales	Nondurable goods — Change in business inventories	Services [1]	Structures	Auto output
1959	1,928.8	1,915.2	13.6	825.2	811.6	13.6	273.8	8.6	537.8	5.0	843.7	259.9	59.5
1960	1,970.8	1,962.7	8.1	835.3	827.1	8.1	277.8	4.6	549.3	3.5	877.3	258.2	63.8
1961	2,023.8	2,016.6	7.2	840.9	833.7	7.2	273.5	−.3	560.2	7.5	916.7	266.1	53.1
1962	2,128.1	2,112.5	15.6	889.6	874.0	15.6	296.5	8.6	577.5	7.0	956.8	281.7	63.3
1963	2,215.6	2,199.6	16.0	914.9	898.9	16.0	310.4	7.5	588.5	8.6	999.9	300.8	68.9
1964	2,340.6	2,324.9	15.7	967.6	952.0	15.7	334.3	11.3	617.6	4.4	1,052.6	320.4	69.5
1965	2,470.5	2,445.4	25.1	1,033.0	1,007.9	25.1	364.1	18.3	643.8	6.9	1,102.1	335.4	83.2
1966	2,616.2	2,579.5	36.7	1,113.3	1,076.6	36.7	399.4	27.1	677.2	9.6	1,168.4	334.5	80.4
1967	2,685.2	2,657.5	27.6	1,129.4	1,101.7	27.6	413.7	14.5	688.0	13.1	1,226.6	329.3	72.4
1968	2,796.9	2,773.2	23.6	1,168.9	1,145.3	23.6	430.4	12.8	714.9	10.9	1,277.8	350.1	86.6
1969	2,873.0	2,848.2	24.8	1,193.9	1,169.1	24.8	438.4	15.7	730.7	9.1	1,324.6	354.5	82.9
1970	2,873.9	2,868.0	5.9	1,173.0	1,167.1	5.9	428.0	−.9	739.1	6.9	1,362.0	338.9	65.4
1971	2,955.9	2,935.2	20.8	1,182.0	1,161.3	20.8	419.2	8.9	742.1	11.9	1,401.8	372.1	85.3
1972	3,107.1	3,084.5	22.5	1,251.0	1,228.4	22.5	458.4	16.2	770.0	6.4	1,454.1	401.9	89.9
1973	3,268.6	3,230.9	37.7	1,349.8	1,312.1	37.7	528.0	31.2	784.1	6.5	1,508.3	410.4	98.7
1974	3,248.1	3,217.2	30.9	1,328.2	1,297.3	30.9	524.6	19.6	772.7	11.3	1,553.9	366.1	79.0
1975	3,221.7	3,235.6	−13.9	1,291.8	1,305.7	−13.9	521.6	−11.5	784.1	−2.5	1,602.2	327.7	74.8
1976	3,380.8	3,355.3	25.5	1,372.7	1,347.2	25.5	540.6	17.0	806.6	8.5	1,649.1	359.0	96.8
1977	3,533.3	3,499.0	34.3	1,436.9	1,402.6	34.3	583.6	15.6	819.0	18.7	1,701.2	395.2	106.0
1978	3,703.5	3,666.3	37.2	1,507.3	1,470.1	37.2	623.7	28.7	846.4	8.5	1,770.6	425.6	104.2
1979	3,796.8	3,783.2	13.6	1,537.1	1,523.5	13.6	654.1	11.7	869.3	1.9	1,821.7	438.0	94.8
1980	3,776.3	3,784.6	−8.3	1,509.5	1,517.7	−8.3	626.4	−4.3	891.4	−4.0	1,864.3	402.5	79.1
1981	3,843.1	3,818.6	24.6	1,547.4	1,522.9	24.6	619.4	6.3	903.4	18.3	1,895.7	400.0	86.8
1982	3,760.3	3,777.8	−17.5	1,468.7	1,486.2	−17.5	578.9	−16.0	907.3	−1.5	1,922.8	368.8	79.2
1983	3,906.6	3,902.2	4.4	1,531.7	1,527.3	4.4	601.5	6.3	925.8	−1.8	1,976.8	398.1	101.7
1984	4,148.5	4,080.6	67.9	1,667.7	1,599.8	67.9	655.1	45.7	944.7	22.3	2,033.1	447.7	115.8
1985	4,279.8	4,257.6	22.1	1,695.0	1,672.9	22.1	703.4	9.3	969.5	12.9	2,115.3	469.4	125.0
1986	4,404.5	4,395.9	8.5	1,740.1	1,731.6	8.5	731.5	1.9	1,000.1	6.7	2,185.0	479.3	124.4
1987	4,539.9	4,513.7	26.3	1,794.5	1,768.2	26.3	753.5	21.6	1,014.7	4.7	2,267.2	478.2	118.9
1988	4,718.6	4,698.6	19.9	1,892.5	1,872.6	19.9	833.1	23.3	1,039.5	−3.4	2,349.7	476.4	127.3
1989	4,838.0	4,808.3	29.8	1,961.7	1,932.0	29.8	868.1	23.8	1,063.9	6.0	2,403.9	472.5	128.0
1990	4,877.5	4,871.3	6.2	1,956.8	1,950.7	6.2	881.0	−.7	1,069.7	6.9	2,463.0	457.7	121.7
1991	4,821.0	4,830.3	−9.3	1,911.2	1,920.5	−9.3	851.6	−17.5	1,069.0	8.2	2,497.6	412.2	109.3
1982: IV	3,759.6	3,804.5	−44.9	1,447.7	1,492.6	−44.9	580.9	−41.9	911.6	−3.0	1,942.1	369.8	75.3
1983: IV	4,012.1	3,982.8	29.3	1,597.8	1,568.5	29.3	639.4	26.7	929.1	2.6	1,998.3	416.0	113.7
1984: IV	4,194.2	4,146.2	47.9	1,680.9	1,633.0	47.9	677.6	39.7	955.3	8.3	2,058.1	455.1	122.4
1985: IV	4,333.5	4,303.3	30.2	1,708.1	1,677.9	30.2	703.1	11.9	974.9	18.3	2,148.8	476.5	122.4
1986: IV	4,427.1	4,447.2	−20.1	1,741.8	1,761.8	−20.1	750.4	−11.9	1,011.4	−8.2	2,208.2	477.2	124.1
1987: IV	4,625.5	4,565.6	59.9	1,850.8	1,790.9	59.9	769.4	36.9	1,021.5	23.0	2,290.9	483.8	120.3
1988: IV	4,779.7	4,758.7	20.9	1,926.0	1,905.0	20.9	852.9	33.5	1,052.2	−12.5	2,372.4	481.3	134.6
1989: I	4,817.6	4,776.3	41.2	1,956.8	1,915.5	41.2	853.6	38.5	1,061.9	2.7	2,382.3	478.4	133.3
II	4,839.0	4,802.0	36.9	1,973.9	1,937.0	36.9	874.1	15.9	1,062.8	21.0	2,394.5	470.5	130.4
III	4,839.0	4,823.0	16.0	1,959.4	1,943.4	16.0	882.3	9.6	1,061.2	6.4	2,408.5	471.1	124.6
IV	4,856.7	4,831.8	24.9	1,956.9	1,932.0	24.9	862.3	31.0	1,069.6	−6.1	2,430.0	469.8	123.8
1990: I	4,890.8	4,883.3	7.5	1,972.0	1,964.5	7.5	900.1	−1.3	1,064.4	8.8	2,440.8	478.0	122.6
II	4,902.7	4,870.0	32.8	1,975.3	1,942.6	32.8	879.1	10.0	1,063.4	22.7	2,462.6	464.8	124.6
III	4,882.6	4,871.4	11.2	1,957.7	1,946.5	11.2	877.1	9.5	1,069.4	1.7	2,472.1	452.8	129.6
IV	4,833.8	4,860.6	−26.8	1,922.3	1,949.1	−26.8	867.6	−21.2	1,081.5	−5.6	2,476.5	435.1	110.2
1991: I	4,796.7	4,821.8	−25.1	1,903.1	1,928.2	−25.1	847.4	−32.2	1,080.8	7.1	2,480.5	413.2	104.8
II	4,817.1	4,837.4	−20.4	1,907.6	1,928.0	−20.4	860.2	−24.0	1,067.8	3.6	2,497.3	412.1	110.7
III	4,831.8	4,831.2	.6	1,918.3	1,917.7	.6	851.7	−6.4	1,066.0	7.0	2,503.7	409.8	112.2
IV	4,838.5	4,830.9	7.5	1,915.7	1,908.2	7.5	846.8	−7.4	1,061.3	15.0	2,509.0	413.7	109.4
1992: I	4,873.7	4,886.3	−12.6	1,924.0	1,936.6	−12.6	859.6	−17.3	1,077.0	4.7	2,520.1	429.5	111.2
II	4,892.4	4,884.6	7.8	1,936.7	1,929.0	7.8	865.7	8.6	1,063.3	−.8	2,522.4	433.3	121.4
III	4,933.7	4,918.7	15.0	1,966.2	1,951.3	15.0	880.2	3.3	1,071.1	11.6	2,537.5	429.9	118.6

[1] Exports and imports of certain goods, primarily military equipment purchased and sold by the Federal Government, are included in services.

Source: Department of Commerce, Bureau of Economic Analysis.

357

TABLE B-8.—Gross domestic product by sector, 1959–92

[Billions of dollars; quarterly data at seasonally adjusted annual rates]

Year or quarter	Gross domestic product	Business [1]				House-holds and institu-tions	General government [2]		
		Total [1]	Nonfarm [1]	Farm	Statis-tical discrep-ancy		Total	Federal	State and local
1959	494.2	436.9	419.8	18.9	−1.8	12.4	44.9	21.7	23.1
1960	513.4	451.4	434.7	19.8	−3.1	13.9	48.1	22.6	25.5
1961	531.8	465.7	447.9	20.1	−2.2	14.5	51.6	23.7	27.9
1962	571.6	500.5	481.4	20.2	−1.0	15.6	55.5	25.2	30.2
1963	603.1	527.1	508.7	20.4	−2.0	16.7	59.3	26.5	32.9
1964	648.0	565.8	547.2	19.3	−.7	17.9	64.4	28.5	35.9
1965	702.7	614.1	592.9	21.9	−.7	19.3	69.3	30.0	39.3
1966	769.8	670.1	644.4	22.9	2.8	21.3	78.4	34.3	44.1
1967	814.3	703.5	680.5	22.2	.8	23.4	87.4	37.9	49.5
1968	889.3	765.4	742.8	22.7	−.1	26.1	97.8	41.9	55.9
1969	959.5	822.5	799.9	25.2	−2.6	29.5	107.5	44.9	62.6
1970	1,010.7	858.7	832.5	26.2	.0	32.4	119.5	48.5	71.1
1971	1,097.2	931.2	900.0	28.1	3.1	35.6	130.4	51.1	79.3
1972	1,207.0	1,025.3	991.7	32.6	1.1	39.0	142.6	54.9	87.7
1973	1,349.6	1,151.5	1,102.2	49.8	−.5	43.0	155.1	57.2	97.9
1974	1,458.6	1,242.7	1,193.9	47.4	1.4	47.2	168.8	61.1	107.6
1975	1,585.9	1,346.1	1,291.4	48.8	6.0	52.0	187.7	66.6	121.1
1976	1,768.4	1,507.4	1,450.6	46.4	10.4	57.1	203.9	71.0	132.9
1977	1,974.1	1,691.1	1,633.0	47.2	10.9	62.4	220.6	75.6	145.0
1978	2,232.7	1,921.1	1,858.7	54.7	7.6	71.0	240.7	81.8	158.9
1979	2,488.6	2,147.9	2,069.7	64.5	13.8	78.9	261.9	87.1	174.8
1980	2,708.0	2,328.9	2,259.2	56.1	13.6	89.3	289.8	96.3	193.5
1981	3,030.6	2,611.7	2,530.9	69.9	10.9	100.5	318.4	107.7	210.7
1982	3,149.6	2,692.1	2,634.4	65.1	−7.4	111.6	345.8	117.3	228.5
1983	3,405.0	2,914.8	2,855.5	49.2	10.2	121.3	368.9	125.0	243.9
1984	3,777.2	3,251.1	3,191.6	68.5	−9.0	132.0	394.1	132.2	261.9
1985	4,038.7	3,473.5	3,420.3	67.1	−13.9	141.7	423.6	140.3	283.2
1986	4,268.6	3,665.7	3,601.5	62.9	1.2	153.3	449.6	143.7	305.9
1987	4,539.9	3,890.8	3,849.5	66.0	−24.8	170.5	478.7	151.4	327.3
1988	4,900.4	4,201.0	4,161.8	67.6	−28.4	187.6	511.7	159.8	351.9
1989	5,250.8	4,495.9	4,413.7	81.1	1.1	206.1	548.8	169.1	379.8
1990	5,522.2	4,702.8	4,612.4	85.0	5.4	227.8	591.6	180.3	411.4
1991	5,677.5	4,803.8	4,702.8	79.1	21.9	246.1	627.6	192.0	435.6
1982: IV	3,195.1	2,724.0	2,674.1	60.0	−10.1	115.5	355.6	121.1	234.5
1983: IV	3,547.3	3,046.6	2,986.9	45.8	13.8	125.1	375.6	126.2	249.4
1984: IV	3,869.1	3,330.3	3,283.2	67.5	−20.5	135.6	403.2	134.1	269.2
1985: IV	4,140.5	3,561.2	3,501.5	65.7	−5.9	145.6	433.6	142.4	291.2
1986: IV	4,336.6	3,718.3	3,656.0	64.3	−2.0	157.8	460.5	144.9	315.6
1987: IV	4,683.0	4,016.6	3,970.9	70.6	−24.9	177.6	488.8	153.2	335.6
1988: IV	5,044.6	4,327.3	4,291.9	60.8	−25.4	194.3	523.0	161.3	361.7
1989: I	5,150.0	4,413.9	4,342.9	82.5	−11.4	199.3	536.7	167.9	368.8
II	5,229.5	4,481.5	4,397.6	82.3	1.7	203.7	544.3	168.5	375.8
III	5,278.9	4,518.2	4,437.6	79.4	1.2	208.2	552.5	169.3	383.3
IV	5,344.8	4,569.8	4,476.6	80.4	12.8	213.3	561.7	170.6	391.2
1990: I	5,445.2	4,649.1	4,547.5	85.4	16.1	218.8	577.3	177.8	399.5
II	5,522.6	4,709.3	4,619.8	88.2	1.2	225.0	588.4	180.5	407.9
III	5,559.6	4,732.9	4,634.0	85.5	13.4	231.3	595.3	179.8	415.6
IV	5,561.3	4,719.9	4,648.2	80.8	−9.1	235.9	605.5	182.9	422.6
1991: I	5,585.8	4,726.2	4,635.8	77.0	13.4	237.4	622.2	193.3	428.9
II	5,657.6	4,786.7	4,677.1	82.5	27.1	244.1	626.8	192.4	434.5
III	5,713.1	4,835.2	4,725.5	79.2	30.5	249.3	628.7	191.3	437.4
IV	5,753.3	4,867.2	4,772.9	77.9	16.4	253.5	632.7	191.1	441.6
1992: I	5,840.2	4,937.4	4,826.9	81.6	29.0	258.3	644.4	198.2	446.2
II	5,902.2	4,988.6	4,877.6	80.1	30.9	261.5	652.2	198.7	453.5
III	5,978.5	5,057.5	4,940.0	82.5	35.1	264.8	656.2	199.0	457.2

[1] Includes compensation of employees in government enterprises.
[2] Compensation of government employees.
Source: Department of Commerce, Bureau of Economic Analysis.

TABLE B–9.—*Gross domestic product by sector in 1987 dollars, 1959–92*

[Billions of 1987 dollars; quarterly data at seasonally adjusted annual rates]

Year or quarter	Gross domestic product	Business [1]				House-holds and institu-tions	General government [2]		
		Total [1]	Nonfarm [1]	Farm	Statis-tical discrep-ancy		Total	Federal	State and local
1959	1,928,8	1,582.1	1,543.4	45.2	−6.5	80.1	266.5	130.5	136.0
1960	1,970.8	1,609.5	1,574.3	46.4	−11.2	86.5	274.8	132.1	142.7
1961	2,023.8	1,650.7	1,611.6	46.9	−7.8	87.5	285.6	135.3	150.3
1962	2,128.1	1,740.8	1,698.0	46.3	−3.6	91.1	296.2	141.6	154.7
1963	2,215.6	1,818.8	1,778.6	47.1	−6.8	93.6	303.2	140.9	162.3
1964	2,340.6	1,930.4	1,886.8	46.0	−2.4	96.5	313.7	141.7	172.0
1965	2,470.5	2,045.3	2,001.7	46.1	−2.5	100.4	324.8	142.3	182.5
1966	2,616.2	2,162.6	2,109.1	44.5	9.0	104.7	348.9	155.4	193.5
1967	2,685.2	2,208.0	2,158.8	46.5	2.6	108.3	368.9	168.1	200.8
1968	2,796.9	2,303.0	2,258.0	45.1	−.1	111.8	382.1	170.7	211.4
1969	2,873.0	2,366.2	2,326.7	46.8	−7.2	115.5	391.3	171.2	220.1
1970	2,873.9	2,368.4	2,318.9	49.5	.0	114.1	391.4	161.6	229.8
1971	2,955.9	2,447.4	2,388.6	50.5	8.3	116.7	391.8	152.4	239.5
1972	3,107.1	2,594.8	2,541.3	50.7	2.8	120.0	392.2	143.7	248.6
1973	3,268.6	2,749.7	2,702.0	48.6	−1.0	123.2	395.7	138.0	257.7
1974	3,248.1	2,719.6	2,666.0	50.7	3.0	124.3	404.1	137.9	266.2
1975	3,221.7	2,684.6	2,619.6	53.1	11.9	128.0	409.1	137.1	272.0
1976	3,380.8	2,840.1	2,768.1	52.5	19.5	128.6	412.0	137.0	275.0
1977	3,533.3	2,987.8	2,914.6	53.8	19.4	129.8	415.6	137.0	278.6
1978	3,703.5	3,144.2	3,083.8	48.2	12.2	135.1	424.2	138.4	285.8
1979	3,796.8	3,226.0	3,155.0	50.4	20.6	138.3	432.5	137.5	295.0
1980	3,776.3	3,193.4	3,123.4	51.0	19.0	142.6	440.3	139.2	301.1
1981	3,843.1	3,253.6	3,179.2	60.8	13.6	145.6	443.9	140.9	303.0
1982	3,760.3	3,167.3	3,115.8	60.2	−8.7	148.9	444.2	142.4	301.8
1983	3,906.6	3,308.2	3,243.1	53.7	11.5	151.0	447.4	144.8	302.6
1984	4,148.5	3,541.7	3,496.4	55.1	−9.8	154.9	451.9	146.4	305.4
1985	4,279.8	3,658.1	3,608.6	64.2	−14.7	159.9	461.8	148.6	313.2
1986	4,404.5	3,768.3	3,702.8	64.3	1.3	166.3	469.9	149.0	320.8
1987	4,539.9	3,890.8	3,849.5	66.0	−24.8	170.5	478.7	151.4	327.3
1988	4,718.6	4,050.6	4,014.8	63.2	−27.4	180.6	487.4	153.5	333.9
1989	4,838.0	4,150.5	4,083.4	66.2	.9	190.5	497.0	154.2	342.7
1990	4,877.5	4,170.1	4,094.7	70.5	4.9	197.7	509.6	156.3	353.5
1991	4,821.0	4,103.9	4,015.8	69.4	18.7	202.4	514.7	157.1	357.5
1982: IV	3,759.6	3,166.3	3,116.9	61.1	−11.7	149.6	443.8	143.2	300.6
1983: IV	4,012.1	3,411.5	3,349.0	47.0	15.5	151.7	448.9	145.2	303.7
1984: IV	4,194.2	3,583.0	3,548.9	56.1	−22.0	156.8	454.4	147.1	307.3
1985: IV	4,333.5	3,706.1	3,646.8	65.5	−6.2	162.3	465.1	148.7	316.5
1986: IV	4,427.1	3,786.7	3,724.4	64.4	−2.1	166.9	473.5	149.8	323.7
1987: IV	4,625.5	3,969.9	3,925.5	69.0	−24.6	173.2	482.3	152.8	329.5
1988: IV	4,779.7	4,104.2	4,074.5	53.8	−24.1	184.7	490.7	154.0	336.7
1989: I	4,817.6	4,137.2	4,082.5	65.4	−10.7	187.5	492.9	154.0	338.9
II	4,839.0	4,153.9	4,083.8	68.5	1.6	190.0	495.1	153.8	341.3
III	4,839.0	4,149.3	4,082.4	65.8	1.1	191.6	498.2	154.3	343.9
IV	4,856.7	4,161.9	4,085.0	65.2	11.7	193.2	501.7	154.8	346.9
1990: I	4,890.8	4,191.1	4,107.8	68.7	14.5	194.8	505.0	155.1	349.9
II	4,902.7	4,196.5	4,124.6	70.8	1.1	197.0	509.3	156.6	352.7
III	4,882.6	4,172.8	4,089.9	71.0	11.8	199.3	510.6	155.7	354.8
IV	4,833.8	4,120.1	4,056.4	71.6	−7.9	199.6	514.2	157.7	356.5
1991: I	4,796.7	4,078.2	3,998.3	68.3	11.5	200.0	518.5	161.1	357.4
II	4,817.1	4,098.3	4,007.1	68.0	23.2	201.9	516.9	158.6	358.3
III	4,831.8	4,116.1	4,021.6	68.5	26.0	203.1	512.6	155.5	357.1
IV	4,838.5	4,123.1	4,036.3	72.8	13.9	204.8	510.6	153.4	357.3
1992: I	4,873.7	4,156.8	4,058.8	73.6	24.4	206.7	510.3	152.5	357.7
II	4,892.4	4,174.4	4,076.1	72.5	25.9	206.7	511.3	151.8	359.5
III	4,933.7	4,212.5	4,109.2	74.0	29.2	208.8	512.3	151.1	361.2

[1] Includes compensation of employees in government enterprises.
[2] Compensation of government employees.

Source: Department of Commerce, Bureau of Economic Analysis.

TABLE B-10.—Gross domestic product of nonfinancial corporate business, 1959–92

[Billions of dollars; quarterly data at seasonally adjusted annual rates]

Year or quarter	Gross domestic product of nonfinancial corporate business	Consumption of fixed capital	Net domestic product Total	Indirect business taxes [1]	Domestic income Total	Compensation of employees	Corporate profits w/ IVA & CCAdj Total	Profits before tax	Profits tax liability	Profits after tax Total	Dividends	Undistributed profits	Inventory valuation adjustment	Capital consumption adjustment	Net interest
1959	267.5	24.2	243.2	26.0	217.2	171.5	42.6	43.6	20.7	22.9	10.0	12.9	-0.3	-0.7	3.1
1960	278.1	25.2	252.9	28.3	224.6	181.2	40.0	40.3	19.2	21.1	10.6	10.6	-.2	-.2	3.5
1961	285.5	26.0	259.6	29.5	230.1	185.3	40.8	40.1	19.5	20.7	10.6	10.1	.3	.3	4.0
1962	311.7	26.9	284.8	32.0	252.8	200.1	48.2	45.0	20.6	24.3	11.4	13.0	.0	3.2	4.5
1963	331.8	28.1	303.7	34.0	269.7	211.1	53.8	49.8	22.8	27.0	12.6	14.4	.1	3.9	4.8
1964	358.1	29.5	328.6	36.6	292.0	226.7	60.0	56.0	24.0	32.1	13.7	18.4	-.5	4.5	5.3
1965	393.5	31.5	362.0	39.2	322.8	246.5	70.3	66.2	27.2	39.0	15.6	23.4	-1.2	5.3	6.1
1966	431.0	34.3	396.7	40.5	356.2	274.0	74.9	71.4	29.5	41.9	16.8	25.1	-2.1	5.6	7.4
1967	453.4	37.5	415.9	43.1	372.8	292.3	71.8	67.5	27.8	39.7	17.5	22.2	-1.6	5.8	8.8
1968	500.5	41.4	459.1	49.7	409.3	323.2	76.0	74.0	33.6	40.4	19.1	21.3	-3.7	5.6	10.1
1969	543.3	45.3	498.0	54.7	443.3	358.8	71.3	70.8	33.3	37.5	19.1	18.4	-5.9	6.3	13.2
1970	561.4	49.7	511.6	58.8	452.8	378.7	57.1	58.1	27.2	31.0	18.5	12.5	-6.6	5.5	17.1
1971	606.4	54.6	551.7	64.5	487.3	402.0	67.2	67.1	29.9	37.1	18.5	18.7	-4.6	4.7	18.1
1972	673.3	61.0	612.4	69.2	543.2	447.1	77.0	78.6	33.8	44.8	20.1	24.7	-6.6	5.0	19.2
1973	754.5	66.2	688.3	76.3	612.0	505.9	83.6	98.6	40.2	58.4	21.1	37.3	-20.0	5.0	22.5
1974	814.6	77.5	737.1	81.4	655.7	556.8	70.6	109.2	42.2	67.0	21.7	45.2	-39.5	.9	28.3
1975	881.2	93.3	788.0	87.4	700.6	580.3	91.5	109.9	41.5	68.4	24.8	43.6	-11.0	-7.4	28.7
1976	994.6	103.8	890.8	95.1	795.7	656.7	111.5	137.3	53.0	84.4	27.8	56.6	-14.9	-10.9	27.5
1977	1,124.7	116.2	1,008.5	104.1	904.4	741.8	132.0	158.6	59.9	98.7	32.0	66.8	-16.6	-10.0	30.6
1978	1,279.4	132.3	1,147.2	114.6	1,032.6	850.2	146.1	183.5	67.1	116.4	37.2	79.1	-25.0	-12.3	36.3
1979	1,423.7	153.0	1,270.7	123.3	1,147.4	964.2	138.1	195.5	69.6	125.9	39.3	86.7	-41.6	-15.9	45.1
1980	1,546.5	174.8	1,371.7	139.4	1,232.4	1,053.5	120.7	181.6	67.0	114.6	45.5	69.1	-43.0	-17.8	58.2
1981	1,748.6	207.0	1,541.5	167.9	1,373.6	1,164.8	136.9	181.0	63.9	117.1	53.4	63.7	-25.7	-18.4	71.9
1982	1,802.8	229.4	1,573.4	169.4	1,404.0	1,209.9	111.5	132.9	46.3	86.7	56.4	30.2	-9.9	-11.5	82.5
1983	1,936.1	242.1	1,694.0	185.8	1,508.2	1,271.6	159.9	155.9	59.4	96.4	66.5	29.9	-8.5	12.5	76.7
1984	2,166.5	248.1	1,918.3	206.9	1,711.4	1,409.2	214.3	189.0	73.7	115.4	69.5	45.9	-4.1	29.4	87.9
1985	2,293.6	258.0	2,035.5	220.3	1,815.3	1,503.2	221.4	165.5	69.9	95.6	74.5	21.1	.2	55.6	90.7
1986	2,386.3	271.4	2,114.9	231.4	1,883.6	1,581.5	203.8	149.1	75.6	73.5	76.3	-2.8	9.7	44.9	98.3
1987	2,547.3	281.4	2,265.9	241.0	2,024.9	1,675.0	244.2	212.0	93.5	118.5	77.9	40.6	-14.5	46.7	105.8
1988	2,764.8	297.5	2,467.3	257.1	2,210.2	1,814.2	274.4	256.6	101.7	154.9	82.0	72.9	-27.3	45.0	121.6
1989	2,913.5	317.4	2,596.2	274.2	2,322.0	1,920.2	255.2	232.9	99.5	133.3	101.9	31.5	-17.5	39.9	146.6
1990	3,036.5	329.3	2,707.2	290.9	2,416.3	2,019.0	248.3	232.9	92.8	140.2	118.5	21.6	-14.2	29.5	149.0
1991	3,073.8	341.2	2,732.6	310.8	2,421.8	2,048.6	229.9	207.3	81.1	126.2	117.3	8.8	3.1	19.4	143.4
1982: IV	1,806.3	238.8	1,567.5	172.6	1,394.9	1,213.9	101.5	116.5	40.6	75.9	59.0	16.9	-8.6	-6.4	79.6
1983: IV	2,037.2	261.5	1,775.7	194.0	1,581.7	1,327.6	175.2	168.1	64.4	103.7	67.4	36.3	-7.6	14.7	78.9
1984: IV	2,228.2	258.9	1,969.4	212.4	1,756.9	1,449.7	211.4	169.0	62.6	106.4	68.7	37.7	3.5	38.9	95.8
1985: IV	2,338.8	263.4	2,075.4	223.8	1,851.6	1,540.1	211.4	168.4	71.1	97.2	74.7	22.5	-3.8	56.9	90.0
1986: IV	2,422.8	275.8	2,147.1	233.6	1,913.5	1,611.4	198.6	168.5	86.5	82.0	75.2	6.8	-10.7	40.8	103.5
1987: IV	2,627.6	286.1	2,341.4	245.4	2,096.0	1,730.1	256.8	224.8	99.6	125.1	84.0	41.2	-17.8	49.8	109.2
1988: IV	2,843.2	304.5	2,538.8	263.1	2,275.7	1,868.8	278.5	271.4	107.9	163.5	84.3	79.2	-31.7	38.8	128.4
1989: I	2,870.1	308.7	2,561.4	266.6	2,294.9	1,894.9	262.2	260.6	113.2	147.4	102.4	45.0	-37.6	39.2	137.7
II	2,902.3	312.4	2,589.8	272.5	2,317.4	1,907.2	263.2	237.3	101.6	135.7	100.5	35.3	-15.7	41.6	147.0
III	2,930.2	321.7	2,608.5	278.8	2,329.7	1,924.0	254.8	217.8	92.3	125.5	102.3	23.3	-3.3	40.3	150.9
IV	2,951.5	326.5	2,625.0	279.0	2,346.0	1,954.6	240.7	215.9	91.1	124.8	102.3	22.5	-13.5	38.3	150.7
1990: I	2,999.6	324.8	2,674.9	286.1	2,388.8	1,985.3	254.9	224.6	89.3	135.3	118.2	17.2	-6.6	36.9	148.7
II	3,053.1	327.2	2,725.9	286.6	2,439.3	2,017.6	272.0	235.4	93.7	141.7	113.5	28.2	3.8	32.9	149.7
III	3,048.2	330.8	2,717.4	293.5	2,423.9	2,035.7	239.7	245.4	98.0	147.4	118.0	29.5	-32.6	26.9	148.4
IV	3,045.0	334.4	2,710.6	297.5	2,413.2	2,037.3	226.6	226.4	90.1	136.2	124.5	11.7	-21.2	21.5	149.2
1991: I	3,037.1	338.9	2,698.2	304.1	2,394.2	2,022.1	226.2	203.1	78.8	124.2	119.0	5.2	6.7	16.5	145.9
II	3,062.7	341.0	2,721.7	305.5	2,416.2	2,042.0	231.4	205.2	80.3	124.9	115.5	9.3	9.9	16.2	142.9
III	3,084.4	341.5	2,742.9	314.7	2,428.2	2,058.6	226.5	211.2	83.3	127.9	114.1	14.1	-4.8	20.1	143.0
IV	3,111.1	343.5	2,767.5	318.7	2,448.8	2,071.8	235.3	209.7	82.1	127.6	120.9	6.7	.7	24.8	141.7
1992: I	3,138.1	342.7	2,795.4	322.6	2,472.8	2,081.0	255.7	227.3	90.2	137.1	107.1	30.1	-5.4	33.8	136.0
II	3,178.8	347.6	2,831.3	324.1	2,507.1	2,096.4	276.2	254.5	100.8	153.7	113.4	40.4	-15.5	37.1	134.6
III	3,211.6	363.3	2,848.3	330.1	2,518.2	2,109.5	278.5	248.6	96.6	152.0	117.0	35.0	-9.7	39.5	130.3

[1] Indirect business tax and nontax liability plus business transfer payments less subsidies.

Source: Department of Commerce, Bureau of Economic Analysis.

TABLE B-11.—*Output, costs, and profits of nonfinancial corporate business, 1959–92*

[Quarterly data at seasonally adjusted annual rates]

| Year or quarter | Gross domestic product of nonfinancial corporate business (billions of dollars) | | Current-dollar cost and profit per unit of output (dollars) [1] | | | | | | | | Output per hour of all employees (1987 dollars) | Compensation per hour of all employees (dollars) |
| | Current dollars | 1987 dollars | Total cost and profit [2] | Consumption of fixed capital | Indirect business taxes [3] | Compensation of employees | Corporate profits with inventory valuation and capital consumption adjustments | | | Net interest | | |
							Total	Profits tax liability	Profits after tax [4]			
1959	267.5	928.7	0.288	0.026	0.028	0.185	0.046	0.022	0.024	0.003	15.442	2.851
1960	278.1	955.6	.291	.026	.030	.190	.042	.020	.022	.004	15.659	2.968
1961	285.5	978.2	.292	.027	.030	.189	.042	.020	.022	.004	16.168	3.063
1962	311.7	1,047.5	.298	.026	.031	.191	.046	.020	.026	.004	16.661	3.183
1963	331.8	1,104.8	.300	.025	.031	.191	.049	.021	.028	.004	17.192	3.284
1964	358.1	1,179.3	.304	.025	.031	.192	.051	.020	.031	.005	17.843	3.430
1965	393.5	1,262.2	.312	.025	.031	.195	.056	.022	.034	.005	18.062	3.527
1966	431.0	1,336.0	.323	.026	.030	.205	.056	.022	.034	.006	18.147	3.721
1967	453.4	1,367.4	.332	.027	.032	.214	.052	.020	.032	.006	18.354	3.923
1968	500.5	1,444.3	.347	.029	.034	.224	.053	.023	.029	.007	18.854	4.219
1969	543.3	1,492.5	.364	.030	.037	.240	.048	.022	.025	.009	18.743	4.506
1970	561.4	1,473.4	.381	.034	.040	.257	.039	.018	.020	.012	18.776	4.825
1971	606.4	1,525.9	.397	.036	.042	.263	.044	.020	.024	.012	19.482	5.133
1972	673.3	1,629.5	.413	.037	.042	.274	.047	.021	.027	.012	19.774	5.425
1973	754.5	1,706.9	.442	.039	.045	.296	.049	.024	.025	.013	19.754	5.855
1974	814.6	1,669.7	.488	.046	.049	.333	.042	.025	.017	.017	19.238	6.416
1975	881.2	1,625.6	.542	.057	.054	.357	.056	.026	.031	.018	19.755	7.053
1976	994.6	1,748.5	.569	.059	.054	.376	.064	.030	.033	.016	20.354	7.644
1977	1,124.7	1,866.7	.603	.062	.056	.397	.071	.032	.039	.016	20.753	8.247
1978	1,279.4	1,967.1	.650	.067	.058	.432	.074	.034	.040	.018	20.696	8.945
1979	1,423.7	1,995.7	.713	.077	.062	.483	.069	.035	.034	.023	20.215	9.767
1980	1,546.5	1,980.9	.781	.088	.070	.532	.061	.034	.027	.029	20.271	10.780
1981	1,748.6	2,035.1	.859	.102	.082	.572	.067	.031	.036	.035	20.553	11.764
1982	1,802.8	2,001.3	.901	.115	.085	.605	.056	.023	.033	.041	20.819	12.586
1983	1,936.1	2,112.3	.917	.115	.088	.602	.076	.028	.048	.036	21.586	12.995
1984	2,166.5	2,284.1	.949	.109	.091	.617	.094	.032	.062	.038	21.896	13.509
1985	2,293.6	2,364.3	.970	.109	.093	.636	.094	.030	.064	.038	22.125	14.067
1986	2,386.3	2,439.3	.978	.111	.095	.648	.084	.031	.053	.040	22.690	14.711
1987	2,547.3	2,547.3	1.000	.110	.095	.658	.096	.037	.059	.042	23.071	15.170
1988	2,764.8	2,684.8	1.030	.111	.096	.676	.102	.038	.064	.045	23.494	15.781
1989	2,913.5	2,718.9	1.072	.117	.101	.706	.094	.037	.057	.054	23.088	16.306
1990	3,036.5	2,740.0	1.108	.120	.106	.737	.091	.034	.057	.054	23.300	17.169
1991	3,073.8	2,698.0	1.139	.126	.115	.759	.085	.030	.055	.053	23.720	18.011
1982: IV	1,806.3	1,999.6	.903	.119	.086	.607	.051	.020	.030	.040	21.094	12.805
1983: IV	2,037.2	2,204.2	.924	.119	.088	.602	.079	.029	.050	.036	21.895	13.187
1984: IV	2,228.2	2,328.4	.957	.111	.091	.623	.091	.027	.064	.041	22.032	13.718
1985: IV	2,338.8	2,396.9	.976	.110	.093	.643	.092	.030	.063	.038	22.315	14.339
1986: IV	2,422.8	2,463.3	.984	.112	.095	.654	.081	.035	.045	.042	22.838	14.940
1987: IV	2,627.6	2,604.0	1.009	.110	.094	.664	.099	.038	.060	.042	23.286	15.471
1988: IV	2,843.2	2,719.0	1.046	.112	.097	.687	.102	.040	.063	.047	23.446	16.018
1989: I	2,870.1	2,719.1	1.056	.114	.098	.697	.096	.042	.055	.051	23.176	16.151
II	2,902.3	2,715.8	1.069	.115	.100	.702	.097	.037	.060	.054	23.056	16.191
III	2,930.2	2,717.9	1.078	.118	.103	.708	.094	.034	.060	.056	23.062	16.326
IV	2,951.5	2,722.7	1.084	.120	.102	.718	.088	.033	.055	.055	23.054	16.550
1990: I	2,999.6	2,742.0	1.094	.118	.104	.724	.093	.033	.060	.054	23.122	16.741
II	3,053.1	2,763.3	1.105	.118	.104	.730	.098	.034	.065	.054	23.375	17.067
III	3,048.2	2,737.3	1.114	.121	.107	.744	.088	.036	.052	.054	23.293	17.322
IV	3,045.0	2,717.4	1.121	.123	.109	.750	.083	.033	.050	.055	23.437	17.572
1991: I	3,037.1	2,683.5	1.132	.126	.113	.754	.084	.029	.055	.054	23.522	17.724
II	3,062.7	2,687.4	1.140	.127	.114	.760	.086	.030	.056	.053	23.646	17.967
III	3,084.4	2,699.1	1.143	.127	.117	.763	.084	.031	.053	.053	23.769	18.129
IV	3,111.1	2,722.0	1.143	.126	.117	.761	.086	.030	.056	.052	24.014	18.278
1992: I	3,138.1	2,737.6	1.146	.125	.118	.760	.093	.033	.060	.050	24.152	18.359
II	3,178.8	2,760.8	1.151	.126	.117	.759	.100	.037	.064	.049	24.301	18.452
III	3,211.6	2,787.6	1.152	.130	.118	.757	.100	.035	.065	.047	24.610	18.599

[1] Output is measured by gross domestic product of nonfinancial corporate business in 1987 dollars.
[2] This is equal to the deflator for gross domestic product of nonfinancial corporate business with the decimal point shifted two places to the left.
[3] Indirect business tax and nontax liability plus business transfer payments less subsidies.
[4] With inventory valuation and capital consumption adjustments.

Sources: Department of Commerce (Bureau of Economic Analysis) and Department of Labor (Bureau of Labor Statistics).

TABLE B-12.—*Personal consumption expenditures, 1959–92*

[Billions of dollars; quarterly data at seasonally adjusted annual rates]

Year or quarter	Personal con-sumption expendi-tures	Durable goods			Nondurable goods					Services					
		Total [1]	Motor vehi-cles and parts	Furni-ture and house-hold equip-ment	Total [1]	Food	Cloth-ing and shoes	Gaso-line and oil	Fuel oil and coal	Total [1]	Hous-ing [2]	Household operation		Trans-porta-tion	Medi-cal care
												Total [1]	Elec-tricity and gas		
1959	318.1	42.8	18.9	18.1	148.5	80.7	26.4	11.3	4.0	126.8	45.0	18.7	7.6	10.5	16.3
1960	332.4	43.5	19.7	18.0	153.1	82.6	27.0	12.0	3.8	135.9	48.2	20.3	8.3	11.2	17.4
1961	343.5	41.9	17.8	18.3	157.4	84.8	27.6	12.0	3.8	144.1	51.2	21.2	8.8	11.7	18.6
1962	364.4	47.0	21.5	19.3	163.8	87.1	29.0	12.6	3.8	153.6	54.7	22.4	9.4	12.2	20.7
1963	384.2	51.8	24.4	20.7	169.4	89.5	29.8	13.0	4.0	163.1	58.0	23.6	9.9	12.7	22.4
1964	412.5	56.8	26.0	23.2	179.7	94.6	32.4	13.6	4.1	175.9	61.4	25.0	10.4	13.4	25.7
1965	444.6	63.5	29.9	25.1	191.9	101.0	34.1	14.8	4.4	189.2	65.4	26.5	10.9	14.5	27.7
1966	481.6	68.5	30.3	28.2	208.5	109.0	37.4	16.0	4.7	204.6	69.5	28.2	11.5	15.9	30.5
1967	509.3	70.6	30.0	30.0	216.9	112.3	39.2	17.1	4.8	221.7	74.1	30.2	12.2	17.3	33.7
1968	559.1	81.0	36.1	32.9	235.0	121.6	43.2	18.6	4.7	243.1	79.7	32.3	13.0	18.9	39.0
1969	603.7	86.2	38.4	34.7	252.2	130.5	46.5	20.5	4.6	265.3	86.8	35.1	14.0	20.9	44.4
1970	646.5	85.3	35.5	35.7	270.4	142.1	47.8	21.9	4.4	290.8	94.0	37.8	15.2	23.7	50.1
1971	700.3	97.2	44.5	37.8	283.3	147.5	51.7	23.2	4.6	319.8	102.7	41.0	16.6	27.1	56.5
1972	767.8	110.7	51.1	42.4	305.2	158.5	56.4	24.4	5.1	351.9	112.1	45.3	18.4	29.8	63.5
1973	848.1	124.1	56.1	47.9	339.6	176.1	62.5	28.1	6.3	384.5	122.7	49.8	20.0	31.2	71.2
1974	927.7	123.0	49.5	51.5	380.8	198.1	66.0	36.1	7.8	423.9	134.1	55.5	23.5	33.3	80.1
1975	1,024.9	134.3	54.8	54.5	416.0	218.5	70.8	39.7	8.4	474.5	147.0	63.7	28.5	35.7	93.0
1976	1,143.1	160.0	71.3	60.2	451.8	236.0	76.6	43.0	10.1	531.2	161.5	72.4	32.5	41.3	106.2
1977	1,271.5	182.6	83.5	67.1	490.4	255.9	84.1	46.9	11.1	598.4	179.5	81.9	37.6	49.2	122.4
1978	1,421.2	202.3	92.2	74.0	541.5	280.6	94.3	50.1	11.5	677.4	201.7	91.2	42.1	53.6	139.7
1979	1,583.7	214.2	91.5	82.3	613.3	313.0	101.2	66.2	14.4	756.2	226.6	100.0	46.8	59.4	157.8
1980	1,748.1	212.5	84.0	86.0	682.9	341.8	107.3	86.7	15.4	852.7	255.2	113.0	56.3	65.1	181.3
1981	1,926.2	228.5	91.6	91.3	744.2	367.3	117.2	97.9	15.8	953.5	287.1	126.0	63.4	69.4	213.6
1982	2,059.2	236.5	97.7	92.5	772.3	386.0	120.5	94.1	14.5	1,050.4	311.1	141.4	72.6	71.6	240.5
1983	2,257.5	275.0	120.6	104.4	817.8	406.2	130.8	93.3	13.8	1,164.7	334.6	153.6	80.7	78.9	265.7
1984	2,460.3	317.9	144.6	115.3	873.0	430.2	142.5	94.5	14.2	1,269.4	362.3	165.5	84.6	89.1	290.6
1985	2,667.4	352.9	167.4	123.4	919.4	451.1	152.2	96.9	14.1	1,395.1	392.5	176.2	88.7	99.0	319.3
1986	2,850.6	389.6	184.9	135.5	952.2	476.8	163.2	79.7	12.0	1,508.8	421.8	181.1	87.1	105.8	346.4
1987	3,052.2	403.7	183.5	144.0	1,011.1	500.7	174.5	84.7	12.0	1,637.4	452.5	187.8	88.4	116.6	384.7
1988	3,296.1	437.1	197.8	156.7	1,073.8	533.6	186.4	86.9	12.1	1,785.2	484.2	199.5	93.4	128.5	427.7
1989	3,523.1	459.4	205.4	167.9	1,149.5	565.1	200.4	96.2	12.0	1,914.2	514.4	209.8	98.0	135.6	471.9
1990	3,748.4	464.3	202.4	172.1	1,224.5	601.4	206.9	108.5	12.6	2,059.7	547.5	215.0	97.6	142.8	524.9
1991	3,887.7	446.1	185.4	170.4	1,251.5	617.7	209.0	105.5	11.7	2,190.1	574.0	223.7	103.6	147.3	580.2
1982: IV	2,128.7	246.9	105.1	95.6	787.3	394.9	122.7	93.0	14.0	1,094.6	320.2	145.8	74.9	73.6	250.9
1983: IV	2,346.8	297.7	134.8	109.7	839.8	413.9	136.7	94.9	14.1	1,209.3	344.6	159.3	84.8	82.9	274.8
1984: IV	2,526.4	328.2	149.3	118.7	887.8	436.8	145.7	94.9	13.8	1,310.4	373.8	168.8	85.9	92.5	299.9
1985: IV	2,739.8	354.4	162.9	128.1	939.5	460.7	156.2	97.6	14.3	1,446.0	404.6	180.7	90.1	101.5	333.0
1986: IV	2,923.1	406.8	188.2	140.6	963.7	486.7	165.8	73.0	11.3	1,552.6	432.7	182.5	86.8	109.0	358.4
1987: IV	3,124.6	408.8	186.3	145.9	1,029.4	507.4	177.6	87.8	12.2	1,686.4	466.6	189.7	88.6	121.3	398.5
1988: IV	3,398.2	452.9	203.4	162.5	1,105.8	549.5	194.4	88.5	11.7	1,839.5	496.0	203.8	95.3	132.7	444.4
1989: I	3,440.8	450.8	203.7	164.9	1,121.1	555.8	195.2	90.9	11.2	1,868.8	502.9	206.9	96.6	134.5	457.0
II	3,499.1	457.6	204.9	167.3	1,146.5	562.0	199.4	100.4	12.0	1,895.1	510.2	206.0	94.9	134.5	466.0
III	3,553.3	470.8	215.0	168.8	1,157.1	567.6	201.7	97.7	11.5	1,925.4	517.7	208.7	96.6	135.9	475.3
IV	3,599.1	458.3	198.1	170.8	1,173.5	575.3	205.4	95.9	13.2	1,967.3	526.6	217.7	103.7	137.6	489.2
1990: I	3,672.4	478.0	213.0	174.8	1,199.3	589.7	206.9	101.0	12.0	1,995.0	534.7	208.0	92.5	140.0	503.2
II	3,715.3	463.5	202.5	172.2	1,208.7	597.6	206.8	99.3	12.1	2,043.1	543.1	216.2	98.7	141.8	517.2
III	3,787.8	463.0	201.5	171.5	1,235.3	606.4	208.4	109.5	13.3	2,089.6	553.6	218.4	99.9	143.4	533.1
IV	3,818.2	452.7	192.6	169.9	1,254.5	611.8	205.6	124.0	13.0	2,111.1	558.8	217.5	99.4	145.9	546.0
1991: I	3,821.7	439.5	180.9	169.2	1,245.0	613.6	206.2	108.1	12.2	2,137.2	565.0	218.4	100.0	145.1	558.7
II	3,871.9	441.4	180.7	171.5	1,254.2	619.2	210.8	105.5	11.4	2,176.3	571.5	224.8	104.4	146.2	572.5
III	3,914.2	453.0	189.3	172.2	1,255.3	617.9	212.0	104.7	11.8	2,205.9	576.5	226.1	104.6	148.2	586.3
IV	3,942.9	450.4	190.9	168.9	1,251.4	620.0	206.8	103.5	11.3	2,241.1	583.0	225.5	105.2	149.8	603.2
1992: I	4,022.8	469.4	198.9	176.3	1,274.1	627.9	216.5	102.8	11.6	2,279.3	590.9	223.5	101.8	152.6	614.8
II	4,057.1	470.6	200.7	176.3	1,277.5	623.2	217.4	105.4	13.8	2,309.0	597.4	227.9	104.2	152.5	629.0
III	4,108.7	482.5	201.7	182.4	1,292.8	627.3	224.3	107.7	13.0	2,333.3	603.3	225.8	104.8	153.1	642.0

[1] Includes other items not shown separately.
[2] Includes imputed rental value of owner-occupied housing.

Source: Department of Commerce, Bureau of Economic Analysis.

TABLE B-13.—*Personal consumption expenditures in 1987 dollars, 1959–92*

[Billions of 1987 dollars; quarterly data at seasonally adjusted annual rates]

Year or quarter	Personal con-sumption expendi-tures	Durable goods			Nondurable goods					Services					
		Total [1]	Motor vehi-cles and parts	Furni-ture and house-hold equip-ment	Total [1]	Food	Cloth-ing and shoes	Gaso-line and oil	Fuel oil and coal	Total [1]	Hous-ing [2]	Household operation		Trans-porta-tion	Medi-cal care
												Total [1]	Elec-tricity and gas		
1959	1,178.9	114.4	59.7	38.2	518.5	301.9	58.2	38.1	22.6	546.0	159.8	75.0	34.5	45.4	95.0
1960	1,210.8	115.4	61.3	37.7	526.9	305.8	58.7	39.4	21.7	568.5	168.1	78.5	36.3	46.7	98.4
1961	1,238.4	109.4	54.9	38.1	537.7	312.1	59.8	39.8	20.6	591.3	176.0	81.2	38.3	47.0	102.0
1962	1,293.3	120.2	62.2	40.4	553.0	316.3	62.4	41.5	20.6	620.0	185.8	85.2	40.9	48.7	110.2
1963	1,341.9	130.3	68.4	43.1	563.6	319.2	63.6	42.8	21.6	648.0	194.4	88.4	42.8	50.5	117.1
1964	1,417.2	140.7	71.2	48.3	588.2	331.0	68.5	45.1	22.5	688.3	203.5	92.6	45.1	53.0	129.8
1965	1,497.0	156.2	81.2	52.1	616.7	346.5	71.5	47.3	23.5	724.1	214.6	96.8	47.2	55.4	135.8
1966	1,573.8	166.0	81.8	57.6	647.6	359.1	76.3	50.2	24.2	760.2	224.4	101.4	49.7	58.6	142.3
1967	1,622.4	167.2	80.3	59.5	659.0	364.5	76.9	51.8	24.2	796.2	234.5	106.2	52.4	62.0	148.1
1968	1,707.5	184.5	91.8	62.9	686.0	380.7	80.2	55.5	23.0	837.0	246.0	110.1	55.0	65.4	159.5
1969	1,771.2	190.8	95.1	64.3	703.2	389.7	81.9	59.2	21.8	877.2	259.1	115.3	58.0	68.9	171.3
1970	1,813.5	183.7	85.6	64.4	717.2	397.5	81.0	62.9	20.2	912.5	269.3	118.9	60.4	71.0	180.7
1971	1,873.7	201.4	100.8	66.8	725.6	399.2	84.6	65.9	19.5	946.7	280.9	120.8	61.8	73.6	193.7
1972	1,978.4	225.2	114.3	73.6	755.8	411.9	90.4	68.6	21.5	997.4	295.9	126.8	64.9	77.8	207.0
1973	2,066.7	246.6	123.4	81.5	777.9	412.6	96.9	72.1	23.3	1,042.2	310.8	132.0	66.5	79.6	222.4
1974	2,053.8	227.2	102.2	81.9	759.8	404.7	95.4	68.6	18.4	1,066.8	326.9	132.5	66.9	79.9	231.1
1975	2,097.5	226.8	102.9	79.1	767.1	413.2	98.5	70.6	18.1	1,103.6	336.5	138.1	70.4	81.4	243.8
1976	2,207.3	256.4	124.6	84.2	801.3	431.9	103.2	73.4	20.3	1,149.5	346.7	143.9	72.9	84.4	255.5
1977	2,296.6	280.0	137.3	91.4	819.8	441.5	108.7	75.7	19.6	1,196.8	355.4	151.0	76.0	90.2	267.9
1978	2,391.8	292.9	141.5	96.6	844.8	442.8	119.0	77.4	19.5	1,254.1	372.9	158.0	78.8	92.9	279.2
1979	2,448.4	289.0	130.5	101.3	862.8	448.0	124.1	76.4	18.1	1,296.5	387.9	162.9	79.3	96.1	290.9
1980	2,447.1	262.7	111.4	98.5	860.5	448.8	126.0	72.0	14.0	1,323.9	399.4	167.1	81.6	91.3	302.1
1981	2,476.9	264.6	113.5	97.7	867.9	446.6	132.8	73.2	11.8	1,344.4	407.3	165.6	80.3	88.9	318.3
1982	2,503.7	262.5	115.6	94.2	872.2	451.4	133.7	73.9	10.9	1,368.9	409.6	166.7	81.2	87.4	323.7
1983	2,619.4	297.7	138.1	104.3	900.3	463.4	142.4	75.7	11.1	1,421.4	415.5	169.4	83.7	91.6	332.6
1984	2,746.1	338.5	160.3	115.3	934.6	472.3	153.1	77.9	11.2	1,473.0	426.8	173.7	84.3	100.0	341.9
1985	2,865.8	370.1	180.2	123.8	958.7	483.0	158.8	79.2	11.5	1,537.0	435.9	179.1	86.6	109.2	353.0
1986	2,969.1	402.0	193.3	136.3	991.0	494.1	170.3	82.9	12.1	1,576.1	442.1	180.8	85.6	112.6	366.2
1987	3,052.2	403.7	183.5	144.0	1,011.1	500.7	174.5	84.7	12.0	1,637.4	452.5	187.8	88.4	116.6	384.7
1988	3,162.4	428.7	194.8	155.4	1,035.1	513.4	178.9	86.1	12.0	1,698.5	461.8	196.9	92.7	122.5	399.4
1989	3,223.3	440.7	196.4	165.8	1,051.6	515.0	187.8	87.3	11.4	1,731.0	469.2	202.6	94.3	123.8	408.6
1990	3,260.4	439.3	192.2	169.5	1,056.5	520.8	185.9	86.4	10.1	1,764.6	474.7	203.7	92.4	124.7	423.9
1991	3,240.8	414.7	171.0	168.6	1,042.4	515.8	181.3	85.2	9.7	1,783.7	478.2	204.7	95.2	121.2	438.8
1982: IV	2,539.3	272.3	123.7	96.4	880.7	458.3	135.7	73.4	10.5	1,386.2	411.0	166.2	80.2	88.2	327.8
1983: IV	2,678.2	319.1	151.6	109.3	915.2	467.1	147.7	76.9	11.4	1,443.9	419.7	173.3	86.8	94.2	334.8
1984: IV	2,784.8	347.7	164.3	118.7	942.9	475.1	154.7	79.0	11.1	1,494.2	431.3	174.8	84.5	103.5	344.9
1985: IV	2,895.3	369.6	173.9	128.6	968.7	488.2	161.7	79.5	11.4	1,557.1	438.1	182.6	88.5	111.2	359.1
1986: IV	3,012.5	415.7	193.6	141.4	1,000.9	496.9	171.9	84.6	12.4	1,595.8	444.8	182.8	86.8	113.4	372.0
1987: IV	3,074.7	404.7	183.6	145.9	1,014.6	502.4	174.5	85.4	11.9	1,655.5	457.0	189.3	88.6	117.9	390.7
1988: IV	3,202.9	439.2	197.7	160.3	1,046.8	518.0	182.8	87.5	12.0	1,716.9	465.6	198.6	93.0	124.2	403.0
1989: I	3,203.6	435.2	196.2	163.0	1,048.1	516.8	183.3	88.1	11.1	1,720.3	467.0	201.0	94.1	123.6	406.6
II	3,212.2	440.2	195.6	166.1	1,047.0	514.2	186.5	85.4	11.6	1,725.1	468.4	199.5	91.8	123.4	407.0
III	3,235.3	450.6	205.3	166.3	1,052.6	513.2	190.4	87.1	11.0	1,732.2	469.9	201.3	92.6	123.7	408.8
IV	3,242.0	436.8	188.3	167.9	1,058.9	515.6	190.9	88.6	12.0	1,746.3	471.3	208.5	98.8	124.3	411.8
1990: I	3,259.5	453.5	202.6	171.8	1,058.3	518.3	188.6	87.4	9.8	1,747.1	473.3	197.9	87.8	125.2	418.3
II	3,260.1	439.2	192.8	169.7	1,057.1	521.2	185.6	86.4	10.9	1,763.7	474.1	205.3	93.8	125.0	422.1
III	3,273.9	437.7	191.3	168.9	1,059.1	521.6	186.2	86.7	10.9	1,777.1	475.1	207.6	94.8	124.9	426.7
IV	3,248.0	426.6	182.0	167.5	1,051.6	522.0	183.2	85.0	8.8	1,769.8	476.1	204.1	93.2	123.5	428.6
1991: I	3,223.5	412.0	169.6	166.9	1,043.0	516.4	180.8	83.9	9.4	1,768.5	476.5	201.4	92.1	121.5	433.6
II	3,239.3	411.3	167.2	169.3	1,046.3	516.3	183.2	86.0	9.8	1,781.8	477.9	206.5	96.6	121.5	435.6
III	3,251.2	419.4	173.3	170.4	1,044.8	515.0	183.7	86.0	10.0	1,787.0	478.8	206.5	96.3	121.2	440.5
IV	3,249.0	416.1	174.0	167.9	1,035.6	515.3	177.5	84.7	9.4	1,797.4	479.8	204.6	95.6	121.0	447.2
1992: I	3,289.3	432.3	181.5	174.4	1,049.6	518.9	184.1	85.7	10.2	1,807.3	481.2	201.6	92.0	120.3	449.6
II	3,288.5	430.0	182.2	174.4	1,045.9	513.5	184.4	85.8	12.0	1,812.9	483.3	204.2	94.5	121.3	453.7
III	3,318.4	439.8	179.0	181.5	1,052.0	514.3	190.8	86.0	10.9	1,826.6	485.8	205.6	94.0	124.1	458.1

[1] Includes other items not shown separately.
[2] Includes imputed rental value of owner-occupied housing.

Source: Department of Commerce, Bureau of Economic Analysis.

TABLE B–14.—*Gross and net private domestic investment, 1959–92*

[Billions of dollars; quarterly data at seasonally adjusted annual rates]

Year or quarter	Gross private domestic investment	Less: Consumption of fixed capital	Equals: Net private domestic investment						
				Net fixed investment					Change in business inventories
			Total	Total	Nonresidential			Residential	
					Total	Structures	Producers' durable equipment		
1959	78.8	44.6	34.2	30.1	12.3	6.6	5.7	17.8	4.2
1960	78.7	46.3	32.4	29.2	13.8	7.7	6.1	15.4	3.2
1961	77.9	47.7	30.3	27.3	12.2	7.6	4.6	15.1	2.9
1962	87.9	49.3	38.6	32.5	15.3	8.3	7.0	17.2	6.1
1963	93.4	51.3	42.0	36.4	16.4	8.3	8.1	20.0	5.7
1964	101.7	53.9	47.8	42.8	21.3	10.3	11.0	21.5	5.0
1965	118.0	57.3	60.7	51.0	30.3	14.1	16.2	20.7	9.7
1966	130.4	62.1	68.3	54.5	36.7	16.0	20.7	17.8	13.8
1967	128.0	67.4	60.6	50.1	33.2	15.1	18.1	16.9	10.5
1968	139.9	73.9	66.0	56.9	35.0	15.8	19.2	21.9	9.1
1969	155.2	81.5	73.7	64.0	40.5	17.9	22.6	23.5	9.7
1970	150.3	88.8	61.5	59.2	38.4	18.4	20.0	20.8	2.3
1971	175.5	97.6	78.0	69.9	36.8	18.4	18.4	33.1	8.0
1972	205.6	109.9	95.7	85.8	42.5	18.7	23.8	43.2	9.9
1973	243.1	120.4	122.7	105.0	59.0	23.8	35.2	46.0	17.7
1974	245.8	140.2	105.5	91.3	58.9	24.5	34.5	32.3	14.3
1975	226.0	165.2	60.9	66.5	41.5	18.8	22.7	25.1	−5.7
1976	286.4	182.8	103.6	86.8	45.6	19.9	25.6	41.2	16.7
1977	358.3	205.2	153.1	128.3	64.9	23.4	41.5	63.4	24.7
1978	434.0	234.8	199.3	171.3	94.1	35.5	58.6	77.3	27.9
1979	480.2	272.4	207.8	195.1	117.3	49.9	67.4	77.8	12.8
1980	467.6	311.9	155.7	165.2	113.8	59.1	54.7	51.4	−9.5
1981	558.0	362.4	195.6	170.2	127.1	75.5	51.6	43.1	25.4
1982	503.4	399.1	104.3	120.3	99.1	72.4	26.7	21.2	−15.9
1983	546.7	418.4	128.2	133.8	69.1	46.2	22.9	64.6	−5.5
1984	718.9	433.2	285.6	214.6	126.6	65.1	61.5	87.9	71.1
1985	714.5	454.5	260.0	235.4	146.1	75.2	70.9	89.3	24.6
1986	717.6	478.6	239.1	230.4	114.4	51.8	62.6	116.0	8.6
1987	749.3	502.2	247.1	220.9	103.0	46.7	56.3	117.9	26.3
1988	793.6	534.0	259.6	243.4	125.8	47.9	77.9	117.6	16.2
1989	832.3	580.4	251.9	218.6	117.1	48.6	68.5	101.5	33.3
1990	799.5	602.8	196.7	190.4	106.9	51.4	55.5	83.5	6.3
1991	721.1	626.1	95.0	105.3	52.3	25.2	27.1	53.0	−10.2
1982: IV	464.2	412.5	51.7	98.0					−46.3
1983: IV	614.8	439.7	175.1	154.9					20.2
1984: IV	722.8	448.0	274.8	223.8					51.0
1985: IV	737.0	465.6	271.4	238.8					32.6
1986: IV	697.1	488.2	208.9	227.8					−18.8
1987: IV	800.2	512.1	288.1	228.8					59.3
1988: IV	814.8	547.2	267.6	250.3					17.3
1989: I	843.9	557.8	286.1	242.4					43.7
II	840.3	568.4	271.9	232.1					39.8
III	819.6	594.3	225.3	205.7					19.6
IV	825.2	600.8	224.4	194.2					30.2
1990: I	820.3	594.7	225.6	217.5					8.1
II	833.0	599.1	233.9	196.2					37.7
III	805.7	605.8	199.9	189.5					10.4
IV	739.0	611.6	127.3	158.3					−31.0
1991: I	705.4	618.9	86.5	115.0					−28.5
II	710.2	623.5	86.8	108.5					−21.8
III	732.8	624.9	107.9	107.7					.2
IV	736.1	637.1	99.0	89.8					9.2
1992: I	722.4	631.4	91.0	106.8					−15.8
II	773.2	638.2	135.0	126.9					8.1
III	781.6	697.7	83.9	68.9					15.0

Source: Department of Commerce, Bureau of Economic Analysis.

364

TABLE B-15.—*Gross and net private domestic investment in 1987 dollars, 1959-92*

[Billions of 1987 dollars; quarterly data at seasonally adjusted annual rates]

Year or quarter	Gross private domestic investment	Less: Consumption of fixed capital	Equals: Net private domestic investment						
				Net fixed investment					Change in business inventories
			Total	Total	Nonresidential			Residential	
					Total	Structures	Producers' durable equipment		
1959	296.4	168.8	127.5	114.0	39.2	25.4	13.8	74.8	13.6
1960	290.8	173.7	117.1	109.0	44.1	30.5	13.7	64.8	8.1
1961	289.4	178.6	110.8	103.6	39.9	30.6	9.4	63.7	7.2
1962	321.2	183.6	137.6	122.0	49.5	32.9	16.6	72.5	15.6
1963	343.3	189.6	153.7	137.7	52.8	32.1	20.7	84.9	16.0
1964	371.8	196.4	175.4	159.7	69.7	39.5	30.2	90.0	15.7
1965	413.0	205.0	208.1	182.9	99.9	53.0	46.9	83.0	25.1
1966	438.0	214.9	223.0	186.3	118.1	58.3	59.8	68.2	36.7
1967	418.6	225.2	193.4	165.8	103.9	53.0	50.9	61.9	27.6
1968	440.1	235.3	204.7	181.1	105.1	52.2	52.9	76.0	23.6
1969	461.3	246.7	214.6	189.8	112.2	56.0	56.2	77.6	24.8
1970	429.7	258.0	171.7	165.8	98.7	53.5	45.2	67.1	5.9
1971	475.7	269.1	206.6	185.8	85.0	49.0	36.0	100.8	20.8
1972	532.2	285.0	247.2	224.6	98.9	49.2	49.7	125.7	22.5
1973	591.7	296.4	295.3	257.6	134.6	57.9	76.7	123.0	37.7
1974	543.0	310.3	232.6	201.7	122.3	53.4	68.9	79.4	30.9
1975	437.6	322.8	114.8	128.7	72.0	36.7	35.3	56.8	−13.9
1976	520.6	334.6	186.1	160.6	74.5	36.8	37.7	86.1	25.5
1977	600.4	348.4	252.1	217.8	99.0	39.8	59.2	118.8	34.3
1978	664.6	364.5	300.0	262.8	134.4	55.2	79.2	128.4	37.2
1979	669.7	384.5	285.2	271.6	154.1	70.1	84.0	117.5	13.6
1980	594.4	400.7	193.7	201.9	129.5	73.3	56.1	72.5	−8.3
1981	631.1	417.8	213.2	188.7	131.6	82.0	49.6	57.1	24.6
1982	540.5	429.5	111.0	128.5	101.0	75.3	25.7	27.5	−17.5
1983	599.5	447.4	152.1	147.7	71.6	50.3	21.4	76.0	4.4
1984	757.5	455.5	302.0	234.0	134.3	69.3	65.0	99.8	67.9
1985	745.9	471.5	274.4	252.3	154.0	79.4	74.6	98.3	22.1
1986	735.1	486.7	248.4	239.9	118.3	54.9	63.3	121.6	8.5
1987	749.3	502.2	247.1	220.9	103.0	46.7	56.3	117.9	26.3
1988	773.4	518.5	254.9	235.0	122.6	46.7	75.9	112.4	19.9
1989	784.0	545.5	238.5	208.7	114.8	45.9	68.9	94.0	29.8
1990	739.1	554.9	184.2	178.0	102.6	46.9	55.7	75.5	6.2
1991	661.1	569.3	91.8	101.1	53.9	23.4	30.5	47.3	−9.3
1982: IV	503.5	439.2	64.3	109.2					−44.9
1983: IV	669.5	468.5	201.0	171.7					29.3
1984: IV	756.4	467.4	289.0	241.1					47.9
1985: IV	763.1	480.1	283.0	252.8					30.2
1986: IV	705.9	492.5	213.3	233.4					−20.1
1987: IV	793.8	508.1	285.7	225.8					59.9
1988: IV	785.0	524.7	260.3	239.3					20.9
1989: I	802.9	530.1	272.9	231.6					41.2
II	794.5	535.7	258.8	221.8					36.9
III	769.0	556.7	212.4	196.4					16.0
IV	769.5	559.6	209.9	185.0					24.9
1990: I	763.0	549.9	213.0	205.5					7.5
II	770.2	553.5	216.7	183.9					32.8
III	743.1	556.6	186.5	175.3					11.2
IV	680.0	559.6	120.5	147.2					−26.8
1991: I	646.0	562.5	83.4	108.5					−25.1
II	649.5	565.8	83.6	104.0					−20.4
III	672.0	569.6	102.4	101.8					.6
IV	676.9	579.1	97.8	90.2					7.5
1992: I	668.9	576.4	92.5	105.0					−12.6
II	713.6	578.0	135.7	127.9					7.8
III	724.9	628.3	96.6	81.6					15.0

Source: Department of Commerce, Bureau of Economic Analysis.

TABLE B-16.—*Inventories and final sales of domestic business, 1959–92*

[Billions of dollars, except as noted; seasonally adjusted]

Quarter	Inventories [1]							Final sales of domestic business [3]	Ratio of inventories to final sales of domestic business	
	Total [2]	Farm	Nonfarm						Total	Nonfarm
			Total [2]	Manu-facturing	Whole-sale trade	Retail trade	Other			
Fourth quarter:										
1959	141.2	31.6	109.6	55.2	21.0	26.2	7.2	36.2	3.90	3.03
1960	145.2	33.0	112.2	56.2	21.3	27.5	7.2	37.4	3.88	3.00
1961	147.0	33.7	113.4	57.2	21.8	27.0	7.4	39.3	3.74	2.88
1962	153.4	34.8	118.6	60.3	22.4	28.3	7.5	41.5	3.69	2.86
1963	158.7	34.9	123.8	62.2	23.9	29.6	8.0	44.2	3.59	2.80
1964	164.2	33.3	130.9	65.9	25.2	31.0	8.8	47.1	3.49	2.78
1965	178.4	37.4	141.0	70.7	26.9	33.7	9.8	52.1	3.43	2.71
1966	194.0	36.3	157.8	80.9	30.3	36.2	10.4	55.1	3.52	2.86
1967	206.0	36.5	169.5	87.5	32.7	36.9	12.4	58.7	3.51	2.89
1968	221.4	38.7	182.6	94.0	34.6	40.7	13.3	64.5	3.43	2.83
1969	242.5	41.9	200.6	103.4	37.9	44.5	14.9	68.5	3.54	2.93
1970	249.4	40.1	209.2	105.8	41.7	45.8	16.0	72.2	3.45	2.90
1971	267.4	45.0	222.4	107.3	45.2	52.3	17.6	78.6	3.40	2.83
1972	296.6	55.3	241.3	113.6	50.0	57.7	19.9	87.5	3.39	2.76
1973	365.1	78.0	287.1	136.1	59.4	66.4	25.2	96.0	3.80	2.99
1974	435.2	74.3	360.9	177.0	75.6	74.6	33.7	104.0	4.18	3.47
1975	440.1	75.5	364.5	177.8	76.2	74.7	35.8	116.2	3.79	3.14
1976	475.3	72.2	403.1	194.9	86.1	82.7	39.4	127.6	3.72	3.16
1977	521.6	75.2	446.4	210.6	96.2	93.3	46.3	142.7	3.65	3.13
1978	605.3	92.1	513.2	238.0	111.7	107.5	55.9	164.5	3.68	3.12
1979	702.6	97.9	604.7	280.6	141.2	118.9	64.1	182.3	3.85	3.32
1980	784.1	104.9	679.3	309.8	174.2	125.0	70.3	201.2	3.90	3.38
1981	836.2	101.4	734.7	331.9	184.8	137.0	81.1	217.2	3.85	3.38
1982	817.0	103.6	713.5	318.5	174.7	139.5	80.7	228.6	3.57	3.12
1983	827.5	103.2	724.4	319.2	168.9	153.7	82.5	249.6	3.32	2.90
1984	898.9	100.9	797.9	349.0	187.2	173.5	88.3	271.5	3.31	2.94
1985	904.3	96.6	807.7	339.9	184.9	188.6	94.3	292.7	3.09	2.76
1986	887.9	90.5	797.3	328.1	183.4	193.4	92.4	311.1	2.85	2.56
1987	950.6	90.9	859.7	349.3	196.3	216.1	98.0	329.2	2.89	2.61
1988	1,025.1	95.4	929.6	383.2	215.3	229.9	101.2	358.4	2.86	2.59
1989	1,081.6	96.3	985.3	409.7	224.8	250.2	100.6	376.6	2.87	2.62
1990	1,106.8	94.6	1,012.2	422.2	236.0	252.0	102.0	393.3	2.81	2.57
1991	1,082.1	90.5	991.6	406.7	235.5	255.8	93.6	403.9	2.68	2.45
1989: I	1,048.4	97.5	950.9	393.9	216.8	238.9	101.4	363.0	2.89	2.62
II	1,061.4	98.3	963.1	401.8	220.6	239.4	101.3	369.0	2.88	2.61
III	1,067.1	95.1	972.0	407.4	222.5	240.7	101.3	373.6	2.86	2.60
IV	1,081.6	96.3	985.3	409.7	224.8	250.2	100.6	376.6	2.87	2.62
1990: I	1,084.6	96.5	988.1	412.3	226.5	246.7	102.6	385.2	2.82	2.57
II	1,095.8	98.6	997.2	415.0	230.1	249.9	102.3	388.1	2.82	2.57
III.ᴬ	1,117.2	97.2	1,020.0	427.5	236.5	252.3	103.7	392.0	2.85	2.60
IV	1,106.8	94.6	1,012.2	422.2	236.0	252.0	102.0	393.3	2.81	2.57
1991: I	1,093.3	97.6	995.7	416.6	234.8	247.0	97.3	393.8	2.78	2.53
II	1,089.6	101.1	988.5	411.9	231.4	248.9	96.4	399.3	2.73	2.48
III	1,085.5	96.9	988.6	409.9	231.8	252.5	94.5	401.8	2.70	2.46
IV	1,082.1	90.5	991.6	406.7	235.5	255.8	93.6	403.9	2.68	2.45
1992: I	1,085.1	93.0	992.1	404.0	236.0	257.4	94.7	411.1	2.64	2.41
II	1,090.9	91.4	999.4	403.1	238.3	263.3	94.8	414.5	2.63	2.41
III	1,098.5	92.4	1,006.1	405.2	238.7	267.0	95.3	419.1	2.62	2.40

[1] Inventories at end of quarter. Quarter-to-quarter change calculated from this table is not the current-dollar change in business inventories (CBI) component of GDP. The former is the difference between two inventory stocks, each valued at their respective end-of-quarter prices. The latter is the change in the physical volume of inventories valued at average prices of the quarter. In addition, changes calculated from this table are at quarterly rates, whereas CBI is stated at annual rates.

[2] Inventories of construction establishments are included in "other" nonfarm inventories.

[3] Quarterly totals at monthly rates. Final sales of domestic business equals final sales of domestic product less gross product of households and institutions and general government and includes a small amount of final sales by farms.

Note.—The industry classification of inventories is on an establishment basis and is based on the 1987 Standard Industrial Classification (SIC) beginning 1987 and on the 1972 SIC for earlier years shown.

Source: Department of Commerce, Bureau of Economic Analysis.

TABLE B–17.—*Inventories and final sales of domestic business in 1987 dollars, 1959–92*

[Billions of 1987 dollars, except as noted; seasonally adjusted]

Quarter	Inventories[1]		Nonfarm					Final sales of domestic business[3]	Ratio of inventories to final sales of domestic business	
	Total[2]	Farm	Total[2]	Manufacturing	Wholesale trade	Retail trade	Other		Total	Nonfarm
Fourth quarter:										
1959	388.6	79.6	308.9	152.4	61.2	67.6	27.8	130.5	2.98	2.37
1960	396.7	80.5	316.2	153.9	62.4	71.4	28.5	133.2	2.98	2.37
1961	403.9	82.1	321.8	157.9	63.7	70.2	30.0	138.8	2.91	2.32
1962	419.5	83.9	335.7	166.1	65.9	73.8	29.9	143.8	2.92	2.33
1963	435.6	85.4	350.2	171.6	69.6	76.9	32.0	152.1	2.86	2.30
1964	451.2	83.4	367.8	179.6	73.4	80.3	34.5	159.7	2.83	2.30
1965	476.4	84.6	391.7	190.2	77.6	86.8	37.2	172.8	2.76	2.27
1966	513.1	83.5	429.6	212.1	86.5	92.5	38.4	175.9	2.92	2.44
1967	540.7	84.5	456.3	227.6	92.0	92.1	44.6	182.4	2.97	2.50
1968	564.3	86.9	477.5	237.4	94.7	99.3	46.1	191.0	2.95	2.50
1969	589.2	86.9	502.3	246.7	100.3	105.9	49.4	194.0	3.04	2.59
1970	595.1	86.3	508.8	246.1	106.9	105.8	50.0	196.3	3.03	2.59
1971	615.8	89.2	526.7	243.9	112.3	117.8	52.6	203.4	3.03	2.59
1972	638.4	90.6	547.7	249.6	116.3	125.3	56.5	218.5	2.92	2.51
1973	676.1	92.9	583.3	264.9	121.1	134.5	62.7	223.1	3.03	2.61
1974	707.0	92.5	614.5	283.7	130.8	133.6	66.4	218.5	3.24	2.81
1975	693.1	92.9	600.2	277.2	127.3	127.6	68.0	226.5	3.06	2.65
1976	718.6	90.8	627.8	289.6	135.3	134.8	68.1	235.6	3.05	2.66
1977	752.9	93.6	659.2	297.1	144.4	144.5	73.3	246.7	3.05	2.67
1978	790.1	93.0	697.1	309.2	155.8	153.7	78.3	261.3	3.02	2.67
1979	803.7	95.7	708.0	320.1	157.3	153.5	77.1	265.7	3.02	2.66
1980	795.4	92.3	703.1	319.9	161.9	146.7	74.6	265.4	3.00	2.65
1981	820.0	98.3	721.7	324.0	164.8	152.9	80.0	262.7	3.12	2.75
1982	802.5	101.4	701.0	311.3	159.9	151.7	78.1	264.9	3.03	2.65
1983	806.9	93.1	713.8	311.9	159.3	162.8	79.8	279.0	2.89	2.56
1984	874.8	94.8	780.0	339.4	174.7	181.4	84.5	292.7	2.99	2.66
1985	896.9	97.2	799.8	335.7	178.7	194.1	91.3	305.0	2.94	2.62
1986	905.5	95.1	810.4	333.6	185.7	196.7	94.4	316.9	2.86	2.56
1987	931.8	88.7	843.1	340.2	192.7	213.6	96.6	325.2	2.87	2.59
1988	951.7	81.7	870.0	355.3	199.1	219.7	95.9	339.5	2.80	2.56
1989	981.5	81.6	899.9	373.9	202.5	231.0	92.5	343.2	2.86	2.62
1990	987.6	84.0	903.6	377.6	207.0	227.3	91.7	343.3	2.88	2.63
1991	978.3	84.3	894.0	370.7	207.9	229.0	86.3	342.1	2.86	2.61
1989: I	962.0	83.1	878.9	360.2	198.4	225.5	94.8	340.2	2.83	2.58
II	971.3	84.5	886.7	367.0	201.6	224.3	93.9	342.0	2.84	2.59
III	975.2	83.1	892.1	372.2	202.1	224.5	93.3	343.2	2.84	2.60
IV	981.5	81.6	899.9	373.9	202.5	231.0	92.5	343.2	2.86	2.62
1990: I	983.4	82.0	901.4	376.7	203.5	226.5	94.6	347.2	2.83	2.60
II	991.5	83.2	908.4	378.6	206.2	228.9	94.6	345.9	2.87	2.63
III	994.3	84.3	910.0	379.8	207.8	228.8	93.6	345.4	2.88	2.63
IV	987.6	84.0	903.6	377.6	207.0	227.3	91.7	343.3	2.88	2.63
1991: I	981.4	83.9	897.4	378.3	207.4	222.4	89.4	339.8	2.89	2.64
II	976.3	85.0	891.3	375.4	204.6	222.8	88.5	342.0	2.85	2.61
III	976.4	85.4	891.1	373.5	204.6	226.0	87.0	342.0	2.86	2.61
IV	978.3	84.3	894.0	370.7	207.9	229.0	86.3	342.1	2.86	2.61
1992: I	975.2	83.8	891.4	368.5	206.5	229.2	87.1	346.0	2.82	2.58
II	977.1	84.3	892.9	366.9	207.3	232.1	86.5	346.7	2.82	2.58
III	980.9	85.6	895.3	367.9	206.8	234.5	86.1	348.8	2.81	2.57

[1] Inventories at end of quarter. Quarter-to-quarter changes calculated from this table are at quarterly rates, whereas the constant-dollar change in business inventories component of GDP is stated at annual rates.

[2] Inventories of construction establishments are included in "other" nonfarm inventories.

[3] Quarterly totals at monthly rates. Final sales of domestic business equals final sales of domestic product less gross product of households and institutions and general government and includes a small amount of final sales by farms.

Note.—The industry classification of inventories is on an establishment basis and is based on the 1987 Standard Industrial Classification (SIC) beginning 1987 and on the 1972 SIC for earlier years shown.

Source: Department of Commerce, Bureau of Economic Analysis.

[Billions of dollars; quarterly data at seasonally adjusted annual rates]

Year or quarter	Receipts from rest of the world					Payments to rest of the world									
	Total [1]	Exports of goods and services			Receipts of factor income [3]	Total	Imports of goods and services			Payments of factor income [4]	Transfer payments (net)				Net foreign investment
		Total	Merchandise [2]	Services [2]			Total	Merchandise [2]	Services [2]		Total	From persons (net)	From government (net)	From business	
1959	25.0	20.6	16.5	4.2	4.3	25.0	22.3	15.3	7.0	1.5	2.4	0.4	1.8	0.1	-1.2
1960	30.2	25.3	20.5	4.8	5.0	30.2	22.8	15.2	7.6	1.8	2.4	.5	1.9	.1	3.2
1961	31.4	26.0	20.9	5.1	5.4	31.4	22.7	15.1	7.6	1.8	2.7	.5	2.1	.1	4.3
1962	33.5	27.4	21.7	5.7	6.1	33.5	25.0	16.9	8.1	1.8	2.8	.5	2.1	.1	3.9
1963	36.1	29.4	23.3	6.1	6.6	36.1	26.1	17.7	8.4	2.1	2.8	.6	2.1	.1	5.0
1964	41.0	33.6	26.7	6.9	7.4	41.0	28.1	19.4	8.7	2.4	3.0	.7	2.1	.2	7.5
1965	43.5	35.4	27.8	7.6	8.1	43.5	31.5	22.2	9.3	2.7	3.0	.8	2.1	.2	6.2
1966	47.2	38.9	30.7	8.2	8.3	47.2	37.1	26.3	10.7	3.1	3.2	.8	2.2	.2	3.9
1967	50.2	41.4	32.2	9.2	8.9	50.2	39.9	27.8	12.2	3.4	3.4	1.0	2.1	.2	3.5
1968	55.6	45.3	35.3	10.0	10.3	55.6	46.6	33.9	12.6	4.1	3.2	1.0	1.9	.3	1.7
1969	61.2	49.3	38.3	11.0	11.9	61.2	50.5	36.8	13.7	5.8	3.2	1.1	1.8	.3	1.8
1970	70.8	57.0	44.5	12.4	13.0	70.8	55.8	40.9	14.9	6.6	3.6	1.2	2.0	.4	4.9
1971	74.2	59.3	45.6	13.8	14.1	74.2	62.3	46.6	15.8	6.4	4.1	1.3	2.4	.4	1.3
1972	83.4	66.2	51.8	14.4	16.4	83.4	74.2	56.9	17.3	7.7	4.3	1.3	2.5	.5	-2.9
1973	115.6	91.8	73.9	17.8	23.8	115.6	91.2	71.8	19.3	11.1	4.6	1.4	2.5	.7	8.7
1974	152.6	124.3	101.0	23.3	30.3	152.6	127.5	104.5	22.9	14.6	5.4	1.2	3.2	1.0	5.1
1975	164.4	136.3	109.6	26.7	28.2	164.4	122.7	99.0	23.7	14.9	5.4	1.2	3.5	.7	21.4
1976	181.6	148.9	117.8	31.1	32.8	181.6	151.1	124.6	26.5	15.7	6.0	1.2	3.7	1.1	8.8
1977	196.5	158.8	123.7	35.1	37.7	196.5	182.4	152.6	29.8	17.2	6.0	1.2	3.4	1.4	-9.2
1978	233.3	186.1	145.4	40.7	47.1	233.3	212.3	177.4	34.8	25.3	6.4	1.3	3.8	1.4	-10.7
1979	299.7	228.9	184.2	44.7	69.7	299.7	252.7	212.8	39.9	37.5	7.5	1.4	4.1	2.0	2.0
1980	360.9	279.2	226.0	53.2	80.6	360.9	293.9	248.6	45.3	46.5	9.0	1.6	5.0	2.4	11.5
1981	398.2	303.0	239.3	63.7	94.1	398.2	317.7	267.7	49.9	60.9	10.0	1.8	5.0	3.2	9.5
1982	379.9	282.6	215.2	67.4	97.3	379.9	303.2	250.6	52.6	67.1	12.1	2.1	6.4	3.6	-2.5
1983	372.5	276.7	207.5	69.2	95.8	372.5	328.1	272.7	55.4	66.5	12.9	1.8	7.3	3.8	-35.0
1984	410.5	302.4	225.8	76.6	108.1	410.5	405.1	336.3	68.8	83.8	15.6	2.3	9.4	3.9	-94.0
1985	399.3	302.1	222.4	79.7	97.3	399.3	417.6	343.3	74.3	82.4	17.4	2.7	11.4	3.2	-118.1
1986	415.2	319.2	226.2	93.0	96.0	415.2	451.7	370.0	81.7	86.9	18.3	2.5	12.3	3.5	-141.7
1987	469.0	364.0	257.7	106.2	105.1	469.0	507.1	414.8	92.3	100.5	16.6	3.0	10.4	3.2	-155.1
1988	572.9	444.2	325.8	118.4	128.7	572.9	552.2	452.1	100.1	120.8	17.8	2.7	10.4	4.8	-118.0
1989	665.5	508.0	371.6	136.4	157.5	665.5	587.7	485.1	102.6	141.5	25.6	8.9	11.3	5.4	-89.3
1990	717.6	557.0	398.1	159.0	160.6	717.6	625.9	507.8	118.1	139.9	27.9	9.3	13.4	5.2	-76.1
1991	741.7	598.2	423.1	175.1	143.5	741.7	620.0	499.9	120.1	126.0	-13.3	9.7	-28.3	5.3	9.0
1982: IV	357.5	265.6	198.2	67.4	91.9	357.5	295.1	241.6	53.4	64.4	13.8	1.9	8.2	3.7	-15.8
1983: IV	388.3	286.2	218.2	67.9	102.1	388.3	358.0	300.0	58.0	71.0	17.8	2.0	11.0	4.8	-58.5
1984: IV	415.2	308.7	231.4	77.3	106.6	415.2	415.7	344.1	71.6	85.5	20.4	2.5	13.9	4.0	-106.3
1985: IV	402.9	304.7	222.6	82.1	98.1	402.9	440.2	363.0	77.2	82.4	19.4	2.5	13.5	3.4	-139.1
1986: IV	426.7	333.9	235.8	98.1	92.8	426.7	467.1	382.4	84.7	88.9	19.6	2.8	12.8	4.0	-149.0
1987: IV	506.8	392.4	283.3	109.2	114.4	506.8	535.6	437.6	98.0	106.9	21.4	3.1	14.6	3.8	-157.1
1988: IV	606.9	467.0	345.4	121.6	139.9	606.9	573.1	470.1	103.0	130.2	23.8	2.7	15.1	5.9	-120.1
1989: I	642.4	489.7	358.5	131.2	152.6	642.4	574.9	474.1	100.8	138.6	23.7	8.2	10.0	5.5	-94.7
II	670.4	509.5	376.5	132.9	161.0	670.4	589.6	488.4	101.1	147.2	22.8	8.7	8.6	5.5	-89.1
III	666.1	509.0	370.5	138.5	157.1	666.1	588.7	485.5	103.1	141.3	25.7	8.7	11.5	5.4	-89.6
IV	683.1	523.8	380.7	143.1	159.3	683.1	597.7	492.2	105.6	139.1	30.3	9.8	15.1	5.4	-84.0
1990: I	698.0	541.2	390.7	150.4	156.8	698.0	613.3	500.2	113.1	137.9	25.7	8.5	12.0	5.3	-79.0
II	706.1	551.2	396.4	154.9	154.9	706.1	611.2	495.8	115.4	140.5	29.7	9.0	15.5	5.2	-75.3
III	713.7	555.9	395.5	160.4	157.8	713.7	632.2	512.2	120.0	139.5	28.7	10.2	13.3	5.2	-86.7
IV	752.6	579.7	409.6	170.2	172.9	752.6	646.9	523.2	123.7	141.5	27.4	9.5	12.8	5.2	-63.2
1991: I	733.0	572.3	410.0	163.2	159.8	733.0	602.0	485.2	116.7	130.8	-61.8	9.4	-76.4	5.2	62.1
II	737.5	594.3	421.1	173.2	143.2	737.5	609.6	489.5	120.0	126.5	-16.7	9.8	-31.8	5.3	18.2
III	740.1	602.3	423.5	178.8	137.8	740.1	629.5	508.7	120.8	124.5	9.1	9.9	-6.2	5.3	-22.9
IV	756.0	622.9	437.7	185.3	133.1	756.0	638.9	516.2	122.7	122.3	16.2	9.7	1.3	5.3	-21.5
1992: I	761.0	628.1	437.3	190.8	132.9	761.0	636.2	513.1	123.1	113.3	27.4	10.2	12.0	5.3	-16.0
II	756.7	625.4	435.2	190.2	131.3	756.7	662.5	537.0	125.5	124.3	29.3	10.4	13.6	5.3	-59.4
III	767.9	639.0	446.7	192.4	128.8	767.9	675.0	559.7	115.3	115.3	27.1	10.0	12.0	5.1	-49.6

[1] Includes capital grants received by the United States (net), not shown separately. See Table B-26 for data.
[2] Exports and imports of certain goods, primarily military equipment purchased and sold by the Federal Government, are included in services.
[3] Consists largely of receipts by U.S. residents of interest and dividends and reinvested earnings of foreign affiliates of U.S. corporations.
[4] Consists largely of payments to foreign residents of interest and dividends and reinvested earnings of U.S. affiliates of foreign corporations.

Source: Department of Commerce, Bureau of Economic Analysis.

[Billions of 1987 dollars; quarterly data at seasonally adjusted annual rates]

Year or quarter	Exports of goods and services					Receipts of factor income [2]	Imports of goods and services					Payments of factor income [3]
	Total	Merchandise [1]			Services [1]		Total	Merchandise [1]			Services [1]	
		Total	Durable goods	Nondurable goods				Total	Durable goods	Nondurable goods		
1959	73.8	58.0	31.5	26.5	15.8	17.0	95.6	60.2	26.0	34.2	35.4	6.2
1960	88.4	71.2	39.2	32.0	17.2	19.1	96.1	59.1	24.7	34.4	37.0	7.2
1961	89.9	71.5	39.4	32.1	18.4	20.6	95.3	59.2	23.7	35.5	36.1	7.2
1962	95.0	74.8	41.2	33.5	20.3	22.6	105.5	68.0	28.0	40.0	37.5	7.3
1963	101.8	80.3	43.6	36.7	21.5	24.4	107.7	70.9	29.6	41.2	36.8	8.2
1964	115.4	91.4	50.2	41.2	24.0	26.7	112.9	75.6	32.8	42.8	37.3	9.1
1965	118.1	92.1	52.2	39.9	25.9	28.3	124.5	86.5	40.5	46.0	37.9	9.9
1966	125.7	98.4	56.1	42.3	27.3	28.1	143.7	100.2	50.6	49.6	43.5	11.0
1967	130.0	100.1	63.8	36.3	29.9	29.2	153.7	105.2	53.1	52.1	48.6	11.8
1968	140.2	108.8	70.0	38.7	31.5	32.3	177.7	128.1	68.7	59.4	49.6	13.6
1969	147.8	114.4	75.2	39.2	33.3	35.8	189.2	137.0	74.1	62.8	52.3	17.8
1970	161.3	125.2	80.4	44.7	36.1	36.9	196.4	142.1	75.4	66.7	54.4	19.2
1971	161.9	124.1	79.3	44.9	37.8	38.1	207.8	156.1	84.4	71.7	51.7	18.0
1972	173.7	136.5	87.1	49.5	37.2	42.3	230.2	177.5	95.7	81.7	52.8	20.5
1973	210.3	166.9	108.0	58.9	43.4	57.6	244.4	194.7	100.9	93.9	49.7	27.6
1974	234.4	183.4	123.5	59.9	51.0	67.5	238.4	189.3	101.3	87.9	49.2	33.2
1975	232.9	178.5	121.3	57.2	54.4	57.5	209.8	163.3	82.1	81.2	46.5	31.6
1976	243.4	183.9	121.8	62.1	59.5	63.0	249.7	200.4	100.9	99.5	49.3	31.5
1977	246.9	183.9	119.5	64.4	63.0	67.9	274.7	223.2	112.9	110.3	51.5	32.2
1978	270.2	203.0	132.1	70.9	67.2	78.7	300.1	245.2	130.0	115.3	54.8	43.2
1979	293.5	225.7	148.1	77.6	67.8	107.1	304.1	248.7	132.1	116.7	55.3	58.6
1980	320.5	248.2	161.0	87.3	72.3	113.7	289.9	235.6	133.6	102.0	54.2	66.6
1981	326.1	244.0	154.2	89.7	82.2	120.7	304.1	246.1	143.4	102.7	58.0	79.4
1982	296.7	217.7	130.5	87.2	79.0	117.9	304.1	243.1	143.0	100.1	61.1	82.1
1983	285.9	208.3	124.6	83.8	77.6	111.0	342.1	276.5	167.6	108.9	65.6	78.0
1984	305.7	221.3	133.8	87.5	84.4	119.4	427.7	346.1	219.9	126.2	81.6	93.5
1985	309.2	224.8	139.3	85.6	84.4	103.4	454.6	366.5	237.2	129.3	88.1	88.2
1986	329.6	234.3	144.8	89.6	95.3	99.2	484.7	398.0	254.6	143.4	86.7	90.2
1987	364.0	257.7	163.0	94.7	106.2	105.1	507.1	414.8	264.2	150.6	92.3	100.5
1988	421.6	307.4	202.8	104.6	114.2	123.8	525.7	431.3	274.7	156.7	94.3	116.1
1989	471.8	343.8	230.9	112.9	128.0	144.7	545.4	450.4	287.1	163.3	95.0	130.1
1990	510.0	368.5	249.2	119.3	141.4	141.1	561.8	460.3	291.2	169.1	101.5	122.6
1991	539.4	392.5	266.4	126.1	146.9	120.8	561.2	463.5	296.7	166.8	97.7	105.4
1982: IV	280.4	202.8	119.0	83.7	77.6	109.7	299.4	236.3	134.6	101.7	63.1	77.6
1983: IV	291.5	215.5	131.0	84.5	75.9	116.5	375.1	306.6	191.1	115.5	68.6	82.0
1984: IV	312.8	229.0	138.5	90.5	83.8	116.1	444.2	357.9	229.3	128.6	86.3	93.9
1985: IV	312.0	226.4	139.6	86.8	85.5	102.9	467.4	380.0	243.5	136.5	87.4	86.8
1986: IV	342.9	243.5	150.0	93.5	99.4	94.8	498.9	409.1	259.8	149.3	89.8	91.2
1987: IV	386.1	278.0	180.1	97.8	108.1	112.9	522.1	427.4	273.8	153.7	94.6	105.4
1988: IV	438.2	322.0	214.7	107.2	116.2	132.3	540.9	444.8	284.0	160.8	96.1	123.0
1989: I	454.5	330.2	220.9	109.3	124.3	142.5	534.3	440.4	283.3	157.1	93.9	129.4
II	472.0	346.9	233.5	113.5	125.0	148.6	541.9	447.6	286.2	161.4	94.3	136.0
III	472.9	343.3	231.3	112.0	129.6	143.6	550.5	455.0	288.3	166.7	95.5	129.2
IV	487.7	354.8	237.8	116.9	132.9	144.3	555.0	458.5	290.4	168.1	96.5	125.9
1990: I	500.2	363.5	245.2	118.3	136.7	140.3	558.6	458.3	285.1	173.2	100.3	123.3
II	508.7	368.7	251.6	117.1	140.0	136.8	565.6	464.5	291.4	173.0	101.2	124.0
III	508.4	366.7	248.7	118.0	141.7	137.8	567.7	465.7	295.0	170.7	102.0	121.5
IV	522.6	375.3	251.3	123.9	147.3	149.3	555.3	452.7	293.3	159.4	102.6	121.7
1991: I	515.9	377.4	251.1	126.3	138.5	136.2	533.8	438.9	282.2	156.7	94.9	110.9
II	536.1	390.1	267.9	122.1	146.1	120.9	553.5	454.9	286.6	168.3	98.5	106.2
III	544.2	395.2	269.6	125.5	149.0	115.4	575.8	477.9	306.9	171.0	97.9	103.6
IV	561.4	407.3	277.0	130.3	154.0	110.8	581.8	482.2	311.0	171.3	99.6	101.0
1992: I	565.4	408.1	276.1	131.9	157.3	109.7	586.8	488.0	316.3	171.8	98.8	92.7
II	563.4	408.0	278.4	129.6	155.4	107.6	607.3	507.8	327.0	180.8	99.5	101.0
III	575.9	420.4	285.8	134.6	155.5	105.0	628.6	526.4	342.1	184.3	102.2	93.0

[1] Exports and imports of certain goods, primarily military equipment purchased and sold by the Federal Government, are included in services.
[2] Consists largely of receipts by U.S. residents of interest and dividends and reinvested earnings of foreign affiliates of U.S. corporations.
[3] Consists largely of payments to foreign residents of interest and dividends and reinvested earnings of U.S. affiliates of foreign corporations.

Source: Department of Commerce, Bureau of Economic Analysis.

[Billions of dollars; quarterly data at seasonally adjusted annual rates]

Year or quarter	Gross domestic product	Plus: Receipts of factor income from rest of the world [1]	Less: Payments of factor income to rest of the world [2]	Equals: Gross national product	Less: Consumption of fixed capital	Equals: Net national product	Less: Indirect business tax and nontax liability	Less: Business transfer payments	Less: Statistical discrepancy	Plus: Subsidies less current surplus of government enterprises	Equals: National income
1959	494.2	4.3	1.5	497.0	44.6	452.5	41.9	1.4	−1.8	−0.9	410.1
1960	513.4	5.0	1.8	516.6	46.3	470.2	45.5	1.4	−3.1	−.8	425.7
1961	531.8	5.4	1.8	535.4	47.7	487.7	48.1	1.5	−2.2	.2	440.5
1962	571.6	6.1	1.8	575.8	49.3	526.5	51.7	1.6	−1.0	.3	474.5
1963	603.1	6.6	2.1	607.7	51.3	556.4	54.7	1.8	−2.0	−.3	501.5
1964	648.0	7.4	2.4	653.0	53.9	599.2	58.8	2.0	−.7	.1	539.1
1965	702.7	8.1	2.7	708.1	57.3	650.7	62.7	2.2	−.7	.3	586.9
1966	769.8	8.3	3.1	774.9	62.1	712.8	65.4	2.3	2.8	1.4	643.7
1967	814.3	8.9	3.4	819.8	67.4	752.4	70.4	2.5	.8	1.2	679.9
1968	889.3	10.3	4.1	895.5	73.9	821.5	79.0	2.8	−.1	1.2	741.0
1969	959.5	11.9	5.8	965.6	81.5	884.2	86.6	3.1	−2.6	1.5	798.6
1970	1,010.7	13.0	6.6	1,017.1	88.8	928.3	94.3	3.2	.0	2.6	833.5
1971	1,097.2	14.1	6.4	1,104.9	97.6	1,007.3	103.6	3.4	3.1	2.4	899.5
1972	1,207.0	16.4	7.7	1,215.7	109.9	1,105.7	111.4	3.9	1.1	3.4	992.9
1973	1,349.6	23.8	11.1	1,362.3	120.4	1,241.9	121.0	4.5	−.5	2.6	1,119.5
1974	1,458.6	30.3	14.6	1,474.3	140.2	1,334.1	129.3	5.0	1.4	.4	1,198.8
1975	1,585.9	28.2	14.9	1,599.1	165.2	1,433.9	140.0	5.2	6.0	2.6	1,285.3
1976	1,768.4	32.8	15.7	1,785.5	182.8	1,602.7	151.6	6.5	10.4	1.4	1,435.5
1977	1,974.1	37.7	17.2	1,994.6	205.2	1,789.4	165.5	7.3	10.9	3.3	1,609.1
1978	2,232.7	47.1	25.3	2,254.5	234.8	2,019.8	177.8	8.2	7.6	3.6	1,829.8
1979	2,488.6	69.7	37.5	2,520.8	272.4	2,248.4	188.7	9.9	13.8	2.9	2,038.9
1980	2,708.0	80.6	46.5	2,742.1	311.9	2,430.2	212.0	11.2	13.6	4.8	2,198.2
1981	3,030.6	94.1	60.9	3,063.8	362.4	2,701.4	249.3	13.4	10.9	4.7	2,432.5
1982	3,149.6	97.3	67.1	3,179.8	399.1	2,780.8	256.4	15.4	−7.4	6.2	2,522.5
1983	3,405.0	95.8	66.5	3,434.4	418.4	3,016.0	280.1	16.6	10.2	11.7	2,720.8
1984	3,777.2	108.1	83.8	3,801.5	433.2	3,368.3	309.5	19.0	−9.0	9.5	3,058.3
1985	4,038.7	97.3	82.4	4,053.6	454.5	3,599.1	329.9	21.0	−13.9	6.4	3,268.4
1986	4,268.6	96.0	86.9	4,277.7	478.6	3,799.2	345.5	24.2	1.2	9.7	3,437.9
1987	4,539.9	105.1	100.5	4,544.5	502.2	4,042.4	365.0	24.0	−24.8	14.1	3,692.3
1988	4,900.4	128.7	120.8	4,908.2	534.0	4,374.2	385.3	25.6	−28.4	10.9	4,002.6
1989	5,250.8	157.5	141.5	5,266.8	580.4	4,686.4	414.7	26.6	1.1	5.4	4,249.5
1990	5,522.2	160.6	139.9	5,542.9	602.8	4,940.1	444.2	26.4	5.4	4.2	4,468.3
1991	5,677.5	143.5	126.0	5,694.9	626.1	5,068.8	475.2	28.1	21.9	.5	4,544.2
1982: IV	3,195.1	91.9	64.4	3,222.6	412.5	2,810.1	262.3	16.0	−10.1	9.6	2,551.5
1983: IV	3,547.3	102.1	71.0	3,578.4	439.7	3,138.7	291.7	18.1	13.8	19.2	2,834.3
1984: IV	3,869.1	106.6	85.5	3,890.2	448.0	3,442.2	317.7	20.2	−20.5	9.7	3,134.4
1985: IV	4,140.5	98.1	82.4	4,156.2	465.6	3,690.7	335.1	22.2	−5.9	2.6	3,341.9
1986: IV	4,336.6	92.8	88.9	4,340.5	488.2	3,852.3	351.6	24.9	−2.0	8.2	3,486.0
1987: IV	4,683.0	114.4	106.9	4,690.5	512.1	4,178.5	372.3	24.2	−24.9	22.0	3,828.8
1988: IV	5,044.6	139.9	130.2	5,054.3	547.2	4,507.2	394.2	27.2	−25.4	16.5	4,127.6
1989: I	5,150.0	152.6	138.6	5,164.0	557.8	4,606.2	401.7	27.2	−11.4	15.2	4,203.9
II	5,229.5	161.0	147.2	5,243.3	568.4	4,674.9	411.6	26.6	1.7	5.8	4,240.8
III	5,278.9	157.1	141.3	5,294.7	594.3	4,700.4	421.0	26.3	1.2	−3.9	4,248.0
IV	5,344.8	159.3	139.1	5,365.0	600.8	4,764.2	424.4	26.2	12.8	4.4	4,305.2
1990: I	5,445.2	156.8	137.9	5,464.1	594.7	4,869.4	436.0	26.1	16.1	9.5	4,400.7
II	5,522.6	154.9	140.5	5,537.0	599.1	4,937.9	437.7	26.3	1.2	2.7	4,475.3
III	5,559.6	157.8	139.5	5,577.8	605.8	4,972.1	447.3	26.4	13.4	−5.6	4,479.3
IV	5,561.3	172.9	141.5	5,592.7	611.6	4,981.0	455.7	26.8	−9.1	10.3	4,517.9
1991: I	5,585.8	159.8	130.8	5,614.9	618.9	4,996.0	464.7	27.3	13.4	2.5	4,493.0
II	5,657.6	143.2	126.5	5,674.3	623.5	5,050.9	468.2	27.9	27.1	1.6	4,529.2
III	5,713.1	137.8	124.5	5,726.4	624.9	5,101.5	480.0	28.4	30.5	−7.1	4,555.4
IV	5,753.3	133.1	122.3	5,764.1	637.1	5,127.0	487.9	28.6	16.4	5.1	4,599.1
1992: I	5,840.2	132.9	113.3	5,859.8	631.4	5,228.3	493.8	29.4	29.0	3.2	4,679.4
II	5,902.2	131.3	124.3	5,909.3	638.2	5,271.1	497.6	29.8	30.9	3.6	4,716.5
III	5,978.5	128.8	115.3	5,992.0	697.7	5,294.3	506.4	29.9	35.1	−3.4	4,719.6

[1] Consists largely of receipts by U.S. residents of interest and dividends and reinvested earnings of foreign affiliates of U.S. corporations.
[2] Consists largely of payments to foreign residents of interest and dividends and reinvested earnings of U.S. affiliates of foreign corporations.

Source: Department of Commerce, Bureau of Economic Analysis.

TABLE B–21.—*Relation of national income and personal income, 1959–92*

[Billions of dollars; quarterly data at seasonally adjusted annual rates]

Year or quarter	National income	Less: Corporate profits with inventory valuation and capital consumption adjustments	Less: Net interest	Less: Contributions for social insurance	Less: Wage accruals less disbursements	Plus: Personal interest income	Plus: Personal dividend income	Plus: Government transfer payments to persons	Plus: Business transfer payments to persons	Equals: Personal income
1959	410.1	52.3	10.2	18.8	0.0	22.7	12.7	25.7	1.3	391.2
1960	425.7	50.7	11.2	21.9	.0	25.0	13.4	27.5	1.3	409.2
1961	440.5	51.6	13.1	22.9	.0	26.9	14.0	31.5	1.4	426.5
1962	474.5	59.6	14.6	25.4	.0	29.3	15.0	32.6	1.5	453.4
1963	501.5	65.1	16.1	28.5	.0	32.4	16.1	34.5	1.7	476.4
1964	539.1	72.1	18.2	30.1	.0	36.1	18.0	36.0	1.8	510.7
1965	586.9	82.9	21.1	31.6	.0	40.3	20.2	39.1	2.0	552.9
1966	643.7	88.6	24.3	40.6	.0	44.9	20.9	43.6	2.1	601.7
1967	679.9	86.0	28.1	45.5	.0	49.5	22.1	52.3	2.3	646.5
1968	741.0	92.6	30.4	50.4	.0	54.6	24.5	60.6	2.5	709.9
1969	798.6	89.6	33.6	57.9	.0	60.8	25.1	67.5	2.8	773.7
1970	833.5	77.5	40.0	62.2	.0	69.2	23.5	81.8	2.8	831.0
1971	899.5	90.3	45.4	68.9	.6	75.7	23.5	97.0	3.0	893.5
1972	992.9	103.2	49.3	79.0	.0	81.8	25.5	108.4	3.4	980.5
1973	1,119.5	116.4	56.5	97.6	—.1	94.1	27.7	124.1	3.8	1,098.7
1974	1,198.8	104.5	71.8	110.5	—.5	112.4	29.6	147.4	4.0	1,205.7
1975	1,285.3	121.9	80.0	118.5	.1	123.0	29.2	185.7	4.5	1,307.3
1976	1,435.5	147.1	85.1	134.5	.1	134.6	34.7	202.8	5.5	1,446.3
1977	1,609.1	175.7	100.7	149.8	.1	155.7	39.4	217.5	5.9	1,601.3
1978	1,829.8	199.7	120.5	171.8	.3	184.5	44.2	234.8	6.8	1,807.9
1979	2,038.9	202.5	149.9	197.8	—.2	223.2	50.4	262.8	7.9	2,033.1
1980	2,198.2	177.7	191.2	216.6	.0	274.0	57.1	312.6	8.8	2,265.4
1981	2,432.5	182.0	233.4	251.3	.1	336.1	66.9	355.7	10.2	2,534.7
1982	2,522.5	151.5	262.4	269.6	.0	376.8	67.1	396.3	11.8	2,690.9
1983	2,720.8	212.7	270.0	290.2	—.4	397.5	77.8	426.1	12.8	2,862.5
1984	3,058.3	264.2	307.9	325.0	.2	461.9	78.8	437.8	15.1	3,154.6
1985	3,268.4	280.8	326.2	353.8	—.2	498.1	87.9	468.1	17.8	3,379.8
1986	3,437.9	271.6	350.2	379.8	.0	531.7	104.7	497.1	20.7	3,590.4
1987	3,692.3	319.8	360.4	400.7	.0	548.1	100.4	521.3	20.8	3,802.0
1988	4,002.6	365.0	387.7	442.3	.0	583.2	108.4	555.9	20.8	4,075.9
1989	4,249.5	362.8	452.7	473.2	.0	668.2	126.5	603.8	21.1	4,380.3
1990	4,468.3	361.7	460.7	502.3	.1	694.5	140.3	664.6	21.2	4,664.2
1991	4,544.2	346.3	449.5	528.8	—.1	700.6	137.0	748.3	22.8	4,828.3
1982: IV	2,551.5	150.3	256.8	272.8	.0	373.6	69.4	419.9	12.3	2,746.8
1983: IV	2,834.3	229.1	281.8	298.3	.0	418.7	80.6	428.0	13.2	2,965.8
1984: IV	3,134.4	261.3	321.1	332.2	.6	485.4	79.3	442.3	16.2	3,242.5
1985: IV	3,341.9	284.9	331.9	362.3	.0	507.5	92.7	474.8	18.8	3,456.7
1986: IV	3,486.0	264.6	349.7	388.7	.0	532.6	105.6	505.8	20.9	3,647.8
1987: IV	3,828.8	343.3	368.6	409.6	—.2	562.3	100.1	528.1	20.4	3,918.5
1988: IV	4,127.6	378.3	408.1	453.5	.0	608.9	113.8	563.5	21.3	4,195.2
1989: I	4,203.9	369.4	433.8	466.3	.0	643.1	120.2	585.8	21.8	4,305.2
II	4,240.8	369.9	454.9	471.0	.0	670.7	124.2	596.4	21.1	4,357.4
III	4,248.0	357.3	462.4	475.3	.0	677.6	128.7	609.1	20.9	4,389.2
IV	4,305.2	354.5	459.8	480.4	.0	681.2	132.9	624.0	20.8	4,469.4
1990: I	4,400.7	367.6	457.6	493.9	.0	683.8	137.5	648.2	20.8	4,571.7
II	4,475.3	384.0	457.6	499.6	.0	690.5	139.8	655.0	21.1	4,640.5
III	4,479.3	351.4	456.0	506.5	.0	697.3	141.6	667.1	21.2	4,692.6
IV	4,517.9	344.0	471.4	509.1	.2	706.3	142.5	688.1	21.6	4,751.9
1991: I	4,493.0	349.6	456.2	521.5	.2	701.1	141.3	722.8	22.1	4,752.8
II	4,529.2	347.3	444.4	526.5	—.4	696.2	136.7	739.8	22.6	4,806.9
III	4,555.4	341.2	450.5	532.1	.0	701.8	135.6	754.0	23.1	4,846.2
IV	4,599.1	347.1	446.9	535.2	.0	703.3	134.3	776.5	23.3	4,907.2
1992: I	4,679.4	384.0	430.0	546.2	.0	684.8	133.9	818.6	24.1	4,980.5
II	4,716.5	388.4	420.0	550.8	.0	675.2	136.6	835.3	24.4	5,028.9
III	4,719.6	374.1	407.3	554.4	.0	663.2	141.0	849.3	24.8	5,062.0

Source: Department of Commerce, Bureau of Economic Analysis.

TABLE B–22.—*National income by type of income, 1959–92*

[Billions of dollars; quarterly data at seasonally adjusted annual rates]

Year or quarter	National income [1]	Compensation of employees			Proprietors' income with inventory valuation and capital consumption adjustments							
		Total	Wages and salaries	Supplements to wages and salaries [2]	Total	Farm			Nonfarm			
						Total	Proprietors' income [3]	Capital consumption adjustment	Total	Proprietors' income	Inventory valuation adjustment	Capital consumption adjustment
1959	410.1	281.2	259.8	21.4	51.7	10.7	11.6	−0.9	41.1	40.2	0.0	0.9
1960	425.7	296.7	272.8	23.8	51.9	11.2	12.1	−.8	40.6	39.8	.0	.8
1961	440.5	305.6	280.5	25.1	54.3	11.9	12.7	−.8	42.4	41.8	.0	.6
1962	474.5	327.4	299.3	28.1	56.4	11.9	12.7	−.8	44.5	43.9	.0	.6
1963	501.5	345.5	314.8	30.7	57.7	11.8	12.5	−.7	45.9	45.2	.0	.7
1964	539.1	371.0	337.7	33.2	60.5	10.6	11.3	−.7	49.8	49.2	−.1	.7
1965	586.9	399.8	363.7	36.1	65.0	12.9	13.7	−.7	52.1	51.9	−.2	.4
1966	643.7	443.0	400.3	42.7	69.4	14.0	14.8	−.8	55.3	55.4	−.2	.2
1967	679.9	475.5	428.9	46.6	70.9	12.7	13.5	−.8	58.2	58.3	−.2	.1
1968	741.0	524.7	471.9	52.8	75.1	12.7	13.6	−.9	62.4	63.0	−.4	−.2
1969	798.6	578.4	518.3	60.1	78.9	14.4	15.6	−1.1	64.5	65.0	−.5	.0
1970	833.5	618.3	551.5	66.8	79.9	14.6	15.9	−1.3	65.3	66.0	−.5	−.1
1971	899.5	659.4	584.5	74.9	86.2	15.2	16.6	−1.4	70.9	72.0	−.6	−.5
1972	992.9	726.2	638.7	87.6	97.4	19.1	20.9	−1.8	78.3	79.3	−.7	−.2
1973	1,119.5	812.8	708.6	104.2	116.5	32.2	34.3	−2.0	84.3	86.5	−2.0	−.2
1974	1,198.8	891.3	772.2	119.1	115.3	25.5	28.2	−2.8	89.8	94.2	−3.8	−.6
1975	1,285.3	948.7	814.7	134.0	121.2	23.7	27.5	−3.8	97.5	100.2	−1.2	−1.4
1976	1,435.5	1,058.3	899.6	158.7	132.9	18.3	22.5	−4.2	114.6	117.6	−1.3	−1.7
1977	1,609.1	1,177.3	994.0	183.3	146.4	17.1	21.8	−4.8	129.4	132.5	−1.3	−1.8
1978	1,829.8	1,333.0	1,120.9	212.1	167.7	21.5	27.0	−5.5	146.2	150.2	−2.1	−2.0
1979	2,038.9	1,496.4	1,255.3	241.1	181.8	24.7	31.2	−6.4	157.0	161.8	−2.9	−1.9
1980	2,198.2	1,644.4	1,376.6	267.8	171.8	11.5	19.4	−7.9	160.3	165.8	−3.0	−2.5
1981	2,432.5	1,815.5	1,515.6	299.8	180.8	21.2	30.2	−9.0	159.6	160.9	−1.4	.2
1982	2,522.5	1,916.0	1,593.3	322.7	170.7	13.5	23.1	−9.7	157.3	157.8	−.6	.0
1983	2,720.8	2,029.4	1,684.2	345.2	186.7	2.4	12.1	−9.7	184.3	176.1	−.6	8.7
1984	3,058.3	2,226.9	1,850.0	376.9	236.0	21.3	30.8	−9.4	214.7	197.1	−.5	18.1
1985	3,268.4	2,382.8	1,986.3	396.5	259.9	21.5	30.5	−9.0	238.4	212.4	−.2	26.1
1986	3,437.9	2,523.8	2,105.4	418.4	283.7	22.3	31.0	−8.7	261.5	230.6	−.1	30.9
1987	3,692.3	2,698.7	2,261.2	437.4	310.2	31.3	39.6	−8.3	279.0	252.4	−.8	27.4
1988	4,002.6	2,921.3	2,443.0	478.3	324.3	30.9	38.8	−8.0	293.4	266.8	−1.5	28.1
1989	4,249.5	3,100.2	2,586.4	513.8	347.3	40.2	48.3	−8.1	307.0	281.1	−1.2	27.2
1990	4,468.3	3,291.2	2,742.9	548.4	366.9	41.7	49.5	−7.8	325.2	310.0	−.8	16.0
1991	4,544.2	3,390.8	2,812.2	578.7	368.0	35.8	43.4	−7.6	332.2	318.7	−.3	13.8
1982: IV	2,551.5	1,940.4	1,611.8	328.6	179.9	10.2	20.0	−9.8	169.6	168.0	−.6	1.1
1983: IV	2,834.3	2,101.2	1,747.3	353.9	200.1	6.3	15.8	−9.5	193.8	182.5	−1.6	12.9
1984: IV	3,134.4	2,288.1	1,903.9	384.2	239.6	21.9	31.2	−9.3	217.7	196.6	.1	21.0
1985: IV	3,341.9	2,442.5	2,039.1	403.3	268.7	17.8	26.7	−8.9	250.9	223.2	−1.4	29.1
1986: IV	3,486.0	2,582.5	2,153.9	428.6	284.4	23.6	32.1	−8.6	260.9	230.0	.7	30.1
1987: IV	3,828.8	2,785.1	2,336.7	448.4	325.0	42.4	50.6	−8.2	282.6	254.2	1.7	26.7
1988: IV	4,127.6	3,004.9	2,510.6	494.3	333.4	30.9	38.8	−7.9	302.5	274.9	−1.4	29.0
1989: I	4,203.9	3,048.2	2,545.3	502.9	356.6	51.3	59.3	−7.9	305.3	279.2	−3.3	29.4
II	4,240.8	3,077.5	2,567.4	510.1	348.1	42.3	50.3	−8.0	305.8	277.8	−1.0	29.0
III	4,248.0	3,112.2	2,595.1	517.1	334.6	29.0	37.4	−8.4	305.7	278.6	.2	26.9
IV	4,305.2	3,162.8	2,637.9	524.9	349.7	38.4	46.4	−8.0	311.4	288.7	−.7	23.4
1990: I	4,400.7	3,223.7	2,686.1	537.6	367.9	48.1	56.1	−8.0	319.8	300.6	−1.0	20.1
II	4,475.3	3,281.2	2,735.7	545.5	366.3	43.6	51.4	−7.8	322.7	306.7	−.9	16.9
III	4,479.3	3,320.5	2,768.2	552.3	361.0	32.2	40.0	−7.8	328.8	315.4	−.9	14.2
IV	4,517.9	3,339.6	2,781.4	558.2	372.5	42.8	50.5	−7.7	329.7	317.3	−.5	12.9
1991: I	4,493.0	3,343.0	2,774.9	568.1	356.5	34.3	42.0	−7.7	322.2	310.2	−.3	12.4
II	4,529.2	3,379.6	2,804.3	575.2	370.4	41.3	48.9	−7.6	329.1	316.5	−.3	12.9
III	4,555.4	3,407.0	2,824.4	582.6	367.1	29.5	37.1	−7.6	337.6	322.4	−.5	15.6
IV	4,599.1	3,433.8	2,845.0	588.7	377.9	37.9	45.4	−7.5	340.0	325.6	−.1	14.4
1992: I	4,679.4	3,476.3	2,877.6	598.7	393.6	40.1	47.5	−7.4	353.6	339.1	−.8	15.2
II	4,716.5	3,506.3	2,901.3	605.0	398.4	38.5	45.8	−7.3	359.9	344.8	−1.0	16.1
III	4,719.6	3,534.3	2,923.5	610.8	397.4	31.5	39.7	−8.2	365.9	350.2	−.5	16.2

[1] National income is the total net income earned in production. It differs from gross domestic product mainly in that it excludes depreciation charges and other allowances for business and institutional consumption of durable capital goods and indirect business taxes. See Table B–20.

See next page for continuation of table.

372

TABLE B-22.—*National income by type of income, 1959-92*—Continued

[Billions of dollars; quarterly data at seasonally adjusted annual rates]

Year or quarter	Rental income of persons with capital consumption adjustment			Corporate profits with inventory valuation and capital consumption adjustments									Net interest
				Profits with inventory valuation adjustment and without capital consumption adjustment								Capital con-sumption adjust-ment	
	Total	Rental income of persons	Capital con-sumption adjust-ment	Total	Profits						Inven-tory valu-ation adjust-ment		
					Total	Profits before tax	Profits tax liability	Profits after tax					
								Total	Divi-dends	Undis-tributed profits			
1959	14.7	18.0	-3.4	52.3	53.1	53.4	23.6	29.7	12.7	17.0	-0.3	-0.8	10.2
1960	15.3	18.7	-3.4	50.7	51.0	51.1	22.7	28.4	13.4	15.0	-.2	-.3	11.2
1961	15.8	19.2	-3.3	51.6	51.3	51.0	22.8	28.2	14.0	14.3	.3	.3	13.1
1962	16.5	19.8	-3.3	59.6	56.4	56.4	24.0	32.4	15.0	17.4	.0	3.2	14.6
1963	17.1	20.3	-3.2	65.1	61.2	61.2	26.2	34.9	16.1	18.8	.1	3.9	16.1
1964	17.3	20.5	-3.2	72.1	67.5	68.0	28.0	40.0	18.0	22.0	-.5	4.6	18.2
1965	18.0	21.3	-3.3	82.9	77.6	78.8	30.9	47.9	20.2	27.8	-1.2	5.3	21.1
1966	18.5	22.1	-3.6	88.6	83.0	85.1	33.7	51.4	20.9	30.5	-2.1	5.6	24.3
1967	19.4	23.4	-3.9	86.0	80.3	81.8	32.7	49.2	22.1	27.1	-1.6	5.7	28.1
1968	18.2	22.8	-4.6	92.6	86.9	90.6	39.4	51.2	24.6	26.6	-3.7	5.6	30.4
1969	18.0	23.9	-5.9	89.6	83.2	89.0	39.7	49.4	25.2	24.1	-5.9	6.4	33.6
1970	17.8	24.2	-6.4	77.5	71.8	78.4	34.4	44.0	23.7	20.3	-6.6	5.6	40.0
1971	18.2	25.6	-7.4	90.3	85.5	90.1	37.7	52.4	23.7	28.6	-4.6	4.8	45.4
1972	16.8	26.1	-9.3	103.2	97.9	104.5	41.9	62.6	25.8	36.9	-6.6	5.3	49.3
1973	17.3	28.2	-10.9	116.4	110.9	130.9	49.3	81.6	28.1	53.5	-20.0	5.5	56.5
1974	15.8	29.3	-13.5	104.5	103.4	142.8	51.8	91.0	30.4	60.6	-39.5	1.2	71.8
1975	13.5	29.5	-15.9	121.9	129.4	140.4	50.9	89.5	30.1	59.4	-11.0	-7.6	80.0
1976	12.1	29.9	-17.8	147.1	158.8	173.7	64.2	109.5	35.6	73.9	-14.9	-11.7	85.1
1977	9.0	30.0	-21.0	175.7	186.7	203.3	73.0	130.3	40.7	89.5	-16.6	-11.0	100.7
1978	8.9	34.4	-25.5	199.7	212.8	237.9	83.5	154.4	45.9	108.5	-25.0	-13.1	120.5
1979	8.4	39.1	-30.8	202.5	219.8	261.4	88.0	173.4	52.4	121.0	-41.6	-17.3	149.9
1980	13.2	49.0	-35.8	177.7	197.8	240.9	84.8	156.1	59.0	97.1	-43.0	-20.2	191.2
1981	20.8	61.1	-40.2	182.0	203.2	228.9	81.1	147.8	69.2	78.6	-25.7	-21.2	233.4
1982	21.9	64.4	-42.4	151.5	166.4	176.3	63.1	113.2	70.0	43.2	-9.9	-14.9	262.4
1983	22.1	64.8	-42.8	212.7	202.2	210.7	77.2	133.5	81.2	52.3	-8.5	10.4	270.0
1984	23.3	66.5	-43.2	264.2	236.4	240.5	94.0	146.4	82.7	63.8	-4.1	27.8	307.9
1985	18.7	63.4	-44.6	280.8	225.3	225.0	96.5	128.5	92.4	36.1	.2	55.5	326.2
1986	8.7	53.4	-44.7	271.6	227.6	217.8	106.5	111.3	109.8	1.6	9.7	44.1	350.2
1987	3.2	50.0	-46.8	319.8	273.4	287.9	127.1	160.8	106.2	54.6	-14.5	46.4	360.4
1988	3.3	53.4	-49.1	365.0	320.3	347.5	137.0	210.5	115.3	95.2	-27.3	44.7	387.7
1989	-13.5	44.2	-57.7	362.8	325.4	342.9	141.3	201.6	134.6	67.1	-17.5	37.4	452.7
1990	-12.3	44.6	-56.9	361.7	341.2	355.4	136.7	218.7	149.3	69.4	-14.2	20.5	460.7
1991	-10.4	47.5	-57.9	346.3	337.8	334.7	124.0	210.7	146.5	64.2	3.1	8.4	449.5
1982: IV	24.1	66.5	-42.3	150.3	160.0	168.6	58.7	109.9	72.5	37.5	-8.6	-9.6	256.8
1983: IV	22.2	64.5	-42.4	229.1	216.2	223.8	82.2	141.6	84.2	57.4	-7.6	12.9	281.8
1984: IV	24.3	67.6	-43.4	261.3	223.6	220.1	83.8	136.3	83.4	52.9	3.5	37.7	321.1
1985: IV	14.0	60.0	-46.0	284.9	228.0	231.8	97.6	134.2	97.4	36.9	-3.8	56.9	331.9
1986: IV	4.7	50.2	-45.5	264.6	225.0	235.7	116.6	119.2	111.0	8.2	-10.7	39.6	349.7
1987: IV	6.8	54.2	-47.4	343.3	293.4	311.2	135.2	176.0	106.3	69.7	-17.8	49.9	368.6
1988: IV	2.8	52.6	-49.7	378.3	340.5	372.2	146.2	226.0	121.0	105.0	-31.7	37.9	408.1
1989: I	-4.2	47.7	-51.9	369.4	331.3	368.9	154.8	214.1	127.8	86.3	-37.6	38.1	433.8
II	-9.6	44.8	-54.4	369.9	330.0	345.7	143.7	202.0	132.2	69.8	-15.7	40.0	454.9
III	-18.6	44.6	-63.1	357.3	319.8	323.1	132.6	190.5	136.9	53.6	-3.3	37.6	462.4
IV	-21.6	39.8	-61.3	354.5	320.6	334.1	134.2	200.0	141.3	58.7	-13.5	33.9	459.8
1990: I	-16.2	41.0	-57.1	367.6	337.4	344.0	132.4	211.6	146.1	65.5	-6.6	30.2	457.6
II	-13.8	43.0	-56.8	384.0	359.6	355.8	137.6	218.2	148.7	69.5	3.8	24.4	457.6
III	-9.5	47.6	-57.1	351.4	334.4	367.0	143.0	224.0	150.6	73.4	-32.6	17.0	456.0
IV	-9.6	46.9	-56.4	344.0	333.5	354.7	133.7	221.0	151.9	69.1	-21.2	10.5	471.4
1991: I	-12.4	44.0	-56.4	349.6	344.2	337.6	121.3	216.3	150.6	65.7	6.7	5.3	456.2
II	-12.3	44.3	-56.6	347.3	342.2	332.3	122.9	209.4	146.2	63.2	9.9	5.1	444.4
III	-10.3	47.0	-56.6	341.2	331.9	336.7	127.0	209.6	145.1	64.5	-4.8	9.3	450.5
IV	-6.6	54.7	-61.3	347.1	333.1	332.3	125.0	207.4	143.9	63.4	.7	14.1	446.9
1992: I	-4.5	51.7	-56.2	384.0	360.7	366.1	136.4	229.7	143.6	86.2	-5.4	23.3	430.0
II	3.3	60.0	-56.6	388.4	361.4	376.8	144.1	232.7	146.6	86.1	-15.5	27.0	420.0
III	6.4	90.3	-83.9	374.1	344.4	354.1	131.8	222.2	151.1	71.1	-9.7	29.7	407.3

2 Consists mainly of employer contributions for social insurance and to private pension, health, and welfare funds.
3 With inventory valuation adjustment.

Source: Department of Commerce, Bureau of Economic Analysis.

TABLE B–23.—Sources of personal income, 1959–92

[Billions of dollars; quarterly data at seasonally adjusted annual rates]

Year or quarter	Personal income	Wage and salary disbursements [1]						Other labor income [1]	Proprietors' income with inventory valuation and capital consumption adjustments	
		Total	Commodity-producing industries		Distributive industries	Service industries	Government		Farm	Nonfarm
			Total	Manufacturing						
1959	391.2	259.8	109.9	86.9	65.1	38.8	46.0	10.6	10.7	41.1
1960	409.2	272.8	113.4	89.8	68.6	41.7	49.2	11.2	11.2	40.6
1961	426.5	280.5	114.0	89.9	69.6	44.4	52.4	11.8	11.9	42.4
1962	453.4	299.3	122.2	96.8	73.3	47.6	56.3	13.0	11.9	44.5
1963	476.4	314.8	127.4	100.7	76.8	50.7	60.0	14.0	11.8	45.9
1964	510.7	337.7	136.0	107.3	82.0	54.9	64.9	15.7	10.6	49.8
1965	552.9	363.7	146.6	115.7	87.9	59.4	69.9	17.8	12.9	52.1
1966	601.7	400.3	161.6	128.2	95.1	65.3	78.3	19.9	14.0	55.3
1967	646.5	428.9	169.0	134.3	101.6	72.0	86.4	21.7	12.7	58.2
1968	709.9	471.9	184.1	146.0	110.8	80.4	96.6	25.2	12.7	62.4
1969	773.7	518.3	200.4	157.7	121.7	90.6	105.5	28.5	14.4	64.5
1970	831.0	551.5	203.7	158.4	131.2	99.4	117.1	32.5	14.6	65.3
1971	893.5	583.9	209.1	160.5	140.4	107.9	126.5	36.7	15.2	70.9
1972	980.5	638.7	228.2	175.6	153.3	119.7	137.4	43.0	19.1	78.3
1973	1,098.7	708.7	255.9	196.6	170.3	133.9	148.7	49.2	32.2	84.3
1974	1,205.7	772.6	276.5	211.8	186.8	148.6	160.9	56.5	25.5	89.8
1975	1,307.3	814.6	277.1	211.6	198.1	163.4	176.0	65.9	23.7	97.5
1976	1,446.3	899.5	309.7	238.0	219.5	181.6	188.6	79.7	18.3	114.6
1977	1,601.3	993.9	346.1	266.7	242.7	202.8	202.3	94.7	17.1	129.4
1978	1,807.9	1,120.7	392.6	300.1	274.9	233.7	219.4	110.1	21.5	146.2
1979	2,033.1	1,255.4	442.1	334.9	308.4	267.7	237.3	124.3	24.7	157.0
1980	2,265.4	1,376.6	471.9	355.7	336.4	306.9	261.4	139.8	11.5	160.3
1981	2,534.7	1,515.6	513.7	386.9	368.1	348.1	285.7	153.0	21.2	159.6
1982	2,690.9	1,593.3	513.5	384.3	385.8	386.5	307.5	165.4	13.5	157.3
1983	2,862.5	1,684.7	525.1	397.7	406.2	427.4	325.9	174.6	2.4	184.3
1984	3,154.6	1,848.8	580.8	439.8	445.4	475.8	347.8	184.7	21.3	214.7
1985	3,379.8	1,986.5	612.2	461.3	475.9	524.5	373.9	191.8	21.5	238.4
1986	3,590.4	2,105.4	628.5	473.8	501.7	579.5	395.7	200.7	22.3	261.5
1987	3,802.0	2,261.2	651.8	490.1	536.9	650.7	421.8	210.4	31.3	279.0
1988	4,075.9	2,443.0	699.1	524.5	575.3	719.6	449.0	230.5	30.9	293.4
1989	4,380.3	2,586.4	724.2	542.2	607.0	776.8	478.5	251.9	40.2	307.0
1990	4,664.2	2,742.8	745.6	556.1	634.6	847.8	514.8	271.0	41.7	325.2
1991	4,828.3	2,812.2	737.4	556.9	647.4	883.9	543.6	288.3	35.8	332.2
1982: IV	2,746.8	1,611.7	503.9	378.0	391.2	400.9	315.6	169.2	10.2	169.6
1983: IV	2,965.8	1,747.3	547.6	415.7	422.4	445.8	331.5	179.0	6.3	193.8
1984: IV	3,242.5	1,903.3	594.5	450.5	458.4	494.4	356.1	187.7	21.9	217.7
1985: IV	3,456.7	2,039.1	622.6	469.1	487.6	546.8	382.2	193.9	17.8	250.9
1986: IV	3,647.8	2,153.9	635.3	478.5	512.5	602.1	404.0	205.3	23.6	260.9
1987: IV	3,918.5	2,337.0	668.4	501.6	551.9	685.0	431.7	216.5	42.4	282.6
1988: IV	4,195.2	2,510.6	715.3	537.5	589.9	746.8	458.5	240.3	30.9	302.5
1989: I	4,305.2	2,545.3	720.9	542.2	599.8	756.5	468.2	244.8	51.3	305.3
II	4,357.4	2,567.4	719.8	539.6	604.5	768.7	474.4	249.4	42.3	305.8
III	4,389.2	2,595.1	723.8	541.3	607.5	782.1	481.6	254.2	29.0	305.7
IV	4,469.4	2,637.9	732.1	545.7	616.1	800.0	489.7	259.1	38.4	311.4
1990: I	4,571.7	2,686.1	740.0	549.7	625.5	819.0	501.6	264.9	48.1	319.8
II	4,640.5	2,735.7	748.9	558.4	633.7	841.2	511.8	268.9	43.6	322.7
III	4,692.6	2,768.2	749.4	559.4	639.1	861.1	518.5	273.1	32.2	328.8
IV	4,751.9	2,781.3	744.0	556.9	640.2	869.9	527.1	276.9	42.8	329.7
1991: I	4,752.8	2,774.7	734.6	551.2	638.6	861.8	539.7	281.5	34.3	322.2
II	4,806.9	2,804.7	734.6	553.4	647.0	879.4	543.8	286.1	41.3	329.1
III	4,846.2	2,824.4	738.8	559.0	651.1	890.2	544.3	290.6	29.5	337.6
IV	4,907.2	2,845.0	741.5	563.9	652.9	904.3	546.4	295.0	37.9	340.0
1992: I	4,980.5	2,877.6	736.8	559.9	660.9	925.3	554.6	299.2	40.1	353.6
II	5,028.9	2,901.3	743.1	564.7	662.9	933.9	561.4	303.6	38.5	359.9
III	5,062.0	2,923.5	742.4	565.5	667.7	949.1	564.3	307.9	31.5	365.9

[1] The total of wage and salary disbursements and other labor income differs from compensation of employees in Table B–22 in that it excludes employer contributions for social insurance and the excess of wage accruals over wage disbursements.

See next page for continuation of table.

TABLE B-23.—*Sources of personal income, 1959-92*—Continued

[Billions of dollars; quarterly data at seasonally adjusted annual rates]

Year or quarter	Rental income of persons with capital consumption adjustment	Personal dividend income	Personal interest income	Transfer payments to persons							Less: Personal contributions for social insurance	Nonfarm personal income[2]
				Total	Old-age, survivors, disability, and health insurance benefits	Government unemployment insurance benefits	Veterans benefits	Government employees retirement benefits	Aid to families with dependent children (AFDC)	Other		
1959...............	14.7	12.7	22.7	27.0	10.2	2.8	4.6	2.8	0.9	5.7	7.9	376.7
1960...............	15.3	13.4	25.0	28.8	11.1	3.0	4.6	3.1	1.0	6.1	9.3	393.7
1961...............	15.8	14.0	26.9	32.8	12.6	4.3	5.0	3.4	1.1	6.5	9.7	410.4
1962...............	16.5	15.0	29.3	34.1	14.3	3.1	4.7	3.7	1.3	7.0	10.3	437.0
1963...............	17.1	16.1	32.4	36.2	15.2	3.0	4.8	4.2	1.4	7.6	11.8	460.0
1964...............	17.3	18.0	36.1	37.9	16.0	2.7	4.7	4.7	1.5	8.2	12.6	495.3
1965...............	18.0	20.2	40.3	41.1	18.1	2.3	4.9	5.2	1.7	9.0	13.3	534.9
1966...............	18.5	20.9	44.9	45.7	20.8	1.9	4.9	6.1	1.9	10.3	17.8	582.4
1967...............	19.4	22.1	49.5	54.6	25.5	2.2	5.6	6.9	2.3	12.2	20.6	628.3
1968...............	18.2	24.5	54.6	63.2	30.2	2.1	5.9	7.6	2.8	14.5	22.9	691.4
1969...............	18.0	25.1	60.8	70.3	32.9	2.2	6.7	8.7	3.5	16.2	26.2	753.1
1970...............	17.8	23.5	69.2	84.6	38.5	4.0	7.7	10.2	4.8	19.4	27.9	809.8
1971...............	18.2	23.5	75.7	100.1	44.5	5.8	8.8	11.8	6.2	23.0	30.7	871.5
1972...............	16.8	25.5	81.8	111.8	49.6	5.7	9.7	13.8	6.9	26.1	34.5	954.2
1973...............	17.3	27.7	94.1	127.9	60.4	4.4	10.4	16.0	7.2	29.5	42.6	1,058.1
1974...............	15.8	29.6	112.4	151.3	70.1	6.8	11.8	19.0	7.9	35.7	47.9	1,170.2
1975...............	13.5	29.2	123.0	190.2	81.4	17.6	14.5	22.7	9.2	44.7	50.4	1,272.5
1976...............	12.1	34.7	134.6	208.3	92.9	15.8	14.4	26.1	10.1	49.1	55.5	1,415.1
1977...............	9.0	39.4	155.7	223.3	104.9	12.7	13.8	29.0	10.6	52.4	61.2	1,569.9
1978...............	8.9	44.2	184.5	241.6	116.2	9.7	13.9	32.7	10.7	58.4	69.8	1,770.3
1979...............	8.4	50.4	223.2	270.7	131.8	9.8	14.4	36.9	11.0	66.8	81.0	1,989.3
1980...............	13.2	57.1	274.0	321.5	154.2	16.1	15.0	43.0	12.4	80.8	88.6	2,231.6
1981...............	20.8	66.9	336.1	365.9	182.0	15.9	16.1	49.4	13.0	89.7	104.5	2,488.5
1982...............	21.9	67.1	376.8	408.1	204.5	25.2	16.4	54.6	13.3	94.1	112.3	2,649.8
1983...............	22.1	77.8	397.5	438.9	221.7	26.3	16.6	58.0	14.2	102.1	119.7	2,832.6
1984...............	23.3	78.8	461.9	452.9	235.7	15.8	16.4	60.9	14.8	109.2	132.8	3,106.1
1985...............	18.7	87.9	498.1	485.9	253.4	15.7	16.7	66.6	15.4	118.1	149.1	3,333.2
1986...............	8.7	104.7	531.7	517.8	269.2	16.3	16.7	70.7	16.4	128.5	162.1	3,545.6
1987...............	3.2	100.4	548.1	542.2	282.9	14.5	16.6	76.0	16.7	135.5	173.6	3,749.4
1988...............	4.3	108.4	583.2	576.7	300.4	13.4	16.9	82.2	17.3	146.5	194.5	4,023.9
1989...............	−13.5	126.5	668.2	625.0	325.1	14.4	17.3	87.5	18.0	162.6	211.4	4,318.0
1990...............	−12.3	140.3	694.5	685.8	352.0	18.0	17.8	94.0	19.8	184.2	224.8	4,599.6
1991...............	−10.4	137.0	700.6	771.1	382.0	27.5	18.1	101.3	22.0	220.2	238.4	4,770.4
1982: IV............	24.1	69.4	373.6	432.2	216.4	31.8	16.6	56.1	13.6	97.6	113.3	2,708.5
1983: IV............	22.2	80.6	418.7	441.3	226.7	19.9	16.5	59.5	14.5	104.2	123.4	2,932.0
1984: IV............	24.3	79.3	485.4	458.5	241.3	15.6	16.4	58.0	14.8	112.5	135.6	3,193.8
1985: IV............	14.0	92.7	507.5	493.6	256.7	15.3	16.5	68.0	15.7	121.3	152.8	3,414.9
1986: IV............	4.7	105.6	532.6	526.6	273.3	16.7	16.4	72.4	16.7	131.1	165.4	3,602.3
1987: IV............	6.8	100.1	562.3	548.5	285.8	13.4	16.5	77.7	16.7	138.3	177.7	3,854.9
1988: IV............	2.8	113.8	608.9	584.8	303.8	13.0	16.8	83.0	17.5	150.6	199.5	4,142.9
1989: I.............	−4.2	120.2	643.1	607.6	316.5	13.5	17.5	85.9	17.6	156.6	208.2	4,232.2
II............	−9.6	124.2	670.7	617.5	321.6	13.8	17.3	87.0	17.8	160.0	210.3	4,293.2
III...........	−18.6	128.7	677.6	630.0	328.1	14.6	17.3	87.9	18.1	164.0	212.4	4,338.0
IV...........	−21.6	132.9	681.2	644.8	334.4	15.6	17.3	89.3	18.4	169.9	214.7	4,408.5
1990: I.............	−16.2	137.5	683.8	669.0	348.0	16.1	17.9	93.1	19.2	174.7	221.2	4,500.9
II............	−13.8	139.8	690.5	676.1	348.7	17.1	17.8	93.2	19.5	179.7	223.0	4,573.8
III...........	−9.5	141.6	697.3	688.3	352.8	18.1	17.8	94.0	19.9	185.7	227.3	4,637.5
IV...........	−9.6	142.5	706.3	709.7	358.6	20.7	17.7	95.7	20.5	196.5	227.8	4,686.3
1991: I.............	−12.4	141.3	701.1	744.9	374.2	24.3	17.8	101.6	21.3	205.8	234.9	4,696.0
II............	−12.3	136.7	696.2	762.4	378.9	28.3	18.5	100.4	21.8	214.6	237.4	4,743.3
III...........	−10.3	135.6	701.8	777.1	384.2	27.6	18.1	101.0	22.2	224.0	240.1	4,794.7
IV...........	−6.6	134.3	703.3	799.8	390.6	30.0	18.1	102.0	22.7	236.4	241.5	4,847.4
1992: I.............	−4.5	133.9	684.8	842.7	405.7	39.7	20.2	106.4	23.0	247.7	246.8	4,918.2
II............	3.3	136.6	675.2	859.7	412.1	41.7	18.7	106.4	23.4	257.4	249.3	4,967.7
III...........	6.4	141.0	663.2	874.1	417.1	40.4	18.5	106.6	23.6	267.9	251.5	5,007.6

[2] Personal income exclusive of the farm component of wages and salaries, other labor income, proprietors' income with inventory valuation and capital consumption adjustments, and net interest.

Note.—The industry classification of wage and salary disbursements and proprietors' income is on an establishment basis and is based on the 1987 Standard Industrial Classification (SIC) beginning 1987 and on the 1972 SIC for earlier years shown.

Source: Department of Commerce, Bureau of Economic Analysis.

[Billions of dollars, except as noted; quarterly data at seasonally adjusted annual rates]

Year or quarter	Personal income	Less: Personal tax and nontax payments	Equals: Disposable personal income	Less: Personal outlays				Equals: Personal saving	Percent of disposable personal income [1]		
				Total	Personal consumption expenditures	Interest paid by persons	Personal transfer payments to rest of the world (net)		Personal outlays		Personal saving
									Total	Personal consumption expenditures	
1959	391.2	44.5	346.7	324.7	318.1	6.1	0.4	22.0	93.7	91.8	6.3
1960	409.2	48.7	360.5	339.9	332.4	7.0	.5	20.6	94.3	92.2	5.7
1961	426.5	50.3	376.2	351.3	343.5	7.3	.5	24.9	93.4	91.3	6.6
1962	453.4	54.8	398.7	372.8	364.4	7.8	.5	25.9	93.5	91.4	6.5
1963	476.4	58.0	418.4	393.7	384.2	8.9	.6	24.6	94.1	91.8	5.9
1964	510.7	56.0	454.7	423.1	412.5	10.0	.7	31.6	93.1	90.7	6.9
1965	552.9	61.9	491.0	456.5	444.6	11.1	.8	34.6	93.0	90.5	7.0
1966	601.7	71.0	530.7	494.4	481.6	12.0	.8	36.3	93.2	90.7	6.8
1967	646.5	77.9	568.6	522.8	509.3	12.5	1.0	45.8	91.9	89.6	8.1
1968	709.9	92.1	617.8	573.9	559.1	13.8	1.0	43.8	92.9	90.5	7.1
1969	773.7	109.9	663.8	620.5	603.7	15.7	1.1	43.3	93.5	90.9	6.5
1970	831.0	109.0	722.0	664.5	646.5	16.8	1.2	57.5	92.0	89.5	8.0
1971	893.5	108.7	784.9	719.4	700.3	17.8	1.3	65.4	91.7	89.2	8.3
1972	980.5	132.0	848.5	788.7	767.8	19.6	1.3	59.7	93.0	90.5	7.0
1973	1,098.7	140.6	958.1	872.0	848.1	22.4	1.4	86.1	91.0	88.5	9.0
1974	1,205.7	159.1	1,046.5	953.1	927.7	24.2	1.2	93.4	91.1	88.6	8.9
1975	1,307.3	156.4	1,150.9	1,050.6	1,024.9	24.5	1.2	100.3	91.3	89.1	8.7
1976	1,446.3	182.3	1,264.0	1,171.0	1,143.1	26.7	1.2	93.0	92.6	90.4	7.4
1977	1,601.3	210.0	1,391.3	1,303.4	1,271.5	30.7	1.2	87.9	93.7	91.4	6.3
1978	1,807.9	240.1	1,567.8	1,460.0	1,421.2	37.5	1.3	107.8	93.1	90.7	6.9
1979	2,033.1	280.2	1,753.0	1,629.6	1,583.7	44.5	1.4	123.3	93.0	90.3	7.0
1980	2,265.4	312.4	1,952.9	1,799.1	1,748.1	49.4	1.6	153.8	92.1	89.5	7.9
1981	2,534.7	360.2	2,174.5	1,982.6	1,926.2	54.6	1.8	191.8	91.2	88.6	8.8
1982	2,690.9	371.4	2,319.6	2,120.1	2,059.2	58.8	2.1	199.5	91.4	88.8	8.6
1983	2,862.5	368.8	2,493.7	2,325.1	2,257.5	65.7	1.8	168.7	93.2	90.5	6.8
1984	3,154.6	395.1	2,759.5	2,537.5	2,460.3	75.0	2.3	222.0	92.0	89.2	8.0
1985	3,379.8	436.8	2,943.0	2,753.7	2,667.4	83.6	2.7	189.3	93.6	90.6	6.4
1986	3,590.4	459.0	3,131.5	2,944.0	2,850.6	90.9	2.5	187.5	94.0	91.0	6.0
1987	3,802.0	512.5	3,289.5	3,147.5	3,052.2	92.3	3.0	142.0	95.7	92.8	4.3
1988	4,075.9	527.7	3,548.2	3,392.5	3,296.1	93.7	2.7	155.7	95.6	92.9	4.4
1989	4,380.3	593.3	3,787.0	3,634.9	3,523.1	103.0	8.9	152.1	96.0	93.0	4.0
1990	4,664.2	621.3	4,042.9	3,867.3	3,748.4	109.6	9.3	175.6	95.7	92.7	4.3
1991	4,828.3	618.7	4,209.6	4,009.9	3,887.7	112.5	9.7	199.6	95.3	92.4	4.7
1982: IV	2,746.8	372.1	2,374.7	2,190.9	2,128.7	60.2	1.9	183.8	92.3	89.6	7.7
1983: IV	2,965.8	371.6	2,594.3	2,417.9	2,346.8	69.2	2.0	176.3	93.2	90.5	6.8
1984: IV	3,242.5	413.4	2,829.1	2,606.5	2,526.4	77.6	2.5	222.6	92.1	89.3	7.9
1985: IV	3,456.7	448.8	3,007.9	2,828.7	2,739.8	86.4	2.5	179.2	94.0	91.1	6.0
1986: IV	3,647.8	478.5	3,169.3	3,018.2	2,923.1	92.3	2.8	151.1	95.2	92.2	4.8
1987: IV	3,918.5	528.6	3,389.9	3,220.1	3,124.6	92.4	3.1	169.8	95.0	92.2	5.0
1988: IV	4,195.2	542.0	3,653.2	3,496.7	3,398.2	95.8	2.7	156.4	95.7	93.0	4.3
1989: I	4,305.2	575.2	3,730.0	3,548.0	3,440.8	99.0	8.2	182.0	95.1	92.2	4.9
II	4,357.4	599.1	3,758.3	3,609.8	3,499.1	101.9	8.7	148.5	96.0	93.1	4.0
III	4,389.2	593.8	3,795.4	3,666.3	3,553.3	104.3	8.7	129.0	96.6	93.6	3.4
IV	4,469.4	605.1	3,864.3	3,715.5	3,599.1	106.7	9.8	148.8	96.2	93.1	3.9
1990: I	4,571.7	609.4	3,962.3	3,789.2	3,672.4	108.4	8.5	173.1	95.6	92.7	4.4
II	4,640.5	624.6	4,015.9	3,833.2	3,715.3	108.9	9.0	182.7	95.5	92.5	4.6
III	4,692.6	627.3	4,065.3	3,908.0	3,787.8	110.0	10.2	157.3	96.1	93.2	3.9
IV	4,751.9	623.8	4,128.1	3,938.8	3,818.2	111.1	9.5	189.3	95.4	92.5	4.6
1991: I	4,752.8	616.8	4,136.0	3,943.2	3,821.7	112.2	9.4	192.8	95.3	92.4	4.7
II	4,806.9	617.2	4,189.7	3,994.4	3,871.9	112.7	9.8	195.3	95.3	92.4	4.7
III	4,846.2	618.6	4,227.6	4,036.6	3,914.2	112.5	9.9	191.0	95.5	92.6	4.5
IV	4,907.2	622.3	4,284.9	4,065.5	3,942.9	112.8	9.7	219.4	94.9	92.0	5.1
1992: I	4,980.5	619.6	4,360.9	4,146.3	4,022.8	113.3	10.2	214.6	95.1	92.2	4.9
II	5,028.9	617.1	4,411.8	4,179.5	4,057.1	112.0	10.4	232.3	94.7	92.0	5.3
III	5,062.0	628.8	4,433.2	4,229.9	4,108.7	111.2	10.0	203.3	95.4	92.7	4.6

[1] Percents based on data in millions of dollars.

Source: Department of Commerce, Bureau of Economic Analysis.

TABLE B-25.—*Total and per capita disposable personal income and personal consumption expenditures in current and 1987 dollars, 1959–92*

[Quarterly data at seasonally adjusted annual rates, except as noted]

Year or quarter	Disposable personal income				Personal consumption expenditures				Popula-tion (thou-sands) [1]
	Total (billions of dollars)		Per capita (dollars)		Total (billions of dollars)		Per capita (dollars)		
	Current dollars	1987 dollars	Current dollars	1987 dollars	Current dollars	1987 dollars	Current dollars	1987 dollars	
1959	346.7	1,284.9	1,958	7,256	318.1	1,178.9	1,796	6,658	177,073
1960	360.5	1,313.0	1,994	7,264	332.4	1,210.8	1,839	6,698	180,760
1961	376.2	1,356.4	2,048	7,382	343.5	1,238.4	1,869	6,740	183,742
1962	398.7	1,414.8	2,137	7,583	364.4	1,293.3	1,953	6,931	186,590
1963	418.4	1,461.1	2,210	7,718	384.2	1,341.9	2,030	7,089	189,300
1964	454.7	1,562.2	2,369	8,140	412.5	1,417.2	2,149	7,384	191,927
1965	491.0	1,653.5	2,527	8,508	444.6	1,497.0	2,287	7,703	194,347
1966	530.7	1,734.3	2,699	8,822	481.6	1,573.8	2,450	8,005	196,599
1967	568.6	1,811.4	2,861	9,114	509.3	1,622.4	2,562	8,163	198,752
1968	617.8	1,886.8	3,077	9,399	559.1	1,707.5	2,785	8,506	200,745
1969	663.8	1,947.4	3,274	9,606	603.7	1,771.2	2,978	8,737	202,736
1970	722.0	2,025.3	3,521	9,875	646.5	1,813.5	3,152	8,842	205,089
1971	784.9	2,099.9	3,779	10,111	700.3	1,873.7	3,372	9,022	207,692
1972	848.5	2,186.2	4,042	10,414	767.8	1,978.4	3,658	9,425	209,924
1973	958.1	2,334.1	4,521	11,013	848.1	2,066.7	4,002	9,752	211,939
1974	1,046.5	2,317.0	4,893	10,832	927.7	2,053.8	4,337	9,602	213,898
1975	1,150.9	2,355.4	5,329	10,906	1,024.9	2,097.5	4,745	9,711	215,981
1976	1,264.0	2,440.9	5,796	11,192	1,143.1	2,207.3	5,241	10,121	218,086
1977	1,391.3	2,512.6	6,316	11,406	1,271.5	2,296.6	5,772	10,425	220,289
1978	1,567.8	2,638.4	7,042	11,851	1,421.2	2,391.8	6,384	10,744	222,629
1979	1,753.0	2,710.1	7,787	12,039	1,583.7	2,448.4	7,035	10,876	225,106
1980	1,952.9	2,733.6	8,576	12,005	1,748.1	2,447.1	7,677	10,746	227,715
1981	2,174.5	2,795.8	9,455	12,156	1,926.2	2,476.9	8,375	10,770	229,989
1982	2,319.6	2,820.4	9,989	12,146	2,059.2	2,503.7	8,868	10,782	232,201
1983	2,493.7	2,893.6	10,642	12,349	2,257.5	2,619.4	9,634	11,179	234,326
1984	2,759.5	3,080.1	11,673	13,029	2,460.3	2,746.1	10,408	11,617	236,393
1985	2,943.0	3,162.1	12,339	13,258	2,667.4	2,865.8	11,184	12,015	238,510
1986	3,131.5	3,261.9	13,010	13,552	2,850.6	2,969.1	11,843	12,336	240,691
1987	3,289.5	3,289.5	13,545	13,545	3,052.2	3,052.2	12,568	12,568	242,860
1988	3,548.2	3,404.3	14,477	13,890	3,296.1	3,162.4	13,448	12,903	245,093
1989	3,787.0	3,464.9	15,307	14,005	3,523.1	3,223.3	14,241	13,029	247,397
1990	4,042.9	3,516.5	16,174	14,068	3,748.4	3,260.4	14,996	13,044	249,961
1991	4,209.6	3,509.0	16,658	13,886	3,887.7	3,240.8	· 15,384	12,824	252,711
1982: IV	2,374.7	2,832.6	10,189	12,154	2,128.7	2,539.3	9,134	10,895	233,060
1983: IV	2,594.3	2,960.6	11,033	12,591	2,346.8	2,678.2	9,980	11,390	235,146
1984: IV	2,829.1	3,118.5	11,925	13,145	2,526.4	2,784.8	10,649	11,739	237,231
1985: IV	3,007.9	3,178.7	12,565	13,278	2,739.8	2,895.3	11,445	12,095	239,387
1986: IV	3,169.3	3,266.2	13,121	13,522	2,923.1	3,012.5	12,101	12,472	241,550
1987: IV	3,389.9	3,335.8	13,907	13,685	3,124.6	3,074.7	12,819	12,615	243,745
1988: IV	3,653.2	3,443.1	14,850	13,996	3,398.2	3,202.9	13,814	13,020	246,004
1989: I	3,730.0	3,472.9	15,133	14,090	3,440.8	3,203.6	13,959	12,997	246,488
II	3,758.3	3,450.1	15,214	13,967	3,499.1	3,212.2	14,165	13,003	247,026
III	3,795.4	3,455.7	15,322	13,951	3,553.3	3,235.3	14,345	13,061	247,701
IV	3,864.3	3,480.9	15,558	14,015	3,599.1	3,242.0	14,491	13,053	248,372
1990: I	3,962.3	3,516.8	15,917	14,128	3,672.4	3,259.5	14,752	13,094	248,931
II	4,015.9	3,523.9	16,092	14,120	3,715.3	3,260.1	14,887	13,063	249,558
III	4,065.3	3,513.7	16,242	14,038	3,787.8	3,273.9	15,133	13,080	250,303
IV	4,128.1	3,511.6	16,443	13,988	3,818.2	3,248.0	15,209	12,938	251,050
1991: I	4,136.0	3,488.7	16,433	13,861	3,821.7	3,223.5	15,184	12,808	251,687
II	4,189.7	3,505.2	16,604	13,891	3,871.9	3,239.3	15,345	12,838	252,329
III	4,227.6	3,511.5	16,706	13,876	3,914.2	3,251.2	15,468	12,848	253,053
IV	4,284.9	3,530.8	16,885	13,913	3,942.9	3,249.0	15,537	12,803	253,776
1992: I	4,360.9	3,565.7	17,143	14,017	4,022.8	3,289.3	15,814	12,930	254,388
II	4,411.8	3,576.0	17,297	14,021	4,057.1	3,288.5	15,907	12,893	255,054
III	4,433.2	3,580.5	17,332	13,998	4,108.7	3,318.4	16,063	12,973	255,786

[1] Population of the United States including Armed Forces overseas; includes Alaska and Hawaii beginning 1960. Annual data are averages of quarterly data. Quarterly data are averages for the period.

Source: Department of Commerce (Bureau of Economic Analysis and Bureau of the Census).

377

TABLE B–26.—*Gross saving and investment, 1959–92*

[Billions of dollars; quarterly data at seasonally adjusted annual rates]

Year or quarter	Gross saving								Gross investment			Statistical discrepancy
	Total	Gross private saving			Government surplus or deficit (−), national income and product accounts			Capital grants received by the United States (net)[2]	Total	Gross private domestic investment	Net foreign investment[3]	
		Total	Personal saving	Gross business saving[1]	Total	Federal	State and local					
1959	79.4	82.5	22.0	60.5	−3.1	−2.6	−0.5	....	77.6	78.8	−1.2	−1.8
1960	85.1	81.5	20.6	60.9	3.6	3.5	.0	....	82.0	78.7	3.2	−3.1
1961	84.4	87.4	24.9	62.5	−3.0	−2.6	−.4	....	82.2	77.9	4.3	−2.2
1962	92.8	95.8	25.9	69.9	−2.9	−3.4	.5	....	91.8	87.9	3.9	−1.0
1963	100.4	98.8	24.6	74.1	1.6	1.1	.4	....	98.4	93.4	5.0	−2.0
1964	110.0	111.5	31.6	80.0	−1.6	−2.6	1.0	....	109.3	101.7	7.5	−.7
1965	125.0	123.7	34.6	89.2	1.2	1.3	.0	....	124.2	118.0	6.2	−.7
1966	131.5	132.5	36.3	96.1	−1.0	−1.4	.5	....	134.3	130.4	3.9	2.8
1967	130.8	144.5	45.8	98.7	−13.7	−12.7	−1.1	....	131.6	128.0	3.5	.8
1968	141.7	146.4	43.8	102.5	−4.6	−4.7	.1	....	141.7	139.9	1.7	−.1
1969	159.5	149.5	43.3	106.2	10.0	8.5	1.5	....	157.0	155.2	1.8	−2.6
1970	155.2	165.8	57.5	108.2	−11.5	−13.3	1.8	0.9	155.2	150.3	4.9	.0
1971	173.7	192.2	65.4	126.8	−19.2	−21.7	2.5	.7	176.8	175.5	1.3	3.1
1972	201.7	204.9	59.7	145.1	−3.9	−17.3	13.4	.7	202.7	205.6	−2.9	1.1
1973	252.3	245.4	86.1	159.3	6.9	−6.6	13.4	0	251.8	243.1	8.7	−.5
1974	249.5	256.0	93.4	162.6	−4.5	−11.6	7.1	4−2.0	250.9	245.8	5.1	1.4
1975	241.4	306.3	100.3	206.0	−64.8	−69.4	4.6	0	247.4	226.0	21.4	6.0
1976	284.8	323.1	93.0	230.0	−38.3	−52.9	14.6	0	295.2	286.4	8.8	10.4
1977	338.2	355.0	87.9	267.1	−16.8	−42.4	25.6	0	349.1	358.3	−9.2	10.9
1978	415.7	412.8	107.8	305.0	2.9	−28.1	31.1	0	423.3	434.0	−10.7	7.6
1979	468.5	457.9	123.3	334.5	9.4	−15.7	25.1	1.1	482.2	480.2	2.0	13.8
1980	465.4	499.6	153.8	345.7	−35.3	−60.1	24.8	1.2	479.1	467.6	11.5	13.6
1981	556.6	585.9	191.8	394.1	−30.3	−58.8	28.5	1.1	567.5	558.0	9.5	10.9
1982	508.4	616.9	199.5	417.5	−108.6	−135.5	26.9	0	500.9	503.4	−2.5	−7.4
1983	501.6	641.3	168.7	472.7	−139.8	−180.1	40.3	0	511.7	546.7	−35.0	10.2
1984	633.9	742.7	222.0	520.7	−108.8	−166.9	58.1	0	624.9	718.9	−94.0	−9.0
1985	610.4	735.7	189.3	546.4	−125.3	−181.4	56.1	0	596.5	714.5	−118.1	−13.9
1986	574.6	721.4	187.5	533.9	−146.8	−201.0	54.3	0	575.9	717.6	−141.7	1.2
1987	619.0	730.7	142.0	588.7	−111.7	−151.8	40.1	0	594.2	749.3	−155.1	−24.8
1988	704.0	802.3	155.7	646.6	−98.3	−136.6	38.4	0	675.6	793.6	−118.0	−28.4
1989	741.8	819.4	152.1	667.3	−77.5	−122.3	44.8	0	742.9	832.3	−89.3	1.1
1990	718.0	854.1	175.6	678.5	−136.1	−166.2	30.1	0	723.4	799.5	−76.1	5.4
1991	708.2	901.5	199.6	701.9	−193.3	−210.4	17.1	0	730.1	721.1	9.0	21.9
1982: IV	458.5	615.4	183.8	431.6	−156.9	−183.4	26.5	0	448.4	464.2	−15.8	−10.1
1983: IV	542.4	678.7	176.3	502.4	−136.3	−184.6	48.3	0	556.3	614.8	−58.5	13.8
1984: IV	637.0	764.7	222.6	542.1	−127.8	−186.8	59.0	0	616.5	722.8	−106.3	−20.5
1985: IV	603.8	734.7	179.2	555.5	−130.9	−187.2	56.3	0	597.8	737.0	−139.1	−5.9
1986: IV	550.1	676.3	151.1	525.3	−126.2	−177.5	51.2	0	548.1	697.1	−149.0	−2.0
1987: IV	667.9	783.7	169.8	613.9	−115.8	−152.7	37.0	0	643.0	800.2	−157.1	−24.9
1988: IV	720.1	814.8	156.4	658.3	−94.7	−134.9	40.2	0	694.7	814.8	−120.1	−25.4
1989: I	760.6	826.7	182.0	644.7	−66.1	−110.0	43.9	0	749.2	843.9	−94.7	−11.4
II	749.4	811.0	148.5	662.5	−61.5	−109.7	48.2	0	751.1	840.3	−89.1	1.7
III	728.9	811.2	129.0	682.1	−82.3	−128.0	45.7	0	730.1	819.6	−89.6	1.2
IV	728.4	828.6	148.8	679.8	−100.2	−141.5	41.3	0	741.3	825.2	−84.0	12.8
1990: I	725.2	856.9	173.1	683.8	−131.7	−167.8	36.1	0	741.4	820.3	−79.0	16.1
II	756.4	879.5	182.7	696.8	−123.1	−156.9	33.8	0	757.7	833.0	−75.3	1.2
III	705.6	820.9	157.3	663.6	−115.3	−145.6	30.3	0	719.0	805.7	−86.7	13.4
IV	684.8	859.3	189.3	670.0	−174.4	−194.6	20.2	0	675.7	739.0	−63.2	−9.1
1991: I	754.1	889.4	192.8	696.6	−135.3	−149.9	14.6	0	767.5	705.4	62.1	13.4
II	701.3	896.9	195.3	701.6	−195.6	−212.2	16.5	0	728.4	710.2	18.2	27.1
III	679.4	884.9	191.0	693.9	−205.6	−221.0	15.4	0	709.9	732.8	−22.9	30.5
IV	698.2	934.8	219.4	715.3	−236.6	−258.7	22.0	0	714.6	736.1	−21.5	16.4
1992: I	677.5	950.1	214.6	735.5	−272.6	−289.2	16.6	0	706.5	722.4	−16.0	29.0
II	682.9	968.1	232.3	735.8	−285.2	−302.9	17.7	0	713.8	773.2	−59.4	30.9
III	696.9	992.1	203.3	788.8	−295.2	−304.4	9.2	0	732.0	781.6	−49.6	35.1

[1] Undistributed corporate profits with inventory valuation and capital consumption adjustments, corporate and noncorporate consumption of fixed capital, and private wage accruals less disbursements.
[2] Consists mainly of allocations of special drawing rights (SDRs).
[3] Net exports of goods and services plus net receipts of factor income from rest of the world less net transfers plus net capital grants received by the United States. See also Table B–18.
[4] Consists of a U.S. payment to India under the Agricultural Trade Development and Assistance Act. This payment is included in capital grants received by the United States, net.

Source: Department of Commerce, Bureau of Economic Analysis.

TABLE B-27.—Personal saving, flow of funds accounts, 1946-92 [1]

[Billions of dollars; quarterly data at seasonally adjusted annual rates]

Year or quarter	Personal saving	Total	Increase in financial assets								Net investment in tangible assets [7]			Less: Net increase in debt		
			Checkable deposits and currency	Time and savings deposits	Money market fund shares	Securities			Insurance and pension reserves [5]	Other financial assets [6]	Owner-occupied homes	Consumer durables	Noncorporate business assets [8]	Mortgage debt on nonfarm homes	Consumer credit	Other debt [8][9]
						Government securities [2]	Corporate equities [3]	Other securities [4]								
1946	22.3	19.6	5.6	6.3		-1.5	1.2	-0.7	5.1	3.7	3.8	6.7	2.0	4.1	3.1	2.6
1947	12.4	12.6	.0	3.5		.5	1.1	-.7	5.4	2.7	6.8	9.4	-5.1	4.9	3.7	2.7
1948	16.8	8.9	-2.9	2.3		1.0	1.0	.2	5.3	2.2	9.3	10.2	-1.1	4.8	3.2	2.6
1949	13.4	8.9	-2.0	2.6		.5	.7	-.2	5.6	1.6	8.5	10.9	-5.8	4.2	3.2	1.8
1950	23.3	15.0	2.7	2.4		.9	.7	-.6	6.1	2.9	11.9	14.9	-1.8	7.0	4.6	5.2
1951	24.7	19.5	4.6	4.8		-.6	1.8	.6	6.3	2.0	11.9	11.4	-4.9	6.4	3.3	3.5
1952	38.0	28.5	1.6	7.8		7.4	1.5	.2	7.7	2.4	11.5	8.7	2.1	6.4	3.3	3.2
1953	35.0	24.5	.9	8.2		3.7	1.0	.3	7.9	2.4	12.6	10.3	1.1	7.4	4.1	2.0
1954	27.6	20.9	2.1	9.2		.2	.7	-1.1	7.8	2.0	13.0	7.0	2.0	9.0	1.3	4.9
1955	36.9	28.6	1.2	8.6		6.4	1.1	1.0	8.5	1.7	17.1	12.7	3.2	12.2	7.0	5.4
1956	39.2	31.8	1.9	9.4		4.5	2.0	1.2	9.5	3.4	16.0	8.8	1.2	10.8	3.6	4.2
1957	39.1	29.2	-.4	11.9		3.8	1.5	1.1	9.5	1.9	13.6	7.9	2.5	8.6	2.6	2.9
1958	36.2	32.8	3.7	13.9		-2.7	1.8	1.5	10.4	4.3	12.6	3.7	3.2	9.5	.3	6.4
1959	36.7	35.0	.9	11.0		8.3	.6	.5	11.9	1.9	19.5	7.7	1.3	12.9	7.7	6.2
1960	38.5	32.3	.9	12.2		2.1	.0	1.8	11.5	3.7	17.4	7.2	2.2	11.0	4.0	5.6
1961	38.0	35.3	-1.0	18.3		.8	1.1	-.5	12.1	4.4	16.3	4.5	2.9	12.2	2.2	6.6
1962	44.5	39.6	-1.2	26.1		1.0	-1.4	-.5	13.0	2.5	18.2	8.6	4.3	13.8	5.9	6.5
1963	49.0	45.4	4.2	26.2		-1.0	-1.5	1.4	13.9	2.1	20.5	11.9	4.7	16.2	8.5	8.9
1964	61.1	56.0	6.1	26.3		3.7	-.2	.6	16.4	3.2	22.1	15.1	4.4	16.8	9.5	10.2
1965	68.1	57.9	6.7	27.9		3.7	-1.5	1.0	17.0	3.2	21.6	20.2	8.4	16.8	10.1	13.1
1966	82.5	62.9	2.4	19.1		13.6	.0	4.3	19.3	4.1	19.0	23.2	7.9	12.7	5.9	11.8
1967	84.2	72.4	10.3	35.4		-2.5	-3.1	6.9	18.8	6.8	18.5	21.3	7.3	13.1	5.1	17.0
1968	82.4	69.4	9.5	30.9		1.3	-6.1	8.2	19.9	5.7	19.9	26.9	10.2	16.7	10.8	16.4
1969	81.9	70.7	-1.1	8.9		27.6	-2.1	11.7	21.8	3.9	19.9	26.2	11.7	17.4	9.9	19.4
1970	91.1	80.5	7.4	43.5		-5.5	-.5	7.4	24.2	4.1	17.7	19.6	10.1	13.0	4.6	19.2
1971	103.3	107.4	13.4	67.7		-11.0	-4.4	7.2	28.0	6.5	27.8	25.4	15.1	26.3	14.0	32.0
1972	121.2	134.9	13.4	74.0		-.9	-9.1	-.3	48.5	9.4	36.7	34.3	18.1	39.3	19.0	44.5
1973	157.4	146.4	13.1	63.5		16.7	-4.4	9.5	39.9	8.2	40.2	40.6	23.2	43.6	22.7	26.7
1974	122.5	149.3	6.3	56.2	2.4	18.1	-1.7	15.2	43.7	9.2	30.4	29.1	11.6	34.2	9.4	54.3
1975	155.0	174.4	6.0	77.6	1.3	16.8	-5.0	-4.7	71.9	10.3	28.1	27.4	6.1	39.3	8.0	33.7
1976	168.3	209.2	15.6	107.1	.0	8.6	1.2	3.0	56.6	17.0	44.7	41.5	4.0	62.0	22.9	46.1
1977	193.0	264.0	19.7	106.6	-.2	11.6	-6.4	18.6	78.6	25.6	65.8	51.5	16.3	93.0	36.7	64.8
1978	204.1	287.1	22.0	99.6	6.0	29.3	-11.8	12.0	95.0	35.0	78.5	56.8	23.1	109.9	45.1	86.4
1979	214.0	327.6	35.8	74.4	30.6	65.1	-24.8	5.9	101.8	38.8	75.2	50.4	32.0	116.2	40.5	114.5
1980	213.9	326.9	9.2	124.9	24.5	29.9	-10.6	-6.8	118.5	37.3	51.3	26.3	14.2	96.8	2.6	105.3
1981	239.0	322.7	36.3	72.0	90.7	39.6	-37.0	-7.1	117.9	10.3	50.5	27.3	27.5	76.1	16.9	96.1
1982	262.8	386.8	24.8	122.6	32.8	65.9	-15.6	-19.9	153.5	22.6	30.0	22.4	10.1	58.1	16.4	112.0
1983	312.5	502.9	34.3	195.1	-31.1	88.3	-4.1	9.3	180.7	30.3	71.3	50.6	-11.8	125.4	48.9	126.2
1984	384.4	565.1	21.6	218.8	44.0	108.6	-49.4	2.4	183.0	36.1	93.6	81.8	24.3	143.2	81.7	155.5
1985	361.1	581.9	33.9	119.0	8.7	126.1	-52.9	61.3	217.9	67.9	93.6	95.8	26.8	164.2	82.3	190.7
1986	438.2	609.0	102.2	108.9	39.6	-33.5	5.2	63.8	249.0	73.9	119.4	111.4	16.0	251.9	57.5	108.1
1987	339.4	456.8	6.6	114.7	28.1	154.8	-32.1	4.5	130.5	49.6	123.3	102.9	12.3	234.6	32.9	88.4
1988	381.0	535.3	7.4	154.8	23.5	178.2	-119.7	-4.0	218.9	76.1	126.5	112.6	7.4	241.2	50.1	109.5
1989	456.5	593.9	19.3	108.6	85.9	167.4	-97.2	-5.9	250.1	65.7	113.5	109.3	19.4	244.7	41.7	93.2
1990	417.5	522.1	22.4	21.7	44.2	133.0	23.6	19.0	212.4	45.9	97.5	85.1	9.2	218.9	17.5	59.9
1991	351.2	422.0	55.1	-62.2	28.6	-44.5	72.0	13.4	285.5	74.1	74.6	41.6	-21.6	141.7	-12.5	36.3
1990: I	475.8	697.4	-13.9	101.0	100.8	279.9	-24.7	101.7	162.4	-9.8	113.6	104.8	11.6	332.5	40.8	78.2
II	545.0	610.7	68.2	-16.6	-55.3	182.0	41.8	74.7	269.0	46.9	104.3	87.3	15.4	187.9	21.4	63.3
III	286.2	367.5	44.3	-18.9	96.9	130.4	65.1	-163.5	141.6	71.6	91.8	81.5	11.9	193.3	14.4	58.9
IV	363.2	412.8	-9.2	21.3	34.3	-60.3	12.1	63.1	276.7	74.8	80.2	66.7	-2.0	161.8	-6.6	39.4
1991: I	580.4	664.7	57.9	42.5	175.8	-10.3	31.8	6.3	312.0	48.6	67.5	40.0	-17.6	152.6	-10.4	31.9
II	240.7	362.9	41.4	-82.6	-71.4	150.3	49.2	6.8	229.3	40.0	71.0	38.9	-14.3	157.7	-7.8	67.9
III	287.0	297.0	99.4	-138.2	-6.5	-160.3	92.4	-43.8	359.0	95.0	78.8	48.1	-19.2	122.0	-24.0	19.8
IV	296.6	363.2	21.5	-70.7	16.4	-157.7	114.4	84.5	241.7	113.0	81.3	39.6	-35.2	134.7	-8.0	25.7
1992: I	490.9	569.7	162.5	-63.5	96.6	184.2	115.5	-93.2	167.1	.5	82.7	55.8	-19.9	209.1	3.1	-14.6
II	333.6	334.1	78.9	-170.0	-46.1	31.5	215.6	-5.6	215.9	13.9	89.1	52.6	-14.7	121.1	-12.4	18.7
III	298.6	316.0	163.0	-151.7	-20.3	-108.4	230.5	-166.0	332.2	36.8	51.1	61.5	-13.9	146.6	.4	-30.8

[1] Saving by households, personal trust funds, nonprofit institutions, farms, and other noncorporate business.
[2] Consists of U.S. savings bonds, other U.S. Treasury securities, U.S. Government agency securities and sponsored agency securities, mortgage pool securities, and State and local obligations.
[3] Includes mutual fund shares.
[4] Corporate and foreign bonds and open-market paper.
[5] Private life insurance reserves, private insured and noninsured pension reserves, and government insurance and pension reserves.
[6] Consists of security credit, mortgages, accident and health insurance reserves, and nonlife insurance claims for households, and of consumer credit, equity in sponsored agencies, and nonlife insurance claims for noncorporate business.
[7] Purchases of physical assets less depreciation.
[8] Includes data for corporate farms.
[9] Other debt consists of security credit, U.S. Government and policy loans, and noncorporate business debt.

Source: Board of Governors of the Federal Reserve System.

TABLE B-28.—*Median money income (in 1991 dollars) and poverty status of families and persons, by race, selected years, 1971–91*

Year	Families [1] Number (millions)	Median money income (in 1991 dollars) [2]	Below poverty level Total Number (millions)	Total Percent	Female householder Number (millions)	Female householder Percent	Persons below poverty level Number (millions)	Percent	Median money income (in 1991 dollars) of persons 15 years old and over with income [2][3] Males All persons	Males Year-round full-time workers	Females All persons	Females Year-round full-time workers
ALL RACES												
1971	53.3	$32,502	5.3	10.0	2.1	33.9	25.6	12.5	$21,814	$30,435	$7,610	$18,016
1973	55.1	34,774	4.8	8.8	2.2	32.2	23.0	11.1	23,246	33,092	8,068	18,722
1975 [4]	56.2	33,248	5.5	9.7	2.4	32.5	25.9	12.3	21,455	31,345	8,204	18,707
1977	57.2	34,500	5.3	9.3	2.6	31.7	24.7	11.6	21,816	32,477	8,493	18,995
1978	57.8	35,594	5.3	9.1	2.7	31.4	24.5	11.4	22,064	32,410	8,208	19,453
1979 [5]	59.6	36,051	5.5	9.2	2.6	30.4	26.1	11.7	21,680	32,171	8,010	19,383
1980	60.3	34,791	6.2	10.3	3.0	32.7	29.3	13.0	20,736	31,730	8,142	19,182
1981	61.0	33,843	6.9	11.2	3.3	34.6	31.8	14.0	20,367	31,279	8,251	18,831
1982	61.4	33,385	7.5	12.2	3.4	36.3	34.4	15.0	19,874	30,852	8,387	19,465
1983 [4]	62.0	33,741	7.6	12.3	3.6	36.0	35.3	15.2	20,048	30,776	8,759	19,812
1984	62.7	34,650	7.3	11.6	3.5	34.5	33.7	14.4	20,450	31,466	9,003	20,216
1985	63.6	35,107	7.2	11.4	3.5	34.0	33.1	14.0	20,646	31,644	9,135	20,572
1986	64.5	36,607	7.0	10.9	3.6	34.6	32.4	13.6	21,268	32,178	9,457	20,931
1987 [4]	65.2	37,131	7.0	10.7	3.7	34.2	32.2	13.4	21,324	31,989	9,945	21,058
1988	65.8	37,062	6.9	10.4	3.6	33.4	31.7	13.0	21,769	31,479	10,228	21,351
1989	66.1	37,579	6.8	10.3	3.5	32.2	31.5	12.8	21,850	31,215	10,571	21,570
1990	66.3	36,841	7.1	10.7	3.8	33.4	33.6	13.5	21,147	30,198	10,494	21,457
1991	67.2	35,939	7.7	11.5	4.2	35.6	35.7	14.2	20,469	30,331	10,476	21,245
WHITE												
1971	47.6	33,725	3.8	7.9	1.2	26.5	17.8	9.9	22,870	31,291	7,736	18,224
1973	48.9	36,344	3.2	6.6	1.2	24.5	15.1	8.4	24,392	34,050	8,146	19,039
1975 [4]	49.9	34,578	3.8	7.7	1.4	25.9	17.8	9.7	22,538	32,070	8,288	18,751
1977	50.5	36,076	3.5	7.0	1.4	24.0	16.4	8.9	22,850	33,141	8,622	19,115
1978	50.9	37,063	3.5	6.9	1.3	23.5	16.3	8.7	23,110	33,011	8,307	19,637
1979 [5]	52.2	37,619	3.6	6.9	1.4	22.3	17.2	9.0	22,648	33,100	8,085	19,552
1980	52.7	36,249	4.2	8.0	1.6	25.7	19.7	10.2	22,057	32,635	8,187	19,368
1981	53.3	35,550	4.7	8.8	1.8	27.4	21.6	11.1	21,611	32,014	8,343	19,145
1982	53.4	35,052	5.1	9.6	1.8	27.9	23.5	12.0	21,011	31,674	8,501	19,728
1983 [4]	53.9	35,331	5.2	9.7	1.9	28.3	24.0	12.1	21,092	31,598	8,912	20,077
1984	54.4	36,293	4.9	9.1	1.9	27.1	23.0	11.5	21,586	32,544	9,109	20,417
1985	55.0	36,901	5.0	9.1	2.0	27.4	22.9	11.4	21,659	32,522	9,312	20,863
1986	55.7	38,286	4.8	8.6	2.0	28.2	22.2	11.0	22,443	33,077	9,643	21,251
1987 [4]	56.1	38,828	4.6	8.1	2.0	26.9	21.2	10.4	22,666	32,735	10,199	21,448
1988	56.5	39,047	4.5	7.9	1.9	26.5	20.7	10.1	22,979	32,538	10,480	21,671
1989	56.6	39,514	4.4	7.8	1.9	25.4	20.8	10.0	22,916	32,591	10,777	21,826
1990	56.8	38,468	4.6	8.1	2.0	26.8	22.3	10.7	22,061	31,347	10,751	21,716
1991	57.2	37,783	5.0	8.8	2.2	28.4	23.7	11.3	21,395	30,953	10,721	21,555
BLACK												
1971	5.2	20,351	1.5	28.8	.9	53.5	7.4	32.5	13,639	21,397	6,778	16,091
1973	5.4	20,975	1.5	28.1	1.0	52.7	7.4	31.4	14,754	22,949	7,352	16,145
1975 [4]	5.6	21,276	1.5	27.1	1.0	50.1	7.5	31.3	13,475	23,867	7,530	17,914
1977	5.8	20,609	1.6	28.2	1.2	51.0	7.7	31.3	13,560	22,848	7,446	17,865
1978	5.9	21,951	1.6	27.5	1.2	50.6	7.6	30.6	13,844	25,283	7,480	18,200
1979 [5]	6.2	21,302	1.7	27.8	1.2	49.4	8.1	31.0	14,019	23,855	7,358	17,916
1980	6.3	20,974	1.8	28.9	1.3	49.4	8.6	32.5	13,254	22,962	7,580	18,063
1981	6.4	20,054	2.0	30.8	1.4	52.9	9.2	34.2	12,851	22,651	7,412	17,290
1982	6.5	19,373	2.2	33.0	1.5	56.2	9.7	35.6	12,591	22,496	7,498	17,632
1983 [4]	6.7	19,912	2.2	32.3	1.5	53.7	9.9	35.7	12,335	22,529	7,615	17,822
1984	6.8	20,228	2.1	30.9	1.5	51.7	9.5	33.8	12,385	22,210	8,080	18,399
1985	6.9	21,248	2.0	28.7	1.5	50.5	8.9	31.3	13,630	22,748	7,945	18,468
1986	7.1	21,877	2.0	28.0	1.5	50.1	9.0	31.1	13,449	23,321	8,160	18,596
1987 [4]	7.2	22,068	2.1	29.4	1.6	51.1	9.5	32.4	13,446	23,406	8,331	19,157
1988	7.4	22,254	2.1	28.2	1.6	49.0	9.4	31.3	13,866	23,851	8,461	19,419
1989	7.5	22,197	2.1	27.8	1.5	46.5	9.3	30.7	13,850	22,741	8,650	19,629
1990	7.5	22,325	2.2	29.3	1.6	48.1	9.8	31.9	13,409	22,385	8.678	19,324
1991	7.7	21,548	2.3	30.4	1.8	51.2	10.2	32.7	12,962	22,628	8,816	19,134

[1] The term "family" refers to a group of two or more persons related by blood, marriage, or adoption and residing together; all such persons are considered members of the same family. Beginning 1979, based on householder concept and restricted to primary families.
[2] Current dollar median money income deflated by CPI-U-X1.
[3] Prior to 1979, data are for persons 14 years and over.
[4] Based on revised methodology; comparable with succeeding years.
[5] Based on 1980 census population controls; comparable with succeeding years.

Note.—Poverty rates (percent of persons below poverty level) for all races for years not shown above are: 1959, 22.4; 1960, 22.2; 1961, 21.9; 1962, 21.0; 1963, 19.5; 1964, 19.0; 1965, 17.3; 1966, 14.7; 1967, 14.2; 1968, 12.8; 1969, 12.1; 1970, 12.6; 1972, 11.9; 1974, 11.2; and 1976, 11.8.
The poverty level is based on the poverty index adopted by a Federal interagency committee in 1969, with minor revisions implemented in 1981. The poverty thresholds are updated every year to reflect changes in the consumer price index (CPI-U). For further details, see "Current Population Reports," Series P-60, No. 181.
See "Current Population Reports," Series P-60, No. 180 for details regarding the median money income series.

Source: Department of Commerce, Bureau of the Census.

POPULATION, EMPLOYMENT, WAGES, AND PRODUCTIVITY

TABLE B-29.—*Population by age groups, 1929-92*

[Thousands of persons]

July 1	Total	Age (years)						
		Under 5	5-15	16-19	20-24	25-44	45-64	65 and over
1929	121,767	11,734	26,800	9,127	10,694	35,862	21,076	6,474
1933	125,579	10,612	26,897	9,302	11,152	37,319	22,933	7,363
1939	130,880	10,418	25,179	9,822	11,519	39,354	25,823	8,764
1940	132,122	10,579	24,811	9,895	11,690	39,868	26,249	9,031
1941	133,402	10,850	24,516	9,840	11,807	40,383	26,718	9,288
1942	134,860	11,301	24,231	9,730	11,955	40,861	27,196	9,584
1943	136,739	12,016	24,093	9,607	12,064	41,420	27,671	9,867
1944	138,397	12,524	23,949	9,561	12,062	42,016	28,138	10,147
1945	139,928	12,979	23,907	9,361	12,036	42,521	28,630	10,494
1946	141,389	13,244	24,103	9,119	12,004	43,027	29,064	10,828
1947	144,126	14,406	24,468	9,097	11,814	43,657	29,498	11,185
1948	146,631	14,919	25,209	8,952	11,794	44,288	29,931	11,538
1949	149,188	15,607	25,852	8,788	11,700	44,916	30,405	11,921
1950	152,271	16,410	26,721	8,542	11,680	45,672	30,849	12,397
1951	154,878	17,333	27,279	8,446	11,552	46,103	31,362	12,803
1952	157,553	17,312	28,894	8,414	11,350	46,495	31,884	13,203
1953	160,184	17,638	30,227	8,460	11,062	46,786	32,394	13,617
1954	163,026	18,057	31,480	8,637	10,832	47,001	32,942	14,076
1955	165,931	18,566	32,682	8,744	10,714	47,194	33,506	14,525
1956	168,903	19,003	33,994	8,916	10,616	47,379	34,057	14,938
1957	171,984	19,494	35,272	9,195	10,603	47,440	34,591	15,388
1958	174,882	19,887	36,445	9,543	10,756	47,337	35,109	15,806
1959	177,830	20,175	37,368	10,215	10,969	47,192	35,663	16,248
1960	180,671	20,341	38,494	10,683	11,134	47,140	36,203	16,675
1961	183,691	20,522	39,765	11,025	11,483	47,084	36,722	17,089
1962	186,538	20,469	41,205	11,180	11,959	47,013	37,255	17,457
1963	189,242	20,342	41,626	12,007	12,714	46,994	37,782	17,778
1964	191,889	20,165	42,297	12,736	13,269	46,958	38,338	18,127
1965	194,303	19,824	42,938	13,516	13,746	46,912	38,916	18,451
1966	196,560	19,208	43,702	14,311	14,050	47,001	39,534	18,755
1967	198,712	18,563	44,244	14,200	15,248	47,194	40,193	19,071
1968	200,706	17,913	44,622	14,452	15,786	47,721	40,846	19,365
1969	202,677	17,376	44,840	14,800	16,480	48,064	41,437	19,680
1970	205,052	17,166	44,816	15,289	17,202	48,473	41,999	20,107
1971	207,661	17,244	44,591	15,688	18,159	48,936	42,482	20,561
1972	209,896	17,101	44,203	16,039	18,153	50,482	42,898	21,020
1973	211,909	16,851	43,582	16,446	18,521	51,749	43,235	21,525
1974	213,854	16,487	42,989	16,769	18,975	53,051	43,522	22,061
1975	215,973	16,121	42,508	17,017	19,527	54,302	43,801	22,696
1976	218,035	15,617	42,099	17,194	19,986	55,852	44,008	23,278
1977	220,239	15,564	41,298	17,276	20,499	57,561	44,150	23,892
1978	222,585	15,735	40,428	17,288	20,946	59,400	44,286	24,502
1979	225,055	16,063	39,552	17,242	21,297	61,379	44,390	25,134
1980	227,726	16,451	38,838	17,167	21,590	63,470	44,504	25,707
1981	229,966	16,893	38,144	16,812	21,869	65,528	44,500	26,221
1982	232,188	17,228	37,784	16,332	21,902	67,692	44,462	26,787
1983	234,307	17,547	37,526	15,823	21,844	69,733	44,474	27,361
1984	236,348	17,695	37,461	15,295	21,737	71,735	44,547	27,878
1985	238,466	17,842	37,450	15,005	21,478	73,673	44,602	28,416
1986	240,651	17,963	37,404	15,024	20,942	75,651	44,660	29,008
1987	242,804	18,052	37,333	15,215	20,385	77,338	44,854	29,626
1988	245,021	18,195	37,593	15,198	19,846	78,595	45,471	30,124
1989	247,342	18,508	37,972	14,913	19,442	79,943	45,882	30,682
1990	249,924	18,874	38,592	14,452	19,305	81,192	46,284	31,224
1991	252,688	19,222	39,201	13,949	19,372	82,439	46,752	31,754
1992	255,414							

Note.—Includes Armed Forces overseas beginning 1940. Includes Alaska and Hawaii beginning 1950.

All estimates are consistent with decennial census enumerations.

Source: Department of Commerce, Bureau of the Census.

381

TABLE B-30.—*Population and the labor force, 1929–92*

[Monthly data seasonally adjusted, except as noted]

Year or month	Civilian noninstitutional population [1]	Resident Armed Forces [1]	Labor force including resident Armed Forces	Employment including resident Armed Forces	Civilian labor force						Unemployment rate		Civilian labor force participation rate [4]	Civilian employment/population ratio [5]
					Total	Employment				Unemployment	All workers [2]	Civilian workers [3]		
						Total	Agricultural	Nonagricultural						
	Thousands of persons 14 years of age and over										Percent			
1929					49,180	47,630	10,450	37,180	1,550			3.2		
1933					51,590	38,760	10,090	28,670	12,830			24.9		
1939					55,230	45,750	9,610	36,140	9,480			17.2		
1940	99,840				55,640	47,520	9,540	37,980	8,120			14.6	55.7	47.6
1941	99,900				55,910	50,350	9,100	41,250	5,560			9.9	56.0	50.4
1942	98,640				56,410	53,750	9,250	44,500	2,660			4.7	57.2	54.5
1943	94,640				55,540	54,470	9,080	45,390	1,070			1.9	58.7	57.6
1944	93,220				54,630	53,960	8,950	45,010	670			1.2	58.6	57.9
1945	94,090				53,860	52,820	8,580	44,240	1,040			1.9	57.2	56.1
1946	103,070				57,520	55,250	8,320	46,930	2,270			3.9	55.8	53.6
1947	106,018				60,168	57,812	8,256	49,557	2,356			3.9	56.8	54.5
	Thousands of persons 16 years of age and over													
1947	101,827				59,350	57,038	7,890	49,148	2,311			3.9	58.3	56.0
1948	103,068				60,621	58,343	7,629	50,714	2,276			3.8	58.8	56.6
1949	103,994				61,286	57,651	7,658	49,993	3,637			5.9	58.9	55.4
1950	104,995	1,169	63,377	60,087	62,208	58,918	7,160	51,758	3,288	5.2	5.3	59.2	56.1
1951	104,621	2,143	64,160	62,104	62,017	59,961	6,726	53,235	2,055	3.2	3.3	59.2	57.3
1952	105,231	2,386	64,524	62,636	62,138	60,250	6,500	53,749	1,883	2.9	3.0	59.0	57.3
1953 [6]	107,056	2,231	65,246	63,410	63,015	61,179	6,260	54,919	1,834	2.8	2.9	58.9	57.1
1954	108,321	2,142	65,785	62,251	63,643	60,109	6,205	53,904	3,532	5.4	5.5	58.8	55.5
1955	109,683	2,064	67,087	64,234	65,023	62,170	6,450	55,722	2,852	4.3	4.4	59.3	56.7
1956	110,954	1,965	68,517	65,764	66,552	63,799	6,283	57,514	2,750	4.0	4.1	60.0	57.5
1957	112,265	1,948	68,877	66,019	66,929	64,071	5,947	58,123	2,859	4.2	4.3	59.6	57.1
1958	113,727	1,847	69,486	64,883	67,639	63,036	5,586	57,450	4,602	6.6	6.8	59.5	55.4
1959	115,329	1,788	70,157	66,418	68,369	64,630	5,565	59,065	3,740	5.3	5.5	59.3	56.0
1960 [6]	117,245	1,861	71,489	67,639	69,628	65,778	5,458	60,318	3,852	5.4	5.5	59.4	56.1
1961	118,771	1,900	72,359	67,646	70,459	65,746	5,200	60,546	4,714	6.5	6.7	59.3	55.4
1962 [6]	120,153	2,061	72,675	68,763	70,614	66,702	4,944	61,759	3,911	5.4	5.5	58.8	55.5
1963	122,416	2,006	73,839	69,768	71,833	67,762	4,687	63,076	4,070	5.5	5.7	58.7	55.4
1964	124,485	2,018	75,109	71,323	73,091	69,305	4,523	64,782	3,786	5.0	5.2	58.7	55.7
1965	126,513	1,946	76,401	73,034	74,455	71,088	4,361	66,726	3,366	4.4	4.5	58.9	56.2
1966	128,058	2,122	77,892	75,017	75,770	72,895	3,979	68,915	2,875	3.7	3.8	59.2	56.9
1967	129,874	2,218	79,565	76,590	77,347	74,372	3,844	70,527	2,975	3.7	3.8	59.6	57.3
1968	132,028	2,253	80,990	78,173	78,737	75,920	3,817	72,103	2,817	3.5	3.6	59.6	57.5
1969	134,335	2,238	82,972	80,140	80,734	77,902	3,606	74,296	2,832	3.4	3.5	60.1	58.0
1970	137,085	2,118	84,889	80,796	82,771	78,678	3,463	75,215	4,093	4.8	4.9	60.4	57.4
1971	140,216	1,973	86,355	81,340	84,382	79,367	3,394	75,972	5,016	5.8	5.9	60.2	56.6
1972 [6]	144,126	1,813	88,847	83,966	87,034	82,153	3,484	78,669	4,882	5.5	5.6	60.4	57.0
1973 [6]	147,096	1,774	91,203	86,838	89,429	85,064	3,470	81,594	4,365	4.8	4.9	60.8	57.8
1974	150,120	1,721	93,670	88,515	91,949	86,794	3,515	83,279	5,156	5.5	5.6	61.3	57.8
1975	153,153	1,678	95,453	87,524	93,775	85,846	3,408	82,438	7,929	8.3	8.5	61.2	56.1
1976	156,150	1,668	97,826	90,420	96,158	88,752	3,331	85,421	7,406	7.6	7.7	61.6	56.8
1977	159,033	1,656	100,665	93,673	99,009	92,017	3,283	88,734	6,991	6.9	7.1	62.3	57.9
1978 [6]	161,910	1,631	103,882	97,679	102,251	96,048	3,387	92,661	6,202	6.0	6.1	63.2	59.3
1979	164,863	1,597	106,559	100,421	104,962	98,824	3,347	95,477	6,137	5.8	5.8	63.7	59.9
1980	167,745	1,604	108,544	100,907	106,940	99,303	3,364	95,938	7,637	7.0	7.1	63.8	59.2
1981	170,130	1,645	110,315	102,042	108,670	100,397	3,368	97,030	8,273	7.5	7.6	63.9	59.0
1982	172,271	1,668	111,872	101,194	110,204	99,526	3,401	96,125	10,678	9.5	9.7	64.0	57.8
1983	174,215	1,676	113,226	102,510	111,550	100,834	3,383	97,450	10,717	9.5	9.6	64.0	57.9
1984	176,383	1,697	115,241	106,702	113,544	105,005	3,321	101,685	8,539	7.4	7.5	64.4	59.5
1985	178,206	1,706	117,167	108,856	115,461	107,150	3,179	103,971	8,312	7.1	7.2	64.8	60.1
1986 [6]	180,587	1,706	119,540	111,303	117,834	109,597	3,163	106,434	8,237	6.9	7.0	65.3	60.7
1987	182,753	1,737	121,602	114,177	119,865	112,440	3,208	109,232	7,425	6.1	6.2	65.6	61.5
1988	184,613	1,709	123,378	116,677	121,669	114,968	3,169	111,800	6,701	5.4	5.5	65.9	62.3
1989	186,393	1,688	125,557	119,030	123,869	117,342	3,199	114,142	6,528	5.2	5.3	66.5	63.0
1990	188,049	1,637	126,424	119,550	124,787	117,914	3,186	114,728	6,874	5.4	5.5	66.4	62.7
1991	189,765	1,564	126,867	118,440	125,303	116,877	3,233	113,644	8,426	6.6	6.7	66.0	61.6
1992	191,576	1,566	128,548	119,164	126,982	117,598	3,207	114,391	9,384	7.3	7.4	66.3	61.4

[1] Not seasonally adjusted.
[2] Unemployed as percent of labor force including resident Armed Forces.
[3] Unemployed as percent of civilian labor force.
[4] Civilian labor force as percent of civilian noninstitutional population.
[5] Civilian employment as percent of civilian noninstitutional population.
See next page for continuation of table.

TABLE B-30.—*Population and the labor force, 1929-92*—Continued

[Monthly data seasonally adjusted, except as noted]

Year or month	Civilian noninstitutional population[1]	Resident Armed Forces[1]	Labor force including resident Armed Forces	Employment including resident Armed Forces	Civilian labor force					Unemployment rate		Civilian labor force participation rate[4]	Civilian employment/population ratio[5]
					Total	Employment			Unemployment	All workers[2]	Civilian workers[3]		
						Total	Agricultural	Nonagricultural					
	Thousands of persons 16 years of age and over									Percent			
1989: Jan	185,644	1,696	125,071	118,387	123,375	116,691	3,291	113,400	6,684	5.3	5.4	66.5	62.9
Feb	185,777	1,684	124,816	118,461	123,132	116,777	3,231	113,546	6,355	5.1	5.2	66.3	62.9
Mar	185,897	1,684	124,902	118,698	123,218	117,014	3,196	113,818	6,204	5.0	5.0	66.3	62.9
Apr	186,024	1,684	125,230	118,755	123,546	117,071	3,159	113,912	6,475	5.2	5.2	66.4	62.9
May	186,181	1,673	125,158	118,788	123,485	117,115	3,125	113,990	6,370	5.1	5.2	66.3	62.9
June	186,329	1,666	125,646	119,079	123,980	117,413	3,075	114,338	6,567	5.2	5.3	66.5	63.0
July	186,483	1,666	125,631	119,133	123,965	117,467	3,223	114,244	6,498	5.2	5.2	66.5	63.0
Aug	186,598	1,688	125,840	119,339	124,152	117,651	3,275	114,376	6,501	5.2	5.2	66.5	63.1
Sept	186,726	1,702	125,641	119,045	123,939	117,343	3,217	114,126	6,596	5.2	5.3	66.4	62.8
Oct	186,871	1,709	125,946	119,291	124,237	117,582	3,212	114,370	6,655	5.3	5.4	66.5	62.9
Nov	187,017	1,704	126,393	119,669	124,689	117,965	3,147	114,818	6,724	5.3	5.4	66.7	63.1
Dec	187,165	1,700	126,236	119,569	124,536	117,869	3,197	114,672	6,667	5.3	5.4	66.5	63.0
1990: Jan	187,293	1,697	126,246	119,640	124,549	117,943	3,157	114,786	6,606	5.2	5.3	66.5	63.0
Feb	187,412	1,678	126,301	119,728	124,623	118,050	3,119	114,931	6,573	5.2	5.3	66.5	63.0
Mar	187,529	1,669	126,429	119,938	124,760	118,269	3,219	115,050	6,491	5.1	5.2	66.5	63.1
Apr	187,669	1,657	126,406	119,695	124,749	118,038	3,160	114,878	6,711	5.3	5.4	66.5	62.9
May	187,828	1,639	126,559	119,976	124,920	118,337	3,286	115,051	6,583	5.2	5.3	66.5	63.0
June	187,977	1,630	126,275	119,872	124,645	118,242	3,262	114,980	6,403	5.1	5.1	66.3	62.9
July	188,136	1,627	126,274	119,562	124,647	117,935	3,104	114,831	6,712	5.3	5.4	66.3	62.7
Aug	188,261	1,640	126,461	119,449	124,821	117,809	3,138	114,671	7,012	5.5	5.6	66.3	62.6
Sept	188,401	1,601	126,493	119,372	124,892	117,771	3,170	114,601	7,121	5.6	5.7	66.3	62.5
Oct	188,525	1,570	126,535	119,280	124,965	117,710	3,193	114,517	7,255	5.7	5.8	66.3	62.4
Nov	188,697	1,615	126,545	119,043	124,930	117,428	3,171	114,257	7,502	5.9	6.0	66.2	62.2
Dec	188,866	1,617	126,835	119,109	125,218	117,492	3,270	114,222	7,726	6.1	6.2	66.3	62.2
1991: Jan	188,977	1,615	126,315	118,509	124,700	116,894	3,177	113,717	7,806	6.2	6.3	66.0	61.9
Feb	189,115	1,602	126,621	118,498	125,019	116,896	3,223	113,673	8,123	6.4	6.5	66.1	61.8
Mar	189,243	1,460	126,718	118,256	125,258	116,796	3,124	113,672	8,462	6.7	6.8	66.2	61.7
Apr	189,380	1,456	127,069	118,763	125,613	117,307	3,183	114,124	8,306	6.5	6.6	66.3	61.9
May	189,522	1,458	126,644	118,137	125,186	116,679	3,265	113,414	8,507	6.7	6.8	66.1	61.6
June	189,668	1,505	126,876	118,389	125,371	116,884	3,283	113,601	8,487	6.7	6.8	66.1	61.6
July	189,839	1,604	126,693	118,315	125,089	116,711	3,250	113,461	8,378	6.6	6.7	65.9	61.5
Aug	189,973	1,616	126,598	118,138	124,982	116,522	3,258	113,264	8,460	6.7	6.8	65.8	61.3
Sept	190,122	1,624	127,211	118,732	125,587	117,108	3,277	113,831	8,479	6.7	6.8	66.1	61.6
Oct	190,289	1,614	127,289	118,594	125,675	116,980	3,219	113,761	8,695	6.8	6.9	66.0	61.5
Nov	190,452	1,605	127,207	118,537	125,602	116,932	3,289	113,643	8,670	6.8	6.9	65.9	61.4
Dec	190,605	1,604	127,340	118,356	125,736	116,752	3,169	113,583	8,984	7.1	7.1	66.0	61.3
1992: Jan	190,759	1,599	127,627	118,635	126,028	117,036	3,146	113,890	8,992	7.0	7.1	66.1	61.4
Feb	190,884	1,585	127,770	118,547	126,185	116,962	3,213	113,749	9,223	7.2	7.3	66.1	61.3
Mar	191,022	1,585	128,133	118,849	126,548	117,264	3,194	114,070	9,284	7.2	7.3	66.2	61.4
Apr	191,168	1,577	128,320	119,095	126,743	117,518	3,206	114,312	9,225	7.2	7.3	66.3	61.5
May	191,307	1,574	128,613	119,154	127,039	117,580	3,186	114,394	9,459	7.4	7.4	66.4	61.5
June	191,455	1,570	128,868	119,080	127,298	117,510	3,244	114,266	9,788	7.6	7.7	66.5	61.4
July	191,622	1,568	128,918	119,290	127,350	117,722	3,207	114,515	9,628	7.5	7.6	66.5	61.4
Aug	191,790	1,566	128,970	119,346	127,404	117,780	3,218	114,562	9,624	7.5	7.6	66.4	61.4
Sept	191,947	1,566	128,840	119,290	127,274	117,724	3,221	114,503	9,550	7.4	7.5	66.3	61.3
Oct	192,131	1,552	128,618	119,239	127,066	117,687	3,169	114,518	9,379	7.3	7.4	66.1	61.3
Nov	192,316	1,531	128,896	119,595	127,365	118,064	3,209	114,855	9,301	7.2	7.3	66.2	61.4
Dec	192,509	1,517	129,108	119,828	127,591	118,311	3,262	115,049	9,280	7.2	7.3	66.3	61.5

[6] Not strictly comparable with earlier data due to population adjustments as follows: Beginning 1953, introduction of 1950 census data added about 600,000 to population and 350,000 to labor force, total employment, and agricultural employment. Beginning 1960, inclusion of Alaska and Hawaii added about 500,000 to population, 300,000 to labor force, and 240,000 to nonagricultural employment. Beginning 1962, introduction of 1960 census data reduced population by about 50,000 and labor force and employment by 200,000. Beginning 1972, introduction of 1970 census data added about 800,000 to civilian noninstitutional population and 333,000 to labor force and employment. A subsequent adjustment based on 1970 census in March 1973 added 60,000 to labor force and to employment. Beginning 1978, changes in sampling and estimation procedures introduced into the household survey added about 250,000 to labor force and to employment. Unemployment levels and rates were not significantly affected. Beginning 1986, the introduction of revised population controls added about 400,000 to the civilian population and labor force and 350,000 to civilian employment. Unemployment levels and rates were not significantly affected.

Note.—Labor force data in Tables B-30 through B-39 are based on household interviews and relate to the calendar week including the 12th of the month. For definitions of terms, area samples used, historical comparability of the data, comparability with other series, etc., see "Employment and Earnings."

Source: Department of Labor, Bureau of Labor Statistics.

383

TABLE B-31.—Civilian employment and unemployment by sex and age, 1947-92

[Thousands of persons 16 years of age and over; monthly data seasonally adjusted]

Year or month	Civilian employment Total	Males Total	Males 16-19 years	Males 20 years and over	Females Total	Females 16-19 years	Females 20 years and over	Unemployment Total	Males Total	Males 16-19 years	Males 20 years and over	Females Total	Females 16-19 years	Females 20 years and over
1947	57,038	40,995	2,218	38,776	16,045	1,691	14,354	2,311	1,692	270	1,422	619	144	475
1948	58,343	41,725	2,344	39,382	16,617	1,682	14,936	2,276	1,559	256	1,305	717	153	564
1949	57,651	40,925	2,124	38,803	16,723	1,588	15,137	3,637	2,572	353	2,219	1,065	223	841
1950	58,918	41,578	2,186	39,394	17,340	1,517	15,824	3,288	2,239	318	1,922	1,049	195	854
1951	59,961	41,780	2,156	39,626	18,181	1,611	16,570	2,055	1,221	191	1,029	834	145	689
1952	60,250	41,682	2,107	39,578	18,568	1,612	16,958	1,883	1,185	205	980	698	140	559
1953	61,179	42,430	2,136	40,296	18,749	1,584	17,164	1,834	1,202	184	1,019	632	123	510
1954	60,109	41,619	1,985	39,634	18,490	1,490	17,000	3,532	2,344	310	2,035	1,188	191	997
1955	62,170	42,621	2,095	40,526	19,551	1,547	18,002	2,852	1,854	274	1,580	998	176	823
1956	63,799	43,379	2,164	41,216	20,419	1,654	18,767	2,750	1,711	269	1,442	1,039	209	832
1957	64,071	43,357	2,115	41,239	20,714	1,663	19,052	2,859	1,841	300	1,541	1,018	197	821
1958	63,036	42,423	2,012	40,411	20,613	1,570	19,043	4,602	3,098	416	2,681	1,504	262	1,242
1959	64,630	43,466	2,198	41,267	21,164	1,640	19,524	3,740	2,420	398	2,022	1,320	256	1,063
1960	65,778	43,904	2,361	41,543	21,874	1,768	20,105	3,852	2,486	426	2,060	1,366	286	1,080
1961	65,746	43,656	2,315	41,342	22,090	1,793	20,296	4,714	2,997	479	2,518	1,717	349	1,368
1962	66,702	44,177	2,362	41,815	22,525	1,833	20,693	3,911	2,423	408	2,016	1,488	313	1,175
1963	67,762	44,657	2,406	42,251	23,105	1,849	21,257	4,070	2,472	501	1,971	1,598	383	1,216
1964	69,305	45,474	2,587	42,886	23,831	1,929	21,903	3,786	2,205	487	1,718	1,581	385	1,195
1965	71,088	46,340	2,918	43,422	24,748	2,118	22,630	3,366	1,914	479	1,435	1,452	395	1,056
1966	72,895	46,919	3,253	43,668	25,976	2,468	23,510	2,875	1,551	432	1,120	1,324	405	921
1967	74,372	47,479	3,186	44,294	26,893	2,496	24,397	2,975	1,508	448	1,060	1,468	391	1,078
1968	75,920	48,114	3,255	44,859	27,807	2,526	25,281	2,817	1,419	426	993	1,397	412	985
1969	77,902	48,818	3,430	45,388	29,084	2,687	26,397	2,832	1,403	440	963	1,429	413	1,015
1970	78,678	48,990	3,409	45,581	29,688	2,735	26,952	4,093	2,238	599	1,638	1,855	506	1,349
1971	79,367	49,390	3,478	45,912	29,976	2,730	27,246	5,016	2,789	693	2,097	2,227	568	1,658
1972	82,153	50,896	3,765	47,130	31,257	2,980	28,276	4,882	2,659	711	1,948	2,222	598	1,625
1973	85,064	52,349	4,039	48,310	32,715	3,231	29,484	4,365	2,275	653	1,624	2,089	583	1,507
1974	86,794	53,024	4,103	48,922	33,769	3,345	30,424	5,156	2,714	757	1,957	2,441	665	1,777
1975	85,846	51,857	3,839	48,018	33,989	3,263	30,726	7,929	4,442	966	3,476	3,486	802	2,684
1976	88,752	53,138	3,947	49,190	35,615	3,389	32,226	7,406	4,036	939	3,098	3,369	780	2,588
1977	92,017	54,728	4,174	50,555	37,289	3,514	33,775	6,991	3,667	874	2,794	3,324	789	2,535
1978	96,048	56,479	4,336	52,143	39,569	3,734	35,836	6,202	3,142	813	2,328	3,061	769	2,292
1979	98,824	57,607	4,300	53,308	41,217	3,783	37,434	6,137	3,120	811	2,308	3,018	743	2,276
1980	99,303	57,186	4,085	53,101	42,117	3,625	38,492	7,637	4,267	913	3,353	3,370	755	2,615
1981	100,397	57,397	3,815	53,582	43,000	3,411	39,590	8,273	4,577	962	3,615	3,696	800	2,895
1982	99,526	56,271	3,379	52,891	43,256	3,170	40,086	10,678	6,179	1,090	5,089	4,499	886	3,613
1983	100,834	56,787	3,300	53,487	44,047	3,043	41,004	10,717	6,260	1,003	5,257	4,457	825	3,632
1984	105,005	59,091	3,322	55,769	45,915	3,122	42,793	8,539	4,744	812	3,932	3,794	687	3,107
1985	107,150	59,891	3,328	56,562	47,259	3,105	44,154	8,312	4,521	806	3,715	3,791	661	3,129
1986	109,597	60,892	3,323	57,569	48,706	3,149	45,556	8,237	4,530	779	3,751	3,707	675	3,032
1987	112,440	62,107	3,381	58,726	50,334	3,260	47,074	7,425	4,101	732	3,369	3,324	616	2,709
1988	114,968	63,273	3,492	59,781	51,696	3,313	48,383	6,701	3,655	667	2,987	3,046	558	2,487
1989	117,342	64,315	3,477	60,837	53,027	3,282	49,745	6,528	3,525	658	2,867	3,003	536	2,467
1990	117,914	64,435	3,237	61,198	53,479	3,024	50,455	6,874	3,799	629	3,170	3,075	519	2,555
1991	116,877	63,593	2,879	60,714	53,284	2,749	50,535	8,426	4,817	709	4,109	3,609	581	3,028
1992	117,598	63,805	2,786	61,019	53,793	2,613	51,181	9,384	5,380	761	4,619	4,005	591	3,413
1991: Jan	116,894	63,816	3,010	60,806	53,078	2,820	50,258	7,806	4,337	700	3,637	3,469	634	2,835
Feb	116,896	63,623	3,031	60,592	53,273	2,867	50,406	8,123	4,662	667	3,995	3,461	565	2,896
Mar	116,796	63,589	2,982	60,607	53,207	2,861	50,346	8,462	4,896	731	4,165	3,566	571	2,995
Apr	117,307	63,765	2,890	60,875	53,542	2,892	50,650	8,306	4,785	708	4,077	3,521	595	2,926
May	116,679	63,498	2,905	60,593	53,181	2,772	50,409	8,507	4,842	753	4,089	3,665	560	3,105
June	116,884	63,545	2,860	60,685	53,339	2,762	50,577	8,487	4,880	730	4,150	3,607	541	3,066
July	116,711	63,468	2,804	60,664	53,243	2,645	50,598	8,378	4,915	722	4,193	3,463	587	2,876
Aug	116,522	63,417	2,805	60,612	53,105	2,562	50,543	8,460	4,853	678	4,175	3,607	576	3,031
Sept	117,108	63,703	2,866	60,837	53,405	2,680	50,725	8,479	4,939	699	4,240	3,540	535	3,005
Oct	116,980	63,608	2,832	60,776	53,372	2,707	50,665	8,695	4,899	693	4,206	3,796	633	3,163
Nov	116,932	63,589	2,797	60,792	53,343	2,728	50,615	8,670	4,895	707	4,188	3,775	563	3,212
Dec	116,752	63,398	2,729	60,669	53,354	2,672	50,682	8,984	5,101	720	4,381	3,883	610	3,273
1992: Jan	117,036	63,466	2,802	60,664	53,570	2,681	50,889	8,992	5,174	717	4,457	3,818	564	3,254
Feb	116,962	63,351	2,745	60,606	53,611	2,686	50,925	9,223	5,324	769	4,555	3,899	585	3,314
Mar	117,264	63,547	2,704	60,843	53,717	2,603	51,114	9,284	5,360	767	4,593	3,924	580	3,344
Apr	117,518	63,777	2,744	61,033	53,741	2,605	51,136	9,225	5,266	727	4,539	3,959	561	3,398
May	117,580	63,830	2,743	61,087	53,750	2,646	51,104	9,459	5,497	740	4,757	3,962	598	3,364
June	117,510	63,751	2,724	61,027	53,759	2,526	51,233	9,788	5,666	880	4,786	4,122	673	3,449
July	117,722	63,830	2,760	61,070	53,892	2,585	51,307	9,628	5,485	773	4,712	4,143	616	3,527
Aug	117,780	63,901	2,797	61,104	53,879	2,632	51,247	9,624	5,531	778	4,753	4,093	567	3,526
Sept	117,724	63,937	2,851	61,125	53,748	2,607	51,141	9,550	5,477	797	4,680	4,073	603	3,470
Oct	117,687	63,924	2,836	61,088	53,763	2,581	51,182	9,379	5,410	687	4,723	3,969	573	3,396
Nov	118,064	64,043	2,837	61,206	54,021	2,586	51,435	9,301	5,292	758	4,534	4,009	612	3,397
Dec	118,311	64,194	2,868	61,326	54,117	2,623	51,494	9,280	5,200	741	4,459	4,080	564	3,516

Note.—See footnote 6 and Note, Table B-30.

Source: Department of Labor, Bureau of Labor Statistics.

TABLE B-32.—*Civilian employment by demographic characteristic, 1954–92*

[Thousands of persons 16 years of age and over; monthly data seasonally adjusted]

Year or month	All civilian workers	White				Black and other				Black			
		Total	Males	Fe-males	Both sexes 16–19	Total	Males	Fe-males	Both sexes 16–19	Total	Males	Fe-males	Both sexes 16–19
1954	60,109	53,957	37,846	16,111	3,078	6,152	3,773	2,379	396				
1955	62,170	55,833	38,719	17,114	3,225	6,341	3,904	2,437	418				
1956	63,799	57,269	39,368	17,901	3,389	6,534	4,013	2,521	430				
1957	64,071	57,465	39,349	18,116	3,374	6,604	4,006	2,598	407				
1958	63,036	56,613	38,591	18,022	3,216	6,423	3,833	2,590	365				
1959	64,630	58,006	39,494	18,512	3,475	6,623	3,971	2,652	362				
1960	65,778	58,850	39,755	19,095	3,700	6,928	4,149	2,779	430				
1961	65,746	58,913	39,588	19,325	3,693	6,833	4,068	2,765	414				
1962	66,702	59,698	40,016	19,682	3,774	7,003	4,160	2,843	420				
1963	67,762	60,622	40,428	20,194	3,851	7,140	4,229	2,911	404				
1964	69,305	61,922	41,115	20,807	4,076	7,383	4,359	3,024	440				
1965	71,088	63,446	41,844	21,602	4,562	7,643	4,496	3,147	474				
1966	72,895	65,021	42,331	22,690	5,176	7,877	4,588	3,289	545				
1967	74,372	66,361	42,833	23,528	5,114	8,011	4,646	3,365	568				
1968	75,920	67,750	43,411	24,339	5,195	8,169	4,702	3,467	584				
1969	77,902	69,518	44,048	25,470	5,508	8,384	4,770	3,614	609				
1970	78,678	70,217	44,178	26,039	5,571	8,464	4,813	3,650	574				
1971	79,367	70,878	44,595	26,283	5,670	8,488	4,796	3,692	538				
1972	82,153	73,370	45,944	27,426	6,173	8,783	4,952	3,832	573	7,802	4,368	3,433	509
1973	85,064	75,708	47,085	28,623	6,623	9,356	5,265	4,092	647	8,128	4,527	3,601	570
1974	86,794	77,184	47,674	29,511	6,796	9,610	5,352	4,258	652	8,203	4,527	3,677	554
1975	85,846	76,411	46,697	29,714	6,487	9,435	5,161	4,275	615	7,894	4,275	3,618	507
1976	88,752	78,853	47,775	31,078	6,724	9,899	5,363	4,536	611	8,227	4,404	3,823	508
1977	92,017	81,700	49,150	32,550	7,068	10,317	5,579	4,739	619	8,540	4,565	3,975	508
1978	96,048	84,936	50,544	34,392	7,367	11,112	5,936	5,177	703	9,102	4,796	4,307	571
1979	98,824	87,259	51,452	35,807	7,356	11,565	6,156	5,409	727	9,359	4,923	4,436	579
1980	99,303	87,715	51,127	36,587	7,021	11,588	6,059	5,529	689	9,313	4,798	4,515	547
1981	100,397	88,709	51,315	37,394	6,588	11,688	6,083	5,606	637	9,355	4,794	4,561	505
1982	99,526	87,903	50,287	37,615	5,984	11,624	5,983	5,641	565	9,189	4,637	4,552	428
1983	100,834	88,893	50,621	38,272	5,799	11,941	6,166	5,775	543	9,375	4,753	4,622	416
1984	105,005	92,120	52,462	39,659	5,836	12,885	6,629	6,256	607	10,119	5,124	4,995	474
1985	107,150	93,736	53,046	40,690	5,768	13,414	6,845	6,569	666	10,501	5,270	5,231	532
1986	109,597	95,660	53,785	41,876	5,792	13,937	7,107	6,830	681	10,814	5,428	5,386	536
1987	112,440	97,789	54,647	43,142	5,898	14,652	7,459	7,192	742	11,309	5,661	5,648	587
1988	114,968	99,812	55,550	44,262	6,030	15,156	7,722	7,434	774	11,658	5,824	5,834	601
1989	117,342	101,584	56,352	45,232	5,946	15,757	7,963	7,795	813	11,953	5,928	6,025	625
1990	117,914	102,087	56,432	45,654	5,518	15,827	8,003	7,825	743	11,966	5,915	6,051	573
1991	116,877	101,039	55,557	45,482	4,989	15,838	8,036	7,802	639	11,863	5,880	5,983	474
1992	117,598	101,479	55,709	45,770	4,761	16,119	8,096	8,023	637	11,933	5,846	6,087	474
1991: Jan	116,894	101,108	55,795	45,313	5,193	15,820	8,050	7,770	664	11,886	5,883	6,003	506
Feb	116,896	101,189	55,645	45,544	5,238	15,781	8,031	7,750	657	11,862	5,893	5,969	486
Mar	116,796	100,957	55,525	45,432	5,137	15,848	8,075	7,773	679	11,947	5,943	6,004	505
Apr	117,307	101,398	55,706	45,692	5,115	15,906	8,048	7,858	672	11,957	5,901	6,056	493
May	116,679	100,985	55,576	45,409	5,003	15,696	7,895	7,801	673	11,772	5,749	6,023	499
June	116,884	101,056	55,498	45,558	4,960	15,804	8,010	7,794	656	11,833	5,856	5,977	483
July	116,711	100,828	55,433	45,395	4,795	15,896	8,057	7,839	650	11,893	5,885	6,008	475
Aug	116,522	100,803	55,438	45,365	4,823	15,783	8,004	7,779	578	11,770	5,826	5,944	416
Sept	117,108	101,102	55,585	45,517	4,935	15,968	8,072	7,896	608	11,997	5,936	6,061	469
Oct	116,980	101,163	55,543	45,620	4,936	15,822	8,069	7,753	609	11,796	5,903	5,893	451
Nov	116,932	101,051	55,550	45,501	4,908	15,821	8,065	7,756	630	11,775	5,882	5,893	465
Dec	116,752	100,821	55,352	45,469	4,811	15,912	8,051	7,861	606	11,868	5,889	5,979	449
1992: Jan	117,036	101,172	55,476	45,696	4,856	15,910	8,035	7,875	654	11,860	5,880	5,980	522
Feb	116,962	101,085	55,385	45,700	4,791	15,972	8,045	7,927	649	11,818	5,820	5,998	497
Mar	117,264	101,340	55,523	45,817	4,703	15,943	8,035	7,908	596	11,814	5,808	6,006	463
Apr	117,518	101,479	55,700	45,779	4,749	16,038	8,069	7,969	609	11,857	5,821	6,036	454
May	117,580	101,530	55,724	45,806	4,782	16,049	8,075	7,974	606	11,858	5,819	6,039	450
June	117,510	101,307	55,606	45,701	4,582	16,160	8,090	8,070	637	11,971	5,856	6,115	469
July	117,722	101,558	55,738	45,820	4,691	16,171	8,101	8,070	645	11,979	5,846	6,133	475
Aug	117,780	101,524	55,762	45,762	4,756	16,306	8,147	8,159	700	12,098	5,876	6,222	510
Sept	117,724	101,412	55,800	45,612	4,807	16,253	8,127	8,126	642	12,033	5,859	6,174	469
Oct	117,687	101,458	55,811	45,647	4,788	16,212	8,117	8,095	637	11,984	5,847	6,137	443
Nov	118,064	101,816	55,880	45,936	4,786	16,190	8,178	8,012	632	11,948	5,867	6,081	454
Dec	118,311	102,043	56,062	45,981	4,833	16,214	8,118	8,096	645	11,960	5,838	6,122	482

Note.—See footnote 6 and Note, Table B–30.
Source: Department of Labor, Bureau of Labor Statistics.

TABLE B–33.—*Unemployment by demographic characteristic, 1954–92*

[Thousands of persons 16 years of age and over; monthly data seasonally adjusted]

Year or month	All civilian workers	White				Black and other				Black			
		Total	Males	Fe-males	Both sexes 16–19	Total	Males	Fe-males	Both sexes 16–19	Total	Males	Fe-males	Both sexes 16–19
1954	3,532	2,859	1,913	946	423	673	431	242	79				
1955	2,852	2,252	1,478	774	373	601	376	225	77				
1956	2,750	2,159	1,366	793	382	591	345	246	95				
1957	2,859	2,289	1,477	812	401	570	364	206	96				
1958	4,602	3,680	2,489	1,191	541	923	610	313	138				
1959	3,740	2,946	1,903	1,043	525	793	517	276	128				
1960	3,852	3,065	1,988	1,077	575	788	498	290	138				
1961	4,714	3,743	2,398	1,345	669	971	599	372	159				
1962	3,911	3,052	1,915	1,137	580	861	509	352	142				
1963	4,070	3,208	1,976	1,232	708	863	496	367	176				
1964	3,786	2,999	1,779	1,220	708	787	426	361	165				
1965	3,366	2,691	1,556	1,135	705	678	360	318	171				
1966	2,875	2,255	1,241	1,014	651	622	310	312	186				
1967	2,975	2,338	1,208	1,130	635	638	300	338	203				
1968	2,817	2,226	1,142	1,084	644	590	277	313	194				
1969	2,832	2,260	1,137	1,123	660	571	267	304	193				
1970	4,093	3,339	1,857	1,482	871	754	380	374	235				
1971	5,016	4,085	2,309	1,777	1,011	930	481	450	249				
1972	4,882	3,906	2,173	1,733	1,021	977	486	491	288	906	448	458	279
1973	4,365	3,442	1,836	1,606	955	924	440	484	280	846	395	451	262
1974	5,156	4,097	2,169	1,927	1,104	1,058	544	514	318	965	494	470	297
1975	7,929	6,421	3,627	2,794	1,413	1,507	815	692	355	1,369	741	629	330
1976	7,406	5,914	3,258	2,656	1,364	1,492	779	713	355	1,334	698	637	330
1977	6,991	5,441	2,883	2,558	1,284	1,550	784	766	379	1,393	698	695	354
1978	6,202	4,698	2,411	2,287	1,189	1,505	731	774	394	1,330	641	690	360
1979	6,137	4,664	2,405	2,260	1,193	1,473	714	759	362	1,319	636	683	333
1980	7,637	5,884	3,345	2,540	1,291	1,752	922	830	377	1,553	815	738	343
1981	8,273	6,343	3,580	2,762	1,374	1,930	997	933	388	1,731	891	840	357
1982	10,678	8,241	4,846	3,395	1,534	2,437	1,334	1,104	443	2,142	1,167	975	396
1983	10,717	8,128	4,859	3,270	1,387	2,588	1,401	1,187	441	2,272	1,213	1,059	392
1984	8,539	6,372	3,600	2,772	1,116	2,167	1,144	1,022	384	1,914	1,003	911	353
1985	8,312	6,191	3,426	2,765	1,074	2,121	1,095	1,026	394	1,864	951	913	357
1986	8,237	6,140	3,433	2,708	1,070	2,097	1,097	999	383	1,840	946	894	347
1987	7,425	5,501	3,132	2,369	995	1,924	969	955	353	1,684	826	858	312
1988	6,701	4,944	2,766	2,177	910	1,757	888	869	316	1,547	771	776	288
1989	6,528	4,770	2,636	2,135	863	1,757	889	868	331	1,544	773	772	300
1990	6,874	5,091	2,866	2,225	856	1,783	933	850	292	1,527	793	734	258
1991	8,426	6,447	3,775	2,672	977	1,979	1,043	936	313	1,679	874	805	270
1992	9,384	7,047	4,121	2,926	983	2,337	1,259	1,079	369	1,958	1,046	912	313
1991: Jan	7,806	5,958	3,405	2,553	1,011	1,911	1,000	911	317	1,632	846	786	283
Feb	8,123	6,204	3,645	2,559	909	1,904	1,015	889	319	1,605	850	755	263
Mar	8,462	6,503	3,874	2,629	966	1,978	1,048	930	357	1,675	867	808	312
Apr	8,306	6,288	3,718	2,570	976	1,989	1,065	924	322	1,699	904	795	284
May	8,507	6,488	3,759	2,729	1,027	1,982	1,066	916	288	1,702	904	798	252
June	8,487	6,565	3,802	2,763	989	1,949	1,060	889	265	1,678	908	770	241
July	8,378	6,528	3,905	2,623	1,020	1,866	1,012	854	295	1,592	862	730	250
Aug	8,460	6,454	3,778	2,676	927	1,976	1,041	935	322	1,668	867	801	270
Sept	8,479	6,464	3,892	2,572	913	2,017	1,056	961	331	1,705	893	812	286
Oct	8,695	6,572	3,841	2,731	981	2,101	1,032	1,069	340	1,773	852	921	288
Nov	8,670	6,653	3,870	2,783	978	1,973	1,005	968	286	1,671	835	836	251
Dec	8,984	6,890	3,959	2,931	1,038	2,099	1,116	983	307	1,752	913	839	263
1992: Jan	8,992	6,820	4,032	2,788	938	2,278	1,251	1,027	338	1,882	1,015	867	288
Feb	9,223	6,986	4,129	2,857	1,008	2,240	1,212	1,028	346	1,897	1,021	876	305
Mar	9,284	7,065	4,151	2,914	1,040	2,240	1,230	1,010	321	1,915	1,049	866	276
Apr	9,225	6,933	4,066	2,867	936	2,261	1,190	1,071	348	1,899	990	909	297
May	9,459	7,021	4,204	2,817	961	2,382	1,268	1,114	381	2,011	1,061	950	333
June	9,788	7,364	4,343	3,021	1,140	2,445	1,297	1,148	395	2,030	1,075	955	326
July	9,628	7,225	4,179	3,046	1,003	2,413	1,293	1,120	389	2,016	1,058	958	323
Aug	9,624	7,183	4,186	2,997	970	2,406	1,305	1,101	368	2,008	1,080	928	305
Sept	9,550	7,194	4,204	2,990	1,009	2,342	1,274	1,068	401	1,948	1,065	883	342
Oct	9,379	7,025	4,078	2,947	880	2,326	1,298	1,028	375	1,964	1,075	889	324
Nov	9,301	6,907	4,028	2,879	984	2,343	1,247	1,096	384	1,946	1,025	921	320
Dec	9,280	6,903	3,918	2,985	936	2,378	1,255	1,123	383	1,975	1,043	932	316

Note.—See footnote 6 and Note, Table B–30.

Source: Department of Labor, Bureau of Labor Statistics.

TABLE B-34.—*Civilian labor force participation rate and employment/population ratio, 1948-92*

[Percent;[1] monthly data seasonally adjusted]

Year or month	Labor force participation rate							Employment/population ratio						
	All civilian workers	Males	Females	Both sexes 16–19 years	White	Black and other	Black	All civilian workers	Males	Females	Both sexes 16–19 years	White	Black and other	Black
1948	58.8	86.6	32.7	52.5				56.6	83.5	31.3	47.7			
1949	58.9	86.4	33.1	52.2				55.4	81.3	31.2	45.2			
1950	59.2	86.4	33.9	51.8				56.1	82.0	32.0	45.5			
1951	59.2	86.3	34.6	52.2				57.3	84.0	33.1	47.9			
1952	59.0	86.3	34.7	51.3				57.3	83.9	33.4	46.9			
1953	58.9	86.0	34.4	50.2				57.1	83.6	33.3	46.4			
1954	58.8	85.5	34.6	48.3	58.2	64.0		55.5	81.0	32.5	42.3	55.2	58.0	
1955	59.3	85.4	35.7	48.9	58.7	64.2		56.7	81.8	34.0	43.5	56.5	58.7	
1956	60.0	85.5	36.9	50.9	59.4	64.9		57.5	82.3	35.1	45.3	57.3	59.5	
1957	59.6	84.8	36.9	49.6	59.1	64.4		57.1	81.3	35.1	43.9	56.8	59.3	
1958	59.5	84.2	37.1	47.4	58.9	64.8		55.4	78.5	34.5	39.9	55.3	56.7	
1959	59.3	83.7	37.1	46.7	58.7	64.3		56.0	79.3	35.0	39.9	55.9	57.5	
1960	59.4	83.3	37.7	47.5	58.8	64.5		56.1	78.9	35.5	40.5	55.9	57.9	
1961	59.3	82.9	38.1	46.9	58.8	64.1		55.4	77.6	35.4	39.1	55.3	56.2	
1962	58.8	82.0	37.9	46.1	58.3	63.2		55.5	77.7	35.6	39.4	55.4	56.3	
1963	58.7	81.4	38.3	45.2	58.2	63.0		55.4	77.1	35.8	37.4	55.3	56.2	
1964	58.7	81.0	38.7	44.5	58.2	63.1		55.7	77.3	36.3	37.3	55.5	57.0	
1965	58.9	80.7	39.3	45.7	58.4	62.9		56.2	77.5	37.1	38.9	56.0	57.8	
1966	59.2	80.4	40.3	48.2	58.7	63.0		56.9	77.9	38.3	42.1	56.8	58.4	
1967	59.6	80.4	41.1	48.4	59.2	62.8		57.3	78.0	39.0	42.2	57.2	58.2	
1968	59.6	80.1	41.6	48.3	59.3	62.2		57.5	77.8	39.6	42.2	57.4	58.0	
1969	60.1	79.8	42.7	49.4	59.9	62.1		58.0	77.6	40.7	43.4	58.0	58.1	
1970	60.4	79.7	43.3	49.9	60.2	61.8		57.4	76.2	40.8	42.3	57.5	56.8	
1971	60.2	79.1	43.4	49.7	60.1	60.9		56.6	74.9	40.4	41.3	56.8	54.9	
1972	60.4	78.9	43.9	51.9	60.4	60.2	59.9	57.0	75.0	41.0	43.5	57.4	54.1	53.7
1973	60.8	78.8	44.7	53.7	60.8	60.5	60.2	57.8	75.5	42.0	45.9	58.2	55.0	54.5
1974	61.3	78.7	45.7	54.8	61.4	60.3	59.8	57.8	74.9	42.6	46.0	58.3	54.3	53.5
1975	61.2	77.9	46.3	54.0	61.5	59.6	58.8	56.1	71.7	42.0	43.3	56.7	51.4	50.1
1976	61.6	77.5	47.3	54.5	61.8	59.8	59.0	56.8	72.0	43.2	44.2	57.5	52.0	50.8
1977	62.3	77.7	48.4	56.0	62.5	60.4	59.8	57.9	72.8	44.5	46.1	58.6	52.5	51.4
1978	63.2	77.9	50.0	57.8	63.3	62.2	61.5	59.3	73.8	46.4	48.3	60.0	54.7	53.6
1979	63.7	77.8	50.9	57.9	63.9	62.2	61.4	59.9	73.8	47.5	48.5	60.6	55.2	53.8
1980	63.8	77.4	51.5	56.7	64.1	61.7	61.0	59.2	72.0	47.7	46.6	60.0	53.6	52.3
1981	63.9	77.0	52.1	55.4	64.3	61.3	60.8	59.0	71.3	48.0	44.6	60.0	52.6	51.3
1982	64.0	76.6	52.6	54.1	64.3	61.6	61.0	57.8	69.0	47.7	41.5	58.8	50.9	49.4
1983	64.0	76.4	52.9	53.5	64.3	62.1	61.5	57.9	68.8	48.0	41.5	58.9	51.0	49.5
1984	64.4	76.4	53.6	53.9	64.6	62.6	62.2	59.5	70.7	49.5	43.7	60.5	53.6	52.3
1985	64.8	76.3	54.5	54.5	65.0	63.3	62.9	60.1	70.9	50.4	44.4	61.0	54.7	53.4
1986	65.3	76.3	55.3	54.7	65.5	63.7	63.3	60.7	71.0	51.4	44.6	61.5	55.4	54.1
1987	65.6	76.2	56.0	54.7	65.8	64.3	63.8	61.5	71.5	52.5	45.5	62.3	56.8	55.6
1988	65.9	76.2	56.6	55.3	66.2	64.0	63.8	62.3	72.0	53.4	46.8	63.1	57.4	56.3
1989	66.5	76.4	57.4	55.9	66.7	64.7	64.2	63.0	72.5	54.3	47.5	63.8	58.2	56.9
1990	66.4	76.1	57.5	53.7	66.8	63.7	63.3	62.7	71.9	54.3	45.4	63.6	57.3	56.2
1991	66.0	75.5	57.3	51.8	66.6	63.1	62.6	61.6	70.2	53.7	42.1	62.6	56.1	54.9
1992	66.3	75.6	57.8	51.3	66.7	63.8	63.3	61.4	69.7	53.8	41.0	62.4	55.7	54.3
1991: Jan	66.0	75.6	57.2	52.8	66.5	63.4	63.0	61.9	70.8	53.7	43.0	62.8	56.6	55.4
Feb	66.1	75.7	57.4	52.7	66.7	63.1	62.7	61.8	70.5	53.9	43.6	62.8	56.3	55.2
Mar	66.2	75.9	57.4	52.9	66.7	63.5	63.3	61.7	70.4	53.8	43.3	62.6	56.5	55.5
Apr	66.3	75.9	57.6	52.7	66.8	63.6	63.4	61.9	70.6	54.1	43.0	62.9	56.6	55.5
May	66.1	75.6	57.4	52.0	66.6	62.8	62.5	61.6	70.2	53.7	42.3	62.6	55.7	54.6
Jun	66.1	75.6	57.4	51.5	66.7	62.9	62.6	61.6	70.2	53.8	42.0	62.6	56.0	54.8
Jul	65.9	75.5	57.1	50.7	66.5	62.8	62.3	61.5	70.1	53.6	40.9	62.4	56.2	55.0
Aug	65.8	75.3	57.1	49.7	66.4	62.7	62.1	61.3	70.0	53.5	40.3	62.4	55.7	54.4
Sep	66.1	75.7	57.3	51.0	66.5	63.4	63.2	61.6	70.2	53.7	41.7	62.5	56.3	55.3
Oct	66.0	75.4	57.5	51.8	66.6	63.0	62.5	61.5	70.0	53.7	41.8	62.5	55.6	54.3
Nov	65.9	75.3	57.4	51.3	66.5	62.4	61.8	61.4	69.9	53.6	41.7	62.4	55.5	54.2
Dec	66.0	75.3	57.5	51.0	66.5	63.1	62.6	61.3	69.7	53.6	40.9	62.2	55.7	54.5
1992: Jan	66.1	75.4	57.6	51.4	66.6	63.6	63.0	61.4	69.7	53.8	41.6	62.4	55.6	54.4
Feb	66.1	75.3	57.7	51.7	66.6	63.5	62.8	61.3	69.5	53.8	41.4	62.4	56.3	54.1
Mar	66.2	75.5	57.8	50.5	66.8	63.3	62.8	61.4	69.6	53.8	40.3	62.4	55.5	54.1
Apr	66.3	75.6	57.8	50.4	66.8	63.6	62.9	61.5	69.8	53.8	40.6	62.5	55.7	54.2
May	66.4	75.9	57.8	51.9	66.8	63.9	63.3	61.5	69.8	53.8	41.0	62.5	55.7	54.1
Jun	66.5	75.9	57.9	51.8	66.8	64.4	63.8	61.4	69.7	53.8	40.0	62.3	56.0	54.6
Jul	66.5	75.7	58.0	51.3	66.9	64.2	63.7	61.4	69.7	53.9	40.8	62.4	55.9	54.5
Aug	66.4	75.8	57.9	51.3	66.8	64.5	64.1	61.4	69.7	53.8	41.3	62.3	55.9	55.0
Sep	66.3	75.7	57.7	52.1	66.7	64.0	63.5	61.3	69.7	53.6	41.4	62.3	55.9	54.6
Oct	66.1	75.5	57.6	50.6	66.5	63.7	63.2	61.3	69.6	53.6	41.0	62.2	55.7	54.3
Nov	66.2	75.4	57.8	51.4	66.6	63.5	63.0	61.3	69.6	53.6	41.1	62.4	55.5	54.1
Dec	66.3	75.4	57.9	51.6	66.7	63.6	63.0	61.5	69.7	53.9	41.7	62.5	55.4	54.0

[1] Civilian labor force or civilian employment as percent of civilian noninstitutional population in group specified.

Note.—Data relate to persons 16 years of age and over.

See footnote 6 and Note, Table B-30.

Source: Department of Labor, Bureau of Labor Statistics.

TABLE B-35.—*Civilian labor force participation rate by demographic characteristic, 1954-92*

[Percent;[1] monthly data seasonally adjusted]

Year or month	All civil- ian work- ers	White							Black and other or black						
		Total	Males			Females			Total	Males			Females		
			Total	16–19 years	20 years and over	Total	16–19 years	20 years and over		Total	16–19 years	20 years and over	Total	16–19 years	20 years and over
											Black and other				
1954	58.8	58.2	85.6	57.6	87.8	33.3	40.6	32.7	64.0	85.2	61.2	87.1	46.1	31.0	47.7
1955	59.3	58.7	85.4	58.6	87.5	34.5	40.7	34.0	64.2	85.1	60.8	87.8	46.1	32.7	47.5
1956	60.0	59.4	85.6	60.4	87.6	35.7	43.1	35.1	64.9	85.1	61.5	87.8	47.3	36.3	48.4
1957	59.6	59.1	84.8	59.2	86.9	35.7	42.2	35.2	64.4	84.2	58.8	87.0	47.1	33.2	48.6
1958	59.5	58.9	84.3	56.5	86.6	35.8	40.1	35.5	64.8	84.1	57.3	87.1	48.0	31.9	49.8
1959	59.3	58.7	83.8	55.9	86.3	36.0	39.6	35.6	64.3	83.4	55.5	86.7	47.7	28.2	49.8
1960	59.4	58.8	83.4	55.9	86.0	36.5	40.3	36.2	64.5	83.0	57.6	86.2	48.2	32.9	49.9
1961	59.3	58.8	83.0	54.5	85.7	36.9	40.6	36.6	64.1	82.2	55.8	85.5	48.3	32.8	50.1
1962	58.8	58.3	82.1	53.8	84.9	36.7	39.8	36.5	63.2	80.8	53.5	84.2	48.0	33.1	49.6
1963	58.7	58.2	81.5	53.1	84.4	37.2	38.7	37.0	63.0	80.2	51.5	83.9	48.1	32.6	49.9
1964	58.7	58.2	81.1	52.7	84.2	37.5	37.8	37.5	63.1	80.1	49.9	84.1	48.6	31.7	50.7
1965	58.9	58.4	80.8	54.1	83.9	38.1	39.2	38.0	62.9	79.6	51.3	83.7	48.6	29.5	51.1
1966	59.2	58.7	80.6	55.9	83.6	39.2	42.6	38.8	63.0	79.0	51.4	83.3	49.4	33.5	51.6
1967	59.6	59.2	80.6	56.3	83.5	40.1	42.5	39.8	62.8	78.5	51.1	82.9	49.5	35.2	51.6
1968	59.6	59.3	80.4	55.9	83.2	40.7	43.0	40.4	62.2	77.7	49.7	82.2	49.3	34.8	51.4
1969	60.1	59.9	80.2	56.8	83.0	41.8	44.6	41.5	62.1	76.9	49.6	81.4	49.8	34.6	52.0
1970	60.4	60.2	80.0	57.5	82.8	42.6	45.6	42.2	61.8	76.5	47.4	81.4	49.5	34.1	51.8
1971	60.2	60.1	79.6	57.9	82.3	42.6	45.4	42.3	60.9	74.9	44.7	80.0	49.2	31.2	51.8
1972	60.4	60.4	79.6	60.1	82.0	43.2	48.1	42.7	60.2	73.9	46.0	78.6	48.8	32.3	51.2
											Black				
1972	60.4	60.4	79.6	60.1	82.0	43.2	48.1	42.7	59.9	73.6	46.3	78.5	48.7	32.2	51.2
1973	60.8	60.8	79.4	62.0	81.6	44.1	50.1	43.5	60.2	73.4	45.7	78.4	49.3	34.2	51.6
1974	61.3	61.4	79.4	62.9	81.4	45.2	51.7	44.4	59.8	72.9	46.7	77.6	49.0	33.4	51.4
1975	61.2	61.5	78.7	61.9	80.7	45.9	51.5	45.3	58.8	70.9	42.6	76.0	48.8	34.2	51.1
1976	61.6	61.8	78.4	62.3	80.3	46.9	52.8	46.2	59.0	70.0	41.3	75.4	49.8	32.9	52.5
1977	62.3	62.5	78.5	64.0	80.2	48.0	54.5	47.3	59.8	70.6	43.2	75.6	50.8	32.9	53.6
1978	63.2	63.3	78.6	65.0	80.1	49.4	56.7	48.7	61.5	71.5	44.9	76.2	53.1	37.3	55.5
1979	63.7	63.9	78.6	64.8	80.1	50.5	57.4	49.8	61.4	71.3	43.6	76.3	53.1	36.8	55.4
1980	63.8	64.1	78.2	63.7	79.8	51.2	56.2	50.6	61.0	70.3	43.2	75.1	53.1	34.9	55.6
1981	63.9	64.3	77.9	62.4	79.5	51.9	55.4	51.5	60.8	70.0	41.6	74.5	53.5	34.0	56.0
1982	64.0	64.3	77.4	60.0	79.2	52.4	55.0	52.2	61.0	70.1	39.8	74.7	53.7	33.5	56.2
1983	64.0	64.3	77.1	59.4	78.9	52.7	54.5	52.5	61.5	70.6	39.9	75.2	54.2	33.0	56.8
1984	64.4	64.6	77.1	59.0	78.7	53.3	55.4	53.1	62.2	70.8	41.7	74.8	55.2	35.0	57.6
1985	64.8	65.0	77.0	59.7	78.5	54.1	55.2	54.0	62.9	70.8	44.6	74.4	56.5	37.9	58.6
1986	65.3	65.5	76.9	59.3	78.5	55.0	56.3	54.9	63.3	71.2	43.7	74.8	56.9	39.1	58.9
1987	65.6	65.8	76.8	59.0	78.4	55.7	56.5	55.6	63.8	71.1	43.6	74.7	58.0	39.6	60.0
1988	65.9	66.2	76.9	60.0	78.3	56.4	57.2	56.3	63.8	71.0	43.8	74.6	58.0	37.9	60.1
1989	66.5	66.7	77.1	61.0	78.5	57.2	57.1	57.2	64.2	71.0	44.6	74.4	58.7	40.4	60.6
1990	66.4	66.8	76.9	59.4	78.3	57.5	55.4	57.6	63.3	70.1	40.6	73.8	57.8	36.7	60.0
1991	66.0	66.6	76.4	57.2	77.8	57.4	54.3	57.7	62.6	69.5	37.4	73.4	57.0	33.5	59.3
1992	66.3	66.7	76.4	56.7	77.8	57.8	52.6	58.1	63.3	69.7	40.7	73.1	58.0	35.2	60.1
1991: Jan	66.0	66.5	76.5	58.7	77.8	57.3	55.4	57.4	63.0	69.8	36.8	73.8	57.4	37.6	59.4
Feb	66.1	66.7	76.5	58.6	77.9	57.5	55.0	57.7	62.7	69.8	35.2	74.0	56.8	35.7	58.9
Mar	66.2	66.7	76.6	58.7	78.0	57.4	54.4	57.6	63.3	70.4	39.4	74.2	57.5	38.2	59.4
Apr	66.3	66.8	76.6	56.8	78.1	57.7	56.6	57.7	63.4	70.3	39.2	74.0	57.8	34.9	60.0
May	66.1	66.6	76.5	58.1	77.8	57.5	54.3	57.7	62.5	68.6	36.9	72.6	57.4	33.7	59.8
June	66.1	66.7	76.4	57.0	77.8	57.7	54.3	57.9	62.6	69.7	38.0	73.5	56.7	30.8	59.3
July	65.9	66.5	76.4	56.7	77.8	57.3	52.4	57.6	62.3	69.4	35.6	73.4	56.6	33.5	58.8
Aug	65.8	66.4	76.2	55.7	77.7	57.3	52.2	57.6	62.1	68.7	36.7	72.6	56.6	28.9	59.3
Sept	66.1	66.5	76.4	56.7	77.9	57.3	53.3	57.6	63.2	70.0	41.1	73.5	57.6	31.3	60.1
Oct	66.0	66.6	76.3	56.8	77.7	57.6	54.7	57.8	62.5	69.2	37.2	73.0	57.0	33.7	59.3
Nov	65.9	66.5	76.2	56.7	77.7	57.5	54.3	57.7	61.8	68.7	36.3	72.5	56.3	32.4	58.5
Dec	66.0	66.5	76.0	56.1	77.5	57.6	54.4	57.8	62.6	69.4	37.2	73.2	56.9	31.3	59.4
1992: Jan	66.1	66.6	76.2	56.7	77.7	57.7	53.0	58.0	63.0	70.3	43.8	73.4	57.1	34.2	59.3
Feb	66.1	66.6	76.2	56.5	77.7	57.7	53.5	58.0	62.8	69.6	42.2	72.8	57.3	35.1	59.4
Mar	66.2	66.8	76.4	56.2	77.8	57.9	52.8	58.2	62.8	69.7	39.5	73.2	57.2	31.7	59.6
Apr	66.3	66.8	76.4	56.2	77.9	57.8	52.0	58.2	62.9	69.1	37.6	72.8	57.7	34.8	59.9
May	66.4	66.8	76.6	56.2	78.1	57.7	53.2	58.0	63.3	69.8	38.2	73.4	58.0	37.4	60.0
June	66.5	66.8	76.6	57.1	78.0	57.8	52.1	58.2	63.8	70.2	40.8	73.6	58.6	36.1	60.8
July	66.5	66.9	76.5	56.5	77.9	58.0	52.3	58.3	63.7	69.8	41.2	73.1	58.7	36.0	60.9
Aug	66.4	66.8	76.4	56.9	77.9	57.8	52.3	58.2	64.1	70.2	41.0	73.6	59.1	37.7	61.2
Sept	66.3	66.7	76.5	58.4	77.8	57.6	52.4	57.9	63.5	69.8	41.6	73.1	58.3	36.6	60.3
Oct	66.1	66.5	76.2	56.0	77.7	57.5	51.9	57.9	63.2	69.6	41.0	73.0	58.0	33.0	60.3
Nov	66.2	66.6	76.2	57.2	77.6	57.8	52.5	58.1	62.9	69.2	39.7	72.6	57.7	34.7	59.9
Dec	66.3	66.7	76.2	57.1	77.6	57.9	52.6	58.3	63.0	69.0	41.6	72.1	58.0	35.1	60.2

[1] Civilian labor force as percent of civilian noninstitutional population in group specified.

Note.—Data relate to persons 16 years of age and over.

See footnote 6 and Note, Table B-30.

Source: Department of Labor, Bureau of Labor Statistics.

TABLE B-36.—*Civilian employment/population ratio by demographic characteristic, 1954–92*

[Percent;[1] monthly data seasonally adjusted]

Year or month	All civilian workers	White Total	White Males Total	White Males 16–19 years	White Males 20 years and over	White Females Total	White Females 16–19 years	White Females 20 years and over	Black and other or black Total	Black Males Total	Black Males 16–19 years	Black Males 20 years and over	Black Females Total	Black Females 16–19 years	Black Females 20 years and over
											Black and other				
1954	55.5	55.2	81.5	49.9	84.0	31.4	36.4	31.1	58.0	76.5	52.4	79.2	41.9	24.7	43.7
1955	56.7	56.5	82.2	52.0	84.7	33.0	37.0	32.7	58.7	77.6	52.7	80.4	42.2	26.4	43.9
1956	57.5	57.3	82.7	54.1	85.0	34.2	38.9	33.8	59.5	78.4	52.2	81.3	43.0	28.0	44.7
1957	57.1	56.8	81.8	52.4	84.1	34.2	38.2	33.9	59.3	77.2	48.0	80.5	43.7	26.5	45.5
1958	55.4	55.3	79.2	47.6	81.8	33.6	35.0	33.5	56.7	72.5	42.0	76.0	42.8	22.8	45.6
1959	56.0	55.9	79.9	48.1	82.8	34.0	34.8	34.0	57.5	73.8	41.4	77.6	43.2	20.3	45.7
1960	56.1	55.9	79.4	48.1	82.4	34.6	35.1	34.5	57.9	74.1	43.8	77.9	43.6	24.8	45.8
1961	55.4	55.3	78.2	45.9	81.4	34.5	34.6	34.5	56.2	71.7	41.0	75.5	42.6	23.2	44.8
1962	55.5	55.4	78.4	46.4	81.5	34.7	34.8	34.7	56.3	72.0	41.7	75.7	42.7	23.1	44.9
1963	55.4	55.3	77.7	44.7	81.1	35.0	32.9	35.2	56.2	71.8	37.4	76.2	42.7	21.3	45.2
1964	55.7	55.5	77.8	45.0	81.3	35.5	32.2	35.8	57.0	72.9	37.8	77.7	43.4	21.8	46.1
1965	56.2	56.0	77.9	47.1	81.5	36.2	33.7	36.5	57.8	73.7	39.4	78.7	44.1	20.2	47.3
1966	56.9	56.8	78.3	50.1	81.7	37.5	37.5	37.5	58.4	74.0	40.5	79.2	45.1	23.1	48.2
1967	57.3	57.2	78.4	50.2	81.7	38.3	37.7	38.3	58.2	73.8	38.8	79.4	45.0	24.8	47.9
1968	57.5	57.4	78.3	50.3	81.6	38.9	37.8	39.1	58.0	73.3	38.7	78.9	45.2	24.7	48.2
1969	58.0	58.0	78.2	51.1	81.4	40.1	39.5	40.1	58.1	72.8	39.0	78.4	45.9	25.1	48.9
1970	57.4	57.5	76.8	49.6	80.1	40.3	39.5	40.4	56.8	70.9	35.5	76.8	44.9	22.4	48.2
1971	56.6	56.8	75.7	49.2	79.0	39.9	38.6	40.1	54.9	68.1	31.8	74.2	43.9	20.2	47.3
1972	57.0	57.4	76.0	51.5	79.0	40.7	41.3	40.6	54.1	67.3	32.4	73.2	43.3	19.9	46.7
											Black				
1972	57.0	57.4	76.0	51.5	79.0	40.7	41.3	40.6	53.7	66.8	31.6	73.0	43.0	19.2	46.5
1973	57.8	58.2	76.5	54.3	79.2	41.8	43.6	41.6	54.5	67.5	32.8	73.7	43.8	22.0	47.2
1974	57.8	58.3	75.9	54.4	78.6	42.4	44.3	42.2	53.5	65.8	31.4	71.9	43.5	20.9	46.9
1975	56.1	56.7	73.0	50.6	75.7	42.0	42.5	41.9	50.1	60.6	26.3	66.5	41.6	20.2	44.9
1976	56.8	57.5	73.4	51.5	76.0	43.2	44.2	43.1	50.8	60.6	25.8	66.8	42.8	19.2	46.4
1977	57.9	58.6	74.1	54.4	76.5	44.5	45.9	44.4	51.4	61.4	26.4	67.5	43.3	18.5	47.0
1978	59.3	60.0	75.0	56.3	77.2	46.3	48.5	46.1	53.6	63.3	28.5	69.1	45.8	22.1	49.3
1979	59.9	60.6	75.1	55.7	77.3	47.5	49.4	47.3	53.8	63.4	28.7	69.1	46.0	22.4	49.3
1980	59.2	60.0	73.4	53.4	75.6	47.8	47.9	47.8	52.3	60.4	27.0	65.8	45.7	21.0	49.1
1981	59.0	60.0	72.8	51.3	75.1	48.3	46.2	48.5	51.3	59.1	24.6	64.5	45.1	19.7	48.5
1982	57.8	58.8	70.6	47.0	73.0	48.1	44.6	48.4	49.4	56.0	20.3	61.4	44.2	17.7	47.5
1983	57.9	58.9	70.4	47.4	72.8	48.5	44.5	48.9	49.5	56.3	20.4	61.6	44.1	17.0	47.4
1984	59.5	60.5	72.1	49.1	74.3	49.8	47.0	50.0	52.3	59.2	23.9	64.1	46.7	20.1	49.8
1985	60.1	61.0	72.3	49.9	74.3	50.7	47.1	51.0	53.4	60.0	26.3	64.6	48.1	23.1	50.9
1986	60.7	61.5	72.3	49.6	74.3	51.7	47.9	52.0	54.1	60.6	26.5	65.1	48.8	23.8	51.6
1987	61.5	62.3	72.7	49.9	74.7	52.8	49.0	53.1	55.6	62.0	28.5	66.4	50.3	25.8	53.0
1988	62.3	63.1	73.2	51.7	75.1	53.8	50.2	54.0	56.3	62.7	29.4	67.1	51.2	25.8	53.9
1989	63.0	63.8	73.7	52.6	75.4	54.6	50.5	54.9	56.9	62.8	30.4	67.0	52.0	27.1	54.6
1990	62.7	63.6	73.2	51.0	75.0	54.8	48.5	55.2	56.2	61.8	27.6	66.1	51.6	25.7	54.2
1991	61.6	62.6	71.5	47.2	73.3	54.3	46.1	54.8	54.9	60.5	23.8	64.9	50.3	21.4	53.1
1992	61.4	62.4	71.1	46.3	72.9	54.3	44.3	54.9	54.3	59.1	23.6	63.3	50.4	22.1	53.1
1991: Jan	61.9	62.8	72.1	48.9	73.8	54.2	46.6	54.7	55.4	61.0	23.8	65.5	50.8	23.9	53.5
Feb	61.8	62.8	71.8	49.3	73.5	54.5	47.5	54.9	55.2	61.0	22.7	65.7	50.4	23.3	53.1
Mar	61.7	62.7	71.6	48.3	73.4	54.3	47.0	54.8	55.5	61.5	24.3	65.9	50.7	23.7	53.3
Apr	61.9	62.9	71.8	47.0	73.7	54.6	48.2	55.0	55.5	61.0	24.7	65.3	51.0	22.3	53.9
May	61.6	62.6	71.6	47.3	73.4	54.2	46.0	54.8	54.6	59.3	23.6	63.7	50.7	23.3	53.4
June	61.6	62.6	71.5	46.5	73.3	54.4	46.3	54.9	54.8	60.3	24.8	64.6	50.3	21.1	53.1
July	61.5	62.4	71.3	45.9	73.2	54.1	44.0	54.8	55.0	60.5	23.7	64.9	50.5	21.6	53.3
Aug	61.3	62.4	71.3	46.5	73.1	54.1	44.1	54.7	54.4	59.8	23.2	64.2	49.9	16.6	53.1
Sept	61.6	62.5	71.4	47.2	73.2	54.2	45.6	54.8	55.3	60.9	24.4	65.2	50.8	20.5	53.7
Oct	61.5	62.5	71.3	47.0	73.1	54.3	46.0	54.9	54.3	60.4	23.7	64.8	49.3	19.6	52.2
Nov	61.4	62.4	71.3	46.7	73.1	54.2	46.0	54.7	54.2	60.1	23.0	64.5	49.3	21.6	51.9
Dec	61.3	62.2	71.0	45.8	72.8	54.1	45.2	54.7	54.5	60.1	23.4	64.4	49.9	19.8	52.8
1992: Jan	61.4	62.4	71.1	46.8	72.9	54.3	45.1	55.0	54.4	59.9	28.0	63.7	49.9	22.2	52.5
Feb	61.3	62.3	70.9	45.7	72.8	54.3	45.1	54.9	54.1	59.2	25.9	63.1	50.0	22.1	52.6
Mar	61.4	62.4	71.0	44.9	73.0	54.4	44.4	55.1	54.1	59.0	24.4	63.1	50.0	20.3	52.8
Apr	61.5	62.5	71.2	46.2	73.1	54.4	44.2	55.0	54.2	59.1	21.4	63.5	50.2	22.4	52.8
May	61.5	62.5	71.2	45.8	73.1	54.4	45.3	55.0	54.1	59.0	21.8	63.3	50.1	21.7	52.8
June	61.4	62.3	71.0	45.0	72.9	54.2	42.5	55.0	54.6	59.3	22.4	63.6	50.7	22.9	53.3
July	61.4	62.4	71.1	45.9	73.0	54.3	43.8	55.0	54.5	59.1	23.8	63.2	50.8	22.2	53.5
Aug	61.4	62.4	71.1	46.4	72.9	54.2	44.4	54.9	55.0	59.3	23.5	63.5	51.5	25.7	53.9
Sept	61.3	62.3	71.1	47.4	72.8	54.0	44.2	54.7	54.6	59.1	23.2	63.2	51.0	22.1	53.7
Oct	61.3	62.2	71.0	47.1	72.8	54.0	44.1	54.7	54.3	58.8	22.9	63.0	50.6	19.8	53.5
Nov	61.4	62.4	71.1	47.1	72.8	54.4	43.9	55.0	54.1	58.9	22.0	63.2	50.1	21.7	52.8
Dec	61.5	62.5	71.2	47.2	73.0	54.4	44.6	55.0	54.0	58.5	24.0	62.5	50.4	22.3	53.0

[1] Civilian employment as percent of civilian noninstitutional population in group specified.

Note.—Data relate to persons 16 years of age and over.
See footnote 6 and Note, Table B–30.

Source: Department of Labor, Bureau of Labor Statistics.

[Percent;[1] monthly data seasonally adjusted]

Year or month	All civilian workers	Males Total	Males 16–19 years	Males 20 years and over	Females Total	Females 16–19 years	Females 20 years and over	Both sexes 16–19 years	White	Black and other	Black	Experienced wage and salary workers	Married men, spouse present[2]	Women who maintain families
1948	3.8	3.6	9.8	3.2	4.1	8.3	3.6	9.2	3.5	5.9		4.3		
1949	5.9	5.9	14.3	5.4	6.0	12.3	5.3	13.4	5.6	8.9		6.8	3.5	
1950	5.3	5.1	12.7	4.7	5.7	11.4	5.1	12.2	4.9	9.0		6.0	4.6	
1951	3.3	2.8	8.1	2.5	4.4	8.3	4.0	8.2	3.1	5.3		3.7	1.5	
1952	3.0	2.8	8.9	2.4	3.6	8.0	3.2	8.5	2.8	5.4		3.4	1.4	
1953	2.9	2.8	7.9	2.5	3.3	7.2	2.9	7.6	2.7	4.5		3.2	1.7	
1954	5.5	5.3	13.5	4.9	6.0	11.4	5.5	12.6	5.0	9.9		6.2	4.0	
1955	4.4	4.2	11.6	3.8	4.9	10.2	4.4	11.0	3.9	8.7		4.8	2.6	
1956	4.1	3.8	11.1	3.4	4.8	11.2	4.2	11.1	3.6	8.3		4.4	2.3	
1957	4.3	4.1	12.4	3.6	4.7	10.6	4.1	11.6	3.8	7.9		4.6	2.8	
1958	6.8	6.8	17.1	6.2	6.8	14.3	6.1	15.9	6.1	12.6		7.3	5.1	
1959	5.5	5.2	15.3	4.7	5.9	13.5	5.2	14.6	4.8	10.7		5.7	3.6	
1960	5.5	5.4	15.3	4.7	5.9	13.9	5.1	14.7	5.0	10.2		5.7	3.7	
1961	6.7	6.4	17.1	5.7	7.2	16.3	6.3	16.8	6.0	12.4		6.8	4.6	
1962	5.5	5.2	14.7	4.6	6.2	14.6	5.4	14.7	4.9	10.9		5.6	3.6	
1963	5.7	5.2	17.2	4.5	6.5	17.2	5.4	17.2	5.0	10.8		5.6	3.4	
1964	5.2	4.6	15.8	3.9	6.2	16.6	5.2	16.2	4.6	9.6		5.0	2.8	
1965	4.5	4.0	14.1	3.2	5.5	15.7	4.5	14.8	4.1	8.1		4.3	2.4	
1966	3.8	3.2	11.7	2.5	4.8	14.1	3.8	12.8	3.4	7.3		3.5	1.9	
1967	3.8	3.1	12.3	2.3	5.2	13.5	4.2	12.9	3.4	7.4		3.6	1.8	4.9
1968	3.6	2.9	11.6	2.2	4.8	14.0	3.8	12.7	3.2	6.7		3.4	1.6	4.4
1969	3.5	2.8	11.4	2.1	4.7	13.3	3.7	12.2	3.1	6.4		3.3	1.5	4.4
1970	4.9	4.4	15.0	3.5	5.9	15.6	4.8	15.3	4.5	8.2		4.8	2.6	5.4
1971	5.9	5.3	16.6	4.4	6.9	17.2	5.7	16.9	5.4	9.9		5.7	3.2	7.3
1972	5.6	5.0	15.9	4.0	6.6	16.7	5.4	16.2	5.1	10.0	10.4	5.3	2.8	7.2
1973	4.9	4.2	13.9	3.3	6.0	15.3	4.9	14.5	4.3	9.0	9.4	4.5	2.3	7.1
1974	5.6	4.9	15.6	3.8	6.7	16.6	5.5	16.0	5.0	9.9	10.5	5.3	2.7	7.0
1975	8.5	7.9	20.1	6.8	9.3	19.7	8.0	19.9	7.8	13.8	14.8	8.2	5.1	10.0
1976	7.7	7.1	19.2	5.9	8.6	18.7	7.4	19.0	7.0	13.1	14.0	7.3	4.2	10.1
1977	7.1	6.3	17.3	5.2	8.2	18.3	7.0	17.8	6.2	13.1	14.0	6.6	3.6	9.4
1978	6.1	5.3	15.8	4.3	7.2	17.1	6.0	16.4	5.2	11.9	12.8	5.6	2.8	8.5
1979	5.8	5.1	15.9	4.2	6.8	16.4	5.7	16.1	5.1	11.3	12.3	5.5	2.8	8.3
1980	7.1	6.9	18.3	5.9	7.4	17.2	6.4	17.8	6.3	13.1	14.3	6.9	4.2	9.2
1981	7.6	7.4	20.1	6.3	7.9	19.0	6.8	19.6	6.7	14.2	15.6	7.3	4.3	10.4
1982	9.7	9.9	24.4	8.8	9.4	21.9	8.3	23.2	8.6	17.3	18.9	9.3	6.5	11.7
1983	9.6	9.9	23.3	8.9	9.2	21.3	8.1	22.4	8.4	17.8	19.5	9.2	6.5	12.2
1984	7.5	7.4	19.6	6.6	7.6	18.0	6.8	18.9	6.5	14.4	15.9	7.1	4.6	10.3
1985	7.2	7.0	19.5	6.2	7.4	17.6	6.6	18.6	6.2	13.7	15.1	6.8	4.3	10.4
1986	7.0	6.9	19.0	6.1	7.1	17.6	6.2	18.3	6.0	13.1	14.5	6.6	4.4	9.8
1987	6.2	6.2	17.8	5.4	6.2	15.9	5.4	16.9	5.3	11.6	13.0	5.8	3.9	9.2
1988	5.5	5.5	16.0	4.8	5.6	14.4	4.9	15.3	4.7	10.4	11.7	5.2	3.3	8.1
1989	5.3	5.2	15.9	4.5	5.4	14.0	4.7	15.0	4.5	10.0	11.4	5.0	3.0	8.1
1990	5.5	5.6	16.3	4.9	5.4	14.7	4.8	15.5	4.7	10.1	11.3	5.3	3.4	8.2
1991	6.7	7.0	19.8	6.3	6.3	17.4	5.7	18.6	6.0	11.1	12.4	6.5	4.4	9.1
1992	7.4	7.8	21.5	7.0	6.9	18.5	6.3	20.0	6.5	12.7	14.1	7.1	5.0	9.9
1991: Jan	6.3	6.4	18.9	5.6	6.1	18.4	5.3	18.6	5.6	10.8	12.1	6.0	4.1	9.2
Feb	6.5	6.8	18.0	6.2	6.1	16.5	5.4	17.3	5.8	10.8	11.9	6.3	4.2	9.1
Mar	6.8	7.1	19.7	6.4	6.3	16.6	5.6	18.2	6.1	11.1	12.3	6.6	4.5	9.0
Apr	6.6	7.0	19.7	6.3	6.2	17.1	5.5	18.4	5.8	11.1	12.4	6.4	4.4	9.5
May	6.8	7.1	20.6	6.3	6.4	16.8	5.8	18.8	6.0	11.2	12.6	6.5	4.4	9.2
June	6.8	7.1	20.3	6.4	6.3	16.4	5.7	18.4	6.1	11.0	12.4	6.5	4.4	9.1
July	6.7	7.2	20.5	6.5	6.1	18.2	5.4	19.4	6.1	10.5	11.8	6.5	4.3	8.3
Aug	6.8	7.1	19.5	6.4	6.4	18.4	5.7	18.9	6.0	11.1	12.4	6.5	4.3	9.3
Sept	6.8	7.2	19.6	6.5	6.2	16.6	5.6	18.2	6.0	11.2	12.4	6.5	4.5	9.1
Oct	6.9	7.2	19.7	6.5	6.6	19.0	5.9	19.3	6.1	11.7	13.1	6.6	4.2	9.6
Nov	6.9	7.1	20.2	6.4	6.6	17.1	6.0	18.7	6.2	11.1	12.4	6.7	4.6	9.1
Dec	7.1	7.4	20.9	6.7	6.8	18.6	6.1	19.8	6.4	11.7	12.9	6.9	4.8	9.2
1992: Jan	7.1	7.5	20.4	6.8	6.7	17.4	6.0	18.9	6.3	12.5	13.7	6.9	4.8	9.1
Feb	7.3	7.8	21.9	7.0	6.8	17.9	6.1	20.0	6.5	12.3	13.8	7.0	5.0	9.5
Mar	7.3	7.8	22.1	7.0	6.8	18.2	6.1	20.2	6.5	12.3	13.9	7.1	4.9	9.9
Apr	7.3	7.6	20.9	6.9	6.9	17.7	6.2	19.4	6.4	12.4	13.8	7.0	4.8	10.0
May	7.4	7.9	21.2	7.2	6.9	18.4	6.2	19.9	6.5	12.9	14.5	7.2	5.0	9.9
June	7.7	8.2	24.4	7.3	7.1	21.0	6.3	22.8	6.8	13.1	14.5	7.3	5.1	10.1
July	7.6	7.9	21.9	7.2	7.1	19.2	6.4	20.6	6.6	13.0	14.4	7.2	5.2	10.3
Aug	7.6	8.0	21.8	7.2	7.1	17.7	6.4	19.9	6.6	12.9	14.2	7.2	5.3	10.3
Sept	7.5	7.9	21.8	7.1	7.0	18.8	6.4	20.4	6.6	12.6	13.9	7.2	5.2	9.1
Oct	7.4	7.8	19.5	7.2	6.9	18.2	6.2	18.9	6.5	12.5	14.1	7.1	5.1	9.3
Nov	7.3	7.6	21.1	6.9	6.9	19.1	6.2	20.2	6.4	12.6	14.0	7.0	4.9	10.4
Dec	7.3	7.5	20.5	6.8	7.0	17.7	6.4	19.2	6.3	12.8	14.2	7.0	4.8	10.3

[1] Unemployed as percent of civilian labor force in group specified.
[2] Data for 1949 and 1951–54 are for April; 1950, for March.

Note.—Data relate to persons 16 years of age and over.
See footnote 6 and Note, Table B–30.

Source: Department of Labor, Bureau of Labor Statistics.

TABLE B-38.—*Civilian unemployment rate by demographic characteristic, 1950-92*

[Percent; [1] monthly data seasonally adjusted]

Year or month	All civilian workers	White Total	White Males Total	White Males 16-19 years	White Males 20 years and over	White Females Total	White Females 16-19 years	White Females 20 years and over	Black and other or black Total	Males Total	Males 16-19 years	Males 20 years and over	Females Total	Females 16-19 years	Females 20 years and over
											Black and other				
1950	5.3	4.9	4.7			5.3			9.0	9.4			8.4		
1951	3.3	3.1	2.6			4.2			5.3	4.9			6.1		
1952	3.0	2.8	2.5			3.3			5.4	5.2			5.7		
1953	2.9	2.7	2.5			3.1			4.5	4.8			4.1		
1954	5.5	5.0	4.8	13.4	4.4	5.5	10.4	5.1	9.9	10.3	14.4	9.9	9.2	20.6	8.4
1955	4.4	3.9	3.7	11.3	3.3	4.3	9.1	3.9	8.7	8.8	13.4	8.4	8.5	19.2	7.7
1956	4.1	3.6	3.4	10.5	3.0	4.2	9.7	3.7	8.3	7.9	15.0	7.4	8.9	22.8	7.8
1957	4.3	3.8	3.6	11.5	3.2	4.3	9.5	3.8	7.9	8.3	18.4	7.6	7.3	20.2	6.4
1958	6.8	6.1	6.1	15.7	5.5	6.2	12.7	5.6	12.6	13.7	26.8	12.7	10.8	28.4	9.5
1959	5.5	4.8	4.6	14.0	4.1	5.3	12.0	4.7	10.7	11.5	25.2	10.5	9.4	27.7	8.3
1960	5.5	5.0	4.8	14.0	4.2	5.3	12.7	4.6	10.2	10.7	24.0	9.6	9.4	24.8	8.3
1961	6.7	6.0	5.7	15.7	5.1	6.5	14.8	5.7	12.4	12.8	26.8	11.7	11.9	29.2	10.6
1962	5.5	4.9	4.6	13.7	4.0	5.5	12.8	4.7	10.9	10.9	22.0	10.0	11.0	30.2	9.6
1963	5.7	5.0	4.7	15.9	3.9	5.8	15.1	4.8	10.8	10.5	27.3	9.2	11.2	34.7	9.4
1964	5.2	4.6	4.1	14.7	3.4	5.5	14.9	4.6	9.6	8.9	24.3	7.7	10.7	31.6	9.0
1965	4.5	4.1	3.6	12.9	2.9	5.0	14.0	4.0	8.1	7.4	23.3	6.0	9.2	31.7	7.5
1966	3.8	3.4	2.8	10.5	2.2	4.3	12.1	3.3	7.3	6.3	21.3	4.9	8.7	31.3	6.6
1967	3.8	3.4	2.7	10.7	2.1	4.6	11.5	3.8	7.4	6.0	23.9	4.3	9.1	29.6	7.1
1968	3.6	3.2	2.6	10.1	2.0	4.3	12.1	3.4	6.7	5.6	22.1	3.9	8.3	28.7	6.3
1969	3.5	3.1	2.5	10.0	1.9	4.2	11.5	3.4	6.4	5.3	21.4	3.7	7.8	27.6	5.8
1970	4.9	4.5	4.0	13.7	3.2	5.4	13.4	4.4	8.2	7.3	25.0	5.6	9.3	34.5	6.9
1971	5.9	5.4	4.9	15.1	4.0	6.3	15.1	5.3	9.9	9.1	28.8	7.3	10.9	35.4	8.7
1972	5.6	5.1	4.5	14.2	3.6	5.9	14.2	4.9	10.0	8.9	29.7	6.9	11.4	38.4	8.8
											Black				
1972	5.6	5.1	4.5	14.2	3.6	5.9	14.2	4.9	10.4	9.3	31.7	7.0	11.8	40.5	9.0
1973	4.9	4.3	3.8	12.3	3.0	5.3	13.0	4.3	9.4	8.0	27.8	6.0	11.1	36.1	8.6
1974	5.6	5.0	4.4	13.5	3.5	6.1	14.5	5.1	10.5	9.8	33.1	7.4	11.3	37.4	8.8
1975	8.5	7.8	7.2	18.3	6.2	8.6	17.4	7.5	14.8	14.8	38.1	12.5	14.8	41.0	12.2
1976	7.7	7.0	6.4	17.3	5.4	7.9	16.4	6.8	14.0	13.7	37.5	11.4	14.3	41.6	11.7
1977	7.1	6.2	5.5	15.0	4.7	7.3	15.9	6.2	14.0	13.3	39.2	10.7	14.9	43.4	12.3
1978	6.1	5.2	4.6	13.5	3.7	6.2	14.4	5.2	12.8	11.8	36.7	9.3	13.8	40.8	11.2
1979	5.8	5.1	4.5	13.9	3.6	5.9	14.0	5.0	12.3	11.4	34.2	9.3	13.3	39.1	10.9
1980	7.1	6.3	6.1	16.2	5.3	6.5	14.8	5.6	14.3	14.5	37.5	12.4	14.0	39.8	11.9
1981	7.6	6.7	6.5	17.9	5.6	6.9	16.6	5.9	15.6	15.7	40.7	13.5	15.6	42.2	13.4
1982	9.7	8.6	8.8	21.7	7.8	8.3	19.0	7.3	18.9	20.1	48.9	17.8	17.6	47.1	15.4
1983	9.6	8.4	8.8	20.2	7.9	7.9	18.3	6.9	19.5	20.3	48.8	18.1	18.6	48.2	16.5
1984	7.5	6.5	6.4	16.8	5.7	6.5	15.2	5.8	15.9	16.4	42.7	14.3	15.4	42.6	13.5
1985	7.2	6.2	6.1	16.5	5.4	6.4	14.8	5.7	15.1	15.3	41.0	13.2	14.9	39.2	13.1
1986	7.0	6.0	6.0	16.3	5.3	6.1	14.9	5.4	14.5	14.8	39.3	12.9	14.2	39.2	12.4
1987	6.2	5.3	5.4	15.5	4.8	5.2	13.4	4.6	13.0	12.7	34.4	11.1	13.2	34.9	11.6
1988	5.5	4.7	4.7	13.9	4.1	4.7	12.3	4.1	11.7	11.7	32.7	10.1	11.7	32.0	10.4
1989	5.3	4.5	4.5	13.7	3.9	4.5	11.5	4.0	11.4	11.5	31.9	10.0	11.4	33.0	9.8
1990	5.5	4.7	4.8	14.2	4.3	4.6	12.6	4.1	11.3	11.8	32.1	10.4	10.8	30.0	9.6
1991	6.7	6.0	6.4	17.5	5.7	5.5	15.2	4.9	12.4	12.9	36.5	11.5	11.9	36.1	10.5
1992	7.4	6.5	6.9	18.4	6.3	6.0	15.7	5.4	14.1	15.2	42.0	13.4	13.0	37.2	11.7
1991: Jan	6.3	5.6	5.8	16.7	5.1	5.3	15.9	4.6	12.1	12.6	35.4	11.2	11.6	36.3	10.0
Feb	6.5	5.8	6.1	15.9	5.6	5.3	13.6	4.8	11.9	12.6	35.6	11.3	11.2	34.6	9.8
Mar	6.8	6.1	6.5	17.7	5.9	5.5	13.8	4.9	12.3	12.7	38.3	11.1	11.9	38.1	10.2
Apr	6.6	5.8	6.3	17.3	5.7	5.3	14.7	4.7	12.4	13.3	36.9	11.8	11.6	36.1	10.2
May	6.8	6.0	6.3	18.6	5.6	5.7	15.3	5.1	12.6	13.6	36.0	12.2	11.7	30.8	10.6
June	6.8	6.1	6.4	18.4	5.8	5.7	14.8	5.1	12.4	13.4	34.7	12.1	11.4	31.6	10.4
July	6.7	6.1	6.6	18.9	5.9	5.5	16.0	4.8	11.8	12.8	33.4	11.6	10.8	35.6	9.5
Aug	6.8	6.0	6.4	16.6	5.8	5.6	15.6	5.0	12.4	13.0	36.7	11.5	11.9	42.6	10.4
Sept	6.8	6.0	6.5	16.7	6.0	5.3	14.4	4.8	12.4	13.1	40.5	11.3	11.8	34.5	10.7
Oct	6.9	6.1	6.5	17.3	5.9	5.6	15.9	5.0	13.1	12.6	36.4	11.2	13.5	41.8	12.0
Nov	6.9	6.2	6.5	17.7	5.9	5.8	15.4	5.2	12.4	12.4	36.5	11.0	12.4	33.4	11.3
Dec	7.1	6.4	6.7	18.5	6.0	6.1	17.0	5.4	12.9	13.4	37.2	12.0	12.3	36.6	11.1
1992: Jan	7.1	6.3	6.8	17.3	6.2	5.8	14.9	5.2	13.7	14.7	36.1	13.2	12.7	34.9	11.4
Feb	7.3	6.5	6.9	19.0	6.3	5.9	15.6	5.3	13.8	14.9	38.7	13.3	12.7	37.2	11.4
Mar	7.3	6.5	7.0	20.0	6.3	6.0	16.0	5.4	13.9	15.3	38.3	13.8	12.6	36.1	11.4
Apr	7.3	6.4	6.8	17.8	6.2	5.9	15.0	5.4	13.8	14.5	43.2	12.8	13.1	35.7	11.8
May	7.4	6.5	7.0	18.4	6.4	5.8	14.9	5.2	14.5	15.4	43.0	13.8	13.6	42.1	11.9
June	7.7	6.8	7.2	21.2	6.5	6.2	18.4	5.5	14.5	15.5	45.1	13.6	13.5	36.4	12.2
July	7.6	6.6	7.0	18.8	6.4	6.2	16.3	5.6	14.4	15.3	42.3	13.6	13.5	38.4	12.1
Aug	7.6	6.6	7.0	18.5	6.4	6.1	15.2	5.6	14.2	15.5	42.7	13.8	13.0	31.8	11.9
Sept	7.5	6.6	7.0	18.7	6.4	6.2	15.8	5.6	13.9	15.4	43.5	12.5	12.5	39.8	11.0
Oct	7.4	6.5	6.8	15.9	6.3	6.1	15.1	5.5	14.1	15.5	44.2	13.7	12.7	39.8	11.3
Nov	7.3	6.4	6.7	17.7	6.1	5.9	16.4	5.3	14.0	14.9	44.8	13.0	13.2	37.5	11.8
Dec	7.3	6.3	6.5	17.2	6.0	6.1	15.1	5.6	14.2	15.2	42.2	13.3	13.2	36.5	11.9

[1] Unemployed as percent of civilian labor force in group specified.

Note.—See Note, Table B-37.

Source: Department of Labor, Bureau of Labor Statistics.

TABLE B-39.—*Unemployment by duration and reason, 1948-92*

[Thousands of persons, except as noted; monthly data seasonally adjusted [1]]

Year or month	Unemployment	Duration of unemployment						Reason for unemployment					
		Less than 5 weeks	5–14 weeks	15–26 weeks	27 weeks and over	Average (mean) duration (weeks)	Median duration (weeks)	Job losers			Job leavers	Reentrants	New entrants
								Total	On layoff	Other			
1948	2,276	1,300	669	193	116	8.6							
1949	3,637	1,756	1,194	428	256	10.0							
1950	3,288	1,450	1,055	425	357	12.1							
1951	2,055	1,177	574	166	137	9.7							
1952	1,883	1,135	516	148	84	8.4							
1953	1,834	1,142	482	132	78	8.0							
1954	3,532	1,605	1,116	495	317	11.8							
1955	2,852	1,335	815	366	336	13.0							
1956	2,750	1,412	805	301	232	11.3							
1957	2,859	1,408	891	321	239	10.5							
1958	4,602	1,753	1,396	785	667	13.9							
1959	3,740	1,585	1,114	469	571	14.4							
1960	3,852	1,719	1,176	503	454	12.8							
1961	4,714	1,806	1,376	728	804	15.6							
1962	3,911	1,663	1,134	534	585	14.7							
1963	4,070	1,751	1,231	535	553	14.0							
1964	3,786	1,697	1,117	491	482	13.3							
1965	3,366	1,628	983	404	351	11.8							
1966	2,875	1,573	779	287	239	10.4							
1967	2,975	1,634	893	271	177	8.7	2.3	1,229	394	836	438	945	396
1968	2,817	1,594	810	256	156	8.4	4.5	1,070	334	736	431	909	407
1969	2,832	1,629	827	242	133	7.8	4.4	1,017	339	678	436	965	413
1970	4,093	2,139	1,290	428	235	8.6	4.9	1,811	675	1,137	550	1,228	504
1971	5,016	2,245	1,585	668	519	11.3	6.3	2,323	735	1,588	590	1,472	630
1972	4,882	2,242	1,472	601	566	12.0	6.2	2,108	582	1,526	641	1,456	677
1973	4,365	2,224	1,314	483	343	10.0	5.2	1,694	472	1,221	683	1,340	649
1974	5,156	2,604	1,597	574	381	9.8	5.2	2,242	746	1,495	768	1,463	681
1975	7,929	2,940	2,484	1,303	1,203	14.2	8.4	4,386	1,671	2,714	827	1,892	823
1976	7,406	2,844	2,196	1,018	1,348	15.8	8.2	3,679	1,050	2,628	903	1,928	895
1977	6,991	2,919	2,132	913	1,028	14.3	7.0	3,166	865	2,300	909	1,963	953
1978	6,202	2,865	1,923	766	648	11.9	5.9	2,585	712	1,873	874	1,857	885
1979	6,137	2,950	1,946	706	535	10.8	5.4	2,635	851	1,784	880	1,806	817
1980	7,637	3,295	2,470	1,052	820	11.9	6.5	3,947	1,488	2,459	891	1,927	872
1981	8,273	3,449	2,539	1,122	1,162	13.7	6.9	4,267	1,430	2,837	923	2,102	981
1982	10,678	3,883	3,311	1,708	1,776	15.6	8.7	6,268	2,127	4,141	840	2,384	1,185
1983	10,717	3,570	2,937	1,652	2,559	20.0	10.1	6,258	1,780	4,478	830	2,412	1,216
1984	8,539	3,350	2,451	1,104	1,634	18.2	7.9	4,421	1,171	3,250	823	2,184	1,110
1985	8,312	3,498	2,509	1,025	1,280	15.6	6.8	4,139	1,157	2,982	877	2,256	1,039
1986	8,237	3,448	2,557	1,045	1,187	15.0	6.9	4,033	1,090	2,943	1,015	2,160	1,029
1987	7,425	3,246	2,196	943	1,040	14.5	6.5	3,566	943	2,623	965	1,974	920
1988	6,701	3,084	2,007	801	809	13.5	5.9	3,092	851	2,241	983	1,809	816
1989	6,528	3,174	1,978	730	646	11.9	4.8	2,983	850	2,133	1,024	1,843	677
1990	6,874	3,169	2,201	809	695	12.1	5.4	3,322	1,018	2,305	1,014	1,883	654
1991	8,426	3,380	2,724	1,225	1,098	13.8	6.9	4,608	1,279	3,329	979	2,087	753
1992	9,384	3,270	2,760	1,424	1,930	17.9	8.8	5,291	1,246	4,045	975	2,228	890
1991: Jan	7,806	3,397	2,547	1,004	856	12.4	5.9	4,151	1,186	2,965	908	2,009	695
Feb	8,123	3,465	2,683	1,057	915	12.8	6.2	4,412	1,433	2,979	1,016	2,014	659
Mar	8,462	3,470	2,846	1,203	947	13.0	6.6	4,593	1,378	3,215	1,098	2,068	724
Apr	8,306	3,348	2,728	1,203	1,007	13.5	6.8	4,501	1,339	3,162	978	2,085	754
May	8,507	3,565	2,763	1,195	1,016	12.9	6.5	4,531	1,335	3,196	1,023	2,194	770
June	8,487	3,369	2,811	1,256	1,085	13.8	6.9	4,670	1,316	3,354	1,046	2,102	702
July	8,378	3,323	2,732	1,227	1,102	13.9	7.0	4,629	1,195	3,434	975	2,033	769
Aug	8,460	3,353	2,657	1,255	1,161	14.2	7.3	4,671	1,284	3,387	875	2,103	759
Sept	8,479	3,320	2,715	1,288	1,168	14.3	7.3	4,776	1,094	3,682	953	2,026	774
Oct	8,695	3,306	2,782	1,466	1,147	14.4	7.4	4,738	1,217	3,521	996	2,116	836
Nov	8,670	3,309	2,687	1,342	1,374	15.1	7.7	4,788	1,217	3,571	985	2,130	776
Dec	8,984	3,359	2,771	1,381	1,508	15.5	8.0	5,066	1,264	3,802	918	2,174	816
1992: Jan	8,992	3,332	2,701	1,455	1,594	16.3	8.1	4,884	1,213	3,671	971	2,316	810
Feb	9,223	3,105	2,882	1,452	1,720	16.8	8.2	5,226	1,261	3,965	927	2,169	838
Mar	9,284	3,291	2,698	1,417	1,768	17.0	8.1	5,269	1,235	4,034	947	2,203	832
Apr	9,225	3,269	2,706	1,303	1,769	17.2	8.6	5,219	1,227	3,992	1,009	2,137	853
May	9,459	3,362	2,663	1,405	1,944	17.9	8.8	5,430	1,211	4,219	992	2,194	863
June	9,788	3,512	2,783	1,363	2,069	18.2	8.7	5,535	1,312	4,223	1,017	2,266	999
July	9,628	3,373	2,776	1,459	2,088	18.3	8.6	5,462	1,296	4,166	1,003	2,273	958
Aug	9,624	3,289	2,846	1,502	2,045	18.3	8.9	5,414	1,255	4,159	1,009	2,246	941
Sept	9,550	3,281	2,847	1,427	2,095	18.5	9.3	5,438	1,335	4,103	963	2,274	944
Oct	9,379	3,192	2,666	1,475	2,089	19.2	9.3	5,492	1,265	4,227	913	2,206	784
Nov	9,301	3,120	2,835	1,438	2,008	18.4	9.4	5,207	1,195	4,012	977	2,194	930
Dec	9,280	3,042	2,688	1,540	2,065	19.2	9.4	5,138	1,204	3,934	972	2,237	930

[1] Because of independent seasonal adjustment of the various series, detail will not add to totals.
[2] Data for 1967 by reason for unemployment are not strictly comparable with those for later years and the total by reason is not equal to total unemployment.

Note.—Data relate to persons 16 years of age and over.
See footnote 6 and Note, Table B-30.

392

TABLE B–40.—*Unemployment insurance programs, selected data, 1960–92*

Year or month	All programs			State programs					
	Covered employ-ment [1]	Insured unemploy-ment (weekly aver-age) [2][3]	Total benefits paid (millions of dollars) [2][4]	Insured unem-ployment	Initial claims	Exhaus-tions [5]	Insured unemploy-ment as percent of covered employ-ment	Benefits paid	
								Total (millions of dollars) [4]	Average weekly check (dollars) [6]
	Thousands			Weekly average; thousands					
1960	46,334	2,071	3,022.8	1,908	331	31	4.8	2,726.7	32.87
1961	46,266	2,994	4,358.1	2,290	350	46	5.6	3,422.7	33.80
1962	47,776	1,946	3,145.1	1,783	302	32	4.4	2,675.4	34.56
1963	48,434	7 1,973	3,025.9	7 1,806	7 298	30	4.3	2,774.7	35.27
1964	49,637	1,753	2,749.2	1,605	268	26	3.8	2,522.1	35.92
1965	51,580	1,450	2,360.4	1,328	232	21	3.0	2,166.0	37.19
1966	54,739	1,129	1,890.9	1,061	203	15	2.3	1,771.3	39.75
1967	56,342	1,270	2,221.5	1,205	226	17	2.5	2,092.3	41.25
1968	57,977	1,187	2,191.0	1,111	201	16	2.2	2,031.6	43.43
1969	59,999	1,177	2,298.6	1,101	200	16	2.1	2,127.9	46.17
1970	59,526	2,070	4,209.3	1,805	296	25	3.4	3,848.5	50.34
1971	59,375	2,608	6,154.0	2,150	295	39	4.1	4,957.0	54.02
1972	66,458	2,192	5,491.1	1,848	261	35	3.5	4,471.0	56.76
1973	69,897	1,793	4,517.3	1,632	247	29	2.7	4,007.6	59.00
1974	72,451	2,558	6,933.9	2,262	363	37	3.5	5,974.9	64.25
1975	71,037	4,937	16,802.4	3,986	478	81	6.0	11,754.7	70.23
1976	73,459	3,846	12,344.8	2,991	386	63	4.6	8,974.5	75.16
1977	76,419	3,308	10,998.9	2,655	375	55	3.9	8,357.2	78.79
1978	88,804	2,645	9,006.9	2,359	346	39	3.3	7,717.2	83.67
1979	92,062	2,592	9,401.3	2,434	388	39	2.9	8,612.9	89.67
1980	92,659	3,837	16,175.4	3,350	488	59	3.9	13,761.1	98.95
1981	93,300	3,410	15,287.1	3,047	460	57	3.5	13,262.1	106.70
1982	91,628	4,594	23,774.8	4,061	583	80	4.6	20,649.5	119.34
1983	91,898	3,775	20,206.2	3,396	438	80	3.9	17,762.8	123.59
1984	96,474	2,561	13,109.6	2,476	377	50	2.8	12,594.7	123.47
1985	99,186	2,693	15,056.3	2,611	397	49	2.9	14,130.8	128.14
1986	101,099	2,746	16,292.5	2,650	378	52	2.8	15,329.3	135.65
1987	103,933	2,401	14,501.0	2,332	328	46	2.4	13,606.8	140.55
1988	107,157	2,135	13,694.4	2,081	310	38	2.0	12,564.7	144.97
1989	109,926	2,205	14,957.0	2,158	330	37	2.1	13,760.3	151.73
1990	111,498	2,575	18,746.7	2,522	388	45	2.4	17,356.0	161.56
1991	8 109,613	3,406	27,505.4	3,342	447	67	3.2	24,525.7	169.88
1991: Jan		4,015	2,585.9	3,136	** 460	** 58	** 3.0	2,529.5	166.83
Feb		4,090	2,430.7	3,303	498	57	3.1	2,382.2	169.51
Mar		4,060	2,575.3	3,467	511	62	3.3	2,525.6	170.45
Apr		3,864	2,586.3	3,490	460	70	3.3	2,485.7	170.01
May		3,262	2,323.5	3,475	433	68	3.3	2,236.5	170.46
June		3,177	1,939.7	3,406	421	69	3.2	1,864.5	170.50
July		3,270	2,201.0	3,336	418	76	3.1	2,134.6	169.16
Aug		2,999	1,964.3	3,283	415	72	3.1	1,911.0	169.02
Sept		2,795	1,731.5	3,267	415	66	3.1	1,681.4	170.70
Oct		2,795	1,888.7	3,273	418	66	3.1	1,831.1	171.27
Nov		2,845	1,729.5	3,313	448	62	3.1	1,681.0	170.79
Dec		3,575	2,248.1	3,317	464	71	3.1	2,183.3	170.99
1992: Jan		4,211	2,807.8	3,349	446	78	3.2	2,723.8	171.65
Feb		4,214	2,555.7	3,324	452	76	3.1	2,476.2	173.39
Mar		4,116	2,750.1	3,340	440	78	3.2	2,664.1	173.87
Apr		3,639	2,477.1	3,348	412	83	3.2	2,397.9	173.88
May		3,202	2,016.6	3,328	407	77	3.2	1,946.0	173.70
June		3,148	2,058.4	3,249	415	76	3.1	1,983.2	173.22
July		3,124	2,129.5	3,327	420	77	3.2	2,049.0	171.70
Aug		3,120	1,978.0	3,185	409	74	3.0	1,899.5	174.19
Sept		2,820	1,861.0	3,185	406	67	3.0	1,778.1	174.42
Oct		2,543	1,682.9	3,029	366	63	2.9	1,601.3	175.37
Nov [p]				2,935	361		2.8		

**Monthly data are seasonally adjusted.
[1] Includes persons under the State, UCFE (Federal employee, effective January 1955), and RRB (Railroad Retirement Board) programs. Beginning October 1958, also includes the UCX program (unemployment compensation for ex-servicemembers).
[2] Includes State, UCFE, RR, UCX, UCV (unemployment compensation for veterans, October 1952–January 1960), and SRA (Servicemen's Readjustment Act, September 1944–September 1951) programs. Also includes Federal and State extended benefit programs. Does not include FSB (Federal supplemental benefits), SUA (special unemployment assistance), Federal Supplemental Compensation, and Emergency Unemployment Compensation programs.
[3] Covered workers who have completed at least 1 week of unemployment.
[4] Annual data are net amounts and monthly data are gross amounts.
[5] Individuals receiving final payments in benefit year.
[6] For total unemployment only.
[7] Programs include Puerto Rican sugarcane workers for initial claims and insured unemployment beginning July 1963.
[8] Latest data available for all programs combined. Workers covered by State programs account for about 97 percent of wage and salary earners.

Source: Department of Labor, Employment and Training Administration.

TABLE B-41.—*Employees on nonagricultural payrolls, by major industry, 1946–92*

[Thousands of persons; monthly data seasonally adjusted]

Year or month	Total	Goods-producing industries					
		Total	Mining	Con-struction	Manufacturing		
					Total	Durable goods	Nondura-ble goods
1946	41,652	17,248	862	1,683	14,703	7,785	6,918
1947	43,857	18,509	955	2,009	15,545	8,358	7,187
1948	44,866	18,774	994	2,198	15,582	8,298	7,285
1949	43,754	17,565	930	2,194	14,441	7,462	6,979
1950	45,197	18,506	901	2,364	15,241	8,066	7,175
1951	47,819	19,959	929	2,637	16,393	9,059	7,334
1952	48,793	20,198	898	2,668	16,632	9,320	7,313
1953	50,202	21,074	866	2,659	17,549	10,080	7,468
1954	48,990	19,751	791	2,646	16,314	9,101	7,213
1955	50,641	20,513	792	2,839	16,882	9,511	7,370
1956	52,369	21,104	822	3,039	17,243	9,802	7,442
1957	52,853	20,964	828	2,962	17,174	9,825	7,351
1958	51,324	19,513	751	2,817	15,945	8,801	7,144
1959	53,268	20,411	732	3,004	16,675	9,342	7,333
1960	54,189	20,434	712	2,926	16,796	9,429	7,367
1961	53,999	19,857	672	2,859	16,326	9,041	7,285
1962	55,549	20,451	650	2,948	16,853	9,450	7,403
1963	56,653	20,640	635	3,010	16,995	9,586	7,410
1964	58,283	21,005	634	3,097	17,274	9,785	7,489
1965	60,765	21,926	632	3,232	18,062	10,374	7,688
1966	63,901	23,158	627	3,317	19,214	11,250	7,963
1967	65,803	23,308	613	3,248	19,447	11,408	8,039
1968	67,897	23,737	606	3,350	19,781	11,594	8,187
1969	70,384	24,361	619	3,575	20,167	11,862	8,304
1970	70,880	23,578	623	3,588	19,367	11,176	8,190
1971	71,214	22,935	609	3,704	18,623	10,604	8,019
1972	73,675	23,668	628	3,889	19,151	11,022	8,129
1973	76,790	24,893	642	4,097	20,154	11,863	8,291
1974	78,265	24,794	697	4,020	20,077	11,897	8,181
1975	76,945	22,600	752	3,525	18,323	10,662	7,661
1976	79,382	23,352	779	3,576	18,997	11,051	7,946
1977	82,471	24,346	813	3,851	19,682	11,570	8,112
1978	86,697	25,585	851	4,229	20,505	12,245	8,259
1979	89,823	26,461	958	4,463	21,040	12,730	8,310
1980	90,406	25,658	1,027	4,346	20,285	12,159	8,127
1981	91,156	25,497	1,139	4,188	20,170	12,082	8,089
1982	89,566	23,813	1,128	3,905	18,781	11,014	7,767
1983	90,200	23,334	952	3,948	18,434	10,707	7,726
1984	94,496	24,727	966	4,383	19,378	11,479	7,899
1985	97,519	24,859	927	4,673	19,260	11,464	7,796
1986	99,525	24,558	777	4,816	18,965	11,203	7,761
1987	102,200	24,708	717	4,967	19,024	11,167	7,858
1988	105,536	25,173	713	5,110	19,350	11,381	7,969
1989	108,329	25,322	693	5,187	19,442	11,420	8,022
1990	109,782	24,960	710	5,133	19,117	11,130	7,988
1991	108,310	23,830	691	4,685	18,455	10,602	7,852
1992 ᴾ	108,434	23,421	635	4,594	18,192	10,340	7,852
1991: Jan	108,845	24,195	710	4,790	18,695	10,816	7,879
Feb	108,557	24,081	710	4,798	18,573	10,710	7,863
Mar	108,344	23,938	708	4,740	18,490	10,646	7,844
Apr	108,178	23,860	704	4,701	18,455	10,630	7,825
May	108,265	23,864	699	4,706	18,459	10,622	7,837
June	108,227	23,809	697	4,692	18,420	10,587	7,833
July	108,190	23,792	693	4,674	18,425	10,586	7,839
Aug	108,267	23,791	686	4,662	18,443	10,582	7,861
Sept	108,293	23,755	679	4,662	18,414	10,557	7,857
Oct	108,285	23,704	674	4,642	18,388	10,530	7,858
Nov	108,139	23,613	667	4,585	18,361	10,498	7,863
Dec	108,154	23,584	663	4,592	18,329	10,466	7,863
1992: Jan	108,100	23,527	657	4,587	18,283	10,422	7,861
Feb	108,142	23,525	653	4,582	18,290	10,430	7,860
Mar	108,200	23,532	651	4,603	18,278	10,417	7,861
Apr	108,377	23,530	646	4,605	18,279	10,409	7,870
May	108,496	23,548	641	4,632	18,275	10,398	7,877
June	108,423	23,470	634	4,600	18,236	10,371	7,865
July	108,594	23,459	633	4,584	18,242	10,347	7,895
Aug	108,485	23,362	626	4,591	18,145	10,298	7,847
Sept	108,497	23,296	620	4,574	18,102	10,271	7,831
Oct	108,571	23,270	623	4,601	18,046	10,231	7,815
Nov ᴾ	108,647	23,277	622	4,584	18,071	10,248	7,823
Dec ᴾ	108,711	23,273	620	4,579	18,074	10,243	7,831

Note.—Data in Tables B–41 and B–42 are based on reports from employing establishments and relate to full- and part-time wage and salary workers in nonagricultural establishments who received pay for any part of the pay period that includes the 12th of the month. Not comparable with labor force data (Tables B–30 through B–39), which include both agricultural and nonagricultural industries; which include self-employed persons, unpaid family workers, and private household workers, as well as other wage and salary workers; See next page for continuation of table.

TABLE B-41.—*Employees on nonagricultural payrolls, by major industry, 1946–92*—Continued

[Thousands of persons; monthly data seasonally adjusted]

Year or month	Total	Service-producing industries							
		Transportation and public utilities	Wholesale trade	Retail trade	Finance, insurance, and real estate	Services	Government		
							Total	Federal	State and local
1946	24,404	4,061	2,298	6,077	1,675	4,697	5,595	2,254	3,341
1947	25,348	4,166	2,478	6,477	1,728	5,025	5,474	1,892	3,582
1948	26,092	4,189	2,612	6,659	1,800	5,181	5,650	1,863	3,787
1949	26,189	4,001	2,610	6,654	1,828	5,239	5,856	1,908	3,948
1950	26,691	4,034	2,643	6,743	1,888	5,356	6,026	1,928	4,098
1951	27,860	4,226	2,735	7,007	1,956	5,547	6,389	2,302	4,087
1952	28,595	4,248	2,821	7,184	2,035	5,699	6,609	2,420	4,188
1953	29,128	4,290	2,862	7,385	2,111	5,835	6,645	2,305	4,340
1954	29,239	4,084	2,875	7,360	2,200	5,969	6,751	2,188	4,563
1955	30,128	4,141	2,934	7,601	2,298	6,240	6,914	2,187	4,727
1956	31,266	4,244	3,027	7,831	2,389	6,497	7,278	2,209	5,069
1957	31,889	4,241	3,037	7,848	2,438	6,708	7,616	2,217	5,399
1958	31,811	3,976	2,989	7,761	2,481	6,765	7,839	2,191	5,648
1959	32,857	4,011	3,092	8,035	2,549	7,087	8,083	2,233	5,850
1960	33,755	4,004	3,153	8,238	2,628	7,378	8,353	2,270	6,083
1961	34,142	3,903	3,142	8,195	2,688	7,619	8,594	2,279	6,315
1962	35,098	3,906	3,207	8,359	2,754	7,982	8,890	2,340	6,550
1963	36,013	3,903	3,258	8,520	2,830	8,277	9,225	2,358	6,868
1964	37,278	3,951	3,347	8,812	2,911	8,660	9,596	2,348	7,248
1965	38,839	4,036	3,477	9,239	2,977	9,036	10,074	2,378	7,696
1966	40,743	4,158	3,608	9,637	3,058	9,498	10,784	2,564	8,220
1967	42,495	4,268	3,700	9,906	3,185	10,045	11,391	2,719	8,672
1968	44,160	4,318	3,791	10,308	3,337	10,567	11,839	2,737	9,102
1969	46,023	4,442	3,919	10,785	3,512	11,169	12,195	2,758	9,437
1970	47,302	4,515	4,006	11,034	3,645	11,548	12,554	2,731	9,823
1971	48,278	4,476	4,014	11,338	3,772	11,797	12,881	2,696	10,185
1972	50,007	4,541	4,127	11,822	3,908	12,276	13,334	2,684	10,649
1973	51,897	4,656	4,291	12,315	4,046	12,857	13,732	2,663	11,068
1974	53,471	4,725	4,447	12,539	4,148	13,441	14,170	2,724	11,446
1975	54,345	4,542	4,430	12,630	4,165	13,892	14,686	2,748	11,937
1976	56,030	4,582	4,562	13,193	4,271	14,551	14,871	2,733	12,138
1977	58,125	4,713	4,723	13,792	4,467	15,302	15,127	2,727	12,399
1978	61,113	4,923	4,985	14,556	4,724	16,252	15,672	2,753	12,919
1979	63,363	5,136	5,221	14,972	4,975	17,112	15,947	2,773	13,174
1980	64,748	5,146	5,292	15,018	5,160	17,890	16,241	2,866	13,375
1981	65,659	5,165	5,376	15,172	5,298	18,619	16,031	2,772	13,259
1982	65,753	5,082	5,296	15,161	5,341	19,036	15,837	2,739	13,098
1983	66,866	4,954	5,286	15,595	5,468	19,694	15,869	2,774	13,096
1984	69,769	5,159	5,574	16,526	5,689	20,797	16,024	2,807	13,216
1985	72,660	5,238	5,736	17,336	5,955	21,999	16,394	2,875	13,519
1986	74,967	5,255	5,774	17,909	6,283	23,053	16,693	2,899	13,794
1987	77,492	5,372	5,865	18,462	6,547	24,235	17,010	2,943	14,067
1988	80,363	5,527	6,055	19,077	6,649	25,669	17,386	2,971	14,415
1989	83,007	5,644	6,221	19,549	6,695	27,120	17,779	2,988	14,791
1990	84,822	5,808	6,200	19,677	6,729	28,103	18,304	3,085	15,219
1991	84,480	5,772	6,069	19,259	6,678	28,323	18,380	2,966	15,414
1992 ᵖ	85,013	5,741	5,983	19,137	6,672	28,903	18,578	2,967	15,610
1991: Jan	84,650	5,817	6,127	19,464	6,711	28,215	18,316	2,951	15,365
Feb	84,476	5,781	6,109	19,366	6,701	28,181	18,338	2,952	15,386
Mar	84,406	5,770	6,098	19,340	6,699	28,158	18,341	2,953	15,388
Apr	84,318	5,768	6,082	19,275	6,688	28,145	18,360	2,955	15,405
May	84,401	5,769	6,081	19,281	6,683	28,209	18,378	2,957	15,421
June	84,418	5,763	6,069	19,268	6,674	28,251	18,393	2,970	15,423
July	84,398	5,767	6,064	19,238	6,662	28,289	18,378	2,965	15,413
Aug	84,476	5,773	6,050	19,244	6,661	28,366	18,382	2,970	15,412
Sept	84,538	5,769	6,049	19,220	6,663	28,450	18,387	2,978	15,409
Oct	84,581	5,766	6,040	19,175	6,665	28,525	18,410	2,980	15,430
Nov	84,526	5,761	6,031	19,130	6,666	28,514	18,424	2,981	15,443
Dec	84,570	5,758	6,021	19,112	6,670	28,559	18,450	2,983	15,467
1992: Jan	84,573	5,746	6,010	19,118	6,665	28,577	18,457	2,981	15,476
Feb	84,617	5,753	6,003	19,143	6,673	28,584	18,461	2,981	15,480
Mar	84,668	5,754	5,997	19,092	6,675	28,643	18,507	2,989	15,518
Apr	84,847	5,746	5,993	19,177	6,682	28,707	18,542	2,986	15,556
May	84,948	5,745	5,993	19,150	6,681	28,833	18,546	2,984	15,562
June	84,953	5,745	5,988	19,156	6,672	28,854	18,538	2,972	15,566
July	85,135	5,742	5,972	19,184	6,660	28,971	18,606	2,957	15,649
Aug	85,123	5,729	5,964	19,106	6,661	28,981	18,682	2,959	15,723
Sept	85,201	5,738	5,957	19,122	6,669	29,065	18,650	2,967	15,683
Oct	85,301	5,731	5,969	19,146	6,680	29,152	18,623	2,942	15,681
Nov ᵖ	85,370	5,733	5,974	19,125	6,669	29,183	18,686	2,942	15,744
Dec ᵖ	85,438	5,737	5,967	19,140	6,677	29,253	18,664	2,944	15,720

Note (cont'd).—which count persons as employed when they are not at work because of industrial disputes, bad weather, etc., even if they are not paid for the time off; and which are based on a sample of the working-age population. For description and details of the various establishment data, see "Employment and Earnings."

Source: Department of Labor, Bureau of Labor Statistics.

TABLE B-42.—*Hours and earnings in private nonagricultural industries and hourly compensation in the total economy, 1959-92*

[Monthly data seasonally adjusted, except as noted]

Year or month	Private nonagricultural industries [1]										Total economy, hourly compensation [4]	
	Average weekly hours			Average hourly earnings			Average weekly earnings, total private						
		Manufacturing		Total private			Level		Percent change from a year earlier [3]				1982 CPI-U-X1 dollars [5]
	Total private	Total	Overtime	Current dollars	1982 dollars [2]	Manufacturing (current dollars)	Current dollars	1982 dollars [2]	Current dollars	1982 dollars [2]	Current dollars	
1959	39.0	40.3	2.7	$2.02	$6.69	$2.19	$78.78	$260.86	4.9	4.2	$2.32	$7.02
1960	38.6	39.7	2.5	2.09	6.79	2.26	80.67	261.92	2.4	.4	2.43	7.20
1961	38.6	39.8	2.4	2.14	6.88	2.32	82.60	265.59	2.4	1.4	2.52	7.40
1962	38.7	40.4	2.8	2.22	7.07	2.39	85.91	273.60	4.0	3.0	2.62	7.64
1963	38.8	40.5	2.8	2.28	7.17	2.45	88.46	278.18	3.0	1.7	2.73	7.84
1964	38.7	40.7	3.1	2.36	7.33	2.53	91.33	283.63	3.2	2.0	2.87	8.14
1965	38.8	41.2	3.6	2.46	7.52	2.61	95.45	291.90	4.5	2.9	2.99	8.35
1966	38.6	41.4	3.9	2.56	7.62	2.71	98.82	294.11	3.5	.8	3.18	8.65
1967	38.0	40.6	3.4	2.68	7.72	2.82	101.84	293.49	3.1	-.2	3.35	8.82
1968	37.8	40.7	3.6	2.85	7.89	3.01	107.73	298.42	5.8	1.7	3.64	9.23
1969	37.7	40.6	3.6	3.04	7.98	3.19	114.61	300.81	6.4	.8	3.91	9.48
1970	37.1	39.8	3.0	3.23	8.03	3.35	119.83	298.08	4.6	-.9	4.25	9.83
1971	36.9	39.9	2.9	3.45	8.21	3.57	127.31	303.12	6.2	1.7	4.54	10.07
1972	37.0	40.5	3.5	3.70	8.53	3.82	136.90	315.44	7.5	4.1	4.85	10.45
1973	36.9	40.7	3.8	3.94	8.55	4.09	145.39	315.38	6.2	-.0	5.27	10.66
1974	36.5	40.0	3.3	4.24	8.28	4.42	154.76	302.27	6.4	-4.2	5.77	10.62
1975	36.1	39.5	2.6	4.53	8.12	4.83	163.53	293.06	5.7	-3.0	6.32	10.74
1976	36.1	40.1	3.1	4.86	8.24	5.22	175.45	297.37	7.3	1.5	6.87	11.07
1977	36.0	40.3	3.5	5.25	8.36	5.68	189.00	300.96	7.7	1.2	7.40	11.20
1978	35.8	40.4	3.6	5.69	8.40	6.17	203.70	300.89	7.8	-.0	8.02	11.36
1979	35.7	40.2	3.3	6.16	8.17	6.70	219.91	291.66	8.0	-3.1	8.79	11.36
1980	35.3	39.7	2.8	6.66	7.78	7.27	235.10	274.65	6.9	-5.8	9.70	11.27
1981	35.2	39.8	2.8	7.25	7.69	7.99	255.20	270.63	8.5	-1.5	10.67	11.33
1982	34.8	38.9	2.3	7.68	7.68	8.49	267.26	267.26	4.7	-1.2	11.49	11.49
1983	35.0	40.1	3.0	8.02	7.79	8.83	280.70	272.52	5.0	2.0	11.95	11.47
1984	35.2	40.7	3.4	8.32	7.80	9.19	292.86	274.73	4.3	.8	12.49	11.49
1985	34.9	40.5	3.3	8.57	7.77	9.54	299.09	271.16	2.1	-1.3	13.07	11.60
1986	34.8	40.7	3.4	8.76	7.81	9.73	304.85	271.94	1.9	.3	13.69	11.95
1987	34.8	41.0	3.7	8.98	7.73	9.91	312.50	269.16	2.5	-1.0	14.25	11.99
1988	34.7	41.1	3.9	9.28	7.69	10.19	322.02	266.79	3.0	-.9	14.86	12.02
1989	34.6	41.0	3.8	9.66	7.64	10.48	334.24	264.22	3.8	-1.0	15.42	11.89
1990	34.5	40.8	3.6	10.01	7.52	10.83	345.35	259.47	3.3	-1.8	16.29	11.91
1991	34.3	40.7	3.6	10.33	7.45	11.18	354.32	255.64	2.6	-1.5	17.12	12.01
1992 ᵖ	34.4	41.0	3.8	10.59		11.45	364.30		2.8			
1991: Jan	34.2	40.5	3.4	10.18	7.43	11.02	348.16	254.13	2.4	-2.9		
Feb	34.3	40.4	3.4	10.20	7.44	11.03	349.86	255.19	2.2	-2.7		
Mar	34.2	40.3	3.3	10.23	7.45	11.07	349.87	254.64	1.9	-2.6		
Apr	34.1	40.4	3.4	10.26	7.45	11.12	349.87	253.90	2.3	-2.3		
May	34.3	40.5	3.4	10.30	7.46	11.14	353.29	255.02	2.4	-2.4		
June	34.5	40.7	3.6	10.35	7.48	11.17	357.08	258.01	3.0	-1.5		
July	34.2	40.7	3.6	10.34	7.46	11.21	353.63	255.14	1.8	-2.4		
Aug	34.3	40.9	3.7	10.38	7.47	11.24	356.03	256.32	2.8	-.7		
Sept	34.4	40.9	3.7	10.39	7.46	11.25	357.42	256.58	2.7	-.4		
Oct	34.3	40.9	3.7	10.40	7.45	11.27	356.72	255.53	3.2	.5		
Nov	34.4	40.9	3.7	10.42	7.44	11.30	358.45	255.85	3.0	.2		
Dec	34.5	41.0	3.7	10.46	7.45	11.32	360.87	257.03	3.1	.4		
1992: Jan	34.3	40.9	3.6	10.46	7.44	11.27	358.78	255.36	3.0	.6		
Feb	34.6	41.1	3.7	10.51	7.46	11.34	363.65	258.27	3.9	1.1		
Mar	34.5	41.1	3.8	10.55	7.46	11.37	363.98	257.23	4.2	1.2		
Apr	34.3	41.1	3.9	10.52	7.42	11.42	360.84	254.47	3.1	.1		
May	34.6	41.3	4.1	10.56	7.44	11.44	365.38	257.31	3.4	.6		
June	34.3	41.0	3.8	10.58	7.43	11.44	362.89	254.84	1.9	-1.0		
July	34.3	41.0	3.8	10.58	7.41	11.45	362.89	254.30	2.6	-.4		
Aug	34.6	41.0	3.7	10.66	7.44	11.51	368.84	257.57	3.5	.4		
Sept	34.3	40.9	3.5	10.63	7.41	11.51	364.61	254.08	1.2	-1.7		
Oct	34.5	41.1	3.8	10.65	7.40	11.51	367.43	255.16	2.8	-.3		
Nov ᵖ	34.6	41.2	3.9	10.71	7.42	11.55	370.57	256.81	3.5	.5		
Dec ᵖ	34.3	41.3	3.9	10.70		11.57	367.01		1.6			

[1] For production or nonsupervisory workers; total includes private industry groups shown in Table B-41.
[2] Current dollars divided by the consumer price index for urban wage earners and clerical workers on a 1982=100 base.
[3] Percent changes are based on data that are not seasonally adjusted.
[4] Compensation (wages and salaries of employees plus employer contributions for social insurance and private benefit plans, and all other fringe benefits, as well as an estimate of the wages, salaries, and supplemental payments of the self-employed) divided by hours of all persons.
[5] See Table B-58.
Note.—See Note, Table B-41.
Source: Department of Labor, Bureau of Labor Statistics.

TABLE B-43.—*Employment cost index, private industry, 1979–92*

Year and month	Total private			Goods-producing			Service-producing			Manufacturing			Nonmanufacturing		
	Total compensation	Wages and salaries	Benefits[1]	Total compensation	Wages and salaries	Benefits[1]	Total compensation	Wages and salaries	Benefits[1]	Total compensation	Wages and salaries	Benefits[1]	Total compensation	Wages and salaries	Benefits[1]
Index, June 1989=100; not seasonally adjusted															
December:															
1979	59.1	61.5	53.2	60.7	63.7	54.6	57.7	60.0	51.9	60.1	63.0	54.2	58.5	60.8	52.5
1980	64.8	67.1	59.4	66.7	69.7	60.5	63.3	65.3	58.4	66.0	68.9	59.9	64.2	66.2	59.1
1981	71.2	73.0	66.6	73.3	75.7	68.2	69.5	71.1	65.1	72.5	74.9	67.5	70.4	72.1	66.1
1982	75.8	77.6	71.4	77.8	80.0	73.2	74.1	75.9	69.6	76.9	79.1	72.4	75.1	76.8	70.6
1983	80.1	81.4	76.7	81.6	83.2	78.3	78.9	80.2	75.2	80.8	82.5	77.5	79.6	81.0	76.2
1984	84.0	84.8	81.7	85.4	86.4	83.2	82.9	83.7	80.4	85.0	86.1	82.7	83.4	84.2	81.1
1985	87.3	88.3	84.6	88.2	89.4	85.7	86.6	87.7	83.6	87.8	89.2	85.0	87.0	88.0	84.4
1986	90.1	91.1	87.5	91.0	92.3	88.3	89.3	90.3	86.8	90.7	92.1	87.5	89.7	90.6	87.5
1987	93.1	94.1	90.5	93.8	95.2	90.9	92.6	93.4	90.2	93.4	95.2	89.8	92.9	93.7	91.0
1988	97.6	98.0	96.7	97.9	98.2	97.3	97.3	97.8	96.1	97.6	98.1	96.6	97.5	97.8	96.8
1989	102.3	102.0	102.6	102.1	102.0	102.6	102.3	102.2	102.6	102.0	101.9	102.3	102.3	102.2	102.8
1990	107.0	106.1	109.4	107.0	105.8	109.9	107.0	106.3	109.0	107.2	106.2	109.5	106.9	106.1	109.3
1991	111.7	110.0	116.2	111.9	109.7	116.7	111.6	110.2	115.7	112.2	110.3	116.1	111.5	109.8	116.2
1991: Mar	108.5	107.3	111.6	108.5	107.0	111.9	108.5	107.5	111.4	108.6	107.4	111.2	108.5	107.3	111.9
June	109.8	108.4	113.5	109.8	108.0	113.9	109.8	108.7	113.0	110.0	108.4	113.3	109.7	108.4	113.5
Sept	111.0	109.3	115.2	111.0	108.7	115.8	111.0	109.7	114.6	111.2	109.3	115.3	110.9	109.3	115.1
Dec	111.7	110.0	116.2	111.9	109.7	116.7	111.6	110.2	115.7	112.2	110.3	116.1	111.5	109.8	116.2
1992: Mar	113.1	110.9	118.6	113.5	110.7	119.7	112.8	111.1	117.7	114.0	111.5	119.3	112.7	110.7	118.2
June	113.9	111.6	119.7	114.3	111.4	120.6	113.6	111.7	118.8	114.7	112.2	120.1	113.5	111.3	119.4
Sept	114.8	112.2	121.2	115.3	112.1	122.3	114.4	112.3	120.4	115.7	112.9	121.5	114.4	111.9	121.0
Index, June 1989=100; seasonally adjusted															
1991: Mar	108.5	107.3	111.4	108.4	107.0	111.6	108.5	107.6	111.1	108.5	107.4	110.8	108.5	107.4	111.5
June	109.7	108.4	113.2	109.7	108.0	113.7	109.7	108.6	112.8	109.9	108.4	113.1	109.6	108.4	113.3
Sept	110.8	109.2	115.1	110.8	108.7	115.8	110.8	109.5	114.7	111.2	109.3	115.2	110.8	109.2	115.1
Dec	111.9	110.1	116.7	112.0	109.7	117.2	111.9	110.4	116.4	112.4	110.3	116.7	111.8	109.9	116.8
1992: Mar	113.0	111.0	118.4	113.4	110.7	119.7	112.8	111.2	117.4	113.9	111.5	119.0	112.7	110.8	117.8
June	113.7	111.5	119.4	114.1	111.4	120.4	113.4	111.6	118.6	114.7	112.2	119.9	113.4	111.2	119.2
Sept	114.6	112.1	121.3	115.2	112.1	122.2	114.3	112.1	120.5	115.6	112.9	121.4	114.3	111.8	121.0
Percent change from 12 months earlier, not seasonally adjusted															
December:															
1980	9.6	9.1	11.7	9.9	9.4	10.8	9.7	8.8	12.5	9.8	9.4	10.5	9.7	8.9	12.6
1981	9.9	8.8	12.1	9.9	8.6	12.7	9.8	8.9	11.5	9.8	8.7	12.7	9.7	8.9	11.8
1982	6.5	6.3	7.2	6.1	5.7	7.3	6.6	6.8	6.9	6.1	5.6	7.3	6.7	6.5	6.8
1983	5.7	4.9	7.4	4.9	4.0	7.0	6.5	5.7	8.0	5.1	4.3	7.0	6.0	5.5	7.9
1984	4.9	4.2	6.5	4.7	3.8	6.3	5.1	4.4	6.9	5.2	4.4	6.7	4.8	4.0	6.4
1985	3.9	4.1	3.5	3.3	3.5	3.0	4.5	4.8	4.0	3.3	3.6	2.8	4.3	4.5	4.1
1986	3.2	3.2	3.4	3.2	3.2	3.0	3.1	3.0	3.8	3.3	3.3	2.9	3.1	3.0	3.7
1987	3.3	3.3	3.4	3.1	3.1	2.9	3.7	3.4	3.9	3.0	3.4	2.6	3.6	3.4	4.0
1988	4.8	4.1	6.9	4.4	3.2	7.0	5.1	4.7	6.5	4.5	3.0	7.6	5.0	4.4	6.4
1989	4.8	4.1	6.1	4.3	3.9	5.4	5.1	4.5	6.8	4.5	3.9	5.9	4.9	4.5	6.2
1990	4.6	4.0	6.6	4.8	3.7	7.1	4.6	4.0	6.2	5.1	4.2	7.0	4.5	3.8	6.3
1991	4.4	3.7	6.2	4.6	3.7	6.2	4.3	3.7	6.1	4.7	3.9	6.0	4.3	3.5	6.3
1991: Mar	4.4	4.0	5.8	4.4	3.8	5.9	4.5	4.1	5.8	4.4	4.0	5.4	4.5	4.0	6.2
June	4.4	3.7	6.2	4.4	3.6	6.3	4.4	3.9	6.0	4.5	3.7	6.0	4.4	3.7	6.2
Sept	4.5	3.7	6.4	4.5	3.4	6.5	4.5	3.8	6.2	4.5	3.7	6.4	4.4	3.7	6.4
Dec	4.4	3.7	6.2	4.6	3.7	6.2	4.3	3.7	6.1	4.7	3.9	6.0	4.3	3.5	6.3
1992: Mar	4.2	3.4	6.3	4.6	3.5	7.0	4.0	3.3	5.7	5.0	3.8	7.3	3.9	3.2	5.6
June	3.7	3.0	5.5	4.1	3.1	5.9	3.5	2.8	5.1	4.3	3.5	6.0	3.5	2.7	5.2
Sept	3.4	2.7	5.2	3.9	3.1	5.6	3.1	2.4	5.1	4.0	3.3	5.4	3.2	2.4	5.1
Percent change from 3 months earlier, seasonally adjusted															
1991: Mar	1.2	1.0	1.4	1.1	1.1	1.2	1.2	1.0	1.5	0.9	1.1	0.6	1.3	1.1	1.5
June	1.1	1.0	1.6	1.2	.9	1.9	1.1	.9	1.5	1.3	.9	2.1	1.0	.9	1.6
Sept	1.0	.7	1.7	1.0	.6	1.8	1.0	.8	1.7	1.2	.8	1.9	1.1	.7	1.6
Dec	1.0	.8	1.4	1.1	.9	1.2	1.0	.8	1.5	1.1	.9	1.3	1.0	.9	1.5
1992: Mar	1.0	.8	1.5	1.3	.9	2.0	.8	.7	.9	1.3	1.1	2.0	.8	.8	.9
June	.6	.5	.8	.6	.6	.8	.5	.4	1.0	.7	.6	.8	.6	.4	1.2
Sept	.8	.5	1.6	1.0	.6	1.5	.8	.4	1.6	.8	.6	1.3	.8	.5	1.5

[1] Employer costs for employee benefits.

Note.—The employment cost index is a measure of the change in the cost of labor, free from the influence of employment shifts among occupations and industries.

Data exclude farm and household workers.

Through December 1981, percent changes are based on unrounded data; thereafter changes are based on indexes as published.

Source: Department of Labor, Bureau of Labor Statistics.

Year or quarter	Output per hour of all persons		Output [1]		Hours of all persons [2]		Compensation per hour [3]		Real compensation per hour [4]		Unit labor costs		Implicit price deflator [5]	
	Business sector	Nonfarm business sector	Business sector	Nonfarm business sector	Business sector	Nonfarm business sector	Business sector	Nonfarm business sector	Business sector	Nonfarm business sector	Business sector	Nonfarm business sector	Business sector	Nonfarm business sector
1959	64.5	69.1	51.4	51.0	79.6	73.8	20.2	21.3	67.0	70.5	31.3	30.8	32.1	31.8
1960	65.5	69.8	52.2	51.8	79.7	74.2	21.1	22.2	68.7	72.3	32.2	31.8	32.6	32.3
1961	68.0	72.1	53.3	52.9	78.5	73.4	21.9	22.9	70.7	74.0	32.2	31.8	32.8	32.5
1962	70.4	74.3	56.1	55.7	79.7	74.9	22.9	23.9	73.2	76.2	32.6	32.1	33.5	33.1
1963	73.2	77.0	58.7	58.3	80.1	75.8	23.8	24.7	75.0	77.9	32.5	32.1	33.7	33.4
1964	76.4	79.9	62.2	61.9	81.4	77.5	25.0	25.8	77.9	80.4	32.8	32.3	34.1	33.9
1965	78.5	81.7	65.9	65.7	83.9	80.4	26.0	26.7	79.6	81.8	33.1	32.7	35.0	34.6
1966	80.7	83.3	69.3	69.3	85.8	83.1	27.8	28.3	82.9	84.2	34.5	33.9	36.1	35.8
1967	82.7	85.1	70.8	70.8	85.6	83.1	29.4	29.9	84.9	86.5	35.5	35.1	37.2	36.9
1968	85.3	87.6	74.0	74.0	86.8	84.5	31.8	32.3	88.2	89.5	37.3	36.8	38.8	38.6
1969	85.7	87.6	76.2	76.2	88.9	87.0	34.1	34.5	89.7	90.7	39.8	39.4	40.6	40.4
1970	86.9	88.5	75.8	75.7	87.2	85.6	36.7	37.0	91.2	92.0	42.2	41.8	42.4	42.2
1971	89.8	91.2	78.0	77.9	86.9	85.4	39.0	39.4	93.0	93.8	43.5	43.1	44.5	44.3
1972	92.6	94.0	83.0	83.0	89.6	88.3	41.5	41.9	95.8	96.7	44.8	44.5	46.2	45.8
1973	95.0	96.3	88.2	88.4	92.8	91.7	45.1	45.4	98.0	98.6	47.5	47.1	49.0	47.9
1974	93.2	94.5	86.6	86.7	92.9	91.8	49.5	49.9	97.0	97.6	53.1	52.8	53.7	52.8
1975	95.4	96.6	85.0	84.9	89.1	88.0	54.5	54.8	97.7	98.3	57.1	56.7	59.0	58.3
1976	98.2	99.1	89.9	90.0	91.5	90.8	59.4	59.5	100.8	101.0	60.5	60.1	62.4	61.9
1977	99.8	100.6	94.9	95.0	95.1	94.5	64.2	64.3	102.3	102.4	64.3	63.9	66.5	66.1
1978	100.4	101.3	100.1	100.5	99.7	99.3	69.9	70.0	103.4	103.6	69.6	69.1	71.8	71.2
1979	99.3	99.9	102.1	102.5	102.8	102.7	76.7	76.7	102.0	101.9	77.2	76.8	78.3	77.5
1980	98.6	99.0	100.5	100.8	101.9	101.8	85.0	84.9	99.5	99.4	86.2	85.7	85.9	85.6
1981	99.9	99.9	102.4	102.4	102.5	102.5	93.0	93.0	98.7	98.8	93.1	93.1	94.5	94.2
1982	100.0	100.0	100.0	100.0	100.0	100.0	100.0	100.0	100.0	100.0	100.0	100.0	100.0	100.0
1983	102.2	102.4	104.1	104.4	101.8	102.0	103.7	103.9	100.5	100.7	101.5	101.5	103.4	104.0
1984	104.6	104.5	112.6	113.0	107.6	108.1	108.1	108.1	100.4	100.4	103.3	103.4	107.7	107.6
1985	106.1	105.4	116.7	116.8	109.9	110.8	113.0	112.6	101.3	101.0	106.5	106.8	111.2	111.6
1986	108.3	107.5	119.9	120.1	110.7	111.8	118.6	118.1	104.4	104.0	109.5	109.9	113.6	114.2
1987	109.4	108.3	124.8	125.0	114.1	115.4	122.7	122.1	104.3	103.7	112.2	112.8	116.6	117.2
1988	110.4	109.2	130.1	130.6	117.9	119.5	128.0	127.2	104.4	103.7	116.0	116.4	120.8	121.4
1989	109.5	108.2	132.3	132.7	120.9	122.7	132.3	131.3	103.0	102.2	120.9	121.4	126.1	126.5
1990	109.7	108.2	132.7	132.9	120.9	122.9	139.7	138.4	103.2	102.2	127.3	127.9	131.2	131.8
1991	110.1	108.7	129.8	130.0	117.9	119.6	146.6	145.4	103.9	103.0	133.1	133.8	136.2	137.0
1982: IV	101.1	101.1	100.0	100.0	98.9	98.9	102.1	102.1	100.6	100.6	101.0	101.0	101.4	101.4
1983: IV	103.0	103.2	107.5	108.1	104.3	104.7	105.2	105.1	100.4	100.3	102.1	101.8	104.8	105.2
1984: IV	105.2	105.1	114.4	114.8	108.7	109.2	109.7	109.7	100.6	100.5	104.3	104.4	109.0	109.0
1985: IV	106.9	105.8	118.0	118.2	110.4	111.7	115.4	114.8	102.2	101.6	108.0	108.4	112.4	112.9
1986: IV	108.0	107.1	120.6	120.8	111.6	112.8	120.6	120.1	105.3	104.9	111.6	112.1	114.6	115.2
1987: IV	110.3	109.1	127.4	127.6	115.5	116.9	125.3	124.6	104.8	104.2	113.6	114.2	117.9	118.5
1988: IV	110.5	109.6	131.7	132.5	119.2	120.9	130.2	129.3	104.3	103.6	117.8	118.0	122.8	123.4
1989: IV	109.3	108.0	132.3	132.7	121.1	122.8	134.3	133.3	102.9	102.1	122.9	123.3	127.8	128.2
1990: I	109.4	107.9	133.1	133.5	121.7	123.7	136.2	134.9	102.6	101.6	124.5	125.0	129.1	129.6
II	110.2	108.6	133.7	134.0	121.4	123.4	138.9	137.5	103.6	102.5	126.0	126.6	130.6	131.1
III	109.8	108.1	132.5	132.7	120.7	122.8	141.0	139.6	103.4	102.4	128.4	129.1	131.9	132.5
IV	109.7	108.1	131.3	131.5	119.8	121.6	142.9	141.6	103.0	102.1	130.3	131.0	133.3	134.1
1991: I	109.3	107.9	129.2	129.4	118.1	119.9	144.1	143.0	103.1	102.3	131.8	132.5	134.9	135.7
II	109.8	108.4	129.5	129.7	117.9	119.7	146.1	145.0	103.9	103.1	133.1	133.8	136.0	136.6
III	110.3	108.9	130.0	130.2	117.8	119.6	147.5	146.4	104.2	103.4	133.7	134.4	136.7	137.5
IV	111.2	109.6	130.6	130.7	117.5	119.3	148.8	147.5	104.2	103.3	133.8	134.4	137.3	138.3
1992: I	112.3	110.6	131.4	131.5	117.0	118.9	150.2	148.9	104.5	103.5	133.8	134.6	138.2	139.1
II	112.5	111.1	131.9	132.0	117.2	118.9	151.0	149.8	104.1	103.3	134.1	134.9	139.0	139.9
III	113.5	111.9	133.1	133.2	117.2	119.1	152.4	151.1	104.4	103.5	134.3	135.1	138.8	139.8

[1] Output refers to gross domestic product originating in the sector in 1987 dollars.
[2] Hours at work of all persons engaged in the sector, including hours of proprietors and unpaid family workers. Estimates based primarily on establishment data.
[3] Wages and salaries of employees plus employers' contributions for social insurance and private benefit plans. Also includes an estimate of wages, salaries, and supplemental payments for the self-employed.
[4] Hourly compensation divided by the consumer price index for all urban consumers.
[5] Current dollar gross domestic product divided by constant dollar gross domestic product.

Source: Department of Labor, Bureau of Labor Statistics.

[Percent change from preceding period; quarterly data at seasonally adjusted annual rates]

Year or quarter	Output per hour of all persons		Output [1]		Hours of all persons [2]		Compensation per hour [3]		Real compensation per hour [4]		Unit labor costs		Implicit price deflator [5]	
	Business sector	Nonfarm business sector	Business sector	Nonfarm business sector	Business sector	Nonfarm business sector	Business sector	Nonfarm business sector	Business sector	Nonfarm business sector	Business sector	Nonfarm business sector	Business sector	Nonfarm business sector
1960	1.6	1.1	1.7	1.7	0.1	0.6	4.3	4.4	2.6	2.6	2.7	3.3	1.5	1.5
1961	3.7	3.3	2.1	2.1	-1.6	-1.1	3.9	3.3	2.8	2.2	.1	0	.5	.6
1962	3.5	3.1	5.1	5.3	1.6	2.1	4.7	4.1	3.6	3.0	1.2	1.0	2.0	2.1
1963	4.1	3.6	4.6	4.7	.5	1.1	3.8	3.5	2.4	2.2	-.3	-.1	.8	.9
1964	4.3	3.8	6.0	6.2	1.6	2.3	5.2	4.6	3.9	3.3	.9	.8	1.1	1.4
1965	2.7	2.3	6.0	6.1	3.2	3.8	3.8	3.3	2.2	1.7	1.1	1.0	2.5	2.2
1966	2.8	1.9	5.2	5.4	2.3	3.4	7.0	6.0	4.1	3.0	4.1	3.9	3.3	3.3
1967	2.5	2.2	2.2	2.2	-.3	-.0	5.7	5.8	2.5	2.6	3.1	3.5	2.9	3.3
1968	3.0	2.9	4.5	4.6	1.4	1.7	8.2	7.9	3.8	3.6	5.0	4.8	4.4	4.5
1969	.5	-.0	2.9	2.9	2.4	2.9	7.3	6.8	1.7	1.3	6.7	6.8	4.7	4.6
1970	1.4	1.0	-.5	-.6	-1.9	-1.6	7.6	7.2	1.7	1.4	6.1	6.2	4.3	4.5
1971	3.3	3.1	2.9	2.9	-.4	-.3	6.4	6.4	1.9	1.9	3.0	3.2	4.9	5.0
1972	3.1	3.1	6.4	6.5	3.2	3.3	6.3	6.4	3.0	3.1	3.1	3.2	3.8	3.5
1973	2.6	2.4	6.2	6.4	3.6	3.9	8.7	8.3	2.3	1.9	5.9	5.7	6.1	4.5
1974	-1.8	-2.0	-1.8	-1.9	.1	.1	9.9	9.9	-1.0	-1.0	11.9	12.1	9.5	10.2
1975	2.3	2.2	-1.9	-2.0	-4.1	-4.2	10.0	9.9	.8	.7	7.5	7.5	10.0	10.4
1976	2.9	2.6	5.8	5.9	2.8	3.2	9.1	8.6	3.2	2.7	6.0	5.9	5.8	6.3
1977	1.7	1.5	5.6	5.6	3.8	4.1	8.0	8.0	1.4	1.4	6.3	6.4	6.5	6.8
1978	.6	.7	5.5	5.8	4.9	5.0	8.8	8.9	1.2	1.2	8.2	8.1	8.0	7.6
1979	-1.1	-1.4	2.0	2.0	3.1	3.4	9.8	9.5	-1.4	-1.6	11.0	11.1	9.1	8.9
1980	-.7	-.9	-1.6	-1.7	-.9	-.8	10.7	10.7	-2.4	-2.4	11.5	11.7	9.7	10.4
1981	1.3	.9	1.9	1.6	.6	.7	9.4	9.6	-.8	-.7	8.0	8.6	10.1	10.1
1982	.1	-.1	-2.3	-2.4	-2.5	-2.4	7.6	7.5	1.3	1.2	7.4	7.4	5.8	6.1
1983	2.2	2.4	4.1	4.4	1.8	2.0	3.7	3.9	.5	.7	1.5	1.5	3.4	4.0
1984	2.3	2.1	8.2	8.2	5.7	6.0	4.2	4.0	-.1	-.3	1.9	1.9	4.1	3.5
1985	1.4	.8	3.6	3.4	2.1	2.5	4.5	4.2	.9	.6	3.0	3.3	3.3	3.7
1986	2.0	1.9	2.8	2.8	.7	.9	4.9	4.9	3.0	3.0	2.8	2.9	2.2	2.4
1987	1.0	.8	4.1	4.1	3.1	3.3	3.5	3.4	-.1	-.2	2.5	2.6	2.6	2.6
1988	.9	.9	4.3	4.4	3.3	3.5	4.3	4.1	.1	.0	3.3	3.2	3.6	3.6
1989	-.8	-1.0	1.7	1.7	2.6	2.7	3.4	3.2	-1.4	-1.5	4.2	4.3	4.4	4.2
1990	.3	.0	.2	.1	-.0	.1	5.6	5.4	.2	-.0	5.3	5.4	4.1	4.2
1991	.3	.5	-2.2	-2.2	-2.5	-2.6	4.9	5.1	.7	.8	4.6	4.6	3.8	4.0
1990: I	.4	-.5	2.6	2.2	2.2	2.8	5.8	5.0	-1.2	-1.9	5.3	5.6	4.2	4.2
II	2.9	2.5	1.8	1.6	-1.1	-.9	8.0	7.8	3.8	3.5	5.0	5.1	4.7	4.7
III	-1.4	-1.7	-3.6	-3.7	-2.3	-2.1	6.3	6.4	-.7	-.6	7.8	8.2	4.2	4.5
IV	-.5	.1	-3.5	-3.6	-3.0	-3.7	5.4	5.9	-1.4	-.9	5.9	5.8	4.2	4.8
1991: I	-1.1	-.7	-6.4	-6.1	-5.3	-5.5	3.6	3.8	.4	.6	4.8	4.6	4.8	4.9
II	1.6	1.7	.9	.9	-.7	-.8	5.6	5.8	3.0	3.2	3.9	4.0	3.2	2.7
III	1.9	1.9	1.6	1.5	-.3	-.3	3.9	3.9	1.1	1.2	1.9	2.0	2.3	2.7
IV	3.3	2.5	2.0	1.6	-1.3	-.9	3.5	3.1	-.0	-.4	.2	.6	1.6	2.2
1992: I	3.9	3.7	2.3	2.3	-1.5	-1.3	4.0	3.8	1.1	.9	.1	.1	2.6	2.4
II	1.0	1.7	1.6	1.7	.6	.1	1.9	2.4	-1.4	-.9	.9	.8	2.4	2.5
III	3.4	3.0	3.6	3.5	.2	.6	3.9	3.5	1.3	.9	.5	.6	-.4	-.5

[1] Output refers to gross domestic product originating in the sector in 1987 dollars.
[2] Hours at work of all persons engaged in the sector, including hours of proprietors and unpaid family workers. Estimates based primarily on establishment data.
[3] Wages and salaries of employees plus employers' contributions for social insurance and private benefit plans. Also includes an estimate of wages, salaries, and supplemental payments for the self-employed.
[4] Hourly compensation divided by the consumer price index for all urban consumers.
[5] Current dollar gross domestic product divided by constant dollar gross domestic product.

Note.—Percent changes are based on original data and therefore may differ slightly from percent changes based on indexes in Table B-44.

Source: Department of Labor, Bureau of Labor Statistics.

TABLE B-46.—*Industrial production indexes, major industry divisions, 1947-92*

[1987 = 100; monthly data seasonally adjusted]

Year or month	Total industrial production	Manufacturing			Mining	Utilities
		Total	Durable	Nondur-able		
1991 proportion	*100.0*	*84.7*	*47.3*	*37.5*	*7.5*	*7.8*
1947	22.7	21.2	19.9	22.6	55.5	11.7
1948	23.6	22.0	20.8	23.4	58.3	13.0
1949	22.3	20.8	18.9	23.0	51.7	13.9
1950	25.8	24.2	23.0	25.6	57.7	15.8
1951	28.0	26.1	25.9	26.4	63.4	18.1
1952	29.1	27.2	27.5	26.9	62.8	19.6
1953	31.6	29.6	31.1	28.0	64.5	21.3
1954	29.9	27.7	27.4	28.2	63.2	22.9
1955	33.7	31.3	31.3	31.3	70.5	25.6
1956	35.1	32.5	32.4	32.9	74.2	28.1
1957	35.6	32.9	32.6	33.5	74.3	30.0
1958	33.3	30.6	28.5	33.7	68.1	31.4
1959	37.3	34.5	32.8	37.1	71.3	34.5
1960	38.1	35.2	33.3	38.0	72.7	36.9
1961	38.4	35.3	32.7	39.1	73.1	39.0
1962	41.6	38.4	36.3	41.5	75.2	41.9
1963	44.0	40.7	38.7	43.8	78.2	44.8
1964	47.0	43.5	41.4	46.6	81.4	48.7
1965	51.7	48.2	47.1	49.8	84.4	51.7
1966	56.3	52.6	52.3	52.9	88.9	55.6
1967	57.5	53.6	52.9	54.6	90.6	58.4
1968	60.7	56.6	55.5	58.1	94.1	63.1
1969	63.5	59.1	57.7	61.1	97.8	68.7
1970	61.4	56.4	53.3	61.1	100.4	72.9
1971	62.2	57.3	53.1	63.6	97.8	76.4
1972	68.3	63.3	59.3	69.3	99.9	81.3
1973	73.8	68.9	66.2	72.7	100.8	84.5
1974	72.7	67.9	64.8	72.3	100.3	83.5
1975	66.3	61.1	56.7	67.7	98.0	84.3
1976	72.4	67.4	62.6	74.6	98.9	87.6
1977	78.2	73.3	68.7	80.1	101.5	89.9
1978	82.6	77.8	73.9	83.5	104.6	92.7
1979	85.7	80.9	78.3	84.6	106.6	95.3
1980	84.1	78.8	75.7	83.1	110.0	95.9
1981	85.7	80.3	77.4	84.5	114.3	94.3
1982	81.9	76.6	72.7	82.5	109.3	91.8
1983	84.9	80.9	76.8	87.0	104.8	93.6
1984	92.8	89.3	88.4	90.8	111.9	97.0
1985	94.4	91.6	91.8	91.5	109.0	99.5
1986	95.3	94.3	93.9	94.9	101.0	96.3
1987	100.0	100.0	100.0	100.0	100.0	100.0
1988	105.4	105.8	107.6	103.6	101.8	104.4
1989	108.1	108.9	110.9	106.4	100.5	107.1
1990	109.2	109.9	111.6	107.8	102.6	108.0
1991	107.1	107.4	107.1	107.9	101.1	109.2
1991: Jan	106.6	107.0	107.2	106.8	101.7	107.6
Feb	105.7	106.1	106.1	106.0	102.9	104.6
Mar	105.0	105.2	105.0	105.4	101.5	106.4
Apr	105.5	105.9	106.0	105.9	100.9	105.9
May	106.4	106.6	106.7	106.5	100.2	111.4
June	107.3	107.5	107.3	107.6	102.1	111.5
July	108.1	108.3	108.1	108.6	102.7	110.9
Aug	108.0	108.4	107.8	109.0	101.3	110.7
Sept	108.4	108.9	108.4	109.6	101.4	109.7
Oct	108.4	109.0	108.2	110.1	100.7	109.4
Nov	108.1	108.6	107.8	109.6	99.6	111.0
Dec	107.4	108.1	107.1	109.5	98.8	107.9
1992: Jan	106.6	107.4	105.8	109.5	97.8	106.8
Feb	107.2	108.1	107.0	109.6	98.4	106.4
Mar	107.6	108.5	107.0	110.4	97.5	107.7
Apr	108.1	109.0	107.6	110.7	99.1	108.2
May	108.9	109.9	109.1	110.9	99.7	107.3
June	108.5	109.6	108.5	111.0	98.0	106.7
July	109.4	110.2	109.0	111.7	100.6	109.3
Aug	109.1	110.1	109.2	111.3	98.8	108.8
Sept	108.8	109.7	108.2	111.6	98.8	109.1
Oct ᴾ	109.3	110.3	109.2	111.6	98.9	108.6
Nov ᴾ	109.7	110.8	109.7	112.2	99.5	107.9

Source: Board of Governors of the Federal Reserve System.

TABLE B-47.—*Industrial production indexes, market groupings, 1947-92*

[1987=100; monthly data seasonally adjusted]

Year or month	Total industrial production	Final products									Materials			
		Total	Consumer goods				Equipment			Intermediate products	Total	Durable	Non-durable	Energy
			Total	Automotive products	Other durable goods	Non-durable goods	Total [1]	Business	Defense and space					
1991 proportion	*100.0*	*47.1*	*26.1*	*2.3*	*3.1*	*20.8*	*21.0*	*15.8*	*4.6*	*14.2*	*38.6*	*19.4*	*8.9*	*10.4*
1947	22.7	20.8	25.4	21.7	22.8	27.0	15.0	14.7	7.5	22.4	25.1	21.5		
1948	23.6	21.5	26.2	22.6	23.8	27.7	15.8	15.3	8.8	23.6	26.2	22.1		
1949	22.3	20.9	26.1	22.5	22.0	27.9	14.1	13.4	9.2	22.4	23.9	19.8		
1950	25.8	23.5	29.7	28.3	30.4	30.3	15.3	14.3	10.8	26.1	28.6	24.9		
1951	28.0	25.4	29.4	25.0	26.2	31.3	21.2	17.5	26.5	27.4	31.6	28.3		
1952	29.1	27.3	30.1	22.5	26.2	32.6	25.5	19.8	37.2	27.2	32.1	28.9		
1953	31.6	29.1	31.9	28.4	29.6	33.5	27.6	20.6	44.6	29.1	35.6	33.8		
1954	29.9	27.6	31.7	26.5	27.3	33.9	24.2	18.1	39.3	29.0	32.9	29.2	25.2	52.7
1955	33.7	29.8	35.4	35.2	32.2	36.5	24.7	19.6	35.9	32.9	38.9	35.7	28.9	59.3
1956	35.1	31.6	36.7	28.9	33.9	38.8	27.1	22.7	35.1	34.4	39.9	35.8	30.2	62.7
1957	35.6	32.5	37.6	30.3	33.2	40.1	28.2	23.6	36.7	34.4	39.9	35.8	30.1	63.4
1958	33.3	31.0	37.2	24.1	31.3	41.3	25.2	19.9	36.8	33.6	35.9	30.1	29.9	58.8
1959	37.3	34.0	40.9	30.2	36.0	44.1	27.7	22.4	38.8	37.1	41.4	35.9	34.2	62.3
1960	38.1	35.1	42.4	34.6	36.2	45.5	28.5	23.0	39.9	37.4	42.0	36.3	34.8	63.1
1961	38.4	35.4	43.3	31.6	37.3	47.0	28.1	22.3	40.6	38.1	42.0	35.5	36.2	63.6
1962	41.6	38.4	46.2	38.3	40.5	49.2	31.3	24.3	46.9	40.4	45.8	39.4	39.2	65.8
1963	44.0	40.6	48.8	41.9	43.7	51.4	33.1	25.5	50.6	42.7	48.7	42.1	41.6	69.7
1964	47.0	42.9	51.5	43.9	47.7	54.0	35.0	28.5	49.0	45.5	52.6	45.9	45.2	72.5
1965	51.7	47.1	55.5	54.1	54.1	56.3	39.6	32.6	54.3	48.4	58.7	52.6	49.6	75.8
1966	56.3	51.6	58.4	53.9	59.6	59.0	46.1	37.8	63.7	51.4	63.9	57.9	53.6	80.6
1967	57.5	53.7	59.8	47.4	60.4	62.0	49.0	38.6	72.7	53.5	63.3	55.9	54.5	83.4
1968	60.7	56.3	63.4	56.4	64.7	64.5	50.4	40.3	72.9	56.6	67.5	59.2	59.9	87.2
1969	63.5	58.1	65.8	56.7	69.0	66.7	51.8	42.9	69.4	59.6	71.5	62.3	64.9	91.7
1970	61.4	56.0	65.0	47.7	66.9	67.8	48.1	41.3	58.7	58.7	69.0	56.5	65.2	96.2
1971	62.2	56.5	68.8	60.8	70.8	69.7	45.0	39.3	52.8	60.5	70.0	56.8	68.0	97.1
1972	68.3	61.3	74.3	65.6	81.0	74.2	49.3	44.8	51.3	67.6	77.2	64.2	74.9	100.8
1973	73.8	65.9	77.6	72.4	85.7	76.5	55.0	52.4	50.1	71.9	84.5	73.3	80.4	101.5
1974	72.7	65.7	75.2	62.6	79.3	76.5	56.8	54.7	49.4	69.4	82.8	71.2	80.8	98.8
1975	66.3	61.8	72.3	59.0	69.8	74.9	52.0	48.8	48.5	62.6	72.6	59.3	71.9	96.7
1976	72.4	66.2	79.4	73.2	78.2	80.4	53.8	50.6	49.2	69.0	81.2	68.4	81.4	99.0
1977	78.2	71.6	85.1	84.0	87.4	84.4	58.8	56.7	49.2	74.9	87.3	75.3	86.7	101.1
1978	82.6	76.1	88.4	86.3	91.2	87.8	64.2	63.1	49.5	79.1	91.8	81.4	89.7	102.2
1979	85.7	79.0	87.3	78.5	89.8	87.7	71.0	71.5	51.5	81.2	95.4	85.3	92.9	105.0
1980	84.1	80.0	85.3	59.5	85.1	89.1	74.6	73.5	57.4	77.0	91.3	79.3	88.7	106.2
1981	85.7	82.1	85.8	59.2	86.3	89.6	78.2	76.1	58.5	77.0	92.8	82.1	90.5	104.3
1982	81.9	80.8	84.5	57.5	78.1	89.7	77.0	72.9	65.7	75.1	85.1	73.4	82.1	100.7
1983	84.9	83.0	88.8	71.9	86.2	91.9	76.8	71.9	71.8	80.3	88.3	79.2	89.2	98.9
1984	92.8	91.0	92.8	86.6	94.6	93.4	89.2	85.4	78.9	86.2	96.6	92.1	93.0	103.8
1985	94.4	94.2	93.7	92.7	90.6	94.4	94.8	91.1	89.4	88.3	96.6	92.9	91.7	103.4
1986	95.3	95.7	96.8	95.2	93.9	97.6	94.5	93.2	96.0	92.0	95.9	93.7	94.4	99.4
1987	100.0	100.0	100.0	100.0	100.0	100.0	100.0	100.0	100.0	100.0	100.0	100.0	100.0	100.0
1988	105.4	105.6	104.0	105.9	104.1	103.7	107.6	111.8	98.0	104.4	105.6	109.0	103.0	101.8
1989	108.1	109.1	106.7	106.9	108.7	106.4	112.3	119.1	97.4	106.8	107.4	111.6	105.3	101.4
1990	109.2	110.9	107.3	102.3	109.4	107.6	115.5	123.1	97.3	107.7	107.8	111.8	106.0	102.1
1991	107.1	109.6	107.5	97.8	105.8	109.0	112.2	121.5	91.1	103.4	105.5	107.1	105.9	102.3
1991: Jan	106.6	109.1	105.6	90.6	103.2	107.8	113.6	121.6	94.4	103.8	104.8	106.8	104.9	101.1
Feb	105.7	108.3	104.7	88.1	100.7	107.3	112.9	120.6	94.5	102.6	103.9	105.5	103.6	101.1
Mar	105.0	108.1	104.7	88.9	101.4	107.1	112.5	120.3	93.9	101.3	102.6	103.3	102.8	101.3
Apr	105.5	108.7	105.5	94.2	103.4	107.2	112.8	121.3	92.5	101.2	103.4	104.9	103.1	101.1
May	106.4	109.3	106.6	97.4	104.1	108.1	112.7	121.7	91.5	102.7	104.5	106.2	103.7	102.4
June	107.3	110.1	108.0	100.4	107.3	109.0	112.8	121.9	91.0	104.0	105.4	106.7	104.9	103.4
July	108.1	110.2	108.3	102.3	108.1	109.0	112.8	122.5	90.0	104.0	107.0	108.2	108.1	104.1
Aug	108.0	109.8	108.4	98.6	108.3	109.6	111.6	121.3	89.8	104.4	107.2	109.1	107.8	103.3
Sept	108.4	110.4	109.4	106.5	108.7	109.8	111.8	122.2	89.1	104.3	107.5	109.3	108.3	103.6
Oct	108.4	110.6	109.7	106.7	108.1	110.3	111.9	122.3	89.1	104.1	107.4	108.8	109.6	103.1
Nov	108.1	110.6	110.0	103.6	108.0	111.1	111.4	121.8	88.8	103.9	106.6	108.6	107.7	102.2
Dec	107.4	109.9	109.1	101.3	107.2	110.3	110.9	121.4	88.1	103.8	105.8	108.1	107.8	102.5
1992: Jan	106.6	108.7	108.1	94.2	106.9	110.0	109.4	119.9	86.7	103.9	105.2	107.0	107.3	100.4
Feb	107.2	109.4	108.8	101.6	108.3	109.8	110.2	121.0	86.2	104.0	105.8	108.1	107.1	100.5
Mar	107.6	109.8	109.3	103.6	108.3	110.2	110.4	121.5	85.6	104.4	106.1	108.3	108.9	100.1
Apr	108.1	110.6	110.1	106.5	109.1	110.7	111.3	123.0	84.7	103.9	106.8	108.7	109.4	101.3
May	108.9	111.4	110.8	110.6	111.5	110.7	112.3	124.5	84.2	104.4	107.7	110.4	109.7	101.3
June	108.5	110.5	109.6	108.0	110.2	109.7	111.6	124.1	83.6	104.4	107.6	110.2	110.4	100.6
July	109.4	111.0	110.4	106.6	110.3	110.8	111.8	124.4	82.7	105.1	109.0	111.2	111.7	102.9
Aug	109.1	111.5	110.8	106.4	111.1	111.2	112.5	125.9	81.8	104.4	108.1	111.1	110.8	100.9
Sept	108.8	111.0	110.3	104.5	108.7	111.3	111.9	125.3	81.0	104.0	108.6	110.1	110.5	100.2
Oct P	109.3	111.9	111.0	108.9	108.3	111.7	112.9	126.7	80.5	104.5	108.1	110.9	110.1	101.3
Nov P	109.7	112.2	111.3	109.2	108.7	112.0	113.4	127.4	79.7	104.8	108.6	111.3	111.8	101.1

[1] Two components—oil and gas well drilling and manufactured homes—are included in total equipment, but not in detail shown.

Source: Board of Governors of the Federal Reserve System.

401

TABLE B–48.—*Industrial production indexes, selected manufactures, 1947–92*

[1987 = 100; monthly data seasonally adjusted]

Year or month	Durable manufactures								Nondurable manufactures				
	Primary metals		Fabricated metal products	Non-electrical machinery	Electrical machinery	Transportation equipment		Lumber and products	Apparel products	Textile mill products	Printing and publishing	Chemicals and products	Foods
	Total	Iron and steel				Total	Motor vehicles and parts						
1991 proportion......	3.1	1.8	5.0	9.9	8.9	9.0	3.9	1.8	2.1	1.7	6.7	8.9	8.9
1947...............	70.2	102.1	37.5	12.0	8.5	19.6	27.3	38.8	43.1	35.2	22.1	8.7	33.1
1948...............	73.0	106.8	38.2	12.1	8.8	21.4	29.6	40.4	45.0	37.7	23.2	9.4	32.8
1949...............	61.4	91.2	34.4	10.3	8.3	21.5	30.4	35.7	44.5	34.8	23.8	9.3	33.1
1950...............	77.3	112.4	42.2	11.6	11.3	25.7	39.0	43.4	47.9	39.6	24.9	11.6	34.3
1951...............	84.1	125.7	45.1	14.7	11.4	28.7	35.8	43.2	47.0	39.2	25.4	13.1	35.0
1952...............	76.8	110.6	44.0	16.0	13.0	33.3	30.7	42.7	49.5	38.9	25.3	13.7	35.7
1953...............	87.0	127.5	49.6	16.7	14.9	41.8	38.7	45.1	50.1	39.9	26.5	14.8	36.4
1954...............	70.4	99.1	44.7	14.2	13.3	36.4	33.3	44.8	49.5	37.3	27.6	15.0	37.2
1955...............	91.5	131.8	51.0	15.6	15.3	41.9	44.6	50.1	54.7	42.5	30.3	17.6	39.3
1956...............	90.9	129.3	51.8	17.9	16.5	40.6	36.2	49.5	56.0	43.7	32.3	18.9	41.5
1957...............	87.1	124.6	53.1	17.9	16.4	43.5	38.0	45.4	55.8	41.6	33.4	19.9	42.2
1958...............	69.0	93.9	47.6	15.0	15.0	34.3	28.0	46.1	54.3	41.1	32.6	20.6	43.2
1959...............	80.7	108.1	53.4	17.5	18.2	38.9	36.4	52.3	59.7	46.4	34.8	24.0	45.4
1960...............	80.4	109.9	53.4	17.6	19.8	40.3	41.1	49.3	60.9	45.6	36.2	24.9	46.6
1961...............	78.9	104.9	52.1	17.1	21.0	37.8	36.0	51.6	61.3	46.9	36.4	26.1	47.9
1962...............	84.6	109.3	56.7	19.2	24.1	43.7	43.9	54.4	63.8	50.1	37.7	29.0	49.5
1963...............	91.2	119.1	58.5	20.5	24.8	48.0	48.6	56.9	66.4	51.9	39.7	31.7	51.2
1964...............	102.9	135.5	62.1	23.3	26.2	49.2	49.9	61.1	68.7	56.0	42.1	34.8	53.6
1965...............	113.2	148.7	68.3	26.2	31.3	58.5	63.7	63.5	72.6	61.0	44.8	38.7	54.8
1966...............	120.2	153.1	73.1	30.5	37.5	62.7	62.6	65.9	74.5	64.7	48.3	42.2	56.9
1967...............	111.1	141.5	76.5	31.1	37.7	61.3	55.1	65.3	74.1	64.8	50.9	44.2	59.4
1968...............	115.1	146.1	80.6	31.3	39.8	66.6	66.0	67.2	76.0	72.3	51.7	49.6	61.0
1969...............	123.8	159.2	81.9	33.9	42.3	66.1	66.3	67.1	78.4	76.0	54.2	53.7	63.0
1970...............	115.2	148.2	75.9	32.8	40.5	55.5	53.3	66.7	75.3	74.4	52.7	55.9	64.0
1971...............	109.2	135.5	75.6	30.5	40.7	60.1	66.9	68.5	76.2	78.5	53.2	59.5	66.0
1972...............	122.4	150.6	82.9	35.4	46.5	64.1	73.0	78.4	80.9	86.0	56.7	66.9	69.5
1973...............	138.9	171.5	92.1	41.4	53.0	73.0	85.0	78.7	81.5	89.6	58.3	73.1	70.9
1974...............	134.5	166.1	88.4	44.1	52.4	66.4	73.4	71.4	77.9	81.5	57.4	75.8	71.9
1975...............	107.2	133.5	76.7	38.1	45.1	59.7	62.2	66.5	71.1	77.7	53.7	69.1	71.4
1976...............	119.9	147.1	84.9	40.0	50.7	68.0	81.9	75.6	83.9	86.3	58.7	77.3	75.5
1977...............	121.5	145.1	92.7	45.1	58.4	73.7	94.7	82.3	91.6	91.6	64.3	83.3	79.0
1978...............	130.7	155.3	96.2	50.2	64.0	79.5	99.2	83.6	93.9	92.0	68.1	88.0	81.8
1979...............	133.0	156.5	99.5	56.9	71.3	81.0	91.0	82.4	89.0	95.0	69.9	91.3	82.6
1980...............	110.8	126.0	92.5	60.6	73.3	72.3	67.0	76.9	89.2	92.1	70.3	87.8	84.6
1981...............	117.5	135.1	91.1	65.9	75.4	68.7	64.4	74.7	91.0	89.4	72.1	89.2	86.5
1982...............	83.2	86.2	83.2	63.9	75.9	64.8	58.8	67.3	90.1	83.0	75.2	81.8	87.7
1983...............	91.0	96.1	85.5	64.3	80.3	72.7	74.5	79.9	93.8	93.2	79.0	87.5	90.1
1984...............	102.4	105.9	93.3	80.8	94.1	83.1	90.6	86.0	95.7	93.7	84.5	91.4	92.1
1985...............	101.8	104.5	94.5	86.8	93.1	91.8	99.0	88.0	92.6	89.7	87.6	91.4	94.9
1986...............	93.8	90.8	93.8	90.4	94.3	96.9	98.5	95.1	96.3	93.9	90.7	94.6	97.4
1987...............	100.0	100.0	100.0	100.0	100.0	100.0	100.0	100.0	100.0	100.0	100.0	100.0	100.0
1988...............	110.3	113.8	106.2	113.8	106.5	105.0	105.5	104.6	102.2	99.8	103.6	105.4	102.8
1989...............	109.2	109.3	107.2	121.8	109.5	107.2	104.9	103.0	104.3	101.9	108.5	108.5	105.5
1990...............	108.4	109.9	105.9	126.5	111.4	105.5	96.8	101.6	98.8	100.8	111.9	110.3	107.6
1991...............	99.5	98.0	100.4	123.5	110.1	98.6	90.4	94.2	96.2	100.5	112.3	110.9	108.6
1991: Jan............	99.7	99.0	101.7	125.5	107.6	97.6	83.0	94.2	92.9	94.0	112.1	110.1	108.3
Feb	99.5	98.0	99.1	124.5	108.2	95.5	79.4	91.5	93.1	94.3	110.9	109.1	107.6
Mar............	94.7	92.0	97.8	123.1	108.6	95.0	79.8	91.2	92.5	95.4	101.4	108.2	107.4
Apr............	94.5	91.6	98.0	123.5	109.7	97.2	86.2	92.7	93.2	97.2	110.7	109.0	107.6
May............	96.9	94.0	99.1	123.6	110.6	98.2	89.8	92.5	95.2	99.2	110.6	109.2	108.6
June............	96.4	92.9	99.8	123.4	111.5	99.7	92.5	96.7	96.2	101.7	111.2	109.6	108.6
July............	101.4	99.5	100.9	123.9	111.0	101.3	96.7	94.8	97.8	104.2	111.9	111.5	108.3
Aug............	102.6	100.6	101.4	123.3	111.5	99.0	91.6	95.3	98.3	104.7	112.3	112.3	108.7
Sept............	102.3	100.8	101.9	123.1	111.0	102.2	99.5	95.2	98.1	103.2	113.3	112.6	109.5
Oct	102.6	102.4	101.9	123.5	109.8	102.4	100.4	93.8	98.7	105.5	114.4	113.5	109.4
Nov............	103.5	105.6	101.8	122.8	110.7	99.7	95.9	96.4	98.8	104.4	114.2	113.0	110.1
Dec............	101.3	101.7	101.2	121.9	110.6	98.0	94.6	95.2	99.0	102.5	114.5	112.6	109.6
1992: Jan............	102.5	105.0	99.7	121.4	110.0	93.8	87.1	97.4	97.5	103.1	114.8	112.7	109.2
Feb	102.7	103.7	100.5	121.9	110.7	96.8	93.8	98.8	97.7	104.7	114.4	113.4	109.6
Mar............	101.4	102.5	100.0	122.9	110.9	96.5	94.2	99.2	97.8	105.3	113.8	114.8	110.2
Apr............	100.9	100.9	100.8	124.1	111.0	98.0	98.5	97.2	98.0	106.3	113.7	115.8	109.9
May............	102.0	102.2	102.2	126.7	112.3	99.6	102.7	97.4	99.0	106.8	113.4	117.0	109.3
June............	102.1	101.8	102.2	126.4	112.2	98.2	100.4	95.4	98.1	105.3	113.0	117.5	109.9
July............	105.6	106.4	102.6	127.8	112.6	96.7	97.7	99.8	99.4	107.1	112.3	118.0	109.8
Aug............	104.3	104.4	102.5	129.3	113.0	97.0	99.4	98.9	97.6	106.1	111.4	117.6	110.6
Sept............	102.0	103.0	101.4	129.1	111.9	95.6	97.2	96.3	97.6	105.9	113.1	118.1	110.0
Oct ᵖ........	104.7	107.1	102.0	130.4	112.5	97.4	101.4	98.2	97.5	104.1	112.6	118.4	110.9
Nov ᵖ........	104.8	107.6	102.9	131.7	113.0	96.9	102.1	101.2	97.9	105.7	111.6	119.6	111.2

Source: Board of Governors of the Federal Reserve System.

TABLE B–49.—*Capacity utilization rates, 1948–92*

[Percent;[1] monthly data seasonally adjusted]

Year or month	Total industry	Manufacturing			Primary processing	Advanced processing	Mining	Utilities
		Total	Durable goods	Non-durable goods				
1948		82.5			87.3	80.0		
1949		74.2			76.2	73.2		
1950		82.8			88.5	79.8		
1951		85.8			90.2	83.4		
1952		85.4			84.9	85.9		
1953		89.3			89.4	89.3		
1954		80.1			80.6	80.0		
1955		87.0			92.0	84.2		
1956		86.1			89.4	84.4		
1957		83.6			84.7	83.1		
1958		75.0			75.4	74.9		
1959		81.6			83.0	81.1		
1960		80.1			79.8	80.5		
1961		77.3			77.9	77.2		
1962		81.4			81.5	81.6		
1963		83.5			83.8	83.4		
1964		85.6			87.8	84.6		
1965		89.5			91.0	88.8		
1966		91.1			91.4	91.1		
1967	86.4	87.2	87.1	86.3	85.4	88.0	81.2	93.4
1968	86.8	87.2	86.8	86.6	86.3	87.4	83.5	94.1
1969	86.9	86.8	86.3	86.6	86.9	86.5	86.6	95.8
1970	80.8	79.7	76.7	82.9	80.4	79.1	88.9	95.4
1971	79.2	78.2	74.3	82.8	79.3	77.4	87.4	93.9
1972	84.3	83.7	80.9	86.6	86.4	82.5	90.4	94.6
1973	88.4	88.1	87.5	87.5	91.5	86.5	92.5	92.9
1974	84.2	83.8	82.7	84.0	86.0	82.8	92.5	86.8
1975	74.6	73.2	70.2	76.4	72.9	73.5	89.9	84.0
1976	79.3	78.5	75.4	81.8	80.1	77.8	90.0	84.8
1977	83.3	82.8	80.3	85.2	84.0	81.9	90.9	84.6
1978	85.5	85.1	83.5	86.2	86.3	84.3	91.3	84.8
1979	86.2	85.4	84.9	85.1	86.4	84.8	91.9	85.9
1980	82.1	80.2	78.6	81.4	78.0	81.3	94.0	85.5
1981	80.9	78.8	76.6	81.0	78.0	79.1	94.6	82.8
1982	75.0	72.8	69.0	78.0	69.0	74.6	86.5	79.5
1983	75.8	74.9	70.5	81.1	74.8	74.9	79.9	80.3
1984	81.1	80.4	78.3	83.1	80.4	80.3	84.4	82.5
1985	80.3	79.5	77.8	81.9	79.8	79.4	82.9	83.5
1986	79.2	79.0	76.1	83.0	80.8	78.2	78.2	80.2
1987	81.4	81.4	78.6	85.4	84.9	79.9	80.0	82.5
1988	84.0	83.9	82.5	86.0	87.8	82.3	84.6	84.2
1989	84.2	83.9	82.8	85.5	87.0	82.7	85.9	85.4
1990	83.0	82.3	81.1	83.9	84.9	81.2	89.4	85.2
1991	79.4	78.2	75.8	81.5	80.1	77.4	88.5	84.7
1991: Jan	80.0	78.9	76.8	81.8	80.6	78.2	89.5	84.1
Feb	79.1	78.0	75.8	81.0	79.5	77.4	90.4	81.6
Mar	78.4	77.2	74.9	80.3	77.9	76.8	89.0	83.0
Apr	78.6	77.5	75.4	80.5	78.2	77.3	88.3	82.6
May	79.1	77.8	75.7	80.7	79.0	77.3	87.6	86.7
June	79.6	78.3	76.0	81.4	79.9	77.6	89.2	86.7
July	80.0	78.7	76.4	82.0	81.1	77.8	89.6	86.2
Aug	79.8	78.6	76.0	82.1	81.2	77.5	88.5	85.9
Sept	79.9	78.8	76.2	82.3	81.3	77.7	88.5	85.1
Oct	79.8	78.7	75.9	82.4	81.4	77.6	87.9	84.8
Nov	79.3	78.2	75.5	81.9	80.8	77.1	86.8	85.9
Dec	78.7	77.7	74.8	81.6	80.2	76.6	86.2	83.4
1992: Jan	78.0	77.0	73.8	81.4	80.2	75.7	85.3	82.6
Feb	78.3	77.4	74.5	81.3	80.4	76.1	85.7	82.2
Mar	78.4	77.5	74.3	81.7	80.8	76.1	84.9	83.1
Apr	78.7	77.7	74.6	81.8	81.1	76.3	86.3	83.4
May	79.1	78.2	75.5	81.8	81.5	76.8	86.9	82.7
June	78.6	77.8	75.0	81.6	81.4	76.3	85.4	82.1
July	79.1	78.1	75.2	82.0	82.7	76.2	87.6	84.1
Aug	78.8	77.9	75.2	81.6	81.7	76.3	86.1	83.6
Sept	78.5	77.4	74.4	81.6	81.3	75.9	86.1	83.8
Oct P	78.7	77.7	75.0	81.4	81.6	76.2	86.2	83.3
Nov P	78.9	77.9	75.2	81.7	82.4	76.2	86.7	82.8

[1] Output as percent of capacity.

Source: Board of Governors of the Federal Reserve System.

TABLE B-50.—*New construction activity, 1929–92*

[Value put in place, billions of dollars; monthly data at seasonally adjusted annual rates]

Year or month	Total new construction	Private construction							Public construction		
		Total	Residential buildings [1]		Nonresidential buildings and other construction [1]				Total	Federal	State and local [5]
			Total [2]	New housing units	Total	Commercial [3]	Industrial	Other [4]			
1929	10.8	8.3	3.6	3.0	4.7	1.1	0.9	2.6	2.5	0.2	2.3
1933	2.9	1.2	.5	.3	.8	.1	.2	.5	1.6	.5	1.1
1939	8.2	4.4	2.7	2.3	1.7	.3	.3	1.2	3.8	.8	3.1
1940	8.7	5.1	3.0	2.6	2.1	.3	.4	1.3	3.6	1.2	2.4
1941	12.0	6.2	3.5	3.0	2.7	.4	.8	1.5	5.8	3.8	2.0
1942	14.1	3.4	1.7	1.4	1.7	.2	.3	1.2	10.7	9.3	1.3
1943	8.3	2.0	.9	.7	1.1	.0	.2	.9	6.3	5.6	.7
1944	5.3	2.2	.8	.6	1.4	.1	.2	1.1	3.1	2.5	.6
1945	5.8	3.4	1.3	.7	2.1	.2	.6	1.3	2.4	1.7	.7
1946	14.3	12.1	6.2	4.8	5.8	1.2	1.7	3.0	2.2	.9	1.4
New series											
1947	20.0	16.7	9.9	7.8	6.9	1.0	1.7	4.2	3.3	.8	2.5
1948	26.1	21.4	13.1	10.5	8.2	1.4	1.4	5.5	4.7	1.2	3.5
1949	26.7	20.5	12.4	10.0	8.0	1.2	1.0	5.9	6.3	1.5	4.8
1950	33.6	26.7	18.1	15.6	8.6	1.4	1.1	6.1	6.9	1.6	5.2
1951	35.4	26.2	15.9	13.2	10.3	1.5	2.1	6.7	9.3	3.0	6.3
1952	36.8	26.0	15.8	12.9	10.2	1.1	2.3	6.8	10.8	4.2	6.6
1953	39.1	27.9	16.6	13.4	11.3	1.8	2.2	7.3	11.2	4.1	7.1
1954	41.4	29.7	18.2	14.9	11.5	2.2	2.0	7.2	11.7	3.4	8.3
1955	46.5	34.8	21.9	18.2	12.9	3.2	2.4	7.3	11.7	2.8	8.9
1956	47.6	34.9	20.2	16.1	14.7	3.6	3.1	8.0	12.7	2.7	10.0
1957	49.1	35.1	19.0	14.7	16.1	3.6	3.6	9.0	14.1	3.0	11.1
1958	50.0	34.6	19.8	15.4	14.8	3.6	2.4	8.8	15.5	3.4	12.1
1959	55.4	39.3	24.3	19.2	15.1	3.9	2.1	9.0	16.1	3.7	12.3
1960	54.7	38.9	23.0	17.3	15.9	4.2	2.9	8.9	15.9	3.6	12.2
1961	56.4	39.3	23.1	17.1	16.2	4.7	2.8	8.7	17.1	3.9	13.3
1962	60.2	42.3	25.2	19.4	17.2	5.1	2.8	9.2	17.9	3.9	14.0
1963	64.8	45.5	27.9	21.7	17.6	5.0	2.9	9.7	19.4	4.0	15.4
New series											
1964	72.1	51.9	30.5	24.1	21.4	6.8	3.6	11.0	20.2	3.7	16.5
1965	78.0	56.1	30.2	23.8	25.8	8.1	5.1	12.6	21.9	3.9	18.0
1966	81.2	57.4	28.6	21.8	28.8	8.1	6.6	14.1	23.8	3.8	20.0
1967	83.0	57.6	28.7	21.5	28.8	8.0	6.0	14.9	25.4	3.3	22.1
1968	92.4	65.0	34.2	26.7	30.8	9.0	6.0	15.8	27.4	3.2	24.2
1969	99.8	72.0	37.2	29.2	34.8	10.8	6.8	17.2	27.8	3.2	24.6
1970	100.7	72.8	35.9	27.1	37.0	11.2	6.6	19.2	27.9	3.1	24.8
1971	117.3	87.6	48.5	38.7	39.1	13.1	5.5	20.5	29.7	3.8	25.9
1972	133.3	103.3	60.7	50.1	42.6	15.7	4.8	22.1	30.0	4.2	25.8
1973	146.8	114.5	65.1	54.6	49.4	18.1	6.4	24.9	32.3	4.7	27.6
1974	147.5	109.3	56.0	43.4	53.4	18.1	8.1	27.2	38.1	5.1	33.0
1975	145.6	102.3	51.6	36.3	50.7	14.3	8.3	28.2	43.3	6.1	37.2
1976	165.4	121.5	68.3	50.8	53.2	14.1	7.4	31.6	44.0	6.8	37.2
1977	193.1	150.0	92.0	72.2	58.0	16.4	8.0	33.7	43.1	7.1	36.0
1978	230.2	180.0	109.8	85.6	70.2	20.6	11.5	38.2	50.1	8.1	42.0
1979	259.8	203.2	116.4	89.3	86.8	28.3	15.6	42.8	56.6	8.6	48.1
1980	259.7	196.1	100.4	69.6	95.7	34.6	14.6	46.6	63.6	9.6	54.0
1981	272.0	207.3	99.2	69.4	108.0	40.2	18.0	49.8	64.7	10.4	54.3
1982	260.6	197.5	84.7	57.0	112.9	44.1	18.5	50.2	63.1	10.0	53.1
1983	294.9	231.5	125.5	94.6	106.0	43.9	13.8	48.2	63.5	10.6	52.9
1984	348.8	278.6	153.8	113.8	124.8	59.1	14.8	50.8	70.2	11.2	59.0
1985	377.4	299.5	158.5	114.7	141.1	72.6	17.1	51.3	77.8	12.0	65.8
1986	407.7	323.1	187.1	133.2	136.0	69.5	14.9	51.6	84.6	12.4	72.2
1987	419.4	328.7	194.7	139.9	134.1	68.9	15.0	50.1	90.6	14.1	76.6
1988	432.3	337.5	198.1	138.9	139.4	71.5	16.5	51.5	94.8	12.3	82.5
1989	443.4	345.3	196.6	139.2	148.8	73.9	20.4	54.5	98.1	12.2	85.9
1990	442.1	334.2	182.9	128.0	151.3	72.5	23.8	54.9	107.9	12.1	95.8
1991	401.0	290.7	157.8	110.6	132.9	54.8	22.3	55.8	110.2	12.9	97.3

See next page for continuation of table.

404

[Value put in place, billions of dollars; monthly data at seasonally adjusted annual rates]

Year or month	Total new construction	Private construction								Public construction		
		Total	Residential buildings [1]		Nonresidential buildings and other construction [1]					Total	Federal	State and local [5]
			Total [2]	New housing units	Total	Commercial [3]	Industrial	Other [4]				
1991: Jan	400.4	298.8	157.4	107.4	141.3	64.0	23.4	53.9		101.7	10.8	90.8
Feb	403.8	295.1	151.8	103.4	143.3	63.3	24.4	55.7		108.6	10.7	97.9
Mar	397.2	286.8	149.4	101.5	137.4	59.4	23.4	54.5		110.4	11.8	98.6
Apr	403.3	294.2	148.3	101.2	146.0	63.2	25.9	56.9		109.0	13.2	95.8
May	396.0	286.1	151.7	104.6	134.3	57.9	21.4	55.1		110.0	12.7	97.3
June	394.3	286.3	154.9	107.7	131.4	54.5	21.2	55.8		107.9	12.9	95.0
July	397.0	287.7	157.0	110.0	130.7	53.5	21.3	55.9		109.3	12.6	96.7
Aug	404.8	291.8	161.5	114.4	130.3	52.5	21.4	56.3		113.1	13.6	99.5
Sept	406.0	293.6	164.2	117.1	129.5	52.3	20.7	56.5		112.4	14.7	97.7
Oct	406.1	291.7	164.7	117.5	127.0	49.0	21.1	56.9		114.4	13.7	100.7
Nov	401.2	288.3	164.5	118.0	123.9	45.9	21.6	56.4		112.9	15.0	97.9
Dec	398.7	287.4	164.1	118.3	123.3	44.9	22.4	56.0		111.4	13.8	97.5
1992: Jan	407.1	292.5	169.5	122.0	123.0	44.5	21.3	57.2		114.6	14.3	100.3
Feb	411.8	294.8	169.8	123.3	125.0	45.0	21.7	58.3		117.0	14.1	102.9
Mar	421.5	301.1	172.7	125.9	128.5	45.4	23.7	59.4		120.4	14.9	105.5
Apr	427.6	309.8	182.6	128.8	127.2	44.6	21.3	61.2		117.8	14.2	103.5
May	428.0	307.0	182.9	128.1	124.1	42.6	21.0	60.5		121.0	14.4	106.5
June	426.7	312.2	184.6	128.7	127.6	46.5	20.3	60.7		114.5	14.6	100.0
July	425.7	305.8	181.2	126.9	124.7	42.9	20.6	61.2		119.9	14.8	105.0
Aug	419.6	302.0	184.2	129.1	117.8	40.1	17.9	59.8		117.6	13.8	103.8
Sept	429.3	308.8	186.3	131.4	122.5	42.2	19.0	61.2		120.5	16.4	104.0
Oct ᴾ	432.8	314.4	190.8	135.1	123.7	44.2	18.6	60.8		118.4	15.1	103.3
Nov ᴾ	441.8	319.6	193.5	138.3	126.2	44.4	19.0	62.8		122.2	15.8	106.3

[1] Beginning 1960, farm residential buildings included in residential buildings; prior to 1960, included in nonresidential buildings and other construction.

[2] Includes residential improvements, not shown separately. Prior to 1964, also includes nonhousekeeping units (hotels, motels, etc.).

[3] Office buildings, warehouses, stores, restaurants, garages, etc., and, beginning 1964, hotels and motels; prior to 1964 hotels and motels are included in total residential.

[4] Religious, educational, hospital and institutional, miscellaneous nonresidential, farm (see also footnote 1), public utilities (telecommunications, gas, electric, railroad, and petroleum pipelines), and all other private.

[5] Includes Federal grants-in-aid for State and local projects.

Source: Department of Commerce, Bureau of the Census.

TABLE B-51.—*New housing units started and authorized, 1959-92*

[Thousands of units]

Year or month	New housing units started						New private housing units authorized [2]			
	Private and public [1]		Private (farm and nonfarm) [1]					Type of structure		
	Total (farm and nonfarm)	Nonfarm	Total	Type of structure			Total		2 to 4 units	5 units or more
				1 unit	2 to 4 units	5 units or more		1 unit		
1959	1,553.7	1,531.3	1,517.0	1,234.0	283.0		1,208.3	938.3	77.1	192.9
1960	1,296.1	1,274.0	1,252.2	994.7	257.4		998.0	746.1	64.6	187.4
1961	1,365.0	1,336.8	1,313.0	974.3	338.7		1,064.2	722.8	67.6	273.8
1962	1,492.5	1,468.7	1,462.9	991.4	471.5		1,186.6	716.2	87.1	383.3
1963	1,634.9	1,614.8	1,603.2	1,012.4	590.8		1,334.7	750.2	118.9	465.6
1964	1,561.0	1,534.0	1,528.8	970.5	108.4	450.0	1,285.8	720.1	100.8	464.9
1965	1,509.7	1,487.5	1,472.8	963.7	86.6	422.5	1,239.8	709.9	84.8	445.1
1966	1,195.8	1,172.8	1,164.9	778.6	61.1	325.1	971.9	563.2	61.0	347.7
1967	1,321.9	1,298.8	1,291.6	843.9	71.6	376.1	1,141.0	650.6	73.0	417.5
1968	1,545.4	1,521.4	1,507.6	899.4	80.9	527.3	1,353.4	694.7	84.3	574.4
1969	1,499.5	1,482.3	1,466.8	810.6	85.0	571.2	1,323.7	625.9	85.2	612.7
1970	1,469.0	([3])	1,433.6	812.9	84.8	535.9	1,351.5	646.8	88.1	616.7
1971	2,084.5	([3])	2,052.2	1,151.0	120.3	780.9	1,924.6	906.1	132.9	885.7
1972	2,378.5	([3])	2,356.6	1,309.2	141.3	906.2	2,218.9	1,033.1	148.6	1,037.2
1973	2,057.5	([3])	2,045.3	1,132.0	118.3	795.0	1,819.5	882.1	117.0	820.5
1974	1,352.5	([3])	1,337.7	888.1	68.1	381.6	1,074.4	643.8	64.3	366.2
1975	1,171.4	([3])	1,160.4	892.2	64.0	204.3	939.2	675.5	63.9	199.8
1976	1,547.6	([3])	1,537.5	1,162.4	85.9	289.2	1,296.2	893.6	93.1	309.5
1977	2,001.7	([3])	1,987.1	1,450.9	121.7	414.4	1,690.0	1,126.1	121.3	442.7
1978	2,036.1	([3])	2,020.3	1,433.3	125.0	462.0	1,800.5	1,182.6	130.6	487.3
1979	1,760.0	([3])	1,745.1	1,194.1	122.0	429.0	1,551.8	981.5	125.4	444.8
1980	1,312.6	([3])	1,292.2	852.2	109.5	330.5	1,190.6	710.4	114.5	365.7
1981	1,100.3	([3])	1,084.2	705.4	91.1	287.7	985.5	564.3	101.8	319.4
1982	1,072.1	([3])	1,062.2	662.6	80.0	319.6	1,000.5	546.4	88.3	365.8
1983	1,712.5	([3])	1,703.0	1,067.6	113.5	522.0	1,605.2	901.5	133.6	570.1
1984	1,755.8	([3])	1,749.5	1,084.2	121.4	544.0	1,681.8	922.4	142.6	616.8
1985	1,745.0	([3])	1,741.8	1,072.4	93.4	576.1	1,733.3	956.6	120.1	656.6
1986	1,807.1	([3])	1,805.4	1,179.4	84.0	542.0	1,769.4	1,077.6	108.4	583.5
1987	1,622.7	([3])	1,620.5	1,146.4	65.3	408.7	1,534.8	1,024.4	89.3	421.1
1988	([4])	([3])	1,488.1	1,081.3	58.8	348.0	1,455.6	993.8	75.7	386.1
1989	([4])	([3])	1,376.1	1,003.3	55.2	317.6	1,338.4	931.7	67.0	339.8
1990	([4])	([3])	1,192.7	894.8	37.5	260.4	1,110.8	793.9	54.3	262.6
1991	([4])	([3])	1,013.9	840.4	35.6	137.9	948.8	753.5	43.1	152.1
						Seasonally adjusted annual rates				
1991: Jan	([4])	([3])	844	644	30	170	801	597	40	164
Feb	([4])	([3])	1,008	803	36	169	857	682	42	133
Mar	([4])	([3])	918	751	27	140	918	704	46	168
Apr	([4])	([3])	978	802	32	144	913	740	46	127
May	([4])	([3])	983	830	36	117	988	761	40	187
June	([4])	([3])	1,036	870	26	140	956	759	49	148
July	([4])	([3])	1,053	881	46	126	971	782	39	150
Aug	([4])	([3])	1,053	881	41	131	940	764	43	133
Sept	([4])	([3])	1,020	864	28	128	974	782	43	149
Oct	([4])	([3])	1,085	887	49	149	994	788	41	165
Nov	([4])	([3])	1,085	907	33	145	979	792	46	141
Dec	([4])	([3])	1,118	972	46	100	1,073	873	43	157
1992: Jan	([4])	([3])	1,180	989	28	163	1,106	913	47	146
Feb	([4])	([3])	1,257	1,109	24	124	1,146	946	44	156
Mar	([4])	([3])	1,340	1,068	53	219	1,094	907	41	146
Apr	([4])	([3])	1,086	933	27	126	1,058	873	44	141
May	([4])	([3])	1,196	1,019	33	144	1,054	879	46	129
June	([4])	([3])	1,147	999	40	108	1,032	872	48	112
July	([4])	([3])	1,100	956	25	119	1,080	879	42	159
Aug	([4])	([3])	1,233	1,042	32	159	1,076	877	53	146
Sept	([4])	([3])	1,222	1,051	27	144	1,125	913	47	165
Oct [p]	([4])	([3])	1,224	1,086	19	119	1,139	959	50	130
Nov [p]	([4])	([3])	1,242	1,100	33	109	1,126	955	49	122

[1] Units in structures built by private developers for sale upon completion to local public housing authorities under the Department of Housing and Urban Development "Turnkey" program are classified as private housing. Military housing starts, including those financed with mortgages insured by FHA under Section 803 of the National Housing Act, are included in publicly owned starts and excluded from total private starts.

[2] Authorized by issuance of local building permit: in 17,000 permit-issuing places beginning 1984; in 16,000 places for 1978-83; in 14,000 places for 1972-77; in 13,000 places for 1967-71; in 12,000 places for 1963-66; and in 10,000 places prior to 1963.

[3] Not available separately beginning January 1970.

[4] Series discontinued December 1988.

Source: Department of Commerce, Bureau of the Census.

TABLE B–52.—*Business expenditures for new plant and equipment, 1947–93*

[Billions of dollars; quarterly data at seasonally adjusted annual rates]

Year or quarter	All indus-tries	Manufacturing			Nonmanufacturing					Total non-farm busi-ness [3]	Manu-fac-tur-ing	Nonmanufacturing		
		Total	Dura-ble goods	Non-durable goods	Total [2]	Min-ing	Trans-porta-tion	Public utili-ties	Com-mercial and other			Total	Sur-veyed quar-terly	Sur-veyed annu-ally [4]
1947	20.11	8.73	3.39	5.34	11.38	0.69	2.69	1.64	6.38	22.27	8.73	13.54	11.38	2.16
1948	22.78	9.25	3.54	5.71	13.53	.93	3.17	2.67	6.77	25.97	9.25	16.73	13.53	3.19
1949	20.28	7.32	2.67	4.64	12.96	.88	2.80	3.28	6.01	24.03	7.32	16.72	12.96	3.76
1950	21.56	7.73	3.22	4.51	13.83	.84	2.87	3.42	6.70	25.81	7.73	18.08	13.83	4.25
1951	26.81	11.07	5.12	5.95	15.74	1.11	3.60	3.75	7.29	31.38	11.07	20.31	15.74	4.57
1952	28.16	12.12	5.75	6.37	16.04	1.21	3.56	3.96	7.31	32.16	12.12	20.04	16.04	4.00
1953	29.96	12.43	5.71	6.72	17.53	1.25	3.58	4.61	8.09	34.20	12.43	21.77	17.53	4.23
1954	28.86	12.00	5.49	6.51	16.85	1.29	2.91	4.23	8.42	33.62	12.00	21.62	16.85	4.76
1955	30.94	12.50	5.87	6.62	18.44	1.31	3.10	4.26	9.77	37.08	12.50	24.58	18.44	6.14
1956	37.90	16.33	8.19	8.15	21.57	1.64	3.56	4.78	11.59	45.25	16.33	28.91	21.57	7.35
1957	40.54	17.50	8.59	8.91	23.04	1.69	3.84	5.95	11.56	48.62	17.50	31.11	23.04	8.08
1958	33.84	12.98	6.21	6.77	20.86	1.43	2.72	5.74	10.97	42.55	12.98	29.57	20.86	8.72
1959	35.88	13.76	6.72	7.04	22.12	1.35	3.47	5.46	11.84	45.17	13.76	31.41	22.12	9.29
1960	39.44	16.36	8.28	8.08	23.08	1.29	3.54	5.40	12.86	48.99	16.36	32.63	23.08	9.55
1961	38.34	15.53	7.43	8.10	22.80	1.26	3.14	5.20	13.21	48.14	15.53	32.60	22.80	9.80
1962	40.86	16.03	7.81	8.22	24.83	1.41	3.59	5.12	14.71	51.61	16.03	35.58	24.83	10.75
1963	43.67	17.27	8.64	8.63	26.40	1.26	3.64	5.33	16.17	53.59	17.27	36.33	26.40	9.93
1964	51.26	21.23	10.98	10.25	30.04	1.33	4.71	5.80	18.20	62.02	21.23	40.80	30.04	10.76
1965	59.52	25.41	13.49	11.92	34.12	1.36	5.66	6.49	20.60	70.79	25.41	45.39	34.12	11.27
1966	70.40	31.37	17.23	14.15	39.03	1.42	6.68	7.82	23.11	82.62	31.37	51.25	39.03	12.22
1967	72.75	32.25	17.83	14.42	40.50	1.38	6.57	9.33	23.22	83.82	32.25	51.57	40.50	11.07
1968	76.42	32.34	17.93	14.40	44.08	1.44	6.91	10.52	25.22	88.92	32.34	56.58	44.08	12.50
1969	85.74	36.27	19.97	16.31	49.47	1.77	7.23	11.70	28.77	100.02	36.27	63.74	49.47	14.27
1970	91.91	36.99	19.80	17.19	54.92	2.02	7.17	13.03	32.71	106.15	36.99	69.16	54.92	14.24
1971	92.91	33.60	16.78	16.82	59.31	2.67	6.42	14.70	35.52	109.18	33.60	75.58	59.31	16.26
1972	103.40	35.42	18.22	17.20	67.98	2.88	7.14	16.26	41.69	120.91	35.42	85.49	67.98	17.51
1973	120.03	42.35	22.63	19.72	77.67	3.30	8.00	17.99	48.39	139.26	42.35	96.91	77.67	19.24
1974	139.67	52.48	26.77	25.71	87.19	4.58	9.16	19.96	53.49	159.83	52.48	107.35	87.19	20.16
1975	142.42	53.66	25.37	28.28	88.76	6.12	9.95	20.23	52.47	162.60	53.66	108.95	88.76	20.19
1976	158.44	58.53	27.50	31.03	99.91	7.63	11.10	22.90	58.29	179.91	58.53	121.38	99.91	21.47
1977	184.82	67.48	32.77	34.71	117.34	9.81	12.20	27.83	67.51	208.15	67.48	140.67	117.34	23.33
1978	216.81	78.13	39.02	39.10	138.69	10.55	12.07	32.10	83.96	244.40	78.13	166.27	138.69	27.58
1979	255.26	95.13	47.72	47.41	160.13	11.05	13.91	37.53	97.64	285.24	95.13	190.11	160.13	29.98
1980	286.40	112.60	54.82	57.77	173.80	12.71	13.56	41.32	106.21	318.08	112.60	205.48	173.80	31.68
1981	324.73	128.68	58.93	69.75	196.06	15.81	12.67	47.17	120.41	358.77	128.68	230.09	196.06	34.04
1982	326.19	123.97	54.58	69.39	202.22	14.11	11.75	53.58	122.79	363.08	123.97	239.11	202.22	36.89
1983	321.16	117.35	51.61	65.73	203.82	10.64	10.81	52.95	129.41	359.73	117.35	242.38	203.82	38.56
1984	373.83	139.61	64.57	75.04	234.22	11.86	13.44	57.53	151.39	418.38	139.61	278.77	234.22	44.55
1985	410.12	152.88	70.87	82.01	257.24	12.00	14.57	59.58	171.09	454.93	152.88	302.05	257.24	44.81
1986	399.36	137.95	65.68	72.28	261.40	8.15	15.05	56.61	181.59	447.11	137.95	309.16	261.40	47.75
1987	410.52	141.06	68.03	73.03	269.46	8.28	15.07	56.26	189.84	461.51	141.06	320.45	269.46	50.99
1988	455.49	163.45	77.04	86.41	292.04	9.29	16.63	60.37	205.76	508.22	163.45	344.77	292.04	52.73
1989	507.40	183.80	82.56	101.24	323.60	9.21	18.84	66.28	229.28	563.93	183.80	380.13	323.60	56.53
1990	532.61	192.61	82.58	110.04	339.99	9.88	21.47	67.21	241.43	591.96	192.61	399.34	339.99	59.35
1991	528.39	182.81	77.64	105.17	345.58	10.02	22.66	66.57	246.32	587.93	182.81	405.12	345.58	59.54
1992 [5]	547.39	173.48	74.07	99.41	373.91	9.25	23.65	72.19	268.81	....	173.48	....	373.91	....
1993 [5]	576.55	182.57	76.08	106.49	393.97	9.97	23.75	79.83	280.43	....	182.57	....	393.97	....
1991: I	534.27	190.83	80.99	109.84	343.44	9.94	22.98	67.01	243.51	....	190.83	....	343.44	....
II	525.02	186.52	79.31	107.20	338.50	10.08	22.87	65.09	240.46	....	186.52	....	338.50	....
III	526.59	177.48	74.94	102.55	349.10	10.09	22.56	66.52	249.94	....	177.48	....	349.10	....
IV	529.87	179.06	76.40	102.66	350.81	9.99	22.29	67.42	251.11	....	179.06	....	350.81	....
1992: I	535.72	173.98	74.19	99.79	361.73	8.87	21.88	68.81	262.17	....	173.98	....	361.73	....
II	540.91	171.78	74.26	97.52	369.13	9.18	23.51	72.63	263.80	....	171.78	....	369.13	....
III	547.53	172.23	71.84	100.39	375.30	9.09	24.69	71.66	269.86	....	172.23	....	375.30	....
IV [5]	565.40	175.93	75.98	99.95	389.48	9.87	24.54	75.65	279.42	....	175.93	....	389.48	....
1993: I [5]	576.07	183.93	77.30	106.63	392.14	10.97	23.47	77.70	280.00	....	183.93	....	392.14	....
II [5]	591.20	185.40	75.87	109.52	405.80	10.36	26.77	79.62	289.05	....	185.40	....	405.80	....

[1] These industries accounted for 90 percent of total nonfarm spending in 1991.
[2] Excludes forestry, fisheries, and agricultural services; professional services; social services and membership organizations; and real estate, which, effective with the April–May 1984 survey, are no longer surveyed quarterly. See last column ("nonmanufacturing surveyed annually") for data for these industries.
[3] "All industries" plus the part of nonmanufacturing that is surveyed annually.
[4] Consists of forestry, fisheries, and agricultural services; professional services; social services and membership organizations; and real estate.
[5] Planned capital expenditures as reported by business in October and November 1992, corrected for biases.

Source: Department of Commerce, Bureau of the Census.

TABLE B-53.—*Manufacturing and trade sales and inventories, 1950-92*

[Amounts in millions of dollars; monthly data seasonally adjusted]

Year or month	Total manufacturing and trade			Manufacturing			Merchant wholesalers			Retail trade		
	Sales¹	Inventories²	Ratio³	Sales¹	Inventories²	Ratio³	Sales¹	Inventories²	Ratio³	Sales¹	Inventories²	Ratio³
1950	38,596	59,822	1.36	18,634	31,078	1.48	7,695	9,284	1.07	12,268	19,460	1.38
1951	43,356	70,242	1.55	21,714	39,306	1.66	8,597	9,886	1.16	13,046	21,050	1.64
1952	44,840	72,377	1.58	22,529	41,136	1.78	8,782	10,210	1.12	13,529	21,031	1.52
1953	47,987	76,122	1.58	24,843	43,948	1.76	9,052	10,686	1.17	14,091	21,488	1.53
1954	46,443	73,175	1.60	23,355	41,612	1.81	8,993	10,637	1.18	14,095	20,926	1.51
1955	51,694	79,516	1.47	26,480	45,069	1.62	9,893	11,678	1.13	15,321	22,769	1.43
1956	54,063	87,304	1.55	27,740	50,642	1.73	10,513	13,260	1.19	15,811	23,402	1.47
1957	55,879	89,052	1.59	28,736	51,871	1.80	10,475	12,730	1.23	16,667	24,451	1.44
1958	54,201	87,055	1.61	28,146	50,203	1.84	10,257	12,739	1.24	16,696	24,113	1.44
1959	59,729	92,097	1.54	30,286	52,913	1.75	11,491	13,879	1.21	17,951	25,305	1.41
1960	60,827	94,719	1.56	30,878	53,786	1.74	11,656	14,120	1.21	18,294	26,813	1.47
1961	61,159	95,580	1.56	30,922	54,871	1.77	11,988	14,488	1.21	18,249	26,221	1.44
1962	65,662	101,049	1.54	33,358	58,172	1.74	12,674	14,936	1.18	19,630	27,941	1.42
1963	68,995	105,463	1.53	35,058	60,029	1.71	13,382	16,048	1.20	20,556	29,386	1.43
1964	73,682	111,504	1.51	37,331	63,410	1.70	14,529	17,000	1.17	21,823	31,094	1.42
1965	80,283	120,929	1.51	40,995	68,207	1.66	15,611	18,317	1.17	23,677	34,405	1.45
1966	87,187	136,824	1.57	44,870	77,986	1.74	16,987	20,765	1.22	25,330	38,073	1.50
1967	90,918	145,681	1.60	46,486	84,646	1.82	19,675	25,786	1.31	24,757	35,249	1.42
1968	98,794	156,611	1.59	50,229	90,560	1.80	21,121	27,166	1.29	27,445	38,885	1.42
1969	105,812	170,400	1.61	53,501	98,145	1.83	22,940	29,800	1.30	29,371	42,455	1.45
1970	108,352	178,594	1.65	52,805	101,599	1.92	24,298	33,354	1.37	31,249	43,641	1.40
1971	117,023	188,991	1.61	55,906	102,567	1.83	26,619	36,568	1.37	34,497	49,856	1.45
1972	131,227	203,227	1.55	63,027	108,121	1.72	30,011	40,297	1.34	38,189	54,809	1.44
1973	153,881	234,406	1.52	72,931	124,499	1.71	38,319	46,918	1.22	42,631	62,989	1.48
1974	178,201	287,144	1.61	84,790	157,625	1.86	48,271	58,667	1.22	45,141	70,852	1.57
1975	182,412	288,992	1.58	86,589	159,708	1.84	46,848	57,774	1.23	48,975	71,510	1.46
1976	204,386	318,345	1.56	98,797	174,636	1.77	50,934	64,622	1.27	54,655	79,087	1.45
1977	229,786	350,706	1.53	113,201	188,378	1.66	56,409	73,179	1.30	60,176	89,149	1.48
1978	260,755	400,929	1.54	126,905	211,689	1.67	66,849	86,934	1.30	67,002	102,306	1.53
1979	298,328	452,636	1.52	143,936	242,153	1.68	79,678	99,679	1.25	74,713	110,804	1.48
1980	328,112	510,124	1.55	154,391	265,213	1.72	93,977	123,833	1.32	79,743	121,078	1.52
1981	356,909	547,169	1.53	168,129	283,401	1.69	102,267	131,049	1.28	86,514	132,719	1.53
1982	348,771	575,486	1.67	163,351	311,834	1.95	96,357	129,024	1.36	89,062	134,628	1.49
1983	370,501	591,858	1.56	172,547	312,362	1.78	100,440	131,663	1.28	97,514	147,833	1.44
1984	411,427	651,527	1.53	190,682	339,492	1.73	113,502	144,223	1.23	107,243	167,812	1.49
1985	423,940	665,837	1.55	194,538	334,801	1.73	114,816	149,155	1.28	114,586	181,881	1.52
1986	431,786	664,654	1.55	194,657	322,699	1.68	116,326	155,445	1.32	120,803	186,510	1.56
1987	459,107	711,745	1.50	206,326	338,095	1.59	124,340	165,814	1.29	128,442	207,836	1.55
1988	496,334	767,387	1.50	223,541	367,396	1.58	135,254	180,717	1.30	137,539	219,274	1.55
1989	522,344	813,018	1.53	232,724	386,784	1.64	144,039	188,635	1.28	145,580	237,599	1.59
1990	540,788	835,985	1.53	239,459	398,851	1.65	149,204	196,917	1.29	152,126	240,217	1.57
1991	533,838	828,184	1.55	235,142	386,043	1.67	145,135	198,979	1.36	153,562	243,162	1.55
1991: Jan	526,917	840,981	1.60	232,505	398,901	1.72	144,931	199,781	1.38	149,481	242,299	1.62
Feb	527,778	838,491	1.59	231,250	398,563	1.72	144,118	199,642	1.39	152,410	240,286	1.58
Mar	521,823	829,818	1.59	225,473	396,329	1.76	142,728	197,863	1.39	153,622	235,626	1.53
Apr	530,940	828,508	1.56	233,029	395,738	1.70	144,902	196,593	1.36	153,009	236,177	1.54
May	535,424	824,177	1.54	235,653	392,533	1.67	145,085	195,308	1.35	154,686	236,336	1.53
June	534,831	820,671	1.53	234,907	391,038	1.66	145,255	194,470	1.34	154,669	235,163	1.52
July	538,852	819,898	1.52	237,616	388,774	1.64	146,576	195,421	1.33	154,660	235,703	1.52
Aug	536,825	819,684	1.53	237,844	387,900	1.63	145,214	195,607	1.35	153,767	236,177	1.54
Sept	538,952	822,418	1.53	238,836	389,552	1.63	146,045	194,386	1.33	154,071	238,480	1.55
Oct	540,772	824,342	1.52	240,912	388,555	1.61	145,396	195,776	1.35	154,464	240,011	1.55
Nov	540,029	825,156	1.53	240,980	388,279	1.61	145,075	195,998	1.35	153,974	240,879	1.56
Dec	531,919	828,184	1.56	232,730	386,043	1.66	144,909	198,979	1.37	154,280	243,162	1.58
1992: Jan	536,977	824,150	1.53	233,247	384,434	1.65	145,922	198,730	1.36	157,808	240,986	1.53
Feb	544,017	824,609	1.52	237,898	383,255	1.61	146,366	199,416	1.36	159,753	241,938	1.51
Mar	545,424	826,204	1.51	240,684	383,239	1.59	146,867	198,677	1.35	157,873	244,288	1.55
Apr	547,081	828,630	1.51	241,749	382,206	1.58	146,947	198,432	1.35	158,385	247,992	1.57
May	546,145	828,032	1.52	241,479	383,286	1.59	145,555	197,397	1.36	159,111	247,349	1.55
June	554,363	831,872	1.50	247,252	382,854	1.55	148,129	200,205	1.35	158,982	248,813	1.57
July	559,701	835,373	1.49	247,216	383,491	1.55	150,467	200,500	1.32	160,784	251,382	1.56
Aug	552,480	836,972	1.51	241,014	385,596	1.60	150,467	201,074	1.34	160,999	250,302	1.55
Sept	558,745	835,457	1.50	245,838	384,390	1.56	150,736	199,925	1.33	162,171	251,142	1.55
Oct ᴾ	560,866	835,819	1.49	244,391	383,708	1.57	151,295	201,713	1.33	165,180	250,398	1.52
Nov ᴾ				246,962	381,772	1.55	151,884	203,582	1.34			

¹ Annual data are averages of monthly not seasonally adjusted figures.
² Seasonally adjusted, end of period. Inventories beginning January 1982 for manufacturing and December 1980 for wholesale and retail trade are not comparable with earlier periods.
³ Inventory/sales ratio. Annual data are: beginning 1982, averages of monthly ratios; for 1958-81, ratio of December inventories to monthly average sales for the year; and for earlier years, weighted averages. Monthly data are ratio of inventories at end of month to sales for month.

Note.—Earlier data are not strictly comparable with data beginning 1958 for manufacturing and beginning 1967 for wholesale and retail trade.

Source: Department of Commerce, Bureau of the Census.

Table B-54.—*Manufacturers' shipments and inventories, 1950–92*

[Millions of dollars; monthly data seasonally adjusted]

Year or month	Shipments [1]			Inventories [2]								
	Total	Durable goods industries	Nondurable goods industries	Total	Durable goods industries				Nondurable goods industries			
					Total	Materials and supplies	Work in process	Finished goods	Total	Materials and supplies	Work in process	Finished goods
1950	18,634	8,845	9,789	31,078	15,539				15,539			
1951	21,714	10,493	11,221	39,306	20,991				18,315			
1952	22,529	11,313	11,216	41,136	23,731				17,405			
1953	24,843	13,349	11,494	43,948	25,878	8,966	10,720	6,206	18,070	8,317	2,472	7,409
1954	23,355	11,828	11,527	47,612	23,710	7,894	9,721	6,040	17,902	8,167	2,440	7,415
1955	26,480	14,071	12,409	45,069	26,405	9,194	10,756	6,348	18,664	8,556	2,571	7,666
1956	27,740	14,715	13,025	50,642	30,447	10,417	12,317	7,565	20,195	8,971	2,721	8,622
1957	28,736	15,237	13,499	51,871	31,728	10,608	12,837	8,125	20,143	8,775	2,864	8,624
1958	27,248	13,553	13,695	50,203	30,194	9,970	12,408	7,816	20,009	8,676	2,827	8,506
1959	30,286	15,597	14,689	52,913	32,012	10,709	13,086	8,217	20,901	9,094	2,942	8,865
1960	30,878	15,870	15,008	53,786	32,337	10,306	12,809	9,222	21,449	9,097	2,947	9,405
1961	30,922	15,601	15,321	54,871	32,496	10,246	13,211	9,039	22,375	9,505	3,108	9,762
1962	33,358	17,247	16,111	58,172	34,565	10,794	14,124	9,647	23,607	9,836	3,304	10,467
1963	35,058	18,255	16,803	60,029	35,776	11,053	14,835	9,888	24,253	10,009	3,420	10,824
1964	37,331	19,611	17,720	63,410	38,421	11,946	16,158	10,317	24,989	10,167	3,531	11,291
1965	40,995	22,193	18,802	68,207	42,189	13,298	18,055	10,836	26,018	10,487	3,825	11,706
1966	44,870	24,617	20,253	77,986	49,852	15,464	21,908	12,480	28,134	11,197	4,226	12,711
1967	46,486	25,233	21,253	84,646	54,896	16,423	24,933	13,540	29,750	11,760	4,431	13,559
1968	50,229	27,624	22,605	90,560	58,732	17,344	27,213	14,175	31,828	12,328	4,852	14,648
1969	53,501	29,403	24,098	98,145	64,598	18,636	30,282	15,680	33,547	12,753	5,120	15,674
1970	52,805	28,156	24,649	101,599	66,651	19,149	29,745	17,757	34,948	13,168	5,271	16,509
1971	55,906	29,924	25,982	102,567	66,136	19,679	28,550	17,907	36,431	13,686	5,678	17,067
1972	63,027	33,987	29,040	108,121	70,067	20,807	30,713	18,547	38,054	14,677	5,998	17,379
1973	72,931	39,635	33,296	124,499	81,192	25,944	35,490	19,758	43,307	18,147	6,729	18,431
1974	84,790	44,173	40,617	157,625	101,493	35,070	42,530	23,893	56,132	23,744	8,189	24,199
1975	86,589	43,598	42,991	159,708	102,590	33,903	43,227	25,460	57,118	23,565	8,834	24,719
1976	98,797	50,623	48,174	174,636	111,988	37,457	46,074	28,457	62,648	25,847	9,929	26,872
1977	113,201	59,168	54,033	188,378	120,877	40,186	50,226	30,465	67,501	27,387	10,961	29,153
1978	126,905	67,731	59,174	211,689	138,176	45,202	58,839	34,135	73,513	29,620	12,084	31,809
1979	143,936	75,927	68,009	242,153	160,728	52,625	69,316	38,737	81,425	32,814	13,911	34,700
1980	154,391	77,419	76,972	265,213	174,783	55,175	76,937	42,671	90,430	36,607	15,886	37,937
1981	168,129	83,727	84,402	283,401	186,429	57,999	80,990	47,440	96,972	38,167	16,194	42,611
1982	163,351	79,212	84,139	311,834	200,423	59,134	86,698	54,591	111,411	44,042	18,613	48,756
1983	172,547	85,481	87,066	312,362	199,831	60,321	86,892	52,618	112,531	44,822	18,696	49,013
1984	190,682	97,940	92,742	339,492	221,304	66,025	98,247	57,032	118,188	45,697	19,331	53,160
1985	194,538	101,279	93,259	334,801	218,211	64,004	98,094	56,113	116,590	44,095	19,451	53,044
1986	194,657	103,238	91,419	322,699	212,027	61,407	96,954	53,666	110,672	42,323	18,125	50,224
1987	206,326	108,128	98,198	338,095	220,786	63,602	102,369	54,815	117,309	45,302	19,275	52,732
1988	223,541	117,993	105,549	367,396	241,356	69,348	112,420	59,588	126,040	49,046	20,440	56,554
1989	232,724	121,703	111,022	386,784	255,911	71,869	121,954	62,088	130,873	49,643	21,248	59,982
1990	239,459	122,387	117,072	398,851	259,746	72,697	122,564	64,485	139,105	51,603	22,434	65,068
1991	235,142	118,548	116,593	386,043	246,966	67,645	117,575	61,746	139,077	51,890	22,002	65,185
1991: Jan	232,505	115,648	116,857	398,901	259,208	72,695	122,542	63,971	139,693	52,208	22,014	65,471
Feb	231,250	115,283	115,967	398,563	259,195	72,540	122,411	64,244	139,368	51,834	21,958	65,576
Mar	255,473	111,617	113,856	396,329	257,407	71,739	122,024	63,644	138,922	51,819	21,602	65,501
Apr	223,029	117,640	115,389	395,738	256,693	70,991	121,490	64,212	139,045	51,721	21,919	65,405
May	235,653	118,439	117,214	392,533	254,099	70,271	120,707	63,121	138,434	51,545	21,867	65,022
June	234,907	118,904	116,003	391,038	252,919	69,305	121,110	62,504	138,119	51,557	22,020	64,542
July	237,616	120,222	117,394	388,774	251,459	68,769	120,484	62,206	137,315	51,711	21,864	63,740
Aug	237,844	121,021	116,823	387,900	250,520	68,816	119,452	62,252	137,380	51,416	21,940	64,024
Sept	238,836	121,958	116,878	389,552	251,319	68,773	120,114	62,432	138,233	51,508	22,383	64,342
Oct	240,912	122,771	118,141	388,555	249,738	68,562	118,868	62,308	138,817	51,811	22,449	64,557
Nov	240,980	122,814	118,166	388,279	249,202	68,264	118,751	62,187	139,077	51,440	22,101	65,536
Dec	232,730	116,869	115,861	386,043	246,966	67,645	117,575	61,746	139,077	51,890	22,002	65,185
1992: Jan	233,247	118,698	114,549	384,434	245,754	67,566	116,593	61,595	138,680	51,608	22,218	64,854
Feb	237,898	121,991	115,907	383,255	244,393	67,002	115,848	61,543	138,862	51,555	22,352	64,955
Mar	240,684	123,503	117,181	383,239	243,787	66,542	115,330	61,915	139,452	51,750	22,374	65,328
Apr	241,749	123,483	118,266	382,206	242,512	66,535	114,004	61,973	139,694	51,880	22,578	65,236
May	241,479	122,344	119,135	383,286	242,447	66,735	113,527	61,985	140,839	52,060	22,611	65,168
June	247,252	125,831	121,421	382,854	241,891	67,304	112,540	62,047	140,963	52,528	22,645	65,790
July	247,216	124,789	122,427	383,491	241,258	66,800	111,644	62,814	142,233	52,962	22,643	66,628
Aug	241,014	123,364	117,650	385,596	242,036	67,304	111,741	62,991	143,560	52,782	22,957	67,821
Sept	245,838	125,346	120,492	384,390	240,550	67,296	110,652	62,602	143,840	52,914	23,075	67,851
Oct ᵖ	244,391	125,162	119,229	383,708	239,390	66,327	111,129	61,934	144,318	52,838	22,963	68,517
Nov ᵖ	246,962	127,556	119,406	381,772	237,735	66,104	109,939	61,692	144,037	52,396	22,898	68,743

[1] Annual data are averages of monthly not seasonally adjusted figures.
[2] Seasonally adjusted, end of period. Data beginning 1982 are not comparable with data for prior periods.

Note.—Data beginning 1958 are not strictly comparable with earlier data.

Source: Department of Commerce, Bureau of the Census.

TABLE B-55.—*Manufacturers' new and unfilled orders, 1950–92*

[Amounts in millions of dollars; monthly data seasonally adjusted]

Year or month	New orders [1]				Unfilled orders [2]			Unfilled orders—shipments ratio [3]		
	Total	Durable goods industries		Non-durable goods industries	Total	Durable goods industries	Non-durable goods industries	Total	Durable goods industries	Non-durable goods industries
		Total	Capital goods industries, nondefense							
1950	20,110	10,165		9,945	41,456	35,435	6,021			
1951	23,907	12,841		11,066	67,266	63,394	3,872			
1952	23,204	12,061		11,143	75,857	72,680	3,177			
1953	23,586	12,147		11,439	61,178	58,637	2,541			
1954	22,335	10,768		11,566	48,266	45,250	3,016	3.42	4.12	0.96
1955	27,465	14,996		12,469	60,004	56,241	3,763	3.63	4.27	1.12
1956	28,368	15,365		13,003	67,375	63,880	3,495	3.87	4.55	1.04
1957	27,559	14,111		13,448	53,183	50,352	2,831	3.35	4.00	.85
1958	27,193	13,387		13,805	46,609	43,807	2,802	3.02	3.62	.85
1959	30,711	15,979		14,732	51,717	48,369	3,348	2.94	3.47	.92
1960	30,232	15,288		14,944	44,213	41,650	2,563	2.71	3.29	.71
1961	31,112	15,753		15,359	46,624	43,582	3,042	2.58	3.08	.78
1962	33,440	17,363		16,078	47,798	45,170	2,628	2.64	3.18	.68
1963	35,511	18,671		16,840	53,417	50,346	3,071	2.74	3.31	.72
1964	38,240	20,507		17,732	64,518	61,315	3,203	2.99	3.59	.71
1965	42,137	23,286		18,851	78,249	74,459	3,790	3.25	3.86	.79
1966	46,420	26,163		20,258	96,846	93,002	3,844	3.74	4.48	.75
1967	47,067	25,803		21,265	103,711	99,735	3,976	3.66	4.37	.73
1968	50,657	28,051	6,314	22,606	108,377	104,393	3,984	3.83	4.64	.69
1969	53,990	29,876	7,046	24,114	114,341	110,161	4,180	3.74	4.50	.69
1970	52,022	27,340	6,072	24,682	105,008	100,412	4,596	3.64	4.40	.76
1971	55,921	29,905	6,682	26,016	105,247	100,225	5,022	3.36	4.06	.76
1972	64,182	35,038	7,745	29,144	119,349	113,034	6,315	3.27	3.88	.86
1973	76,003	42,627	9,926	33,376	156,561	149,204	7,357	3.83	4.55	.91
1974	87,327	46,862	11,594	40,465	187,043	181,519	5,524	4.12	4.97	.62
1975	85,139	41,957	9,886	43,181	169,546	161,664	7,882	3.72	4.50	.82
1976	99,513	51,307	11,490	48,206	178,128	169,857	8,271	3.26	3.90	.74
1977	115,109	61,035	13,681	54,073	202,022	193,321	8,701	3.25	3.87	.71
1978	131,629	72,278	17,588	59,351	259,169	248,281	10,888	3.57	4.20	.81
1979	147,604	79,483	21,154	68,121	303,593	291,320	12,273	3.89	4.62	.82
1980	156,359	79,392	21,135	76,967	327,414	315,200	12,214	3.85	4.58	.75
1981	168,025	83,654	21,806	84,371	326,550	314,709	11,841	3.87	4.68	.69
1982	162,140	78,064	19,213	84,077	311,889	300,799	11,090	3.84	4.74	.62
1983	175,451	88,140	19,624	87,311	347,272	333,113	14,159	3.54	4.29	.69
1984	192,879	100,164	23,669	92,715	373,524	359,644	13,880	3.60	4.37	.64
1985	195,706	102,356	24,545	93,351	387,087	372,017	15,070	3.67	4.47	.68
1986	195,204	103,647	23,983	91,557	393,403	376,613	16,790	3.59	4.40	.70
1987	209,389	110,809	26,095	98,579	430,287	408,600	21,687	3.63	4.42	.83
1988	227,026	121,445	30,729	105,581	471,942	449,989	21,953	3.63	4.45	.76
1989	235,905	124,906	32,725	110,999	510,112	488,431	21,681	3.99	4.89	.77
1990	240,417	123,324	32,227	117,093	521,811	499,828	21,983	4.12	5.09	.77
1991	233,774	117,063	29,862	116,712	505,631	482,208	23,423	4.05	5.00	.83
1991: Jan	233,014	116,327	32,349	116,687	522,320	500,507	21,813	4.16	5.15	.77
Feb	231,894	116,021	31,938	115,873	522,964	501,245	21,719	4.18	5.18	.77
Mar	222,922	109,017	30,548	113,905	520,413	498,645	21,768	4.25	5.29	.78
Apr	229,280	113,934	27,207	115,346	516,664	494,939	21,725	4.11	5.07	.78
May	234,047	115,987	26,616	118,060	515,058	492,487	22,571	4.09	5.04	.80
June	229,219	113,478	27,559	115,741	509,370	487,061	22,309	4.02	4.94	.80
July	244,580	127,153	34,981	117,427	516,334	493,992	22,342	4.05	5.00	.78
Aug	239,750	122,630	29,463	117,120	518,240	495,601	22,639	4.04	4.97	.80
Sept	233,703	116,528	28,762	117,175	513,107	490,171	22,936	3.98	4.89	.81
Oct	238,542	120,227	29,453	118,315	510,737	487,627	23,110	3.94	4.83	.80
Nov	238,679	120,343	33,066	118,336	508,436	485,156	23,280	3.92	4.80	.82
Dec	229,925	113,921	26,969	116,004	505,631	482,208	23,423	4.05	5.00	.83
1992: Jan	232,467	118,011	30,093	114,456	504,851	481,521	23,330	4.01	4.91	.84
Feb	233,388	117,750	29,463	115,638	500,341	477,280	23,061	3.91	4.78	.82
Mar	237,606	120,187	32,163	117,419	497,263	473,964	23,299	3.84	4.68	.82
Apr	240,771	122,393	29,901	118,378	496,285	472,874	23,411	3.83	4.68	.82
May	238,696	119,808	30,469	118,888	493,502	470,338	23,164	3.84	4.71	.81
June	244,542	123,164	30,953	121,378	490,792	467,671	23,121	3.71	4.52	.80
July	242,307	119,861	29,296	122,446	485,883	462,743	23,140	3.67	4.50	.79
Aug	236,880	119,376	28,153	117,504	481,749	458,755	22,994	3.74	4.56	.82
Sept	239,951	119,801	30,571	120,150	475,862	453,210	22,652	3.63	4.41	.79
Oct ᴾ	244,777	125,302	31,665	119,475	476,248	453,350	22,898	3.64	4.44	.79
Nov ᴾ	242,556	122,978	28,651	119,578	471,842	448,772	23,070	3.57	4.34	.81

[1] Annual data are averages of monthly not seasonally adjusted figures.
[2] Seasonally adjusted, end of period.
[3] Ratio of unfilled orders at end of period to shipments for period; excludes industries with no unfilled orders. Annual figures relate to seasonally adjusted data for December.

Note.—Data beginning 1958 are not strictly comparable with earlier data.

Source: Department of Commerce, Bureau of the Census.

TABLE B-56.—Consumer price indexes for major expenditure classes, 1950–92

[For all urban consumers; 1982–84 = 100]

Year or month	All items (CPI–U)	Food and beverages		Housing				Apparel and upkeep	Transportation²	Medical care²	Entertainment	Other goods and services	Energy³
		Total¹	Food²	Total	Shelter²	Fuel and other utilities²	Household furnishings and operation						
1950	24.1		25.4					40.3	22.7	15.1			
1951	26.0		28.2					43.9	24.1	15.9			
1952	26.5		28.7					43.5	25.7	16.7			
1953	26.7		28.3		22.0	22.5		43.1	26.5	17.3			
1954	26.9		28.2		22.5	22.6		43.1	26.1	17.8			
1955	26.8		27.8		22.7	23.0		42.9	25.8	18.2			
1956	27.2		28.0		23.1	23.6		43.7	26.2	18.9			
1957	28.1		28.9		24.0	24.3		44.5	27.7	19.7			21.5
1958	28.9		30.2		24.5	24.8		44.6	28.6	20.6			21.5
1959	29.1		29.7		24.7	25.4		45.0	29.8	21.5			21.9
1960	29.6		30.0		25.2	26.0		45.7	29.8	22.3			22.4
1961	29.9		30.4		25.4	26.3		46.1	30.1	22.9			22.5
1962	30.2		30.6		25.8	26.3		46.3	30.8	23.5			22.6
1963	30.6		31.1		26.1	26.6		46.9	30.9	24.1			22.6
1964	31.0		31.5		26.5	26.6		47.3	31.4	24.6			22.5
1965	31.5		32.2		27.0	26.6		47.8	31.9	25.2			22.9
1966	32.4		33.8		27.8	26.7		49.0	32.3	26.3			23.3
1967	33.4	35.0	34.1	30.8	28.8	27.1	42.0	51.0	33.3	28.2	40.7	35.1	23.8
1968	34.8	36.2	35.3	32.0	30.1	27.4	43.6	53.7	34.3	29.9	43.0	36.9	24.2
1969	36.7	38.1	37.1	34.0	32.6	28.0	45.2	56.8	35.7	31.9	45.2	38.7	24.8
1970	38.8	40.1	39.2	36.4	35.5	29.1	46.8	59.2	37.5	34.0	47.5	40.9	25.5
1971	40.5	41.4	40.4	38.0	37.0	31.1	48.6	61.1	39.5	36.1	50.0	42.9	26.5
1972	41.8	43.1	42.1	39.4	38.7	32.5	49.7	62.3	39.9	37.3	51.5	44.7	27.2
1973	44.4	48.8	48.2	41.2	40.5	34.3	51.1	64.6	41.2	38.8	52.9	46.4	29.4
1974	49.3	55.5	55.1	45.8	44.4	40.7	56.8	69.4	45.8	42.4	56.9	49.8	38.1
1975	53.8	60.2	59.8	50.7	48.8	45.4	63.4	72.5	50.1	47.5	62.0	53.9	42.1
1976	56.9	62.1	61.6	53.8	51.5	49.4	67.3	75.2	55.1	52.0	65.1	57.0	45.1
1977	60.6	65.8	65.5	57.4	54.9	54.7	70.4	78.6	59.0	57.0	68.3	60.4	49.4
1978	65.2	72.2	72.0	62.4	60.5	58.5	74.7	81.4	61.7	61.8	71.9	64.3	52.5
1979	72.6	79.9	79.9	70.1	68.9	64.8	79.9	84.9	70.5	67.5	76.7	68.9	65.7
1980	82.4	86.7	86.8	81.1	81.0	75.4	86.3	90.9	83.1	74.9	83.6	75.2	86.0
1981	90.9	93.5	93.6	90.4	90.5	86.4	93.0	95.3	93.2	82.9	90.1	82.6	97.7
1982	96.5	97.3	97.4	96.9	96.9	94.9	98.0	97.8	97.0	92.5	96.0	91.1	99.2
1983	99.6	99.5	99.4	99.5	99.1	100.2	100.2	100.2	99.3	100.6	100.1	101.1	99.9
1984	103.9	103.2	103.2	103.6	104.0	104.8	101.9	102.1	103.7	106.8	103.8	107.9	100.9
1985	107.6	105.6	105.6	107.7	109.8	106.5	103.8	105.0	106.4	113.5	107.9	114.5	101.6
1986	109.6	109.1	109.0	110.9	115.8	104.1	105.2	105.9	102.3	122.0	111.6	121.4	88.2
1987	113.6	113.5	113.5	114.2	121.3	103.0	107.1	110.6	105.4	130.1	115.3	128.5	88.6
1988	118.3	118.2	118.2	118.5	127.1	104.4	109.4	115.4	108.7	138.6	120.3	137.0	89.3
1989	124.0	124.9	125.1	123.0	132.8	107.8	111.2	118.6	114.1	149.3	126.5	147.7	94.3
1990	130.7	132.1	132.4	128.5	140.0	111.6	113.3	124.1	120.5	162.8	132.4	159.0	102.1
1991	136.2	136.8	136.3	133.6	146.3	115.3	116.0	128.7	123.8	177.0	138.4	171.6	102.5
1991: Jan	134.6	135.9	135.8	131.8	144.0	114.8	114.1	123.8	125.5	171.0	135.5	166.5	107.1
Feb	134.8	136.0	135.5	132.4	144.6	114.7	115.6	126.2	123.7	172.5	136.2	167.4	102.8
Mar	135.0	136.3	135.8	132.6	145.2	114.1	115.7	128.8	122.3	173.7	136.7	167.9	99.7
Apr	135.2	137.2	136.7	132.5	145.2	113.1	115.9	130.1	122.2	174.4	137.7	168.8	99.5
May	135.6	137.3	136.8	132.8	145.2	114.2	116.3	129.4	123.3	175.2	137.8	169.1	102.1
June	136.0	137.7	137.2	133.4	145.8	115.8	115.9	126.9	123.7	176.2	138.1	170.0	103.5
July	136.2	137.1	136.5	134.2	146.8	116.4	116.3	125.2	123.4	177.5	138.6	170.8	102.7
Aug	136.6	136.6	136.0	134.5	147.3	116.2	116.2	127.6	123.8	178.9	139.2	172.2	102.9
Sept	137.2	136.7	136.0	134.7	147.4	116.8	116.4	131.3	123.8	179.7	140.2	175.8	103.6
Oct	137.4	136.5	135.8	134.7	147.7	115.7	116.4	132.7	124.0	180.7	140.5	176.2	101.8
Nov	137.8	136.9	136.2	134.7	147.9	115.3	116.5	132.9	125.0	181.8	140.4	176.9	101.8
Dec	137.9	137.3	136.7	135.0	148.2	116.0	116.3	129.6	125.3	182.6	139.9	177.6	101.9
1992: Jan	138.1	137.9	137.2	135.7	149.2	116.2	116.7	127.9	124.5	184.3	140.1	178.6	100.1
Feb	138.6	138.1	137.1	135.9	149.8	115.9	117.3	130.2	124.1	184.6	140.7	179.4	99.0
Mar	139.3	138.8	138.1	136.6	150.4	115.8	117.7	133.4	124.4	187.3	141.2	179.8	98.9
Apr	139.5	138.8	138.1	136.5	150.4	115.8	118.0	133.3	125.2	188.1	142.0	180.3	99.5
May	139.7	138.3	137.4	136.7	150.2	116.8	117.9	133.1	126.3	188.7	142.0	181.3	102.4
June	140.2	138.3	137.4	136.7	151.1	119.0	118.2	131.0	126.9	189.4	142.0	181.5	105.9
July	140.5	138.1	137.2	138.3	151.8	119.4	118.4	129.2	127.2	190.7	142.4	182.3	106.0
Aug	140.9	138.8	138.0	138.6	152.3	119.4	118.3	130.2	126.9	191.5	142.6	183.9	105.4
Sept	141.3	139.3	138.5	138.4	152.9	119.8	118.3	133.3	126.8	192.3	143.2	187.0	105.9
Oct	141.8	139.2	138.3	138.5	152.5	118.5	118.4	135.0	128.0	193.3	143.5	187.9	104.5
Nov	142.0	139.1	138.3	138.5	152.4	118.3	118.5	134.5	129.2	194.3	143.7	188.0	104.5

[1] Includes alcoholic beverages, not shown separately.
[2] See table B-57 for components.
[3] Household fuels—gas (piped), electricity, fuel oil, etc.—and motor fuel. Motor oil, coolant, etc. also included through 1982. See table B-57 for the components.

Note.—Data beginning 1983 incorporate a rental equivalence measure for homeowners' costs.

Source: Department of Labor, Bureau of Labor Statistics.

TABLE B-57.—*Consumer price indexes for selected expenditure classes, 1950-92*

[For all urban consumers; 1982-84 = 100, except as noted]

Year or month	Food and beverages				Shelter					Fuel and other utilities				
	Total [1]	Food			Renters' costs					Total	Fuels			
		Total	At home	Away from home	Total	Total [2]	Rent, residential	Home-owners' costs [2]	Mainte-nance and repairs		Total	Fuel oil and other house-hold fuel com-modities	Gas (piped) and elec-tricity (energy serv-ices)	Other utilities and public services
1950		25.4	27.3				29.7					11.3	19.2	
1951		28.2	30.3				30.9					11.8	19.3	
1952		28.7	30.8				32.2					12.1	19.5	
1953		28.3	30.3	21.5	22.0		33.9		20.5	22.5		12.6	19.9	
1954		28.2	30.1	21.9	22.5		35.1		20.9	22.6		12.6	20.2	
1955		27.8	29.5	22.1	22.7		35.6		21.4	23.0		12.7	20.7	
1956		28.0	29.6	22.6	23.1		36.3		22.3	23.6		13.3	20.9	
1957		28.9	30.6	23.4	24.0		37.0		23.2	24.3		14.0	21.1	
1958		30.2	32.0	24.1	24.5		37.6		23.6	24.8		13.7	21.9	
1959		29.7	31.2	24.8	24.7		38.2		24.0	25.4		13.9	22.4	
1960		30.0	31.5	25.4	25.2		38.7		24.4	26.0		13.8	23.3	
1961		30.4	31.8	26.0	25.4		39.2		24.8	26.3		14.1	23.5	
1962		30.6	32.0	26.7	25.8		39.7		25.0	26.3		14.2	23.5	
1963		31.1	32.4	27.3	26.1		40.1		25.3	26.6		14.4	23.5	
1964		31.5	32.7	27.8	26.5		40.5		25.8	26.6		14.4	23.5	
1965		32.2	33.5	28.4	27.0		40.9		26.3	26.6		14.6	23.5	
1966		33.8	35.2	29.7	27.8		41.5		27.5	26.7		15.0	23.6	
1967	35.0	34.1	35.1	31.3	28.8		42.2		28.9	27.1	21.4	15.5	23.7	46.6
1968	36.2	35.3	36.3	32.9	30.1		43.3		30.6	27.4	21.7	16.0	23.9	47.1
1969	38.1	37.1	38.0	34.9	32.6		44.7		33.2	28.0	22.1	16.3	24.3	48.4
1970	40.1	39.2	39.9	37.5	35.5		46.5		35.8	29.1	23.1	17.0	25.4	50.0
1971	41.4	40.4	40.9	39.4	37.0		48.7		38.6	31.1	24.7	18.2	27.1	53.4
1972	43.1	42.1	42.7	41.0	38.7		50.4		40.6	32.5	25.7	18.3	28.5	56.2
1973	48.8	48.2	49.7	44.2	40.5		52.5		43.6	34.3	27.5	21.1	29.9	57.8
1974	55.5	55.1	57.1	49.8	44.4		55.2		49.5	40.7	34.4	33.2	34.5	60.7
1975	60.2	59.8	61.8	54.5	48.8		58.0		54.1	45.4	39.4	36.4	40.1	63.9
1976	62.1	61.6	63.1	58.2	51.5		61.1		57.6	49.4	43.3	38.8	44.7	67.7
1977	65.8	65.5	66.8	62.6	54.9		64.8		62.0	54.7	49.0	43.9	50.5	70.8
1978	72.2	72.0	73.8	68.3	60.5		69.3		67.2	58.5	53.0	46.2	55.0	73.7
1979	79.9	79.9	81.8	75.9	68.9		74.3		74.0	64.8	61.3	62.4	61.0	74.3
1980	86.7	86.8	88.4	83.4	81.0		80.9		82.4	75.4	74.8	86.1	71.4	77.0
1981	93.5	93.6	94.8	90.9	90.5		87.9		90.7	86.4	87.2	104.6	81.9	84.3
1982	97.3	97.4	98.1	95.8	96.9		94.6		96.4	94.9	95.6	103.4	93.2	93.3
1983	99.5	99.4	99.1	100.0	99.1	103.0	100.1	102.5	99.9	100.2	100.5	97.2	101.5	99.5
1984	103.2	103.2	102.8	104.2	104.0	108.6	105.3	107.3	103.7	104.8	104.0	99.4	105.4	107.2
1985	105.6	105.6	104.3	108.3	109.8	114.4	111.8	113.1	106.5	106.5	104.5	95.9	107.1	112.1
1986	109.1	109.0	107.3	112.5	115.8	121.9	118.3	119.4	107.9	104.1	99.2	77.6	105.7	117.9
1987	113.5	113.5	111.9	117.0	121.3	128.1	123.1	124.8	111.8	103.0	97.3	77.9	103.8	120.1
1988	118.2	118.2	116.6	121.8	127.1	133.6	127.8	131.1	114.7	104.4	98.0	78.1	104.6	122.9
1989	124.9	125.1	124.2	127.4	132.8	138.9	132.8	137.3	118.0	107.8	100.9	81.7	107.5	127.1
1990	132.1	132.4	132.3	133.4	140.0	146.7	138.4	144.6	122.2	111.6	104.5	99.3	109.3	131.7
1991	136.8	136.3	135.8	137.9	146.3	155.6	143.3	150.2	126.3	115.3	106.7	94.6	112.6	137.9
1991: Jan	135.9	135.8	136.4	135.8	144.0	153.2	141.2	147.9	124.1	114.8	107.7	111.2	111.5	135.0
Feb	136.0	135.5	135.7	136.2	144.6	154.4	141.5	148.2	125.5	114.7	107.1	105.7	111.5	135.7
Mar	136.3	135.8	136.0	136.5	145.2	156.1	142.0	148.4	124.2	114.1	105.7	99.3	110.8	136.3
Apr	137.2	136.7	137.0	137.1	145.2	155.1	142.5	148.8	126.1	113.1	104.0	94.4	109.4	136.5
May	137.3	136.8	136.9	137.5	145.2	154.2	142.8	149.2	126.9	114.2	105.4	90.9	111.5	137.3
June	137.7	137.2	137.4	137.9	145.8	155.1	143.0	149.7	126.2	115.8	107.6	89.3	114.4	137.9
July	137.1	136.5	136.0	138.4	146.8	157.4	143.7	150.2	126.9	116.4	108.2	87.8	115.4	138.5
Aug	136.6	136.0	134.9	138.7	147.3	158.1	143.7	150.7	127.6	116.2	107.7	87.8	114.7	138.9
Sept	136.7	136.0	134.9	138.9	147.4	156.2	144.6	151.6	126.8	116.8	108.5	90.9	112.9	139.6
Oct	136.5	135.8	134.4	139.1	147.7	156.1	144.6	152.1	127.6	115.7	106.5	94.8	111.2	140.1
Nov	136.9	136.2	135.0	139.3	147.5	154.0	145.0	152.6	127.6	115.5	105.5	94.7	112.4	140.2
Dec	137.3	136.7	135.5	139.6	148.2	155.8	145.2	153.0	128.1	116.0	106.5	94.7	112.4	140.2
1992: Jan	137.9	137.2	136.4	139.7	149.2	158.8	145.4	153.2	128.0	116.2	106.6	92.0	112.8	140.5
Feb	138.1	137.5	136.6	139.9	149.8	160.2	145.6	153.5	128.3	115.9	105.9	91.5	112.0	141.2
Mar	138.8	138.1	137.5	140.1	150.4	161.2	146.4	154.1	128.4	115.8	105.2	90.5	111.5	141.7
Apr	138.8	138.1	137.4	140.2	150.2	160.1	146.2	154.2	128.0	115.8	105.1	89.9	111.3	142.2
May	138.3	137.4	136.2	140.4	150.2	159.5	146.3	154.4	128.1	116.8	106.5	89.8	113.0	142.4
June	138.3	137.4	136.1	140.7	151.1	161.0	146.6	155.0	128.5	116.9	110.2	90.1	117.4	142.2
July	138.1	137.2	135.7	140.8	151.8	162.8	147.0	155.5	128.8	119.4	110.4	90.0	117.6	143.1
Aug	138.8	138.0	136.9	141.0	152.3	163.5	147.0	155.8	128.5	119.4	110.3	89.7	117.5	143.3
Sept	139.3	138.5	137.4	141.2	151.9	161.7	147.2	156.0	128.5	119.8	111.1	89.7	118.5	143.0
Oct	139.2	138.3	137.2	141.3	152.5	161.7	148.0	156.8	129.4	118.5	108.7	91.4	115.4	143.4
Nov	139.1	138.3	137.0	141.5	152.4	160.6	148.6	157.2	129.5	118.3	108.2	92.1	114.8	143.7

[1] Includes alcoholic beverages, not shown separately.
[2] December 1982 = 100.

See next page for continuation of table.

412

TABLE B-57.—*Consumer price indexes for selected expenditure classes, 1950-92*—Continued

[For all urban consumers; 1982-84=100, except as noted]

Year or month	Transportation								Medical care		
	Total	Private transportation						Public transportation	Total	Medical care commodities	Medical care services
		Total[3]	New cars	Used cars	Motor fuel[4]	Automobile maintenance and repair	Other				
1950	22.7	24.5	41.1		19.0	18.9		13.4	15.1	39.7	12.8
1951	24.1	25.6	43.1		19.5	20.4		14.8	15.9	40.8	13.4
1952	25.7	27.3	46.8		20.0	20.8		15.8	16.7	41.2	14.3
1953	26.5	27.8	47.2	26.7	21.2	22.0		16.8	17.3	41.5	14.8
1954	26.1	27.1	46.5	22.7	21.8	22.7		18.0	17.8	42.0	15.3
1955	25.8	26.7	44.8	21.5	22.1	23.2		18.5	18.2	42.5	15.7
1956	26.2	27.1	46.1	20.7	22.8	24.2		19.2	18.9	43.4	16.3
1957	27.7	28.6	48.5	23.2	23.8	25.0		19.9	19.7	44.6	17.0
1958	28.6	29.5	50.0	24.0	23.4	25.4		20.9	20.6	46.1	17.9
1959	29.8	30.8	52.2	26.8	23.7	26.0		21.5	21.5	46.8	18.7
1960	29.8	30.6	51.5	25.0	24.4	26.5		22.2	22.3	46.9	19.5
1961	30.1	30.8	51.5	26.0	24.1	27.1		23.2	22.9	46.3	20.2
1962	30.8	31.4	51.3	28.4	24.3	27.5		24.0	23.5	45.6	20.9
1963	30.9	31.6	51.0	28.7	24.2	27.8		24.3	24.1	45.2	21.5
1964	31.4	32.0	50.9	30.0	24.1	28.2		24.7	24.6	45.1	22.0
1965	31.9	32.5	49.7	29.8	25.1	28.7		25.2	25.2	45.0	22.7
1966	32.3	32.9	48.8	29.0	25.6	29.2		26.1	26.3	45.1	23.9
1967	33.3	33.8	49.3	29.9	26.4	30.4	37.9	27.4	28.2	44.9	26.0
1968	34.3	34.8	50.7	(5)	26.8	32.1	39.2	28.7	29.9	45.0	27.9
1969	35.7	36.0	51.5	30.9	27.6	34.1	41.6	30.9	31.9	45.4	30.2
1970	37.5	37.5	53.0	31.2	27.9	36.6	45.2	35.2	34.0	46.5	32.3
1971	39.5	39.4	55.2	33.0	28.1	39.3	48.6	37.8	36.1	47.3	34.7
1972	39.9	39.7	54.7	33.1	28.4	41.1	48.9	39.3	37.3	47.4	35.9
1973	41.2	41.0	54.8	35.2	31.2	43.2	48.4	39.7	38.8	47.5	37.5
1974	45.8	46.2	57.9	36.7	42.2	47.6	50.2	40.6	42.4	49.2	41.4
1975	50.1	50.6	62.9	43.8	45.1	53.7	53.5	43.5	47.5	53.3	46.6
1976	55.1	55.6	66.9	50.3	47.0	57.6	61.8	47.8	52.0	56.5	51.3
1977	59.0	59.7	70.4	54.7	49.7	61.9	67.2	50.0	57.0	60.2	56.4
1978	61.7	62.5	75.8	55.8	51.8	67.0	69.9	51.5	61.8	64.4	61.2
1979	70.5	71.7	81.8	60.2	70.1	73.7	75.2	54.9	67.5	69.0	67.2
1980	83.1	84.2	88.4	62.3	97.4	81.5	84.3	69.0	74.9	75.4	74.8
1981	93.2	93.8	93.7	76.9	108.5	89.2	91.4	85.6	82.9	83.7	82.8
1982	97.0	97.1	97.4	88.8	102.8	96.0	97.7	94.9	92.5	92.3	92.6
1983	99.3	99.3	99.9	98.7	99.4	100.3	98.8	99.5	100.6	100.2	100.7
1984	103.7	103.6	102.8	112.5	97.9	103.8	103.5	105.7	106.8	107.5	106.7
1985	106.4	106.2	106.1	113.7	98.7	106.8	109.0	110.5	113.5	115.2	113.2
1986	102.3	101.2	110.6	108.8	77.1	110.3	115.1	117.0	122.0	122.8	121.9
1987	105.4	104.2	114.6	113.1	80.2	114.8	120.8	121.1	130.1	131.0	130.0
1988	108.7	107.6	116.9	118.0	80.9	119.7	127.9	123.3	138.6	139.9	138.3
1989	114.1	112.9	119.2	120.4	88.5	124.9	135.8	129.5	149.3	150.8	148.9
1990	120.5	118.8	121.0	117.6	101.2	130.1	142.5	142.6	162.8	163.4	162.7
1991	123.8	121.9	125.3	118.1	99.4	136.0	149.1	148.9	177.0	176.8	177.1
1991: Jan	125.5	123.2	124.6	116.1	108.3	133.1	147.3	155.4	171.0	170.4	171.1
Feb	123.7	121.2	125.3	115.1	99.7	133.5	147.8	156.2	172.5	171.6	172.8
Mar	122.3	119.9	125.4	114.4	94.6	134.1	147.7	153.3	173.7	173.2	173.8
Apr	122.2	120.2	125.3	115.0	96.1	134.4	147.5	147.1	174.4	174.3	174.5
May	123.3	121.5	125.4	117.0	100.2	134.7	147.7	146.0	175.2	175.4	175.1
June	123.7	121.9	125.3	118.8	100.5	135.6	148.0	146.6	176.2	176.5	176.1
July	123.4	121.7	124.9	120.4	98.2	136.4	149.0	146.7	177.5	177.7	177.5
Aug	123.8	122.0	124.4	120.0	99.3	136.9	149.7	147.6	178.9	178.9	178.9
Sept	123.8	122.1	124.1	119.8	99.8	137.8	149.7	146.6	179.7	180.0	179.7
Oct	124.0	122.4	125.0	120.2	98.3	138.4	150.9	144.9	180.7	180.3	180.8
Nov	125.0	123.4	126.6	120.6	99.4	138.5	151.8	147.0	181.8	181.1	181.9
Dec	125.3	123.4	127.6	120.1	98.4	138.4	152.0	149.8	182.6	181.7	182.8
1992: Jan	124.5	122.5	128.0	117.8	94.5	139.0	152.4	151.5	184.3	183.0	184.6
Feb	124.1	122.0	128.1	116.1	92.9	139.7	152.2	150.7	186.2	185.1	186.4
Mar	124.4	122.2	128.2	115.7	93.4	140.3	152.2	153.5	187.3	186.7	187.4
Apr	125.2	122.9	128.2	117.9	95.0	140.5	152.4	154.7	188.1	187.9	188.1
May	126.3	124.3	128.4	120.5	99.4	140.8	152.5	151.6	188.7	187.6	188.9
June	126.9	125.4	128.2	123.1	102.9	141.2	152.6	145.3	189.4	188.0	189.7
July	127.2	125.5	127.8	124.8	102.8	141.4	153.0	148.3	190.7	188.6	191.1
Aug	126.9	125.4	127.6	126.4	101.7	141.6	153.1	146.7	191.5	188.9	192.2
Sept	126.8	125.4	127.4	127.7	101.7	142.2	152.7	145.6	192.3	189.5	192.9
Oct	128.0	126.1	128.2	129.1	101.6	142.5	154.4	152.9	193.3	189.8	194.2
Nov	129.2	127.0	129.7	129.9	102.2	142.8	155.3	157.4	194.3	190.4	195.2

[3] Includes other new vehicles, not shown separately. Includes direct pricing of new trucks and motorcycles beginning September 1982.
[4] Includes direct pricing of diesel fuel and gasohol beginning September 1981.
[5] Not available.
Note.—See Note, Table B-56.
Source: Department of Labor, Bureau of Labor Statistics.

413

TABLE B-58.—*Consumer price indexes for commodities, services, and special groups, 1950-92*

[For all urban consumers; 1982-84=100, except as noted]

Year or month	All items (CPI-U)	Commodities			Services			Special indexes				CPI-U-X1 (all items) (Dec. 1982 =97.6) [1]
		All commodities	Food	Commodities less food	All services	Medical care services	Services less medical care services	All items less food	All items less energy	All items less food and energy	All items less medical care	
1950	24.1	29.0	25.4	31.4	16.9	12.8		23.8				26.2
1951	26.0	31.6	28.2	33.8	17.8	13.4		25.3				28.3
1952	26.5	32.0	28.7	34.1	18.6	14.3		25.9				28.8
1953	26.7	31.9	28.3	34.2	19.4	14.8		26.4				29.0
1954	26.9	31.6	28.2	33.8	20.0	15.3		26.6				29.2
1955	26.8	31.3	27.8	33.6	20.4	15.7		26.6				29.1
1956	27.2	31.6	28.0	33.9	20.9	16.3		27.1				29.6
1957	28.1	32.6	28.9	34.9	21.8	17.0	22.8	28.0	28.9	28.9	28.7	30.5
1958	28.9	33.3	30.2	35.3	22.6	17.9	23.6	28.6	29.7	29.6	29.5	31.4
1959	29.1	33.3	29.7	35.8	23.3	18.7	24.2	29.2	29.9	30.2	29.8	31.6
1960	29.6	33.6	30.0	36.0	24.1	19.5	25.0	29.7	30.4	30.6	30.2	32.2
1961	29.9	33.8	30.4	36.1	24.5	20.2	25.4	30.0	30.7	31.0	30.5	32.5
1962	30.2	34.1	30.6	36.3	25.0	20.9	25.9	30.3	31.1	31.4	30.8	32.8
1963	30.6	34.4	31.1	36.6	25.5	21.5	26.3	30.7	31.5	31.8	31.1	33.3
1964	31.0	34.8	31.5	36.9	26.0	22.0	26.8	31.1	32.0	32.3	31.5	33.7
1965	31.5	35.2	32.2	37.2	26.6	22.7	27.4	31.6	32.5	32.7	32.0	34.2
1966	32.4	36.1	33.8	37.7	27.6	23.9	28.3	32.3	33.5	33.5	33.0	35.2
1967	33.4	36.8	34.1	38.6	28.8	26.0	29.3	33.4	34.4	34.7	33.7	36.3
1968	34.8	38.1	35.3	40.0	30.3	27.9	30.8	34.9	35.9	36.3	35.1	37.7
1969	36.7	39.9	37.1	41.7	32.4	30.2	32.9	36.8	38.0	38.4	37.0	39.4
1970	38.8	41.7	39.2	43.4	35.0	32.3	35.6	39.0	40.3	40.8	39.2	41.3
1971	40.5	43.2	40.4	45.1	37.0	34.7	37.5	40.8	42.0	42.7	40.8	43.1
1972	41.8	44.5	42.1	46.1	38.4	35.9	38.9	42.0	43.4	44.0	42.1	44.4
1973	44.4	47.8	48.2	47.7	40.1	37.5	40.6	43.7	46.1	45.6	44.8	47.2
1974	49.3	53.5	55.1	52.8	43.8	41.4	44.3	48.0	50.6	49.4	49.8	51.9
1975	53.8	58.2	59.8	57.6	48.0	46.6	48.3	52.5	55.1	53.9	54.3	56.2
1976	56.9	60.7	61.6	60.5	52.0	51.3	52.2	56.0	58.2	57.4	57.2	59.4
1977	60.6	64.2	65.5	63.8	56.0	56.4	55.9	59.6	61.9	61.0	60.8	63.2
1978	65.2	68.8	72.0	67.5	60.8	61.2	60.7	63.9	66.7	65.5	65.4	67.5
1979	72.6	76.6	79.9	75.3	67.5	67.2	67.5	71.2	73.4	71.9	72.9	74.0
1980	82.4	86.0	86.8	85.7	77.9	74.8	78.2	81.5	81.9	80.8	82.8	82.3
1981	90.9	93.2	93.6	93.1	88.1	82.8	88.7	90.4	90.1	89.2	91.4	90.1
1982	96.5	97.0	97.4	96.9	96.0	92.6	96.4	96.3	96.1	95.8	96.8	95.6
1983	99.6	99.8	99.4	100.0	99.4	100.7	99.2	99.7	99.6	99.6	99.6	99.6
1984	103.9	103.2	103.2	103.1	104.6	106.7	104.4	104.0	104.3	104.6	103.7	103.9
1985	107.6	105.4	105.6	105.2	109.9	113.2	109.6	108.0	108.4	109.1	107.2	107.6
1986	109.6	104.4	109.0	101.7	115.4	121.9	114.6	109.8	112.6	113.5	108.8	109.6
1987	113.6	107.7	113.5	104.3	120.2	130.0	119.1	113.6	117.2	118.2	112.6	113.6
1988	118.3	111.5	118.2	107.7	125.7	138.3	124.3	118.3	122.3	123.4	117.0	118.3
1989	124.0	116.7	125.1	112.0	131.9	148.9	130.1	123.7	128.1	129.0	122.4	124.0
1990	130.7	122.8	132.4	117.4	139.2	162.7	136.8	130.3	134.7	135.5	128.8	130.7
1991	136.2	126.6	136.3	121.3	146.3	177.1	143.3	136.1	140.9	142.1	133.8	136.2
1991: Jan	134.6	126.0	135.8	120.6	143.8	171.1	141.1	134.3	138.6	139.4	132.4	
Feb	134.8	125.7	135.5	120.3	144.5	172.8	141.7	134.6	139.3	140.3	132.6	
Mar	135.0	125.7	135.8	120.1	144.8	173.8	142.0	134.8	139.8	140.9	132.7	
Apr	135.2	126.4	136.7	120.7	144.7	174.5	141.8	134.9	140.2	141.1	133.0	
May	135.6	126.8	136.8	121.3	145.0	175.1	142.1	135.4	140.3	141.3	133.3	
June	136.0	126.7	137.2	120.9	145.8	176.1	142.9	135.7	140.5	141.5	133.6	
July	136.2	126.2	136.5	120.5	146.8	177.5	143.8	136.1	140.9	142.0	133.8	
Aug	136.6	126.4	136.0	121.1	147.3	178.9	144.3	136.7	141.3	142.7	134.2	
Sept	137.2	127.1	136.0	122.1	147.9	179.7	144.8	137.4	141.9	143.4	134.8	
Oct	137.4	127.2	135.8	122.4	148.1	180.8	145.0	137.7	142.3	143.9	134.9	
Nov	137.8	127.8	136.2	123.0	148.3	181.9	145.1	138.0	142.7	144.4	135.2	
Dec	137.9	127.5	136.7	122.4	148.8	182.8	145.5	138.1	142.8	144.4	135.3	
1992: Jan	138.1	127.2	137.2	121.6	149.6	184.6	146.3	138.3	143.3	144.9	135.5	
Feb	138.6	127.6	137.5	122.1	150.1	186.4	146.6	138.8	144.0	145.6	135.9	
Mar	139.3	128.4	138.1	123.0	150.7	187.4	147.1	139.5	144.7	146.4	136.5	
Apr	139.5	128.8	138.1	123.5	150.8	188.1	147.2	139.7	144.9	146.6	136.7	
May	139.7	129.1	137.4	124.4	150.9	188.9	147.3	140.1	144.9	146.7	136.9	
June	140.2	129.2	137.4	124.5	151.7	189.7	148.1	140.7	145.0	146.9	137.4	
July	140.5	129.0	137.2	124.3	152.5	191.1	148.8	141.1	145.3	147.3	137.6	
Aug	140.9	129.3	138.0	124.3	153.0	192.2	149.2	141.4	145.8	147.7	138.0	
Sept	141.3	129.9	138.5	125.1	153.2	192.9	149.4	141.8	146.2	148.1	138.4	
Oct	141.8	130.3	138.3	125.7	153.7	194.2	149.9	142.4	146.9	149.0	138.8	
Nov	142.0	130.5	138.3	126.1	154.0	195.2	150.1	142.7	147.1	149.3	139.0	

[1] CPI-U-X1 is a rental equivalence approach to homeowners' costs for the consumer price index for years prior to 1983, the first year for which the official index (CPI-U) incorporates such a measure. CPI-U-X1 is rebased to the December 1982 value of the CPI-U (1982-84=100); thus it is identical with CPI-U data for December 1982 and all subsequent periods. Data prior to 1967 estimated by Council of Economic Advisers by moving the series at the same rate as the CPI-U for each year.

Note.—See Note, Table B-56.

Source: Department of Labor, Bureau of Labor Statistics (except as noted).

TABLE B-59.—*Changes in special consumer price indexes, 1958-92*

[For all urban consumers; percent change]

Year or month	All items (CPI-U) Dec. to Dec.[1]	All items (CPI-U) Year to year	All items less food Dec. to Dec.[1]	All items less food Year to year	All items less energy Dec. to Dec.[1]	All items less energy Year to year	All items less food and energy Dec. to Dec.[1]	All items less food and energy Year to year	All items less medical care Dec. to Dec.[1]	All items less medical care Year to year
1958	1.8	2.8	1.8	2.1	2.1	2.8	1.7	2.4	1.7	2.8
1959	1.7	.7	2.1	2.1	1.3	.7	2.0	2.0	1.4	1.0
1960	1.4	1.7	1.0	1.7	1.3	1.7	1.0	1.3	1.3	1.3
1961	.7	1.0	1.3	1.0	.7	1.0	1.3	1.3	.3	1.0
1962	1.3	1.0	1.0	1.0	1.3	1.3	1.3	1.3	1.3	1.0
1963	1.6	1.3	1.6	1.3	1.9	1.3	1.6	1.3	1.6	1.0
1964	1.0	1.3	1.0	1.3	1.3	1.6	1.2	1.6	1.0	1.3
1965	1.9	1.6	1.6	1.6	1.9	1.6	1.5	1.2	1.9	1.6
1966	3.5	2.9	3.5	2.2	3.4	3.1	3.3	2.4	3.4	3.1
1967	3.0	3.1	3.3	3.4	3.2	2.7	3.8	3.6	2.7	2.1
1968	4.7	4.2	5.0	4.5	4.9	4.4	5.1	4.6	4.7	4.2
1969	6.2	5.5	5.6	5.4	6.5	5.8	6.2	5.8	6.1	5.4
1970	5.6	5.7	6.6	6.0	5.4	6.1	6.6	6.3	5.2	5.9
1971	3.3	4.4	3.0	4.6	3.4	4.2	3.1	4.7	3.2	4.1
1972	3.4	3.2	2.9	2.9	3.5	3.3	3.0	3.0	3.4	3.2
1973	8.7	6.2	5.6	4.0	8.2	6.2	4.7	3.6	9.1	6.4
1974	12.3	11.0	12.2	9.8	11.7	9.8	11.1	8.3	12.2	11.2
1975	6.9	9.1	7.3	9.4	6.6	8.9	6.7	9.1	6.7	9.0
1976	4.9	5.8	6.1	6.7	4.8	5.6	6.1	6.5	4.5	5.3
1977	6.7	6.5	6.4	6.4	6.7	6.4	6.5	6.3	6.7	6.3
1978	9.0	7.6	8.3	7.2	9.1	7.8	8.5	7.4	9.1	7.6
1979	13.3	11.3	14.0	11.4	11.1	10.0	11.3	9.8	13.4	11.5
1980	12.5	13.5	13.0	14.5	11.7	11.6	12.2	12.4	12.5	13.6
1981	8.9	10.3	9.8	10.9	8.5	10.0	9.5	10.4	8.8	10.4
1982	3.8	6.2	4.1	6.5	4.2	6.7	4.5	7.4	3.6	5.9
1983	3.8	3.2	4.1	3.5	4.5	3.6	4.8	4.0	3.6	2.9
1984	3.9	4.3	3.9	4.3	4.4	4.7	4.7	5.0	3.9	4.1
1985	3.8	3.6	4.1	3.8	4.0	3.9	4.3	4.3	3.5	3.4
1986	1.1	1.9	.5	1.7	3.8	3.9	3.8	4.0	.7	1.5
1987	4.4	3.6	4.6	3.5	4.1	4.1	4.2	4.1·	4.3	3.5
1988	4.4	4.1	4.2	4.1	4.7	4.4	4.7	4.4	4.2	3.9
1989	4.6	4.8	4.5	4.6	4.6	4.7	4.4	4.5	4.5	4.6
1990	6.1	5.4	6.3	5.3	5.2	5.2	5.2	5.0	5.9	5.2
1991	3.1	4.2	3.3	4.5	3.9	4.6	4.4	4.9	2.7	3.9

	Change from preceding period									
	Unadjusted	Seasonally adjusted	Unadjusted	Seasonally adjusted	Unadjusted	Seasonally adjusted	Unadjusted	Seasonally adjusted	Unadjusted	Seasonally adjusted
1991: Jan	0.6	0.4	0.4	0.4	0.9	0.6	0.8	0.7	0.5	0.4
Feb	.1	.1	.2	.2	.5	.6	.6	.6	.2	.2
Mar	.1	.1	.1	.1	.4	.3	.4	.3	.1	0
Apr	.1	.2	.1	.2	.3	.3	.1	.3	.2	.2
May	.3	.2	.4	.2	.1	.2	.1	.2	.2	.2
June	.3	.3	.2	.2	.1	.3	.1	.3	.2	.2
July	.1	.1	.3	.2	.3	.2	.4	.3	.1	.1
Aug	.3	.3	.4	.4	.3	.3	.5	.4	.3	.2
Sept	.4	.4	.5	.4	.4	.4	.5	.4	.4	.4
Oct	.1	.2	.2	.2	.3	.2	.3	.2	.1	.1
Nov	.3	.4	.2	.4	.3	.3	.3	.3	.2	.3
Dec	.1	.2	.1	.2	.1	.2	0	.2	.1	.2
1992: Jan	.1	.1	.1	.1	.4	.2	.3	.3	.1	.1
Feb	.4	.3	.4	.3	.5	.4	.5	.4	.3	.3
Mar	.5	.5	.5	.5	.5	.5	.5	.5	.4	.4
Apr	.1	.2	.1	.3	.1	.2	.1	.3	.1	.2
May	.1	.1	.3	.2	0	.1	.1	.2	.1	.1
June	.4	.3	.4	.4	.1	.2	.1	.2	.4	.4
July	.2	.1	.3	.2	.2	.1	.3	.2	.1	.1
Aug	.3	.3	.2	.1	.3	.3	.3	.2	.3	.2
Sept	.3	.2	.3	.2	.3	.2	.3	.2	.3	.2
Oct	.4	.4	.4	.4	.5	.4	.6	.5	.3	.4
Nov	.1	.2	.2	.4	.1	.2	.2	.3	.1	.2

[1] Changes from December to December are based on unadjusted indexes.
Note.—See Note, Table B-56.
Source: Department of Labor, Bureau of Labor Statistics.

TABLE B-60.—*Changes in consumer price indexes for commodities and services, 1929-91*

[For all urban consumers; percent change]

Year	All items (CPI-U) Dec. to Dec.¹	Year to year	Commodities Total Dec. to Dec.¹	Year to year	Food Dec. to Dec.¹	Year to year	Services Total Dec. to Dec.¹	Year to year	Medical care services Dec. to Dec.¹	Year to year	Medical care Dec. to Dec.¹	Year to year	Energy² Dec. to Dec.¹	Year to year
1929	0.6	0			2.5	1.2								
1933	.8	-5.1			6.9	-2.8								
1939	0	-1.4	-0.7	-2.0	-2.5	-2.5	0	0	1.2	1.2				
1940	.7	.7	1.4	.7	2.5	1.7	.8	.8	0	0				
1941	9.9	5.0	13.3	6.7	15.7	9.2	2.4	.8	1.2	0				
1942	9.0	10.9	12.9	14.5	17.9	17.6	2.3	3.1	3.5	3.5				
1943	3.0	6.1	4.2	9.3	3.0	11.0	2.3	2.3	5.6	4.5				
1944	2.3	1.7	2.0	1.0	0	-1.2	2.2	2.2	3.2	4.3				
1945	2.2	2.3	2.9	3.0	3.5	2.4	.7	1.5	3.1	3.1				
1946	18.1	8.3	24.8	10.6	31.3	14.5	3.6	1.4	9.0	5.1				
1947	8.8	14.4	10.3	20.5	11.3	21.7	5.6	4.3	6.4	8.7				
1948	3.0	8.1	1.7	7.2	-.8	8.3	5.9	6.1	6.9	7.1	5.8	6.7		
1949	-2.1	-1.2	-4.1	-2.7	-3.9	-4.2	3.7	5.1	1.6	3.3	1.4	2.8		
1950	5.9	1.3	7.8	.7	9.8	1.6	3.6	3.0	4.0	2.4	3.4	2.0		
1951	6.0	7.9	5.9	9.0	7.1	11.0	5.2	5.3	5.3	4.7	5.8	5.3		
1952	.8	1.9	-.9	1.3	-1.0	1.8	4.4	4.5	5.8	6.7	4.3	5.0		
1953	.7	.8	-.3	-.3	-1.1	-1.4	4.2	4.3	3.4	3.5	3.5	3.6		
1954	-.7	.7	-1.6	-.9	-1.8	-.4	2.0	3.1	2.6	3.4	2.3	2.9		
1955	.4	-.4	-.3	-.9	-.7	-1.4	2.0	2.0	3.2	2.6	3.3	2.2		
1956	3.0	1.5	2.6	1.0	2.9	.7	3.4	2.5	3.8	3.8	3.2	3.8		
1957	2.9	3.3	2.8	3.2	2.8	3.2	4.2	4.3	4.8	4.3	4.7	4.2		
1958	1.8	2.8	1.2	2.1	2.4	4.5	2.7	3.7	4.6	5.3	4.5	4.6	-0.9	0
1959	1.7	.7	.6	0	-1.0	-1.7	3.9	3.1	4.9	4.5	3.8	4.4	4.7	1.9
1960	1.4	1.7	1.2	.9	3.1	1.0	2.5	3.4	3.7	4.3	3.2	3.7	1.3	2.3
1961	.7	1.0	0	.6	-.7	1.3	2.1	1.7	3.5	3.6	3.1	2.7	-1.3	.4
1962	1.3	1.0	.9	.9	1.3	.7	1.6	2.0	2.9	3.5	2.2	2.6	2.2	.4
1963	1.6	1.3	1.5	.9	2.0	1.6	2.4	2.0	2.8	2.9	2.5	2.6	-.9	0
1964	1.0	1.3	.9	1.2	1.3	1.3	1.6	2.0	2.3	2.3	2.1	2.1	0	-.4
1965	1.9	1.6	1.4	1.1	3.5	2.2	2.7	2.3	3.6	3.2	2.8	2.4	1.8	1.8
1966	3.5	2.9	2.5	2.6	4.0	5.0	4.8	3.8	8.3	5.3	6.7	4.4	1.7	1.7
1967	3.0	3.1	2.5	1.9	1.2	.9	4.3	4.3	8.0	8.8	6.3	7.2	1.7	2.1
1968	4.7	4.2	4.0	3.5	4.4	3.5	5.8	5.2	7.1	7.3	6.2	6.0	1.7	1.7
1969	6.2	5.5	5.4	4.7	7.0	5.1	7.7	6.9	7.3	8.2	6.2	6.7	2.9	2.5
1970	5.6	5.7	3.9	4.5	2.3	5.7	8.1	8.0	8.1	7.0	7.4	6.6	4.8	2.8
1971	3.3	4.4	2.8	3.6	4.3	3.1	4.1	5.7	5.4	7.4	4.6	6.2	3.1	3.9
1972	3.4	3.2	3.4	3.0	4.6	4.2	3.4	3.8	3.7	3.5	3.3	3.3	2.6	2.6
1973	8.7	6.2	10.4	7.4	20.3	14.5	6.2	4.4	6.0	4.5	5.3	4.0	17.0	8.1
1974	12.3	11.0	12.8	11.9	12.0	14.3	11.4	9.2	13.2	10.4	12.6	9.3	21.6	29.6
1975	6.9	9.1	6.2	8.8	6.6	8.5	8.2	9.6	10.3	12.6	9.8	12.0	11.4	10.5
1976	4.9	5.8	3.3	4.3	.5	3.0	7.2	8.3	10.8	10.1	10.0	9.5	7.1	7.1
1977	6.7	6.5	6.1	5.8	8.1	6.3	8.0	7.7	9.0	9.9	8.9	9.6	7.2	9.5
1978	9.0	7.6	8.8	7.2	11.8	9.9	9.3	8.6	9.3	8.5	8.8	8.4	7.9	6.3
1979	13.3	11.3	13.0	11.3	10.2	11.0	13.6	11.0	10.5	9.8	10.1	9.2	37.5	25.1
1980	12.5	13.5	11.0	12.3	10.2	8.6	14.2	15.4	10.1	11.3	9.9	11.0	18.0	30.9
1981	8.9	10.3	6.0	8.4	4.3	7.8	13.0	13.1	12.6	10.7	12.5	10.7	11.9	13.6
1982	3.8	6.2	3.6	4.1	3.1	4.1	4.3	9.0	11.2	11.8	11.0	11.6	1.3	1.5
1983	3.8	3.2	2.9	2.9	2.7	2.1	4.8	3.5	6.2	8.7	6.4	8.8	-.5	.7
1984	3.9	4.3	2.7	3.4	3.8	3.8	5.4	5.2	5.8	6.0	6.1	6.2	.2	1.0
1985	3.8	3.6	2.5	2.1	2.6	2.3	5.1	5.1	6.8	6.1	6.8	6.3	1.8	.7
1986	1.1	1.9	-2.0	-.9	3.8	3.2	4.5	5.0	7.9	7.7	7.7	7.5	-19.7	-13.2
1987	4.4	3.6	4.6	3.2	3.5	4.1	4.3	4.2	5.6	6.6	5.8	6.6	8.2	.5
1988	4.4	4.1	3.8	3.5	5.2	4.1	4.8	4.6	6.9	6.4	6.9	6.5	.5	.8
1989	4.6	4.8	4.1	4.7	5.6	5.8	5.1	4.9	8.6	7.7	8.5	7.7	5.1	5.6
1990	6.1	5.4	6.6	5.2	5.3	5.8	5.7	5.5	9.9	9.3	9.6	9.0	18.1	8.3
1991	3.1	4.2	1.2	3.1	1.9	2.9	4.6	5.1	8.0	8.9	7.9	8.7	-7.4	.4

¹ Changes from December to December are based on unadjusted indexes.
² Household fuels—gas (piped) electricity, fuel oil, etc.—and motor fuel. Motor oil, coolant, etc. also included through 1982.
Note.—See Note, Table B-56.
Source: Department of Labor, Bureau of Labor Statistics.

416

Year or month	Total finished goods	Consumer foods			Finished goods excluding consumer foods					Total finished consumer goods
		Total	Crude	Processed	Total	Consumer goods			Capital equipment	
						Total	Durable	Non-durable		
1947	26.4	31.9	39.3	31.1		27.4	32.9	24.2	19.8	28.6
1948	28.5	34.9	42.4	34.0		29.2	35.2	25.7	21.6	30.8
1949	27.7	32.1	40.1	31.1		28.6	36.1	24.7	22.7	29.4
1950	28.2	32.7	36.5	32.4		29.0	36.5	25.1	23.2	29.9
1951	30.8	36.7	41.9	36.2		31.1	38.9	27.0	25.5	32.7
1952	30.6	36.4	44.6	35.4		30.7	39.2	26.3	25.9	32.3
1953	30.3	34.5	41.6	33.6		31.0	39.5	26.6	26.3	31.7
1954	30.4	34.2	37.5	34.0		31.1	39.8	26.7	26.7	31.7
1955	30.5	33.4	39.1	32.7		31.3	40.2	26.8	27.4	31.5
1956	31.3	33.3	39.1	32.7		32.1	41.6	27.3	29.5	32.0
1957	32.5	34.4	38.5	34.1		32.9	42.8	27.9	31.3	32.9
1958	33.2	36.5	41.0	36.1		32.9	43.4	27.8	32.1	33.6
1959	33.1	34.8	37.3	34.7		33.3	43.9	28.2	32.7	33.3
1960	33.4	35.5	39.8	35.2		33.5	43.8	28.4	32.8	33.6
1961	33.4	35.4	38.0	35.3		33.4	43.6	28.4	32.9	33.6
1962	33.5	35.7	38.4	35.6		33.4	43.4	28.4	33.0	33.7
1963	33.4	35.3	37.8	35.2		33.4	43.1	28.5	33.1	33.5
1964	33.5	35.4	38.9	35.2		33.3	43.3	28.4	33.4	33.6
1965	34.1	36.8	39.0	36.8		33.6	43.2	28.8	33.8	34.2
1966	35.2	39.2	41.5	39.2		34.1	43.4	29.3	34.6	35.4
1967	35.6	38.5	39.6	38.8	35.0	34.7	44.1	30.0	35.8	35.6
1968	36.6	40.0	42.5	40.0	35.9	35.5	45.1	30.6	37.0	36.5
1969	38.0	42.4	45.9	42.3	36.9	36.3	45.9	31.5	38.3	37.9
1970	39.3	43.8	46.0	43.9	38.2	37.4	47.2	32.5	40.1	39.1
1971	40.5	44.5	45.8	44.7	39.6	38.7	48.9	33.5	41.7	40.2
1972	41.8	46.9	48.0	47.2	40.4	39.4	50.0	34.1	42.8	41.5
1973	45.6	56.5	63.6	55.8	42.0	41.2	50.9	36.1	44.2	46.0
1974	52.6	64.4	71.6	63.9	48.8	48.2	55.5	44.0	50.5	53.1
1975	58.2	69.8	71.7	70.3	54.7	53.2	61.0	48.9	58.2	58.2
1976	60.8	69.6	76.7	69.0	58.1	56.5	63.7	52.4	62.1	60.4
1977	64.7	73.3	79.5	72.7	62.2	60.6	67.4	56.8	66.1	64.3
1978	69.8	79.9	85.8	79.4	66.7	64.9	73.6	60.0	71.3	69.4
1979	77.6	87.3	92.3	86.8	74.6	73.5	80.8	69.3	77.5	77.5
1980	88.0	92.4	93.9	92.3	86.7	87.1	91.0	85.1	85.8	88.6
1981	96.1	97.8	104.4	97.2	95.6	96.1	96.4	95.8	94.6	96.6
1982	100.0	100.0	100.0	100.0	100.0	100.0	100.0	100.0	100.0	100.0
1983	101.6	101.0	102.4	100.9	101.8	101.2	102.8	100.5	102.8	101.3
1984	103.7	105.4	111.4	104.9	103.2	102.2	104.5	101.1	105.2	103.3
1985	104.7	104.6	102.9	104.8	104.6	103.3	106.5	101.7	107.5	103.8
1986	103.2	107.3	105.6	107.4	101.9	98.5	108.9	93.3	109.7	101.4
1987	105.4	109.5	107.1	109.6	104.0	100.7	111.5	94.9	111.7	103.6
1988	108.0	112.6	109.8	112.7	106.5	103.1	113.8	97.3	114.3	106.2
1989	113.6	118.7	119.6	118.6	111.8	108.9	117.6	103.8	118.8	112.1
1990	119.2	124.4	123.0	124.4	117.4	115.3	120.4	111.5	122.9	118.2
1991	121.7	124.1	119.3	124.4	120.9	118.7	123.9	115.0	126.7	120.5
1991: Jan	122.3	124.8	124.3	124.7	121.4	119.8	123.5	116.7	125.9	121.4
Feb	121.4	124.6	118.8	124.9	120.4	118.2	123.9	114.4	126.1	120.3
Mar	120.9	125.2	125.0	125.1	119.5	117.0	124.0	112.8	126.2	119.6
Apr	121.1	125.3	128.2	125.1	119.7	117.2	123.7	113.2	126.2	119.8
May	121.8	125.8	137.8	124.9	120.5	118.2	123.2	114.6	126.5	120.6
June	121.9	125.3	130.3	124.8	120.8	118.6	123.1	115.2	126.5	120.7
July	121.6	124.5	121.8	124.7	120.7	118.4	123.1	115.0	126.6	120.4
Aug	121.7	123.3	112.1	124.1	121.1	119.0	122.9	115.8	126.5	120.4
Sept	121.4	122.7	109.9	123.6	121.0	119.0	122.1	116.1	126.2	120.2
Oct	122.2	123.0	104.8	124.3	121.9	119.7	126.0	115.6	127.9	120.8
Nov	122.3	123.0	114.6	123.6	122.0	119.7	125.7	115.8	127.9	120.9
Dec	121.9	122.3	104.5	123.6	121.7	119.2	125.4	115.2	128.0	120.3
1992: Jan	121.8	122.5	109.7	123.4	121.5	118.8	125.8	114.4	128.6	120.0
Feb	122.1	123.4	118.7	123.7	121.6	118.8	125.5	114.6	128.7	120.3
Mar	122.2	123.3	115.8	123.8	121.8	119.0	125.8	114.8	128.9	120.4
Apr	122.4	122.8	105.2	124.0	122.3	119.6	125.6	115.7	129.1	120.7
May	123.2	123.1	98.6	124.8	123.1	120.9	125.6	117.5	129.0	121.7
June	123.9	123.1	96.3	125.1	124.0	122.1	125.2	119.5	128.9	122.6
July [1]	123.7	122.8	97.3	124.7	123.8	122.0	125.4	119.2	128.8	122.4
Aug	123.5	123.2	104.7	124.6	123.5	121.6	125.1	118.7	128.8	122.2
Sept	123.3	123.2	104.5	124.6	123.2	121.4	123.4	119.3	128.0	122.1
Oct	124.3	123.6	110.0	124.6	124.3	122.2	127.0	118.8	130.1	122.8
Nov	123.9	123.3	107.3	124.4	124.0	121.7	127.0	118.0	130.0	122.3

[1] Data have been revised through July 1992 to reflect the availability of late reports and corrections by respondents. All data are subject to revision 4 months after original publication.

See next page for continuation of table.

TABLE B–61.—*Producer price indexes by stage of processing, 1947–92*—Continued

[1982 = 100]

Year or month	Intermediate materials, supplies, and components								Crude materials for further processing				
	Total	Foods and feeds²	Other	Materials and components		Processed fuels and lubricants	Containers	Supplies	Total	Foodstuffs and feedstuffs	Other		
				For manufacturing	For construction						Total	Fuel	Other
1947	23.3		22.2	24.9	22.5	14.4	23.4	28.5	31.7	45.1		7.5	24.0
1948	25.2		24.1	26.8	24.9	16.4	24.4	29.8	34.7	48.8		8.9	26.7
1949	24.2		23.5	25.7	24.9	14.9	24.5	28.0	30.1	40.5		8.8	24.3
1950	25.3		24.6	26.9	26.2	15.2	25.2	29.0	32.7	43.4		8.8	27.8
1951	28.4		27.6	30.5	28.7	15.9	29.6	32.6	37.6	50.2		9.0	32.0
1952	27.5		26.7	29.3	28.5	15.7	28.0	32.6	34.5	47.3		9.0	27.8
1953	27.7		27.0	29.7	29.0	15.8	28.0	31.0	31.9	42.3		9.3	26.6
1954	27.9		27.2	29.8	29.1	15.8	28.5	31.7	31.6	42.3		8.9	26.1
1955	28.4		28.0	30.5	30.3	15.8	28.9	31.2	30.4	38.4		8.9	27.5
1956	29.6		29.3	32.0	31.8	16.3	31.0	32.0	30.6	37.6		9.5	28.6
1957	30.3		30.1	32.7	32.0	17.2	32.4	32.3	31.2	39.2		10.1	28.2
1958	30.4		30.1	32.8	32.0	16.2	33.2	33.1	31.9	41.6		10.2	27.1
1959	30.8		30.5	33.3	32.9	16.2	33.0	33.5	31.1	38.8		10.4	28.1
1960	30.8		30.7	33.3	32.7	16.6	33.4	33.3	30.4	38.4		10.5	26.9
1961	30.6		30.3	32.9	32.2	16.8	33.2	33.7	30.2	37.9		10.5	27.2
1962	30.6		30.2	32.7	32.1	16.7	33.6	34.5	30.5	38.6		10.4	27.1
1963	30.7		30.1	32.7	32.2	16.6	33.2	35.0	29.9	37.5		10.5	26.7
1964	30.8		30.3	33.1	32.5	16.2	32.9	34.7	29.6	36.6		10.5	27.2
1965	31.2		30.7	33.6	32.8	16.5	33.5	35.0	31.1	39.2		10.6	27.7
1966	32.0		31.3	34.3	33.6	16.8	34.5	36.5	33.1	42.7		10.9	28.3
1967	32.2	41.8	31.7	34.5	34.0	16.9	35.0	36.8	31.3	40.3	21.1	11.3	26.5
1968	33.0	41.5	32.5	35.3	35.7	16.5	35.9	37.1	31.8	40.9	21.6	11.5	27.1
1969	34.1	42.9	33.6	36.5	37.7	16.6	37.2	37.8	33.9	44.1	22.5	12.0	28.4
1970	35.4	45.6	34.8	38.0	38.3	17.7	39.0	39.7	35.2	45.2	23.8	13.8	29.1
1971	36.8	46.7	36.2	38.9	40.8	19.5	40.8	40.8	36.0	46.1	24.7	15.7	29.4
1972	38.2	49.5	37.7	40.4	43.0	20.1	42.7	42.5	39.9	51.5	27.0	16.8	32.3
1973	42.4	70.3	40.6	44.1	46.5	22.2	45.2	51.7	54.5	72.6	34.3	18.6	42.9
1974	52.5	83.6	50.5	56.0	55.0	33.6	53.3	56.8	61.4	76.4	44.1	24.8	54.5
1975	58.0	81.6	56.6	61.7	60.1	39.4	60.0	61.8	61.6	77.4	43.7	30.6	50.0
1976	60.9	77.4	60.0	64.0	64.1	42.3	63.1	65.8	63.4	76.8	48.2	34.5	54.9
1977	64.9	79.6	64.1	67.4	69.3	47.7	65.9	69.3	65.5	77.5	51.7	42.0	56.3
1978	69.5	84.8	68.6	72.0	76.5	49.9	71.0	72.9	73.4	87.3	57.5	48.2	61.9
1979	78.4	94.5	77.4	80.9	84.2	61.6	79.4	80.2	85.9	100.0	69.6	57.3	75.5
1980	90.3	105.5	89.4	91.7	91.3	85.0	89.1	89.9	95.3	104.6	84.6	69.4	91.8
1981	98.6	104.6	98.2	98.7	97.9	100.6	96.7	96.9	103.0	103.9	101.8	84.8	109.8
1982	100.0	100.0	100.0	100.0	100.0	100.0	100.0	100.0	100.0	100.0	100.0	100.0	100.0
1983	100.6	103.6	100.5	101.2	102.8	95.4	100.4	101.8	101.3	101.8	100.7	105.1	98.8
1984	103.1	105.7	103.0	104.1	105.6	95.7	105.9	104.1	103.5	104.7	102.2	105.1	101.0
1985	102.7	97.3	103.0	103.3	107.3	92.8	109.0	104.4	95.8	94.8	96.9	102.7	94.3
1986	99.1	96.2	99.3	102.2	108.1	72.7	110.3	105.6	87.7	93.2	81.6	92.2	76.0
1987	101.5	99.2	101.7	105.3	109.8	73.3	114.5	107.7	93.7	96.2	87.9	84.1	88.5
1988	107.1	109.5	106.9	113.2	116.1	71.2	120.1	113.7	96.0	106.1	85.5	82.1	85.9
1989	112.0	113.8	111.9	118.1	121.3	76.4	125.4	118.1	103.1	111.2	93.4	85.3	95.8
1990	114.5	113.3	114.5	118.7	122.9	85.9	127.7	119.4	108.9	113.1	101.5	84.8	107.3
1991	114.4	111.1	114.6	118.1	124.5	85.3	128.1	121.4	101.2	105.5	94.6	82.9	97.5
1991: Jan	116.4	110.4	116.8	119.9	124.0	91.7	129.0	120.9	112.8	107.2	110.8	88.5	120.4
Feb	115.5	110.7	115.7	119.6	123.9	87.5	128.9	121.1	104.1	107.3	97.9	85.6	101.0
Mar	114.2	111.6	114.4	118.9	124.0	82.8	128.7	121.3	101.2	109.9	92.3	84.8	92.2
Apr	113.9	111.5	114.1	118.5	124.3	81.8	128.3	121.4	100.8	109.0	92.2	81.7	94.2
May	114.0	110.8	114.2	118.1	124.5	83.4	128.1	121.3	102.1	108.7	94.2	84.0	95.9
June	114.3	110.8	114.5	117.8	125.2	85.0	127.7	121.4	99.8	107.4	91.5	82.5	92.4
July	114.0	110.0	114.2	117.4	125.3	84.6	127.9	121.1	99.5	105.1	92.3	81.4	94.8
Aug	114.2	111.5	114.4	117.3	124.7	86.0	127.4	121.5	99.1	102.7	93.0	81.8	95.6
Sept	114.6	111.5	114.8	117.3	124.7	87.7	127.4	121.6	98.0	103.0	91.1	77.8	95.4
Oct	114.2	111.8	114.3	117.4	124.5	85.4	127.8	121.5	99.9	102.6	94.2	78.6	99.9
Nov	114.0	111.4	114.1	117.3	124.4	84.7	128.1	121.7	99.7	101.5	94.5	82.2	97.8
Dec	113.7	111.3	113.8	117.3	124.5	83.2	128.0	121.7	97.7	101.6	91.5	85.7	90.1
1992: Jan	113.2	110.7	113.3	117.2	124.9	80.2	127.6	122.0	96.9	103.7	88.8	83.5	87.2
Feb	113.5	110.7	113.6	117.4	125.9	80.6	127.7	122.1	98.6	106.0	90.1	82.6	89.7
Mar	113.6	110.7	113.7	117.5	126.6	80.0	127.7	122.4	97.9	107.2	88.2	79.1	88.8
Apr	113.8	110.4	114.0	117.6	126.8	80.7	127.8	122.4	98.8	105.5	90.7	78.5	93.0
May	114.5	111.5	114.7	117.9	126.8	83.6	127.7	122.7	101.2	108.4	92.8	79.8	95.3
June	115.4	112.3	115.6	118.2	126.5	88.1	127.6	122.7	102.1	107.4	94.8	78.5	99.1
July ¹	115.5	111.2	115.7	118.3	126.3	88.2	127.7	122.7	101.7	105.0	95.7	83.7	97.6
Aug	115.3	110.2	115.6	118.2	126.2	87.6	127.6	122.6	100.9	103.7	95.2	83.5	97.0
Sept	115.6	111.0	115.9	118.3	126.7	88.3	127.6	122.9	102.0	103.0	97.5	86.8	98.6
Oct	115.4	109.6	115.7	118.1	126.6	87.5	127.9	123.1	101.8	103.5	96.7	85.6	98.1
Nov	115.1	109.5	115.4	118.0	126.8	86.0	128.0	123.2	101.5	102.8	96.8	93.0	93.9

² Intermediate materials for food manufacturing and feeds.
Source: Department of Labor, Bureau of Labor Statistics.

TABLE B-62.—*Producer price indexes by stage of processing, special groups, 1974–92*

[1982 = 100]

Year or month	Finished goods						Intermediate materials, supplies, and components				Crude materials for further processing			
	Total	Foods	Energy	Excluding foods and energy			Total	Foods and feeds[1]	Energy	Other	Total	Foodstuffs and feedstuffs	Energy	Other
				Total	Capital equipment	Consumer goods excluding foods and energy								
1974...............	52.6	64.4	26.2	53.6	50.5	55.5	52.5	83.6	33.1	54.0	61.4	76.4	27.8	83.3
1975...............	58.2	69.8	30.7	59.7	58.2	60.6	58.0	81.6	38.7	60.2	61.6	77.4	33.3	69.3
1976...............	60.8	69.6	34.3	63.1	62.1	63.7	60.9	77.4	41.5	63.8	63.4	76.8	35.3	80.2
1977...............	64.7	73.3	39.7	66.9	66.1	67.3	64.9	79.6	46.8	67.6	65.5	77.5	40.4	79.8
1978...............	69.8	79.9	42.3	71.9	71.3	72.2	69.5	84.8	49.1	72.5	73.4	87.3	45.2	87.8
1979...............	77.6	87.3	57.1	78.3	77.5	78.8	78.4	94.5	61.1	80.7	85.9	100.0	54.9	106.2
1980...............	88.0	92.4	85.2	87.1	85.8	87.8	90.3	105.5	84.9	90.3	95.3	104.6	73.1	113.1
1981...............	96.1	97.8	101.5	94.6	94.6	94.6	98.6	104.6	100.5	97.7	103.0	103.9	97.7	111.7
1982...............	100.0	100.0	100.0	100.0	100.0	100.0	100.0	100.0	100.0	100.0	100.0	100.0	100.0	100.0
1983...............	101.6	101.0	95.2	103.0	102.8	103.1	100.6	103.6	95.3	101.6	101.3	101.8	98.7	105.3
1984...............	103.7	105.4	91.2	105.5	105.2	105.7	103.1	105.7	95.5	104.7	103.5	104.7	98.0	111.7
1985...............	104.7	104.6	87.6	108.1	107.5	108.4	102.7	97.3	92.6	105.2	95.8	94.8	93.3	104.9
1986...............	103.2	107.3	63.0	110.6	109.7	111.1	99.1	96.2	72.6	104.9	87.7	93.2	71.8	103.1
1987...............	105.4	109.5	61.8	113.3	111.7	114.2	101.5	99.2	73.0	107.8	93.7	96.2	75.0	115.7
1988...............	108.0	112.6	59.8	117.0	114.3	118.5	107.1	109.5	70.9	115.2	96.0	106.1	67.7	133.0
1989...............	113.6	118.7	65.7	122.1	118.8	124.0	112.0	113.8	76.1	120.2	103.1	111.2	75.9	137.9
1990...............	119.2	124.4	75.0	126.6	122.9	128.8	114.5	113.3	85.5	120.9	108.9	113.1	85.9	136.3
1991...............	121.7	124.2	78.1	131.1	126.7	133.7	114.4	111.1	85.1	121.4	101.2	105.5	80.4	128.2
1991: Jan..........	122.3	124.8	82.6	129.9	125.9	132.3	116.4	110.4	91.5	122.4	112.8	107.2	97.6	133.5
Feb..........	121.4	124.6	78.4	130.2	126.1	132.7	115.5	110.7	87.4	122.2	104.1	107.3	83.1	133.4
Mar..........	120.9	125.2	75.5	130.3	126.2	132.8	114.2	111.6	82.7	121.8	101.2	109.9	77.0	132.2
Apr..........	121.1	125.3	75.7	130.5	126.2	133.1	113.9	111.5	81.7	121.6	100.8	109.0	76.7	132.7
May..........	121.8	125.8	78.0	130.5	126.5	132.9	114.0	110.8	83.2	121.4	102.1	108.7	79.2	131.4
June.........	121.9	125.3	78.4	130.8	126.5	133.3	114.3	110.8	84.8	121.4	99.8	107.4	77.1	126.8
July..........	121.6	124.5	77.5	131.0	126.6	133.7	114.0	110.0	84.4	121.1	99.5	105.1	78.3	125.9
Aug..........	121.7	123.3	78.8	131.0	126.5	133.7	114.2	111.5	85.7	120.9	99.1	102.7	79.0	126.0
Sept........	121.4	122.7	79.1	130.7	126.2	133.4	114.6	111.5	87.4	121.0	98.0	103.0	77.0	125.6
Oct..........	122.2	123.0	78.3	132.4	127.9	135.1	114.2	111.8	85.1	121.0	99.9	102.6	80.6	124.8
Nov..........	122.3	123.0	78.1	132.5	127.9	135.3	114.0	111.4	84.4	121.0	99.7	101.5	81.2	123.4
Dec..........	121.9	122.3	76.6	132.8	128.0	135.7	113.7	111.3	82.8	121.0	97.7	101.6	78.0	122.7
1992: Jan..........	121.8	122.5	74.3	133.4	128.6	136.4	113.2	110.7	80.1	121.1	96.9	103.7	74.4	123.0
Feb..........	122.1	123.4	74.3	133.5	128.7	136.4	113.5	110.7	80.4	121.4	98.6	106.0	75.5	125.2
Mar..........	122.2	123.3	74.4	133.7	128.9	136.6	113.6	110.7	79.9	121.6	97.9	107.2	72.2	128.1
Apr..........	122.4	122.8	75.4	134.0	129.1	137.0	113.8	110.4	80.6	121.8	98.8	105.5	75.0	129.1
May..........	123.2	123.1	77.8	134.2	129.0	137.5	114.5	111.5	83.4	121.9	101.2	108.4	77.4	129.7
June.........	123.9	123.1	81.0	134.1	128.9	137.3	115.4	112.3	87.8	122.0	102.1	107.4	80.1	129.2
July [2]......	123.7	122.8	80.4	134.2	128.8	137.5	115.5	111.2	88.0	122.1	101.7	105.0	81.0	130.0
Aug..........	123.5	123.2	80.3	133.8	128.8	136.9	115.3	110.2	87.3	122.1	100.9	103.7	80.3	130.5
Sept........	123.3	123.2	80.9	133.2	128.0	136.3	115.6	111.0	88.1	122.3	102.0	103.0	83.2	130.5
Oct..........	124.3	123.6	80.0	135.0	130.1	138.1	115.4	109.6	87.3	122.3	101.8	103.5	82.8	128.4
Nov..........	123.9	123.3	78.5	135.1	130.0	138.2	115.1	109.5	85.9	122.2	101.5	102.8	83.3	126.8

[1] Intermediate materials for food manufacturing and feeds.
[2] Data have been revised through July 1992 to reflect the availability of late reports and corrections by respondents. All data are subject to revision 4 months after original publication.

Source: Department of Labor, Bureau of Labor Statistics.

TABLE B-63.—*Producer price indexes for major commodity groups, 1950–92*

[1982=100]

Year or month	Farm products and processed foods and feeds			Industrial commodities				
	Total	Farm products	Processed foods and feeds	Total	Textile products and apparel	Hides, skins, leather, and related products	Fuels and related products and power [1]	Chemicals and allied products [1]
1950................................	37.7	44.0	33.2	25.0	50.2	32.9	12.6	30.4
1951................................	43.0	51.2	36.9	27.6	56.0	37.7	13.0	34.8
1952................................	41.3	48.4	36.4	26.9	50.5	30.5	13.0	33.0
1953................................	38.6	43.8	34.8	27.2	49.3	31.0	13.4	33.4
1954................................	38.5	43.2	35.4	27.2	48.2	29.5	13.2	33.8
1955................................	36.6	40.5	33.8	27.8	48.2	29.4	13.2	33.7
1956................................	36.4	40.0	33.8	29.1	48.2	31.2	13.6	33.9
1957................................	37.7	41.1	34.8	29.9	48.3	31.2	14.3	34.6
1958................................	39.4	42.9	36.5	30.0	47.4	31.6	13.7	34.9
1959................................	37.6	40.2	35.6	30.5	48.1	35.9	13.7	34.8
1960................................	37.7	40.1	35.6	30.5	48.6	34.6	13.9	34.8
1961................................	37.7	39.7	36.2	30.4	47.8	34.9	14.0	34.5
1962................................	38.1	40.4	36.5	30.4	48.2	35.3	14.0	33.9
1963................................	37.7	39.6	36.8	30.3	48.2	34.3	13.9	33.5
1964................................	37.5	39.0	36.7	30.5	48.5	34.4	13.5	33.6
1965................................	39.0	40.7	38.0	30.9	48.8	35.9	13.8	33.9
1966................................	41.6	43.7	40.2	31.5	48.9	39.4	14.1	34.0
1967................................	40.2	41.3	39.8	32.0	48.9	38.1	14.4	34.2
1968................................	41.1	42.3	40.6	32.8	50.7	39.3	14.3	34.1
1969................................	43.4	45.0	42.7	33.9	51.8	41.5	14.6	34.2
1970................................	44.9	45.8	44.6	35.2	52.4	42.0	15.3	35.0
1971................................	45.8	46.6	45.5	36.5	53.3	43.4	16.6	35.6
1972................................	49.2	51.6	48.0	37.8	55.5	50.0	17.1	35.6
1973................................	63.9	72.7	58.9	40.3	60.5	54.5	19.4	37.6
1974................................	71.3	77.4	68.0	49.2	68.0	55.2	30.1	50.2
1975................................	74.0	77.0	72.6	54.9	67.4	56.5	35.4	62.0
1976................................	73.6	78.8	70.8	58.4	72.4	63.9	38.3	64.0
1977................................	75.9	79.4	74.0	62.5	75.3	68.3	43.6	65.9
1978................................	83.0	87.7	80.6	67.0	78.1	76.1	46.5	68.0
1979................................	92.3	99.6	88.5	75.7	82.5	96.1	58.9	76.0
1980................................	98.3	102.9	95.9	88.0	89.7	94.7	82.8	89.0
1981................................	101.1	105.2	98.9	97.4	97.6	99.3	100.2	98.4
1982................................	100.0	100.0	100.0	100.0	100.0	100.0	100.0	100.0
1983................................	102.0	102.4	101.8	101.1	100.3	103.2	95.9	100.3
1984................................	105.5	105.5	105.4	103.3	102.7	109.0	94.8	102.9
1985................................	100.7	95.1	103.5	103.7	102.9	108.9	91.4	103.7
1986................................	101.2	92.9	105.4	100.0	103.2	113.0	69.8	102.6
1987................................	103.7	95.5	107.9	102.6	105.1	120.4	70.2	106.4
1988................................	110.0	104.9	112.7	106.3	109.2	131.4	66.7	116.3
1989................................	115.4	110.9	117.8	111.6	112.3	136.3	72.9	123.0
1990................................	118.6	112.2	121.9	115.8	115.0	141.7	82.3	123.6
1991................................	116.4	105.7	121.9	116.5	116.3	138.9	81.2	125.6
1991: Jan	117.0	106.9	122.1	119.3	115.7	140.2	90.1	128.3
Feb	117.1	106.9	122.3	117.2	115.8	140.0	83.0	128.1
Mar...............	118.3	109.7	122.6	115.7	115.9	140.4	78.5	126.0
Apr	118.1	109.6	122.5	115.6	116.0	141.1	78.1	126.0
May	118.3	110.4	122.3	116.1	116.0	140.4	80.2	125.3
June	117.6	109.1	121.9	116.1	116.2	140.0	80.3	125.0
July	116.3	105.6	121.6	116.0	116.3	138.3	80.1	124.4
Aug...............	115.2	102.9	121.4	116.3	116.5	138.1	81.3	124.5
Sept...............	115.1	103.1	121.1	116.3	116.6	136.6	81.4	124.5
Oct	115.1	101.5	121.9	116.7	116.7	136.3	81.3	124.9
Nov...............	114.8	101.6	121.4	116.7	116.8	137.1	81.2	124.9
Dec...............	114.5	100.6	121.4	116.1	116.9	137.6	79.1	125.0
1992: Jan	115.2	102.8	121.3	115.7	117.4	138.6	76.3	124.6
Feb	116.3	105.5	121.7	116.0	117.6	139.0	76.8	124.5
Mar...............	116.7	106.4	121.8	115.9	117.7	139.8	75.8	124.4
Apr	115.8	103.2	122.0	116.4	117.8	139.9	77.1	124.8
May	117.0	105.8	122.5	117.3	117.7	140.7	79.7	125.2
June	116.9	104.7	123.0	118.2	117.9	140.8	83.2	126.0
July [2]...............	115.8	102.5	122.4	118.3	117.8	140.1	83.3	126.4
Aug...............	115.3	102.1	121.9	118.1	118.1	140.7	82.8	126.9
Sept...............	115.3	101.6	122.1	118.3	118.0	140.8	84.0	126.5
Oct	115.2	102.6	121.5	118.6	118.2	140.8	83.3	127.0
Nov...............	114.9	102.0	121.4	118.3	117.9	140.5	82.3	127.5

[1] Prices for some items in this grouping are lagged and refer to 1 month earlier than the index month.
[2] Data have been revised through July 1992 to reflect the availability of late reports and corrections by respondents. All data are subject to revision 4 months after original publication.
See next page for continuation of table.

420

TABLE B-63.—*Producer price indexes for major commodity groups, 1950-92*—Continued

[1982 = 100]

Year or month	Rubber and plastic products	Lumber and wood products	Pulp, paper, and allied products	Metals and metal products	Machinery and equipment	Furniture and household durables	Non-metallic mineral products	Transportation equipment		Miscella-neous products
								Total	Motor vehicles and equip-ment	
1950	35.6	31.4	25.7	22.0	22.6	40.9	23.5		30.0	28.6
1951	43.7	34.1	30.5	24.5	25.3	44.4	25.0		31.6	30.3
1952	39.6	33.2	29.7	24.5	25.3	43.5	25.0		33.4	30.2
1953	36.9	33.1	29.6	25.3	25.9	44.4	26.0		33.3	31.0
1954	37.5	32.5	29.6	25.5	26.3	44.9	26.6		33.4	31.3
1955	42.4	34.1	30.4	27.2	27.2	45.1	27.3		34.3	31.3
1956	43.0	34.6	32.4	29.6	29.3	46.3	28.5		36.3	31.7
1957	42.8	32.8	33.0	30.2	31.4	47.5	29.6		37.9	32.6
1958	42.8	32.5	33.4	30.0	32.1	47.9	29.9		39.0	33.3
1959	42.6	34.7	33.7	30.6	32.8	48.0	30.3		39.9	33.4
1960	42.7	33.5	34.0	30.6	33.0	47.8	30.4		39.3	33.6
1961	41.1	32.0	33.0	30.5	33.0	47.5	30.5		39.2	33.7
1962	39.9	32.2	33.4	30.2	33.0	47.2	30.5		39.2	33.9
1963	40.1	32.8	33.1	30.3	33.1	46.9	30.3		38.9	34.2
1964	39.6	33.5	33.0	31.1	33.3	47.1	30.4		39.1	34.4
1965	39.7	33.7	33.3	32.0	33.7	46.8	30.4		39.2	34.7
1966	40.5	35.2	34.2	32.8	34.7	47.4	30.7		39.2	35.3
1967	41.4	35.1	34.6	33.2	35.9	48.3	31.2		39.8	36.2
1968	42.8	39.8	35.0	34.0	37.0	49.7	32.4		40.9	37.0
1969	43.6	44.0	36.0	36.0	38.2	50.7	33.6	40.4	41.7	38.1
1970	44.9	39.9	37.5	38.7	40.0	51.9	35.3	41.9	43.3	39.8
1971	45.2	44.7	38.1	39.4	41.4	53.1	38.2	44.2	45.7	40.8
1972	45.3	50.7	39.3	40.9	42.3	53.8	39.4	45.5	47.0	41.5
1973	46.6	62.2	42.3	44.0	43.7	55.7	40.7	46.1	47.4	43.3
1974	56.4	64.5	52.5	57.0	50.0	61.8	47.8	50.3	51.4	48.1
1975	62.2	62.1	59.0	61.5	57.9	67.5	54.4	56.7	57.6	53.4
1976	66.0	72.2	62.1	65.0	61.3	70.3	58.2	60.5	61.2	55.6
1977	69.4	83.0	64.6	69.3	65.2	73.2	62.6	64.6	65.2	59.4
1978	72.4	96.9	67.7	75.3	70.3	77.5	69.6	69.5	70.0	66.7
1979	80.5	105.5	75.9	86.0	76.7	82.8	77.6	75.3	75.8	75.5
1980	90.1	101.5	86.3	95.0	86.0	90.7	88.4	82.9	83.1	93.6
1981	96.4	102.8	94.8	99.6	94.4	95.9	96.7	94.3	94.6	96.1
1982	100.0	100.0	100.0	100.0	100.0	100.0	100.0	100.0	100.0	100.0
1983	100.8	107.9	103.3	101.8	102.7	103.4	101.6	102.8	102.2	104.8
1984	102.3	108.0	110.3	104.8	105.1	105.7	105.4	105.2	104.1	107.0
1985	101.9	106.6	113.3	104.4	107.2	107.1	108.6	107.9	106.4	109.4
1986	101.9	107.2	116.1	103.2	108.8	108.2	110.0	110.5	109.1	111.6
1987	103.0	112.8	121.8	107.1	110.4	109.9	110.0	112.5	111.7	114.9
1988	109.3	118.9	130.4	118.7	113.2	113.1	111.2	114.3	113.1	120.2
1989	112.6	126.7	137.8	124.1	117.4	116.9	112.6	117.7	116.2	126.5
1990	113.6	129.7	141.2	122.9	120.7	119.2	114.7	121.5	118.2	134.2
1991	115.1	132.1	142.9	120.2	123.0	121.2	117.2	126.4	122.1	140.9
1991: Jan	116.0	127.6	143.6	122.4	122.6	120.6	116.9	125.2	121.9	139.1
Feb	116.0	127.2	143.8	121.9	122.9	120.9	117.2	125.7	122.4	138.9
Mar	115.8	127.8	143.7	121.5	123.0	121.0	117.4	125.7	122.2	139.4
Apr	115.5	129.2	143.2	121.3	123.1	121.2	117.3	125.5	121.5	140.0
May	115.2	132.3	143.0	120.5	123.1	121.2	117.3	125.6	120.7	140.1
June	115.0	136.2	142.7	119.7	123.1	121.2	117.3	125.6	120.6	140.9
July	114.8	136.9	142.3	119.6	123.0	121.2	117.2	125.7	120.5	141.8
Aug	114.7	133.3	142.2	119.5	123.0	121.2	117.1	126.0	120.6	141.7
Sept	114.6	133.4	142.3	119.5	123.0	121.2	117.2	125.2	119.2	141.5
Oct	114.7	133.2	142.6	119.3	123.0	121.4	117.4	129.1	125.8	141.4
Nov	114.6	133.4	142.8	118.9	123.1	121.4	117.2	128.9	125.4	141.8
Dec	114.7	134.6	142.7	118.7	123.2	121.5	117.1	129.0	124.9	143.4
1992: Jan	114.7	137.6	144.1	118.2	123.3	121.8	117.2	129.8	124.8	143.9
Feb	114.3	142.9	144.2	118.9	123.5	121.8	117.1	129.7	124.6	143.9
Mar	114.3	145.7	144.4	119.4	123.6	121.9	117.3	130.0	124.9	144.0
Apr	114.6	147.5	144.9	119.6	123.4	122.0	116.9	130.2	124.8	144.8
May	114.9	147.6	145.2	119.5	123.4	122.1	116.9	130.2	124.7	146.4
June	115.0	146.3	145.1	119.6	123.2	122.2	117.0	130.1	124.3	146.2
July [2]	115.2	145.3	145.2	120.0	123.1	122.2	117.1	130.2	124.4	146.3
Aug	115.3	144.9	145.3	120.2	123.1	122.1	117.3	129.6	123.9	143.7
Sept	115.8	148.4	145.8	119.6	123.2	122.2	117.4	128.1	121.1	145.3
Oct	115.6	148.5	146.0	118.9	123.3	122.2	117.5	132.0	126.9	145.3
Nov	115.7	149.2	145.8	118.2	123.2	122.5	117.7	131.9	126.9	145.8

Source: Department of Labor, Bureau of Labor Statistics.

421

TABLE B–64.—*Changes in producer price indexes for finished goods, 1955–92*

[Percent change]

Year or month	Total finished goods		Finished consumer foods		Finished goods excluding consumer foods						Finished energy goods		Finished goods excluding foods and energy	
					Total		Consumer goods		Capital equipment					
	Dec. to Dec.¹	Year to year	Dec. to Dec.¹	Year to year	Dec. to Dec.¹	Year to year	Dec. to Dec.¹	Year to year	Dec. to Dec.¹	Year to year	Dec. to Dec.¹	Year to year	Dec. to Dec.¹	Year to year
1955	1.0	0.3	−3.0	−2.3			1.6	0.6	5.6	2.6				
1956	4.2	2.6	3.7	−.3			2.5	2.6	8.1	7.7				
1957	3.4	3.8	5.1	3.3			1.5	2.5	4.6	6.1				
1958	.3	2.2	.6	6.1			.3	0	1.2	2.6				
1959	−.3	−.3	−3.7	−4.7			.9	1.2	.9	1.9				
1960	1.8	.9	5.3	2.0			.3	.6	.3	.3				
1961	−.6	0	−1.9	−.3			−.3	−.3	0	.3				
1962	.3	.3	.6	.8			0	0	.3	.3				
1963	−.3	−.3	−1.4	−1.1			0	0	.6	.3				
1964	.6	.3	.6	.3			.3	−.3	.9	.9				
1965	3.3	1.8	9.1	4.0			.9	.9	1.5	1.2				
1966	2.0	3.2	1.3	6.5			1.8	1.5	3.8	2.4				
1967	1.7	1.1	−.3	−1.8			2.0	1.8	3.1	3.5				
1968	3.1	2.8	4.6	3.9	2.5	2.6	2.0	2.3	3.0	3.4				
1969	4.9	3.8	8.1	6.0	3.3	2.8	2.8	2.3	4.8	3.5				
1970	2.1	3.4	−2.3	3.3	4.3	3.5	3.8	3.0	4.8	4.7				
1971	3.3	3.1	5.8	1.6	2.0	3.7	2.1	3.5	2.4	4.0				
1972	3.9	3.2	7.9	5.4	2.3	2.0	2.1	1.8	2.1	2.6				
1973	11.7	9.1	22.7	20.5	6.6	4.0	7.5	4.6	5.1	3.3				
1974	18.3	15.4	12.8	14.0	21.1	16.2	20.3	17.0	22.7	14.3			17.7	11.4
1975	6.6	10.6	5.6	8.4	7.2	12.1	6.8	10.4	8.1	15.2	16.3	17.2	6.0	11.4
1976	3.8	4.5	−2.5	−.3	6.2	6.2	6.0	6.2	6.5	6.7	11.6	11.7	5.7	5.7
1977	6.7	6.4	6.9	5.3	6.8	7.1	6.7	7.3	7.2	6.4	12.0	15.7	6.2	6.0
1978	9.3	7.9	11.7	9.0	8.3	7.2	8.5	7.1	8.0	7.9	8.5	6.5	8.4	7.5
1979	12.8	11.2	7.4	9.3	14.8	11.8	17.6	13.3	8.8	8.7	58.1	35.0	9.4	8.9
1980	11.8	13.4	7.5	5.8	13.4	16.2	14.1	18.5	11.4	10.7	27.9	49.2	10.8	11.2
1981	7.1	9.2	1.5	5.8	8.7	10.3	8.6	10.3	9.2	10.3	14.1	19.1	7.7	8.6
1982	3.6	4.1	2.0	2.2	4.2	4.6	4.2	4.1	3.9	5.7	−.1	−1.5	4.9	5.7
1983	.6	1.6	2.3	1.0	0	1.8	−.9	1.2	2.0	2.8	−9.2	−4.8	1.9	3.0
1984	1.7	2.1	3.5	4.4	1.1	1.4	.8	1.0	1.8	2.3	−4.2	−4.2	2.0	2.4
1985	1.8	1.0	.6	−.8	2.2	1.4	2.1	1.1	2.7	2.2	−.2	−3.9	2.7	2.5
1986	−2.3	−1.4	2.8	2.6	−4.0	−2.6	−6.6	−4.6	2.1	2.0	−38.1	−28.1	2.7	2.3
1987	2.2	2.1	−.2	2.1	3.2	2.1	4.1	2.2	1.3	1.8	11.2	−1.9	2.1	2.4
1988	4.0	2.5	5.7	2.8	3.2	2.4	3.1	2.4	3.6	2.3	−3.6	−3.2	4.3	3.3
1989	4.9	5.2	5.2	5.4	4.8	5.0	5.3	5.6	3.8	3.9	9.5	9.9	4.2	4.4
1990	5.7	4.9	2.6	4.8	6.9	5.0	8.7	5.9	3.4	3.5	30.7	14.2	3.5	3.7
1991	−.1	2.1	−1.5	−.2	.3	3.0	−.7	2.9	2.5	3.1	−9.6	4.1	3.1	3.6

Percent change from preceding month

	Unadjusted	Seasonally adjusted	Unadjusted	Seasonally adjusted	Unadjusted	Seasonally adjusted	Unadjusted	Seasonally adjusted	Unadjusted	Seasonally adjusted	Unadjusted	Seasonally adjusted	Unadjusted	Seasonally adjusted
1991: Jan	0.2	0.2	0.5	−0.1	0.1	0.2	−0.2	−0.1	0.8	0.9	−2.5	−2.0	0.9	0.9
Feb	−.7	−.7	−.2	0	−.8	−.7	−1.3	−1.2	.2	.2	−5.1	−4.6	.2	.2
Mar	−.4	−.3	.5	.1	−.7	−.6	−1.0	−.9	.1	.2	−3.7	−3.1	.1	.2
Apr	.2	.2	.1	.3	.2	.1	.2	.1	0	0	.3	−.5	.2	.3
May	.6	.2	.4	−.2	.7	.2	.9	.3	.2	.3	3.0	.9	0	.2
June	.1	−.2	−.4	−.2	.2	−.2	.3	−.3	0	.1	.5	−.8	.2	0
July	−.2	−.2	−.6	−.6	−.1	−.1	−.2	−.1	.1	.1	−1.1	−1.0	.2	.2
Aug	.1	.2	−1.0	−.5	.3	.4	.5	.5	−.1	.1	1.7	1.6	0	.2
Sept	−.2	.2	−.5	−.1	−.1	.5	0	.6	−.2	.2	.4	.4	−.2	.3
Oct	.7	.2	.2	0	.7	.4	.6	.5	1.3	.2	−1.0	1.2	1.3	.2
Nov	.1	.1	0	−.2	.1	.2	0	.2	0	.2	−.3	.1	.1	.2
Dec	−.3	−.1	−.6	−.1	−.2	−.2	−.4	−.3	.1	.2	−1.9	−1.4	.2	.2
1992: Jan	−.1	−.2	.2	−.4	−.2	−.1	−.3	−.4	.5	.5	−3.0	−2.8	.5	.5
Feb	.2	.2	.7	1.0	.1	.1	0	.2	.1	.1	0	.5	.1	.1
Mar	.1	.2	−.1	−.5	.2	.4	.2	.3	.2	.3	.1	.5	.1	.3
Apr	.2	.3	−.4	−.3	.4	.4	.5	.5	.2	.2	1.3	.7	.2	.4
May	.7	.2	.2	−.2	.7	.4	1.1	.6	−.1	.1	3.2	1.0	.1	.3
June	.6	.2	0	.2	.7	.2	1.0	.4	−.1	−.1	4.1	2.5	−.1	−.2
July ²	−.2	0	−.2	−.2	−.2	0	−.1	0	−.1	.1	−.7	−.6	.1	.1
Aug	−.2	.1	.3	.7	−.2	−.1	−.3	−.2	0	.2	−.1	−.3	−.3	−.1
Sept	−.2	.3	0	.4	−.2	.3	−.2	.3	−.6	0	.7	.8	−.4	.2
Oct	.8	.1	.3	.1	.9	.1	.7	.2	1.6	−.2	−1.1	1.4	1.4	−.1
Nov	−.3	−.2	−.2	−.5	−.2	−.2	−.4	−.2	−.1	−.1	−1.9	−1.5	.1	.1

¹ Changes from December to December are based on unadjusted indexes.
² Data have been revised through July 1992 to reflect the availability of late reports and corrections by respondents. All data are subject to revision 4 months after original publication.

Source: Department of Labor, Bureau of Labor Statistics.

TABLE B–65.—*Money stock, liquid assets, and debt measures, 1959–92*

[Averages of daily figures; billions of dollars, seasonally adjusted]

Year and month	M1	M2	M3	L	Debt [1]	Percent change from year or 6 months earlier [2]			
	Sum of currency, demand deposits, travelers checks, and other checkable deposits (OCDs)	M1 plus overnight RPs and Eurodollars, MMMF balances (general purpose and broker/dealer), MMDAs, and savings and small time deposits	M2 plus large time deposits, term RPs, term Eurodollars, and institution-only MMMF balances	M3 plus other liquid assets	Debt of domestic nonfinancial sectors (monthly average)	M1	M2	M3	Debt
December:									
1959	140.0	297.8	299.8	388.7	688.2				7.6
1960	140.7	312.4	315.3	403.7	723.0	0.5	4.9	5.2	5.1
1961	145.2	335.5	341.1	430.8	765.4	3.2	7.4	8.2	5.9
1962	147.9	362.7	371.5	466.1	817.4	1.9	8.1	8.9	6.8
1963	153.4	393.3	406.1	503.8	872.1	3.7	8.4	9.3	6.7
1964	160.4	424.8	442.5	540.4	935.0	4.6	8.0	9.0	7.2
1965	167.9	459.4	482.3	584.5	1,002.9	4.7	8.1	9.0	7.3
1966	172.1	480.0	505.1	614.8	1,069.6	2.5	4.5	4.7	6.7
1967	183.3	524.4	557.1	666.6	1,144.2	6.5	9.3	10.3	7.0
1968	197.5	566.4	606.3	729.0	1,236.2	7.7	8.0	8.8	8.0
1969	204.0	589.6	615.1	763.6	1,327.4	3.3	4.1	1.5	7.4
1970	214.5	628.1	677.4	816.3	1,418.7	5.1	6.5	10.1	6.9
1971	228.4	712.7	776.2	903.0	1,551.2	6.5	13.5	14.6	9.3
1972	249.3	805.2	886.1	1,023.0	1,706.9	9.2	13.0	14.2	10.0
1973	262.9	861.0	985.0	1,142.6	1,892.8	5.5	6.9	11.2	10.9
1974	274.4	908.6	1,070.4	1,250.3	2,062.3	4.4	5.5	8.7	9.0
1975	287.6	1,023.3	1,172.2	1,367.0	2,241.2	4.8	12.6	9.5	8.7
1976	306.4	1,163.7	1,311.8	1,516.6	2,484.3	6.5	13.7	11.9	10.8
1977	331.3	1,286.6	1,472.5	1,705.2	2,804.9	8.1	10.6	12.3	12.9
1978	358.4	1,388.7	1,646.4	1,910.5	3,183.6	8.2	7.9	11.8	13.5
1979	382.7	1,496.7	1,802.8	2,115.8	3,574.2	6.8	7.8	9.5	12.3
1980	408.8	1,629.5	1,987.0	2,323.8	3,913.1	6.8	8.9	10.2	9.5
1981	436.5	1,792.9	2,233.6	2,596.2	4,299.5	6.8	10.0	12.4	9.9
1982	474.6	1,951.9	2,440.6	2,850.4	4,700.2	8.7	8.9	9.3	9.3
1983	521.4	2,186.1	2,693.0	3,154.3	5,244.6	9.9	12.0	10.3	11.6
1984	552.5	2,374.3	2,987.4	3,528.8	6,008.2	6.0	8.6	10.9	14.6
1985	620.2	2,569.4	3,203.2	3,830.4	6,875.3	12.3	8.2	7.2	14.4
1986	724.6	2,811.1	3,494.3	4,134.3	7,795.2	16.8	9.4	9.1	13.4
1987	750.0	2,910.8	3,681.1	4,339.3	8,546.2	3.5	3.5	5.3	9.6
1988	786.9	3,071.1	3,923.1	4,677.1	9,326.3	4.9	5.5	6.6	9.1
1989	794.1	3,227.3	4,059.8	4,890.6	10,076.7	.9	5.1	3.5	8.0
1990	826.1	3,339.0	4,114.9	4,965.5	10,751.4	4.0	3.5	1.4	6.7
1991	898.1	3,439.8	4,171.0	4,988.1	11,201.3	8.7	3.0	1.4	4.2
1991: Jan	826.2	3,344.0	4,125.9	4,980.6	10,777.2	4.0	2.7	1.7	5.3
Feb	836.2	3,369.4	4,160.2	5,007.2	10,825.4	4.9	3.2	2.6	4.9
Mar	842.3	3,386.9	4,165.8	5,002.5	10,863.3	4.7	3.4	2.4	4.5
Apr	842.7	3,394.8	4,168.6	4,976.7	10,886.8	5.0	3.6	2.5	4.3
May	850.9	3,405.6	4,170.5	4,956.7	10,940.8	6.6	4.3	2.7	4.2
June	857.3	3,411.8	4,167.9	4,984.9	10,993.9	7.6	4.4	2.6	4.5
July	860.0	3,407.5	4,157.5	4,990.0	11,026.7	8.2	3.8	1.5	4.6
Aug	866.5	3,409.7	4,156.8	4,983.6	11,062.9	7.2	2.4	–.2	4.4
Sept	872.0	3,411.9	4,152.8	4,972.6	11,094.8	7.1	1.5	–.6	4.3
Oct	880.9	3,417.9	4,159.0	4,976.3	11,133.4	9.1	1.4	–.5	4.5
Nov	891.4	3,431.6	4,166.9	4,989.4	11,174.6	9.5	1.5	–.2	4.3
Dec	898.1	3,439.8	4,171.0	4,988.1	11,201.3	9.5	1.6	.1	3.8
1992: Jan	910.4	3,447.6	4,173.7	4,980.6	11,237.5	11.7	2.4	.8	3.8
Feb	931.0	3,474.4	4,198.7	5,009.1	11,288.2	14.9	3.8	2.0	4.1
Mar	939.0	3,475.7	4,191.8	5,019.9	11,345.0	15.4	3.7	1.9	4.5
Apr	942.8	3,471.5	4,179.4	5,012.7	11,397.4	14.1	3.1	1.0	4.7
May	954.3	3,473.0	4,178.7	5,002.5	11,443.1	14.1	2.4	.6	4.8
June	951.7	3,464.1	4,166.7	5,013.7	11,490.3	11.9	1.4	–.2	5.2
July	960.5	3,461.6	4,162.9	5,006.0	11,527.2	11.0	.8	–.5	5.2
Aug	973.1	3,471.2	4,176.3	5,024.8	11,564.7	9.0	–.2	–1.1	4.9
Sept	988.6	3,481.8	4,183.0	5,043.8	11,596.5	10.6	.4	–.4	4.4
Oct	1,007.3	3,497.1	4,184.7	5,050.7	11,622.4	13.7	1.5	.3	3.9
Nov	1,019.0	3,507.5	4,191.4			13.6	2.0	.6	

[1] Consists of outstanding credit market debt of the U.S. Government, State and local governments, and private nonfinancial sectors; data derived from flow of funds accounts.
[2] Annual changes are from December to December; monthly changes are from 6 months earlier at a simple annual rate.
Note.—See Table B–66 for components.
Source: Board of Governors of the Federal Reserve System.

TABLE B-66.—*Components of money stock measures and liquid assets, 1959-92*

[Averages of daily figures; billions of dollars, seasonally adjusted, except as noted]

Year and month	Currency	Travelers checks	Demand deposits	Other checkable deposits (OCDs)	Overnight repurchase agreements (RPs) net, plus overnight Eurodollars [1] NSA	Money market mutual fund (MMMF) balances General purpose and broker/dealer [2]	Institution only [2]	Savings deposits, including money market deposit accounts (MMDAs) [3]
December:								
1959	28.8	0.4	110.8	0.0	0.0	0.0	0.0	146.5
1960	28.7	.4	111.6	.0	.0	.0	.0	159.1
1961	29.3	.4	115.5	.0	.0	.0	.0	175.5
1962	30.3	.4	117.1	.0	.0	.0	.0	194.7
1963	32.2	.5	120.6	.1	.0	.0	.0	214.4
1964	33.9	.5	125.8	.1	.0	.0	.0	235.3
1965	36.0	.6	131.3	.1	.0	.0	.0	256.9
1966	38.0	.6	133.4	.1	.0	.0	.0	253.2
1967	40.0	.7	142.5	.1	.0	.0	.0	263.7
1968	43.0	.8	153.6	.1	.0	.0	.0	268.9
1969	45.7	.8	157.3	.2	2.2	.0	.0	263.6
1970	48.6	1.0	164.7	.1	1.3	.0	.0	260.9
1971	52.0	1.1	175.1	.2	2.3	.0	.0	292.2
1972	56.2	1.3	191.6	.2	2.8	.0	.0	321.4
1973	60.8	1.5	200.3	.3	5.3	.0	.0	326.7
1974	67.0	1.8	205.1	.4	5.7	1.7	.2	338.5
1975	72.8	2.3	211.6	.9	5.9	2.7	.4	388.6
1976	79.5	2.8	221.5	2.7	10.7	2.4	.6	452.6
1977	87.4	3.1	236.7	4.2	14.9	2.4	.9	491.1
1978	96.0	3.5	250.4	8.5	20.7	6.4	3.1	480.3
1979	104.8	3.8	257.4	16.8	21.7	33.4	9.5	422.0
1980	115.3	4.2	261.2	28.0	28.8	61.6	15.2	398.2
1981	122.6	4.4	231.2	78.3	36.6	150.6	38.0	342.2
1982	132.5	4.3	234.0	103.7	39.9	184.5	51.1	398.5
1983	146.2	4.9	238.5	131.8	55.6	138.3	42.7	684.0
1984	156.1	5.2	243.9	147.2	60.6	167.1	63.7	704.2
1985	167.9	5.9	266.7	179.7	73.5	176.1	65.8	814.4
1986	180.8	6.4	302.0	235.3	82.3	208.0	86.1	940.1
1987	197.0	7.0	286.8	259.3	84.1	221.7	92.1	937.0
1988	212.3	7.5	286.5	280.6	83.2	241.9	91.0	926.2
1989	222.6	7.4	279.0	285.1	77.6	316.3	107.2	891.2
1990	246.8	8.3	277.1	293.9	74.7	348.9	133.7	920.7
1991	267.3	8.2	289.5	333.2	76.2	360.5	179.1	1,042.6
1991: Jan	251.5	8.3	271.8	294.6	71.9	356.6	138.3	922.3
Feb	254.6	8.2	275.9	297.5	70.4	361.0	145.5	931.0
Mar	256.0	8.1	276.9	301.3	69.2	365.0	148.5	941.7
Apr	256.3	7.8	276.1	302.5	69.6	366.6	152.9	953.0
May	256.6	8.0	278.4	307.8	68.5	367.8	155.2	966.1
June	257.6	7.9	280.1	311.6	67.9	368.8	155.3	976.8
July	259.3	7.8	279.3	313.7	65.0	367.9	155.4	986.1
Aug	261.3	7.8	280.1	317.3	67.6	362.4	158.6	994.1
Sept	262.9	7.8	280.6	320.6	66.8	359.9	162.6	1,002.4
Oct	264.8	7.9	283.8	324.5	70.0	359.3	168.2	1,015.0
Nov	266.0	8.0	287.6	329.7	73.7	359.5	173.6	1,028.7
Dec	267.3	8.2	289.5	333.2	76.2	360.5	179.1	1,042.6
1992: Jan	269.4	8.2	293.9	339.0	77.7	358.6	182.4	1,061.2
Feb	271.6	8.1	305.1	346.3	77.6	361.7	188.2	1,083.9
Mar	271.8	8.0	309.6	349.5	74.6	358.3	185.3	1,098.0
Apr	273.6	8.0	311.2	350.0	72.6	355.9	189.2	1,111.2
May	274.7	8.0	315.1	356.4	69.2	356.7	194.8	1,122.4
June	276.2	7.9	311.0	356.7	72.0	355.3	199.7	1,127.0
July	278.9	7.8	315.6	358.2	72.4	351.7	207.7	1,134.4
Aug	282.3	7.9	320.6	362.2	75.8	349.7	217.2	1,145.6
Sept	286.4	8.3	327.8	366.1	74.1	344.7	217.2	1,159.6
Oct	288.4	8.6	336.2	374.0	75.1	347.6	205.6	1,171.6
Nov	290.0	8.6	339.2	381.2	74.9	348.7	203.5	1,181.8

[1] Includes continuing contract RPs.
[2] Data prior to 1983 are not seasonally adjusted.
[3] Data prior to 1982 are savings deposits only; MMDA data begin December 1982.

See next page for continuation of table.

424

[Averages of daily figures; billions of dollars, seasonally adjusted, except as noted]

Year and month	Small denomination time deposits [4]	Large denomination time deposits [4]	Term repurchase agreements (RPs) NSA	Term Euro-dollars NSA	Savings bonds	Short-term Treasury securities	Bankers acceptances	Commercial paper
December:								
1959	11.4	1.2	0.0	0.7	46.1	38.6	0.6	3.6
1960	12.5	2.0	.0	.8	45.7	36.7	.9	5.1
1961	14.8	3.9	.0	1.5	46.5	37.0	1.1	5.2
1962	20.1	7.0	.0	1.6	46.9	39.8	1.1	6.8
1963	25.6	10.8	.0	1.9	48.1	40.7	1.2	7.7
1964	29.2	15.2	.0	2.4	49.0	38.5	1.3	9.1
1965	34.5	21.2	.0	1.8	49.6	40.7	1.6	10.2
1966	55.0	23.1	.0	2.2	50.2	43.2	1.8	14.4
1967	77.8	30.9	.0	2.2	51.2	38.7	1.8	17.8
1968	100.6	37.4	.0	2.9	51.8	46.1	2.3	22.5
1969	120.4	20.4	2.7	2.7	51.7	59.5	3.3	34.0
1970	151.1	45.2	1.6	2.2	52.0	48.8	3.5	34.5
1971	189.7	57.7	2.7	2.7	54.3	36.0	3.8	32.7
1972	231.6	73.4	3.5	3.6	57.6	40.7	3.5	35.2
1973	265.8	111.1	6.7	5.5	60.4	49.3	5.0	42.8
1974	287.9	144.8	7.8	8.1	63.3	52.8	12.6	51.2
1975	338.0	129.8	8.1	9.8	67.2	68.4	10.7	48.5
1976	390.9	118.1	13.9	14.8	71.8	69.8	10.8	52.5
1977	445.7	145.0	18.9	20.2	76.4	78.1	14.1	64.1
1978	521.2	194.9	26.2	31.8	80.3	81.1	22.0	80.7
1979	633.8	221.4	29.1	44.7	79.6	107.8	27.2	98.4
1980	727.0	257.6	33.5	50.3	72.3	133.5	32.1	98.8
1981	820.2	299.1	35.3	67.5	67.8	149.4	40.0	105.3
1982	847.2	323.3	33.4	81.7	68.0	183.6	44.5	113.7
1983	780.8	324.8	49.9	91.5	71.1	211.9	45.0	133.2
1984	884.9	415.6	57.6	82.9	74.2	260.9	45.4	160.8
1985	881.7	436.1	62.4	76.5	79.5	298.2	42.0	207.5
1986	854.8	439.5	80.6	83.8	91.8	279.8	37.1	231.2
1987	917.5	489.1	106.0	91.0	100.6	252.8	44.3	260.5
1988	1,032.9	541.2	121.8	105.7	109.4	268.8	39.8	336.1
1989	1,148.5	559.3	99.1	79.5	117.5	324.7	40.1	348.6
1990	1,168.7	495.2	89.6	68.7	126.0	331.3	34.0	359.3
1991	1,063.0	437.1	70.5	57.2	137.9	316.1	23.3	339.7
1991: Jan	1,169.3	496.7	88.7	69.2	126.9	329.0	35.3	363.4
Feb	1,169.5	499.6	86.7	69.8	127.9	327.3	34.6	357.1
Mar	1,165.9	492.7	83.5	68.2	129.0	322.0	32.1	353.8
Apr	1,159.7	487.5	82.2	65.2	130.1	305.7	30.6	341.6
May	1,150.9	483.5	80.4	62.3	131.3	297.8	29.1	327.9
June	1,140.6	478.5	78.4	61.6	132.4	323.5	28.1	333.0
July	1,129.5	471.4	78.7	62.7	133.5	331.1	28.1	339.8
Aug	1,120.8	465.6	78.2	63.6	134.4	328.9	27.2	336.3
Sept	1,111.0	458.5	76.5	61.5	135.2	321.2	25.8	337.7
Oct	1,095.2	450.0	75.2	62.8	136.1	319.7	25.3	336.2
Nov	1,079.2	442.3	73.3	61.5	137.1	322.9	24.5	337.9
Dec	1,063.0	437.1	70.5	57.2	137.9	316.1	23.3	339.7
1992: Jan	1,042.9	427.9	70.5	55.3	138.9	310.0	23.2	334.8
Feb	1,019.8	420.7	71.7	55.9	140.1	319.9	22.9	327.5
Mar	1,002.8	413.0	73.3	57.9	141.2	327.7	22.2	337.0
Apr	985.3	405.7	72.5	55.0	142.4	327.6	21.6	341.7
May	968.7	400.9	73.4	52.8	143.5	328.9	22.0	329.4
June	956.2	395.3	73.6	51.8	144.6	333.3	22.0	347.1
July	942.4	388.5	72.5	50.8	145.9	325.2	21.7	350.3
Aug	927.9	384.6	73.3	50.8	147.5	327.8	20.9	352.4
Sept	915.2	380.0	75.1	48.6	149.5	326.4	20.4	364.4
Oct	898.8	373.2	77.3	48.2	152.0	322.9	21.6	369.5
Nov	884.4	369.5	79.4	48.8	....	....	....	....

[4] Small denomination and large denomination deposits are those issued in amounts of less than $100,000 and more than $100,000, respectively.

Note.—NSA indicates data are not seasonally adjusted.

See also Table B–65.

Source: Board of Governors of the Federal Reserve System.

[Averages of daily figures [1]; millions of dollars; seasonally adjusted, except as noted]

Year and month	Adjusted for changes in reserve requirements [2]					Borrowings of depository institutions from the Federal Reserve, NSA		
	Reserves of depository institutions							
	Total	Nonborrowed	Nonborrowed plus extended credit	Required	Monetary base	Total	Seasonal	Extended credit
December:								
1959	11,109	10,168	10,168	10,603	40,880	941		
1960	11,247	11,172	11,172	10,503	40,977	74		
1961	11,499	11,366	11,366	10,915	41,853	133		
1962	11,604	11,344	11,344	11,033	42,957	260		
1963	11,730	11,397	11,397	11,239	45,003	332		
1964	12,011	11,747	11,747	11,605	47,161	264		
1965	12,316	11,872	11,872	11,892	49,620	444		
1966	12,223	11,690	11,690	11,884	51,565	532		
1967	13,180	12,952	12,952	12,805	54,579	228		
1968	13,767	13,021	13,021	13,341	58,357	746		
1969	14,168	13,049	13,049	13,882	61,569	1,119		
1970	14,558	14,225	14,225	14,309	65,013	332		
1971	15,230	15,104	15,104	15,049	69,108	126		
1972	16,645	15,595	15,595	16,361	75,167	1,050		
1973	17,021	15,723	15,723	16,717	81,073	1,298	41	
1974	17,550	16,823	16,970	17,292	87,535	727	32	147
1975	17,822	17,692	17,704	17,556	93,887	130	14	12
1976	18,388	18,335	18,335	18,115	101,515	53	13	
1977	18,990	18,420	18,420	18,800	110,323	569	55	
1978	19,753	18,885	18,885	19,521	120,445	868	135	
1979	20,720	19,248	19,248	20,279	131,143	1,473	82	
1980	22,015	20,325	20,328	21,501	142,004	1,690	116	3
1981	22,443	21,807	21,956	22,124	149,021	636	54	148
1982	23,600	22,966	23,152	23,100	160,127	634	33	186
1983	25,367	24,593	24,595	24,806	175,467	774	96	2
1984	26,878	23,692	26,296	26,023	187,248	3,186	113	2,604
1985	31,485	30,167	30,666	30,448	203,601	1,318	56	499
1986	39,005	38,179	38,482	37,635	223,732	827	38	303
1987	38,934	38,157	38,640	37,888	239,967	777	93	483
1988	40,468	38,752	39,996	39,420	256,973	1,716	130	1,244
1989	40,558	40,293	40,313	39,636	267,772	265	84	20
1990	41,832	41,506	41,529	40,167	293,287	326	76	23
1991	45,601	45,409	45,410	44,623	317,254	192	38	1
1991: Jan	42,221	41,687	41,714	40,052	298,001	534	33	27
Feb	42,120	41,868	41,901	40,311	301,466	252	37	34
Mar	41,948	41,707	41,760	40,769	302,779	241	55	53
Apr	41,884	41,652	41,738	40,853	303,017	231	79	86
May	42,389	42,086	42,174	41,359	303,734	303	151	88
June	42,710	42,370	42,377	41,701	305,003	340	222	8
July	42,845	42,238	42,284	41,939	306,794	607	317	46
Aug	43,282	42,517	42,818	42,196	309,132	764	331	300
Sept	43,487	42,841	43,143	42,558	310,929	645	287	302
Oct	44,138	43,877	43,889	43,055	313,281	261	211	12
Nov	44,785	44,677	44,678	43,893	315,332	108	86	1
Dec	45,601	45,409	45,410	44,623	317,254	192	38	1
1992: Jan	46,186	45,953	45,954	45,183	319,695	233	17	1
Feb	47,746	47,668	47,670	46,681	323,411	77	22	2
Mar	48,476	48,385	48,386	47,447	324,512	91	32	2
Apr	49,001	48,911	48,913	47,863	326,500	90	47	2
May	49,494	49,339	49,339	48,494	328,584	155	98	0
June	49,234	49,005	49,005	48,321	329,642	229	149	0
July	49,489	49,205	49,205	48,524	332,255	284	203	0
Aug	50,322	50,071	50,071	49,387	336,865	251	223	0
Sept	51,346	51,058	51,058	50,352	341,545	287	193	0
Oct	53,143	53,000	53,000	52,069	345,610	143	114	0
Nov	54,069	53,965	53,965	53,027	348,116	104	40	0

[1] Data are prorated averages of biweekly (maintenance period) averages of daily figures.
[2] Aggregate reserves incorporate adjustments for discontinuities associated with regulatory changes to reserve requirements. For details on aggregate reserves series see *Federal Reserve Bulletin.*

Note.—NSA indicates data are not seasonally adjusted.

Source: Board of Governors of the Federal Reserve System.

TABLE B–68.—*Commercial bank loans and securities, 1972–92*

[Monthly average; billions of dollars, seasonally adjusted [1]]

Year and month	Total loans and securities [2]	U.S. Government securities	Other securities	Loans and leases											
				Total [2]	Commercial and industrial	Real estate	Individual	Security	Nonbank financial institutions	Agricultural	State and political subdivisions	Foreign banks	Foreign official institutions	Lease financing receivables	Other
December:															
1972	572.5	89.0	93.4	390.1	137.1	98.1	86.3	15.6	21.7	14.3		3.9	1.6	1.4	10.1
1973	647.8	88.2	99.4	460.2	165.0	117.3	98.6	12.9	28.5	17.2		6.2	2.1	2.1	10.2
1974	713.7	86.3	107.5	519.9	196.6	130.1	102.4	12.7	34.5	18.3		8.3	2.2	3.2	11.5
1975	745.1	116.7	111.2	517.2	189.3	134.4	104.9	13.5	28.9	20.1		9.0	2.4	4.0	10.7
1976	804.6	136.3	113.5	554.8	190.9	148.8	116.3	17.7	26.4	23.2		11.7	2.8	5.1	11.9
1977	891.5	136.6	122.7	632.3	211.0	175.2	138.3	21.0	25.8	25.8		13.7	2.7	5.7	12.9
1978	1,013.9	137.6	129.2	747.1	246.2	210.5	164.7	19.7	26.2	28.2		21.5	4.9	7.4	17.8
1979	1,135.6	144.3	141.9	849.4	291.4	241.9	184.5	18.7	29.3	31.1		18.6	6.9	9.3	17.8
1980	1,238.6	170.6	154.4	913.5	325.7	262.6	179.2	18.0	29.3	31.6		23.8	11.5	10.9	21.1
1981	1,307.0	179.3	160.5	967.3	355.4	284.1	182.5	21.4	29.9	33.1		18.1	7.2	12.7	22.9
1982	1,400.4	201.7	164.8	1,033.9	392.5	299.9	188.2	25.3	31.2	36.2		14.7	5.9	13.3	26.8
1983	1,552.2	259.2	169.1	1,123.9	414.2	331.0	212.9	28.0	30.4	39.2	0.0	13.4	9.4	13.7	31.8
1984	1,722.2	260.2	140.9	1,321.1	473.1	376.2	253.8	34.4	31.3	40.1	46.0	11.6	8.4	16.0	30.2
1985	1,909.5	270.8	179.0	1,459.8	500.2	425.8	294.7	43.0	32.4	36.1	56.7	9.9	6.3	19.0	35.6
1986	2,093.2	310.0	193.9	1,589.4	537.0	494.0	315.3	40.3	35.0	31.5	58.5	10.3	6.3	22.4	38.8
1987	2,238.5	335.8	193.6	1,709.1	567.1	586.9	328.3	34.8	32.0	29.4	52.4	7.8	5.7	24.6	40.1
1988	2,422.8	363.5	192.4	1,866.9	606.8	670.1	354.5	41.2	32.3	28.7	45.1	7.7	5.0	29.3	46.2
1989	2,590.8	398.2	181.7	2,010.9	640.2	759.5	374.8	41.5	34.3	29.8	40.0	8.2	3.5	31.8	47.1
1990	2,730.8	454.1	177.9	2,098.8	643.2	843.3	379.6	44.7	35.7	32.0	33.9	7.5	2.8	32.8	43.3
1991	2,838.7	562.6	179.4	2,096.6	618.0	873.1	363.5	54.5	40.6	34.0	29.1	7.4	2.4	31.7	42.4
1991:															
Jan	2,735.8	456.8	178.3	2,100.7	638.6	847.7	374.9	49.8	35.5	31.9	32.8	6.7	2.6	32.7	47.4
Feb	2,747.3	460.7	178.3	2,108.3	638.2	852.8	376.3	51.8	36.1	31.9	32.9	6.6	2.7	33.0	45.9
Mar	2,759.9	470.8	178.5	2,110.5	638.7	857.7	375.2	48.2	36.9	33.0	32.8	7.5	2.8	33.1	44.7
Apr	2,763.5	478.1	177.5	2,108.0	635.1	861.5	374.4	48.5	35.8	33.6	32.3	7.1	2.5	33.1	44.1
May	2,764.8	483.9	176.8	2,104.0	630.5	863.8	373.8	49.1	36.1	33.7	31.7	6.4	2.4	33.0	43.4
June	2,773.3	493.5	176.3	2,103.6	625.8	868.5	373.1	49.0	38.6	33.9	31.4	6.3	2.5	33.3	41.1
July	2,773.8	502.4	175.8	2,095.5	623.8	867.3	370.9	47.4	37.7	34.0	31.0	6.4	2.3	32.5	42.3
Aug	2,776.9	512.6	174.4	2,089.9	619.5	866.7	370.3	48.4	36.9	34.3	30.6	6.5	2.2	31.9	42.7
Sept	2,789.1	523.0	176.3	2,089.8	622.0	868.1	367.3	50.0	37.1	34.5	30.3	6.8	2.3	31.8	39.8
Oct	2,805.5	538.7	177.9	2,099.9	622.6	869.8	364.2	51.1	37.2	34.1	29.7	6.6	2.4	31.6	39.5
Nov	2,822.7	550.8	178.8	2,093.2	621.7	871.9	363.1	53.5	37.8	33.8	29.4	6.9	2.5	31.5	41.1
Dec	2,838.7	562.6	179.4	2,096.6	618.0	873.1	363.5	54.5	40.6	34.0	29.1	7.4	2.4	31.7	42.4
1992:															
Jan	2,852.0	566.2	179.7	2,106.1	617.3	873.5	363.1	59.4	40.8	33.7	28.0	7.2	2.3	31.5	49.2
Feb	2,854.8	571.2	180.5	2,103.1	613.2	877.5	363.6	57.1	42.6	33.5	28.1	6.7	2.1	31.6	47.1
Mar	2,863.1	579.5	178.1	2,105.5	610.9	879.4	362.2	60.4	43.7	34.3	28.0	6.5	2.1	31.5	46.5
Apr	2,877.5	592.3	178.5	2,106.7	609.2	881.4	360.7	64.9	42.7	34.4	27.7	6.5	2.0	31.6	45.6
May	2,877.6	601.7	177.1	2,098.8	607.3	882.6	358.9	61.6	43.0	34.3	27.2	6.9	2.0	31.7	43.3
June	2,883.7	611.7	175.5	2,096.5	604.7	881.2	359.0	63.9	42.0	34.8	26.8	7.5	2.0	32.0	42.4
July	2,884.4	619.5	177.8	2,087.1	603.1	878.9	358.6	60.7	40.7	34.8	26.4	7.8	2.1	31.0	43.1
Aug	2,897.2	634.1	178.1	2,085.1	600.7	878.4	357.2	62.5	41.8	35.3	26.0	7.1	2.1	30.7	43.3
Sept	2,913.3	639.1	178.0	2,096.2	602.9	882.6	356.5	66.2	44.3	35.3	26.0	7.9	2.1	30.8	41.6
Oct	2,924.9	646.2	178.8	2,099.8	603.3	887.1	355.2	65.7	44.3	35.0	25.5	7.2	2.1	30.6	43.8
Nov	2,936.6	653.6	177.9	2,105.0	606.0	889.5	354.6	64.4	45.1	34.7	25.2	6.8	2.5	30.5	45.8

[1] Data are prorated averages of Wednesday figures for domestically chartered banks and for foreign-related institutions beginning July 1981. Prior to July 1981, data for foreign-related institutions are averages of current and previous month-end data.
[2] Excludes loans to commercial banks in the United States.

Note.—Data are not strictly comparable because of breaks in the series.

Source: Board of Governors of the Federal Reserve System.

427

TABLE B-69.—*Bond yields and interest rates, 1929–92*

[Percent per annum]

Year and month	U.S. Treasury securities				Corporate bonds (Moody's)		High-grade munici-pal bonds (Stand-ard & Poor's)	New-home mort-gage yields [3]	Commer-cial paper, 6 months [4]	Prime rate charged by banks [5]	Discount rate, Federal Reserve Bank of New York [5]	Federal funds rate [6]
	Bills (new issues) [1]		Constant maturities [2]		Aaa	Baa						
	3-month	6-month	3-year	10-year								
1929					4.73	5.90	4.27		5.85	5.50–6.00	5.16	
1933	0.515				4.49	7.76	4.71		1.73	1.50–4.00	2.56	
1939	.023				3.01	4.96	2.76		.59	1.50	1.00	
1940	.014				2.84	4.75	2.50		.56	1.50	1.00	
1941	.103				2.77	4.33	2.10		.53	1.50	1.00	
1942	.326				2.83	4.28	2.36		.66	1.50	7 1.00	
1943	.373				2.73	3.91	2.06		.69	1.50	7 1.00	
1944	.375				2.72	3.61	1.86		.73	1.50	7 1.00	
1945	.375				2.62	3.29	1.67		.75	1.50	7 1.00	
1946	.375				2.53	3.05	1.64		.81	1.50	7 1.00	
1947	.594				2.61	3.24	2.01		1.03	1.50–1.75	1.00	
1948	1.040				2.82	3.47	2.40		1.44	1.75–2.00	1.34	
1949	1.102				2.66	3.42	2.21		1.49	2.00	1.50	
1950	1.218				2.62	3.24	1.98		1.45	2.07	1.59	
1951	1.552				2.86	3.41	2.00		2.16	2.56	1.75	
1952	1.766				2.96	3.52	2.19		2.33	3.00	1.75	
1953	1.931		2.47	2.85	3.20	3.74	2.72		2.52	3.17	1.99	
1954	.953		1.63	2.40	2.90	3.51	2.37		1.58	3.05	1.60	
1955	1.753		2.47	2.82	3.06	3.53	2.53		2.18	3.16	1.89	1.78
1956	2.658		3.19	3.18	3.36	3.88	2.93		3.31	3.77	2.77	2.73
1957	3.267		3.98	3.65	3.89	4.71	3.60		3.81	4.20	3.12	3.11
1958	1.839		2.84	3.32	3.79	4.73	3.56		2.46	3.83	2.15	1.57
1959	3.405	3.832	4.46	4.33	4.38	5.05	3.95		3.97	4.48	3.36	3.30
1960	2.928	3.247	3.98	4.12	4.41	5.19	3.73		3.85	4.82	3.53	3.22
1961	2.378	2.605	3.54	3.88	4.35	5.08	3.46		2.97	4.50	3.00	1.96
1962	2.778	2.908	3.47	3.95	4.33	5.02	3.18		3.26	4.50	3.00	2.68
1963	3.157	3.253	3.67	4.00	4.26	4.86	3.23	5.89	3.55	4.50	3.23	3.18
1964	3.549	3.686	4.03	4.19	4.40	4.83	3.22	5.83	3.97	4.50	3.55	3.50
1965	3.954	4.055	4.22	4.28	4.49	4.87	3.27	5.81	4.38	4.54	4.04	4.07
1966	4.881	5.082	5.23	4.92	5.13	5.67	3.82	6.25	5.55	5.63	4.50	5.11
1967	4.321	4.630	5.03	5.07	5.51	6.23	3.98	6.46	5.10	5.61	4.19	4.22
1968	5.339	5.470	5.68	5.65	6.18	6.94	4.51	6.97	5.90	6.30	5.16	5.66
1969	6.677	6.853	7.02	6.67	7.03	7.81	5.81	7.81	7.83	7.96	5.87	8.20
1970	6.458	6.562	7.29	7.35	8.04	9.11	6.51	8.45	7.71	7.91	5.95	7.18
1971	4.348	4.511	5.65	6.16	7.39	8.56	5.70	7.74	5.11	5.72	4.88	4.66
1972	4.071	4.466	5.72	6.21	7.21	8.16	5.27	7.60	4.73	5.25	4.50	4.43
1973	7.041	7.178	6.95	6.84	7.44	8.24	5.18	7.96	8.15	8.03	6.44	8.73
1974	7.886	7.926	7.82	7.56	8.57	9.50	6.09	8.92	9.84	10.81	7.83	10.50
1975	5.838	6.122	7.49	7.99	8.83	10.61	6.89	9.00	6.32	7.86	6.25	5.82
1976	4.989	5.266	6.77	7.61	8.43	9.75	6.49	9.00	5.34	6.84	5.50	5.04
1977	5.265	5.510	6.69	7.42	8.02	8.97	5.56	9.02	5.61	6.83	5.46	5.54
1978	7.221	7.572	8.29	8.41	8.73	9.49	5.90	9.56	7.99	9.06	7.46	7.93
1979	10.041	10.017	9.71	9.44	9.63	10.69	6.39	10.78	10.91	12.67	10.28	11.19
1980	11.506	11.374	11.55	11.46	11.94	13.67	8.51	12.66	12.29	15.27	11.77	13.36
1981	14.029	13.776	14.44	13.91	14.17	16.04	11.23	14.70	14.76	18.87	13.42	16.38
1982	10.686	11.084	12.92	13.00	13.79	16.11	11.57	15.14	11.89	14.86	11.02	12.26
1983	8.63	8.75	10.45	11.10	12.04	13.55	9.47	12.57	8.89	10.79	8.50	9.09
1984	9.58	9.80	11.89	12.44	12.71	14.19	10.15	12.38	10.16	12.04	8.80	10.23
1985	7.48	7.66	9.64	10.62	11.37	12.72	9.18	11.55	8.01	9.93	7.69	8.10
1986	5.98	6.03	7.06	7.68	9.02	10.39	7.38	10.17	6.39	8.33	6.33	6.81
1987	5.82	6.05	7.68	8.39	9.38	10.58	7.73	9.31	6.85	8.21	5.66	6.66
1988	6.69	6.92	8.26	8.85	9.71	10.83	7.76	9.19	7.68	9.32	6.20	7.57
1989	8.12	8.04	8.55	8.49	9.26	10.18	7.24	10.13	8.80	10.87	6.93	9.21
1990	7.51	7.47	8.26	8.55	9.32	10.36	7.25	10.05	7.95	10.01	6.98	8.10
1991	5.42	5.49	6.82	7.86	8.77	9.80	6.89	9.32	5.85	8.46	5.45	5.69
1992	3.45	3.57	5.30	7.01	8.14	8.98	6.41		3.80	6.25	3.25	3.52
										High-low	High-low	
1987:												
Jan	5.45	5.47	6.41	7.08	8.36	9.72	6.63	9.51	5.76	7.50– 7.50	5.50–5.50	6.43
Feb	5.59	5.60	6.56	7.25	8.38	9.65	6.66	9.23	5.99	7.50– 7.50	5.50–5.50	6.10
Mar	5.56	5.56	6.58	7.25	8.36	9.61	6.71	9.14	6.10	7.50– 7.50	5.50–5.50	6.13
Apr	5.76	5.93	7.32	8.02	8.85	10.04	7.62	9.21	6.50	7.75– 7.50	5.50–5.50	6.37
May	5.75	6.11	8.02	8.61	9.33	10.51	8.10	9.37	7.04	8.25– 7.75	5.50–5.50	6.85
June	5.69	5.99	7.82	8.40	9.32	10.52	7.89	9.45	7.00	8.25– 8.25	5.50–5.50	6.73
July	5.78	5.86	7.74	8.45	9.42	10.61	7.83	9.41	6.72	8.25– 8.25	5.50–5.50	6.58
Aug	6.00	6.14	8.03	8.76	9.67	10.80	7.90	9.38	6.81	8.25– 8.25	5.50–5.50	6.73
Sept	6.32	6.57	8.67	9.42	10.18	11.31	8.36	9.37	7.55	8.75– 8.25	6.00–5.50	7.22
Oct	6.40	6.86	8.75	9.52	10.52	11.62	8.84	9.25	7.96	9.25– 8.75	6.00–6.00	7.29
Nov	5.81	6.23	7.99	8.86	10.01	11.23	8.09	9.30	7.17	9.00– 8.75	6.00–6.00	6.69
Dec	5.80	6.36	8.13	8.99	10.11	11.29	8.07	9.15	7.49	8.75– 8.75	6.00–6.00	6.77

[1] Rate on new issues within period; bank-discount basis.
[2] Yields on the more actively traded issues adjusted to constant maturities by the Treasury Department.
[3] Effective rate (in the primary market) on conventional mortgages, reflecting fees and charges as well as contract rate and assuming, on the average, repayment at end of 10 years. Rates beginning January 1973 not strictly comparable with prior rates. *See next page for continuation of table.*

428

[Percent per annum]

Year and month	U.S. Treasury securities				Corporate bonds (Moody's)		High-grade municipal bonds (Standard & Poor's)	New-home mortgage yields[3]	Commercial paper, 6 months[4]	Prime rate charged by banks[5]	Discount rate, Federal Reserve Bank of New York[5]	Federal funds rate[6]
	Bills (new issues)[1]		Constant maturities[2]									
	3-month	6-month	3-year	10-year	Aaa	Baa						
										High-low	High-low	
1988:												
Jan....	5.90	6.31	7.87	8.67	9.88	11.07	7.81	9.10	6.92	8.75- 8.75	6.00–6.00	6.83
Feb....	5.69	5.96	7.38	8.21	9.40	10.62	7.55	9.12	6.58	8.75- 8.50	6.00–6.00	6.58
Mar....	5.69	5.91	7.50	8.37	9.39	10.57	7.80	9.15	6.64	8.50- 8.50	6.00–6.00	6.58
Apr....	5.92	6.21	7.83	8.72	9.67	10.90	7.91	9.13	6.92	8.50- 8.50	6.00–6.00	6.87
May....	6.27	6.53	8.24	9.09	9.90	11.04	8.01	8.95	7.31	9.00- 8.50	6.00–6.00	7.09
June...	6.50	6.76	8.22	8.92	9.86	11.00	7.86	9.26	7.53	9.00- 9.00	6.00–6.00	7.51
July....	6.73	6.97	8.44	9.06	9.96	11.11	7.87	9.17	7.90	9.50- 9.00	6.00–6.00	7.75
Aug....	7.02	7.36	8.77	9.26	10.11	11.21	7.86	9.06	8.36	10.00- 9.50	6.50–6.00	8.01
Sept...	7.23	7.43	8.57	8.98	9.82	10.90	7.71	9.26	8.23	10.00-10.00	6.50–6.50	8.19
Oct....	7.34	7.50	8.43	8.80	9.51	10.41	7.54	9.10	8.24	10.00-10.00	6.50–6.50	8.30
Nov....	7.68	7.76	8.72	8.96	9.45	10.48	7.58	9.43	8.55	10.50-10.00	6.50–6.50	8.35
Dec....	8.09	8.24	9.11	9.11	9.57	10.65	7.66	9.39	8.97	10.50-10.50	6.50–6.50	8.76
1989:												
Jan....	8.29	8.38	9.20	9.09	9.62	10.65	7.41	9.52	9.02	10.50-10.50	6.50–6.50	9.12
Feb....	8.48	8.49	9.32	9.17	9.64	10.61	7.47	9.82	9.35	11.50-10.50	7.00–6.50	9.36
Mar....	8.83	8.87	9.61	9.36	9.80	10.67	7.61	9.99	9.97	11.50-11.50	7.00–7.00	9.85
Apr....	8.70	8.73	9.40	9.18	9.79	10.61	7.49	10.17	9.78	11.50-11.50	7.00–7.00	9.84
May....	8.40	8.39	8.98	8.86	9.57	10.46	7.25	10.18	9.29	11.50-11.50	7.00–7.00	9.81
June...	8.22	8.00	8.37	8.28	9.10	10.03	6.97	10.42	8.80	11.50-11.00	7.00–7.00	9.53
July....	7.92	7.63	7.83	8.02	8.93	9.87	6.97	10.48	8.35	11.00-10.50	7.00–7.00	9.24
Aug....	7.91	7.72	8.13	8.11	8.96	9.88	7.08	10.22	8.32	10.50-10.50	7.00–7.00	8.99
Sept...	7.72	7.74	8.26	8.19	9.01	9.91	7.27	10.24	8.50	10.50-10.50	7.00–7.00	9.02
Oct....	7.63	7.61.	8.02	8.01	8.92	9.81	7.22	10.11	8.24	10.50-10.50	7.00–7.00	8.84
Nov....	7.65	7.46	7.80	7.87	8.89	9.81	7.13	10.09	8.00	10.50-10.50	7.00–7.00	8.55
Dec....	7.64	7.45	7.77	7.84	8.86	9.82	7.01	10.07	7.93	10.50-10.50	7.00–7.00	8.45
1990:												
Jan....	7.64	7.52	8.13	8.21	8.99	9.94	7.13	9.91	7.96	10.50-10.00	7.00–7.00	8.23
Feb....	7.76	7.72	8.39	8.47	9.22	10.14	7.21	9.88	8.04	10.00-10.00	7.00–7.00	8.24
Mar....	7.87	7.83	8.63	8.59	9.37	10.21	7.29	10.03	8.23	10.00-10.00	7.00–7.00	8.28
Apr....	7.78	7.82	8.78	8.79	9.46	10.30	7.36	10.17	8.29	10.00-10.00	7.00–7.00	8.26
May....	7.78	7.82	8.69	8.76	9.47	10.41	7.34	10.28	8.23	10.00-10.00	7.00–7.00	8.18
June...	7.74	7.64	8.40	8.48	9.26	10.22	7.22	10.13	8.06	10.00-10.00	7.00–7.00	8.29
July....	7.66	7.57	8.26	8.47	9.24	10.20	7.15	10.08	7.90	10.00-10.00	7.00–7.00	8.15
Aug....	7.44	7.36	8.22	8.75	9.41	10.41	7.31	10.11	7.77	10.00-10.00	7.00–7.00	8.13
Sept...	7.38	7.33	8.27	8.89	9.56	10.64	7.40	9.90	7.83	10.00-10.00	7.00–7.00	8.20
Oct....	7.19	7.20	8.07	8.72	9.53	10.74	7.40	9.98	7.81	10.00-10.00	7.00–7.00	8.11
Nov....	7.07	7.04	7.74	8.39	9.30	10.62	7.10	9.90	7.74	10.00-10.00	7.00–7.00	7.81
Dec....	6.81	6.76	7.47	8.08	9.05	10.43	7.04	9.76	7.49	10.00-10.00	7.00–6.50	7.31
1991:												
Jan....	6.30	6.34	7.38	8.09	9.04	10.45	7.05	9.65	7.02	10.00- 9.50	6.50–6.50	6.91
Feb....	5.95	5.93	7.08	7.85	8.83	10.07	6.90	9.57	6.41	9.50- 9.00	6.50–6.00	6.25
Mar....	5.91	5.91	7.35	8.11	8.93	10.09	7.07	9.43	6.36	9.00- 9.00	6.00–6.00	6.12
Apr....	5.67	5.73	7.23	8.04	8.86	9.94	7.05	9.60	6.07	9.00- 9.00	6.00–5.50	5.91
May....	5.51	5.65	7.12	8.07	8.86	9.86	6.95	9.52	5.94	9.00- 8.50	5.50–5.50	5.78
June...	5.60	5.76	7.39	8.28	9.01	9.96	7.09	9.46	6.16	8.50- 8.50	5.50–5.50	5.90
July....	5.58	5.71	7.38	8.27	9.00	9.89	7.03	9.43	6.14	8.50- 8.50	5.50–5.50	5.82
Aug....	5.39	5.47	6.80	7.90	8.75	9.65	6.89	9.48	5.76	8.50- 8.50	5.50–5.50	5.66
Sept...	5.25	5.29	6.50	7.65	8.61	9.51	6.80	9.30	5.59	8.50- 8.00	5.50–5.00	5.45
Oct....	5.03	5.08	6.23	7.53	8.55	9.49	6.59	9.04	5.33	8.00- 8.00	5.00–5.00	5.21
Nov....	4.60	4.66	5.90	7.42	8.48	9.45	6.64	8.64	4.93	8.00- 7.50	5.00–4.50	4.81
Dec....	4.12	4.16	5.39	7.09	8.31	9.26	6.63	8.53	4.49	7.50- 6.50	4.50–3.50	4.43
1992:												
Jan....	3.84	3.88	5.40	7.03	8.20	9.13	6.41	8.49	4.06	6.50–6.50	3.50–3.50	4.03
Feb....	3.84	3.94	5.72	7.34	8.29	9.23	6.67	8.65	4.13	6.50–6.50	3.50–3.50	4.06
Mar....	4.05	4.19	6.18	7.54	8.35	9.25	6.69	8.51	4.38	6.50–6.50	3.50–3.50	3.98
Apr....	3.81	3.93	5.93	7.48	8.33	9.21	6.64	8.58	4.13	6.50–6.50	3.50–3.50	3.73
May....	3.66	3.78	5.81	7.39	8.28	9.13	6.57	8.59	3.97	6.50–6.50	3.50–3.50	3.82
June...	3.70	3.81	5.60	7.26	8.22	9.05	6.50	8.43	3.99	6.50–6.50	3.50–3.50	3.76
July....	3.28	3.36	4.91	6.84	8.07	8.84	6.12	8.00	3.53	6.50–6.00	3.50–3.00	3.25
Aug....	3.14	3.23	4.72	6.59	7.95	8.65	6.08	8.00	3.44	6.00–6.00	3.00–3.00	3.30
Sept...	2.97	3.01	4.42	6.42	7.92	8.62	6.24	7.93	3.26	6.00–6.00	3.00–3.00	3.22
Oct....	2.84	2.98	4.64	6.59	7.99	8.84	6.38	7.90	3.33	6.00–6.00	3.00–3.00	3.10
Nov....	3.14	3.35	5.14	6.87	8.10	8.96	6.35	8.07	3.67	6.00–6.00	3.00–3.00	3.09
Dec....	3.25	3.39	5.21	6.77	7.98	8.81	6.24	....	3.70	6.00–6.00	3.00–3.00	2.92

[4] Bank-discount basis; prior to November 1979, data are for 4–6 months paper.
[5] For monthly data, high and low for the period. Prime rate for 1929–33 and 1947–48 are ranges of the rate in effect during the period.
[6] Since July 19, 1975, the daily effective rate is an average of the rates on a given day weighted by the volume of transactions at these rates. Prior to that date, the daily effective rate was the rate considered most representative of the day's transactions, usually the one at which most transactions occurred.
[7] From October 30, 1942, to April 24, 1946, a preferential rate of 0.50 percent was in effect for advances secured by Government securities maturing in 1 year or less.

Sources: Department of the Treasury, Board of Governors of the Federal Reserve System, Federal Housing Finance Board, Moody's Investors Service, and Standard & Poor's Corporation.

TABLE B-70.—*Total funds raised in credit markets by nonfinancial sectors, 1983-92*

[Billions of dollars; quarterly data at seasonally adjusted annual rates]

Item	1983	1984	1985	1986	1987	1988	1989	1990	1991
	Net credit market borrowing by nonfinancial sectors								
Total net borrowing by domestic nonfinancial sectors................	553.3	765.4	903.1	893.8	721.2	775.8	740.8	665.0	452.7
U.S. Government................................	185.2	197.2	225.7	216.0	143.9	155.1	146.4	246.9	278.2
Treasury issues	185.3	197.4	225.8	215.6	142.4	137.7	144.7	238.7	292.0
Agency issues and mortgages.....................	−.1	−.2	−.1	.4	1.5	17.4	1.6	8.2	−13.8
Private domestic nonfinancial sectors..................	368.1	568.2	677.4	677.9	577.3	620.7	594.4	418.2	174.4
Debt capital instruments.............................	263.8	334.6	503.0	523.1	487.2	474.1	441.8	342.3	254.6
Tax-exempt obligations.....................	54.4	58.7	178.6	45.7	83.5	53.7	65.0	51.2	45.8
Corporate bonds............................	16.0	46.1	74.2	127.1	78.8	103.1	73.8	47.1	78.8
Mortgages	193.4	229.9	250.3	350.3	325.0	317.3	303.0	244.0	130.0
Home mortgages.........................	125.9	143.8	164.8	252.6	235.3	241.8	245.3	219.4	142.2
Multi-family residential	14.1	25.2	29.8	33.5	24.4	16.7	16.4	3.7	−2.0
Commercial...................................	51.0	62.2	62.2	73.6	71.6	60.8	42.7	21.0	−9.4
Farm	2.4	−1.2	−6.6	−9.5	−6.4	−2.1	−1.5	−.1	−.8
Other debt instruments..............................	104.4	233.5	174.4	154.8	90.1	146.6	152.6	75.8	−80.2
Consumer credit..............................	48.9	81.7	82.3	57.5	32.9	50.1	41.7	17.5	−12.5
Bank loans n.e.c............................	25.0	67.9	40.6	63.6	9.9	41.0	40.2	4.4	−33.4
Open-market paper.........................	−.8	21.7	14.6	−9.3	1.6	11.9	21.4	9.7	−18.4
Other	31.3	62.2	36.9	43.0	45.7	43.6	49.3	44.2	−15.8
By borrowing sector:..............................	368.1	568.2	677.4	677.9	577.3	620.7	594.4	418.2	174.4
State and local governments................	34.6	35.7	134.0	59.2	83.0	48.9	63.2	48.3	38.5
Households...	185.7	232.7	284.9	319.4	296.4	318.6	305.6	254.2	158.0
Nonfinancial business	147.8	299.8	258.5	299.3	197.8	253.1	225.6	115.6	−22.1
Farm	3.9	−.4	−14.5	−16.3	−10.6	−7.5	1.6	2.5	.9
Nonfarm noncorporate.....................	83.9	123.2	130.0	100.7	65.3	61.8	50.4	26.7	−23.6
Corporate...	60.1	177.0	143.0	214.8	143.1	198.8	173.6	86.4	.6
Foreign net borrowing in United States......................	17.3	8.4	1.2	9.7	6.2	6.4	10.2	23.9	14.1
Bonds..	3.1	3.8	3.8	3.1	7.4	6.9	4.9	21.4	14.9
Bank loans n.e.c..................................	3.6	−6.6	−2.8	−1.0	−3.6	−1.8	−.1	−2.9	3.1
Open-market paper.............................	6.5	6.2	6.2	11.5	3.8	8.7	13.1	12.3	6.4
U.S. Government and other loans...............	4.1	5.0	−6.0	−3.9	−1.4	−7.5	−7.6	−6.9	−10.2
Total domestic plus foreign..............................	570.7	773.7	904.3	903.5	727.4	782.2	750.9	688.9	466.8
	Direct and indirect supply of funds to credit markets								
Total funds supplied to domestic nonfinancial sectors...............	553.3	765.4	903.1	893.8	721.2	775.8	740.8	665.0	452.7
Private domestic nonfinancial sectors..................	382.2	473.4	537.9	424.6	423.1	460.7	424.6	290.4	50.1
Deposits and currency	232.7	313.9	210.2	296.4	185.7	234.5	215.1	86.6	28.5
Checkable deposits and currency	45.0	37.5	55.2	115.6	17.5	27.3	11.7	21.9	69.4
Time and savings deposits	200.5	222.7	131.9	111.5	120.2	165.3	105.6	16.5	−66.0
Money market fund shares...................	−39.0	49.0	7.2	43.2	28.9	20.2	86.4	54.4	33.8
Security repurchase agreements	23.1	9.8	17.7	20.2	21.6	32.9	6.9	−18.2	−18.7
Foreign deposits...................................	3.1	−5.1	−1.7	5.9	−2.5	−11.2	4.4	12.0	10.0
Credit market instruments..........................	149.5	159.5	327.7	128.1	237.4	226.2	209.6	203.8	21.6
Foreign funds	40.8	68.6	80.9	111.1	105.5	105.6	64.1	82.3	20.6
At banks..	14.6	8.8	19.7	12.9	43.7	9.3	−9.9	23.8	−24.1
Credit market instruments......................	26.2	59.8	61.2	98.2	61.8	96.3	74.1	58.4	44.7
U.S. Government and related loans, net..............	9.0	16.5	37.0	18.6	8.1	−14.3	−46.3	17.3	32.0
U.S. Government cash balances.......................	−5.3	4.0	10.3	1.7	−5.8	7.3	−3.4	5.3	5.5
Private insurance and pension reserves...............	133.3	159.8	143.4	187.6	107.8	182.8	210.2	175.9	204.3
Other sources..	−6.6	43.0	93.6	150.3	82.5	33.7	91.5	93.9	140.1

See next page for continuation of table.

TABLE B–70.—*Total funds raised in credit markets by nonfinancial sectors, 1983–92*—Continued

[Billions of dollars; quarterly data at seasonally adjusted annual rates]

Item	1990 I	1990 II	1990 III	1990 IV	1991 I	1991 II	1991 III	1991 IV	1992 I	1992 II	1992 III
	Net credit market borrowing by nonfinancial sectors										
Total net borrowing by domestic nonfinancial sectors	883.5	619.0	653.9	503.9	455.4	543.3	405.6	406.3	667.5	535.1	379.9
U.S. Government	244.8	203.8	268.2	270.8	227.4	276.7	288.4	320.4	368.9	351.9	193.4
Treasury issues	215.2	198.4	269.5	271.8	251.4	282.9	317.2	316.6	380.1	351.5	184.4
Agency issues and mortgages	29.6	5.4	−1.3	−1.0	−24.0	−6.2	−28.8	3.8	−11.2	.4	9.0
Private domestic nonfinancial sectors	638.7	415.2	385.7	233.0	228.0	266.6	117.2	85.9	298.6	183.2	186.5
Debt capital instruments	486.9	321.0	283.4	277.9	296.1	329.9	182.0	210.6	312.9	218.4	196.4
Tax-exempt obligations	70.3	54.7	39.2	40.6	35.6	48.5	53.5	45.5	52.0	73.0	52.3
Corporate bonds	27.5	65.8	29.8	65.2	76.7	96.5	81.7	60.3	76.3	77.5	61.3
Mortgages	389.1	200.4	214.5	172.1	183.8	184.8	46.8	104.8	184.7	67.9	82.8
Home mortgages	333.1	188.5	193.8	162.3	153.0	158.1	122.4	135.1	209.6	121.6	147.2
Multi-family residential	1.2	−7.1	16.6	3.9	6.3	12.5	−29.4	2.7	−1.3	−31.6	−10.7
Commercial	55.4	18.6	2.8	7.2	24.6	14.9	−43.8	−33.1	−22.6	−24.9	−54.7
Farm	−.7	.4	1.3	−1.3	−.1	−.7	−2.5	.0	−1.1	2.7	1.1
Other debt instruments	151.8	94.2	102.3	−44.9	−68.0	−63.3	−64.8	−124.7	−14.4	−35.2	−10.0
Consumer credit	40.8	21.4	14.4	−6.6	−10.4	−7.8	−24.0	−8.0	3.1	−12.4	.4
Bank loans n.e.c	−7.6	22.8	10.9	−8.4	−15.0	−34.5	−18.2	−66.1	−26.9	−21.5	−23.3
Open-market paper	48.2	−.4	25.3	−34.1	−14.3	−15.9	−36.3	−7.0	12.6	−3.4	1.7
Other	70.4	50.4	51.6	4.3	−28.3	−5.2	13.7	−43.6	−3.2	2.1	11.2
By borrowing sector:	638.7	415.2	385.7	233.0	228.0	266.6	117.2	85.9	298.6	183.2	186.5
State and local governments	73.9	47.4	37.3	34.7	36.0	38.6	37.6	41.9	46.1	63.4	50.0
Households	390.0	234.6	232.5	159.8	160.8	188.8	136.1	146.3	217.1	143.3	148.1
Nonfinancial business	174.8	133.2	116.0	38.6	31.2	39.2	−56.5	−102.4	35.4	−23.4	−11.7
Farm	5.8	−3.6	8.2	−.3	3.9	2.1	−.3	−2.2	−1.6	7.1	2.4
Nonfarm noncorporate	45.1	25.4	28.3	7.9	13.2	9.8	−65.9	−51.5	−20.7	−65.6	−51.4
Corporate	123.9	111.4	79.4	31.0	14.0	27.2	9.7	−48.7	57.7	35.2	37.4
Foreign net borrowing in United States	11.5	35.8	23.9	24.2	63.1	−63.2	15.6	41.0	9.9	55.9	30.1
Bonds	34.2	19.6	2.0	29.6	11.1	10.6	15.5	22.3	4.9	22.8	23.2
Bank loans n.e.c	−9.7	1.3	2.0	−5.2	8.1	−3.5	1.4	6.5	1.5	14.1	3.4
Open-market paper	−14.9	23.1	25.6	15.6	46.7	−51.9	16.0	14.9	−7.8	27.7	12.8
U.S. Government and other loans	1.9	−8.2	−5.6	−15.8	−2.8	−18.3	−17.2	−2.7	11.4	−8.8	−9.3
Total domestic plus foreign	895.0	654.8	677.8	528.1	518.5	480.1	421.2	447.3	677.3	591.0	410.1
	Direct and indirect supply of funds to credit markets										
Total funds supplied to domestic nonfinancial sectors	883.5	619.0	653.9	503.9	455.4	543.3	405.6	406.3	667.5	535.1	379.9
Private domestic nonfinancial sectors	569.6	307.5	184.3	100.2	313.0	98.4	−164.6	−46.5	343.4	−77.6	−275.3
Deposits and currency	184.8	21.4	94.8	45.3	263.6	−92.1	−29.3	−28.2	204.3	−151.1	−22.6
Checkable deposits and currency	43.4	22.1	28.0	−6.0	84.3	23.3	121.4	48.7	158.7	60.3	156.2
Time and savings deposits	91.8	−4.3	−30.6	9.2	47.4	−63.5	−143.0	104.9	−86.1	−182.8	−161.0
Money market fund shares	108.2	−43.6	109.2	43.6	182.6	−66.4	−2.1	21.1	101.4	−41.6	−15.6
Security repurchase agreements	−23.9	17.3	−27.3	−38.7	−52.2	−4.5	−20.6	2.3	33.4	42.9	12.5
Foreign deposits	−34.7	29.9	15.4	37.2	1.4	18.9	15.1	4.6	−3.1	−30.1	−14.8
Credit market instruments	384.7	286.1	89.5	54.8	49.4	190.5	−135.3	−18.2	139.2	73.5	−252.7
Foreign funds	18.4	88.0	158.8	63.8	17.9	−47.0	73.9	37.8	93.6	214.1	173.6
At banks	8.4	27.4	80.9	−21.3	−1.3	−98.4	36.5	−33.2	5.2	71.6	115.2
Credit market instruments	10.1	60.6	77.9	85.1	19.1	51.4	37.3	71.0	88.4	142.5	58.4
U.S. Government and related loans, net	39.1	18.8	93.3	−81.9	44.5	91.3	43.5	−51.4	118.8	−79.7	−35.6
U.S. Government cash balances	5.3	1.4	14.2	.4	20.5	−19.6	6.5	14.6	−43.2	21.2	5.4
Private insurance and pension reserves	94.0	233.5	147.5	228.6	277.7	144.0	267.2	128.5	54.6	169.4	263.2
Other sources	157.0	−30.3	55.9	192.9	−218.0	276.2	179.2	323.1	100.4	287.6	248.6

Source: Board of Governors of the Federal Reserve System.

TABLE B-71.—*Mortgage debt outstanding by type of property and of financing, 1940-92*

[Billions of dollars]

End of year or quarter	All properties	Farm properties	Nonfarm properties				Nonfarm properties by type of mortgage					
							Government underwritten				Conventional²	
			Total	1- to 4-family houses	Multifamily properties	Commercial properties	Total¹	1- to 4-family houses			Total	1- to 4-family houses
								Total	FHA insured	VA guaranteed		
1940	36.5	6.5	30.0	17.4	5.7	6.9	2.3	2.3	2.3		27.7	15.1
1941	37.6	6.4	31.2	18.4	5.9	7.0	3.0	3.0	3.0		28.2	15.4
1942	36.7	6.0	30.8	18.2	5.8	6.7	3.7	3.7	3.7		27.1	14.5
1943	35.3	5.4	29.9	17.8	5.8	6.3	4.1	4.1	4.1		25.8	13.7
1944	34.7	4.9	29.7	17.9	5.6	6.2	4.2	4.2	4.2		25.5	13.7
1945	35.5	4.8	30.8	18.6	5.7	6.4	4.3	4.3	4.1	0.2	26.5	14.3
1946	41.8	4.9	36.9	23.0	6.1	7.7	6.3	6.1	3.7	2.4	30.6	16.9
1947	48.9	5.1	43.9	28.2	6.6	9.1	9.8	9.3	3.8	5.5	34.1	18.9
1948	56.2	5.3	50.9	33.3	7.5	10.2	13.6	12.5	5.3	7.2	37.3	20.8
1949	62.7	5.6	57.1	37.6	8.6	10.8	17.1	15.0	6.9	8.1	40.0	22.6
1950	72.8	6.1	66.7	45.2	10.1	11.5	22.1	18.8	8.5	10.3	44.7	26.3
1951	82.3	6.7	75.6	51.7	11.5	12.5	26.6	22.9	9.7	13.2	49.1	28.9
1952	91.4	7.2	84.2	58.5	12.3	13.4	29.3	25.4	10.8	14.6	54.9	33.2
1953	101.3	7.7	93.6	66.1	12.9	14.5	32.1	28.1	12.0	16.1	61.5	38.0
1954	113.7	8.2	105.4	75.7	13.5	16.3	36.2	32.1	12.8	19.3	69.3	43.6
1955	129.9	9.0	120.9	88.2	14.3	18.3	42.9	38.9	14.3	24.6	78.0	49.3
1956	144.5	9.8	134.6	99.0	14.9	20.7	47.8	43.9	15.5	28.4	86.8	55.1
1957	156.5	10.4	146.1	107.6	15.3	23.2	51.6	47.2	16.5	30.7	94.6	60.4
1958	171.8	11.1	160.7	117.7	16.8	26.1	55.2	50.1	19.7	30.4	105.5	67.6
1959	190.8	12.1	178.7	130.9	18.7	29.2	59.3	53.8	23.8	30.0	119.4	77.0
1960	207.5	12.8	194.7	141.9	20.3	32.4	62.3	56.4	26.7	29.7	132.3	85.5
1961	228.0	13.9	214.1	154.6	23.0	36.5	65.6	59.1	29.5	29.6	148.5	95.5
1962	251.4	15.2	236.2	169.3	25.8	41.1	69.4	62.2	32.3	29.9	166.9	107.1
1963	278.5	16.8	261.7	186.4	29.0	46.2	73.4	65.9	35.0	30.9	188.2	120.5
1964	305.9	18.9	287.0	203.4	33.6	50.0	77.2	69.2	38.3	30.9	209.8	134.1
1965	333.3	21.2	312.1	220.5	37.2	54.5	81.2	73.1	42.0	31.1	231.0	147.4
1966	356.5	23.1	333.4	232.9	40.3	60.1	84.1	76.1	44.8	31.3	249.3	156.9
1967	381.2	25.1	356.1	247.3	43.9	64.8	88.2	⁰79.9	⁰7.4	32.5	267.9	167.4
1968	411.1	27.5	383.5	264.8	47.3	71.4	93.4	84.4	50.6	33.8	290.1	180.4
1969	441.6	29.4	412.2	283.2	52.2	76.9	100.2	90.2	54.5	35.7	312.0	193.0
1970	473.7	30.5	443.2	297.4	60.1	85.6	109.2	97.3	59.9	37.3	333.9	200.2
1971	524.2	32.4	491.8	325.9	70.1	95.9	120.7	105.2	65.7	39.5	371.1	220.7
1972	597.4	35.4	562.0	366.5	82.8	112.7	131.1	113.0	68.2	44.7	430.9	253.5
1973	672.6	39.8	632.8	407.9	93.1	131.7	135.0	116.2	66.2	50.0	497.7	291.7
1974	732.5	44.9	687.5	440.7	100.0	146.9	140.2	121.3	65.1	56.2	547.3	319.4
1975	791.9	49.9	742.0	482.1	100.6	159.3	147.0	127.7	66.1	61.6	595.0	354.3
1976	878.6	55.4	823.2	546.3	105.7	171.2	154.1	133.5	66.5	67.0	669.0	412.8
1977	1,010.3	63.9	946.4	642.7	114.0	189.7	161.7	141.6	68.0	73.6	784.6	501.0
1978	1,163.0	72.8	1,090.2	753.5	124.9	211.8	176.4	153.4	71.4	82.0	913.9	600.2
1979	1,328.4	86.8	1,241.7	870.5	134.9	236.3	199.0	172.9	81.0	92.0	1,042.7	697.6
1980	1,460.4	97.5	1,362.9	965.1	142.3	255.5	225.1	195.2	93.6	101.6	1,137.8	769.9
1981	1,566.7	107.2	1,459.5	1,039.8	142.1	277.7	238.9	207.6	101.3	106.2	1,220.6	832.2
1982	1,637.9	111.3	1,526.6	1,080.0	145.7	300.9	248.9	217.9	108.0	109.9	1,277.8	862.2
1983	1,825.4	113.7	1,711.7	1,198.5	160.7	352.4	279.8	248.8	127.4	121.4	1,431.9	949.6
1984	2,051.9	112.4	1,939.5	1,334.5	185.5	419.5	294.8	265.9	136.7	129.1	1,644.7	1,068.6
1985	2,309.5	105.9	2,203.6	1,502.5	214.8	486.3	328.3	288.8	153.0	135.8	1,875.3	1,213.7
1986	2,644.8	96.5	2,548.3	1,726.9	260.9	560.5	370.5	328.6	185.5	143.1	2,177.8	1,398.3
1987	3,001.8	87.5	2,914.3	1,967.3	284.1	662.9	431.4	387.9	235.5	152.4	2,482.9	1,579.4
1988	3,288.1	85.2	3,202.8	2,208.2	296.6	698.0	459.7	414.2	258.8	155.4	2,743.1	1,794.0
1989	3,575.0	84.0	3,491.0	2,435.2	306.8	749.0	486.8	440.1	282.8	157.3	3,004.1	1,995.1
1990	3,797.7	84.0	3,713.8	2,644.7	310.3	758.8	517.9	470.9	310.9	160.0	3,195.8	2,173.7
1991	3,919.5	83.2	3,836.3	2,777.9	308.6	749.8	537.2	493.3	330.6	162.7	3,299.1	2,284.6
1990: I	3,642.1	83.9	3,558.2	2,498.9	306.9	752.4	495.1	448.2	289.8	158.4	3,063.1	2,050.7
II	3,700.9	84.0	3,617.0	2,555.1	305.1	756.7	502.3	455.0	296.2	158.8	3,114.6	2,100.1
III	3,757.8	84.3	3,673.5	2,606.2	309.3	758.0	510.9	464.1	304.8	159.3	3,162.6	2,142.1
IV	3,797.7	84.0	3,713.8	2,644.7	310.3	758.8	517.9	470.9	310.9	160.0	3,195.8	2,173.7
1991: I	3,834.9	83.9	3,751.0	2,674.0	311.9	765.1	525.3	478.0	317.0	161.0	3,225.6	2,196.0
II	3,891.2	83.8	3,807.5	2,723.2	315.2	769.3	545.7	497.3	334.1	163.2	3,261.8	2,225.7
III	3,904.4	83.2	3,821.2	2,755.4	307.8	758.0	535.3	491.4	329.1	162.2	3,285.9	2,264.0
IV	3,919.5	83.2	3,836.3	2,777.9	308.6	749.8	537.2	493.3	330.6	162.7	3,299.1	2,284.6
1992: I	3,966.8	82.9	3,883.9	2,831.2	308.4	744.3	538.1	494.3	330.6	163.7	2,345.8	2,336.9
II	3,992.9	83.6	3,909.3	2,870.7	300.5	738.1	536.1	492.4	328.8	163.6	3,373.2	2,378.3
III	4,008.6	83.9	3,924.7	2,900.7	297.8	726.2	535.4	491.9	327.5	164.4	3,389.3	2,408.9

¹ Includes FHA insured multifamily properties, not shown separately.
² Derived figures. Total includes multifamily and commercial properties, not shown separately.

Source: Board of Governors of the Federal Reserve System, based on data from various Government and private organizations.

TABLE B-72.—*Mortgage debt outstanding by holder, 1940–92*

[Billions of dollars]

End of year or quarter	Total	Major financial institutions				Other holders	
		Total	Savings institutions [1]	Commercial banks [2]	Life insurance companies	Federal and related agencies [3]	Individuals and others [4]
1940	36.5	19.5	9.0	4.6	6.0	4.9	12.0
1941	37.6	20.7	9.4	4.9	6.4	4.7	12.2
1942	36.7	20.7	9.2	4.7	6.7	4.3	11.7
1943	35.3	20.2	9.0	4.5	6.7	3.6	11.5
1944	34.7	20.2	9.1	4.4	6.7	3.0	11.5
1945	35.5	21.0	9.6	4.8	6.6	2.4	12.1
1946	41.8	26.0	11.5	7.2	7.2	2.0	13.8
1947	48.9	31.8	13.8	9.4	8.7	1.8	15.3
1948	56.2	37.8	16.1	10.9	10.8	1.8	16.6
1949	62.7	42.9	18.3	11.6	12.9	2.3	17.5
1950	72.8	51.7	21.9	13.7	16.1	2.8	18.4
1951	82.3	59.5	25.5	14.7	19.3	3.5	19.3
1952	91.4	66.9	29.8	15.9	21.3	4.1	20.4
1953	101.3	75.1	34.9	16.9	23.3	4.6	21.7
1954	113.7	85.7	41.1	18.6	26.0	4.8	23.2
1955	129.9	99.3	48.9	21.0	29.4	5.3	25.3
1956	144.5	111.2	55.5	22.7	33.0	6.2	27.1
1957	156.5	119.7	61.2	23.3	35.2	7.7	29.1
1958	171.8	131.5	68.9	25.5	37.1	8.0	32.3
1959	190.8	145.5	78.1	28.1	39.2	10.2	35.1
1960	207.5	157.6	87.0	28.8	41.8	11.5	38.4
1961	228.0	172.6	98.0	30.4	44.2	12.2	43.1
1962	251.4	192.5	111.1	34.5	46.9	12.6	46.3
1963	278.5	217.1	127.2	39.4	50.5	11.8	49.5
1964	305.9	241.0	141.9	44.0	55.2	12.2	52.7
1965	333.3	264.6	154.9	49.7	60.0	13.5	55.2
1966	356.5	280.8	161.8	54.4	64.6	17.5	58.2
1967	381.2	298.8	172.3	59.0	67.5	20.9	61.4
1968	411.1	319.9	184.3	65.7	70.0	25.1	66.1
1969	441.6	339.1	196.4	70.7	72.0	31.1	71.4
1970	473.7	355.9	208.3	73.3	74.4	38.3	79.4
1971	524.2	394.2	236.2	82.5	75.5	46.4	83.6
1972	597.4	450.0	273.7	99.3	76.9	54.6	92.8
1973	672.6	505.4	305.0	119.1	81.4	64.8	102.4
1974	732.5	542.6	324.2	132.1	86.2	82.2	107.7
1975	791.9	581.2	355.8	136.2	89.2	101.1	109.6
1976	878.6	647.5	404.6	151.3	91.6	116.7	114.4
1977	1,010.3	745.2	469.4	179.0	96.8	140.5	124.6
1978	1,163.0	848.2	528.0	214.0	106.2	170.6	144.3
1979	1,328.4	938.2	574.6	245.2	118.4	216.0	174.3
1980	1,460.4	996.8	603.1	262.7	131.1	256.8	206.8
1981	1,566.7	1,040.5	618.5	284.2	137.7	289.4	236.8
1982	1,637.9	1,021.3	578.1	301.3	142.0	355.4	261.2
1983	1,825.4	1,108.2	626.7	330.5	151.0	433.4	283.7
1984	2,051.9	1,245.9	709.7	379.5	156.7	491.1	314.9
1985	2,309.5	1,361.5	760.5	429.2	171.8	582.0	366.0
1986	2,644.8	1,474.3	778.0	502.5	193.8	735.4	435.0
1987	3,001.8	1,665.3	860.5	592.4	212.4	863.1	473.4
1988	3,288.1	1,831.5	924.6	674.0	232.9	945.9	510.7
1989	3,575.0	1,931.5	910.3	767.1	254.2	1,079.0	564.4
1990	3,797.7	1,914.3	801.6	844.8	267.9	1,270.6	612.8
1991	3,919.5	1,846.9	705.4	876.3	265.3	1,439.3	633.2
1990: I	3,642.1	1,939.0	891.9	786.8	260.3	1,125.1	578.0
II	3,700.9	1,940.4	860.9	814.6	264.9	1,172.0	588.5
III	3,757.8	1,933.3	836.0	831.2	266.1	1,221.2	603.3
IV	3,797.7	1,914.3	801.6	844.8	267.9	1,270.6	612.8
1991: I	3,834.9	1,902.3	776.5	856.8	269.0	1,314.5	618.1
II	3,891.2	1,898.5	755.4	871.4	271.7	1,365.2	627.6
III	3,904.4	1,860.7	719.7	870.9	270.1	1,405.4	638.3
IV	3,919.5	1,846.9	705.4	876.3	265.3	1,439.3	633.2
1992: I	3,966.8	1,826.0	682.3	880.4	263.3	1,476.4	664.4
II	3,992.9	1,806.1	659.6	884.6	261.9	1,516.3	670.5
III	4,008.6	1,794.5	648.1	886.5	259.9	1,539.9	674.3

[1] Includes savings banks and savings and loan associations. Data reported by Federal Savings and Loan Insurance Corporation-insured institutions include loans in process for 1987 and exclude loans in process beginning 1988.

[2] Includes loans held by nondeposit trust companies, but not by bank trust departments.

[3] Includes Government National Mortgage Association (GNMA), Federal Housing Administration, Veterans Administration, Farmers Home Administration (FmHA), and in earlier years Reconstruction Finance Corporation, Homeowners Loan Corporation, Federal Farm Mortgage Corporation, and Public Housing Administration. Also includes U.S.-sponsored agencies such as Federal National Mortgage Association (FNMA), Federal Land Banks, Federal Home Loan Mortgage Corporation (FHLMC), and mortgage pass-through securities issued or guaranteed by GNMA, FHLMC, FNMA or FmHA. Other U.S. agencies (amounts small or current separate data not readily available) included with "individuals and others."

[4] Includes private mortgage pools.

Source: Board of Governors of the Federal Reserve System, based on data from various Government and private organizations.

TABLE B-73.—*Consumer credit outstanding, 1950–92*

[Amount outstanding (end of month); millions of dollars, seasonally adjusted]

Year and month	Total consumer credit	Installment credit [1] Total	Automobile	Revolving [2]	Other [3]	Noninstallment credit [4]
December:						
1950	23,295	15,166	6,035		9,131	8,129
1951	24,624	15,859	5,981		9,878	8,765
1952	29,766	20,121	7,651		12,470	9,645
1953	33,769	23,870	9,702		14,168	9,899
1954	35,027	24,470	9,755		14,715	10,557
1955	41,885	29,809	13,485		16,324	12,076
1956	45,503	32,660	14,499		18,161	12,843
1957	48,132	34,914	15,493		19,421	13,218
1958	48,356	34,736	14,267		20,469	13,620
1959	55,878	40,421	16,641		23,780	15,457
1960	60,035	44,335	18,108		26,227	15,700
1961	62,340	45,438	17,656		27,782	16,902
1962	68,231	50,375	20,001		30,374	17,856
1963	76,606	57,056	22,891		34,165	19,550
1964	85,989	64,674	25,865		38,809	21,315
1965	95,948	72,814	29,378		43,436	23,134
1966	101,839	78,162	31,024		47,138	23,677
1967	106,716	81,783	31,136		50,647	24,933
1968	117,231	90,112	34,352	2,022	53,738	27,119
1969	126,928	99,381	36,946	3,563	58,872	27,547
1970	131,600	103,905	36,348	4,900	62,657	27,695
1971	147,058	116,434	40,522	8,252	67,660	30,624
1972	166,009	131,258	47,835	9,391	74,032	34,751
1973	190,601	152,910	53,740	11,318	87,852	37,691
1974	199,365	162,203	54,241	13,232	94,730	37,162
1975	204,963	167,043	56,989	14,507	95,547	37,920
1976	228,162	187,782	66,821	16,595	104,366	40,380
1977	263,808	221,475	80,948	36,689	103,838	42,333
1978	308,272	261,976	98,739	45,202	118,035	46,296
1979	347,507	296,483	112,475	53,357	130,651	51,024
1980	350,269	298,154	111,991	55,111	131,053	52,115
1981	366,869	311,259	119,008	61,070	131,182	55,610
1982	383,132	325,805	125,945	66,454	133,406	57,327
1983	431,170	368,966	143,560	79,088	146,318	62,204
1984	511,315	442,602	173,564	100,280	168,758	68,713
1985	591,291	517,659	210,238	121,758	185,664	73,631
1986	647,982	572,006	247,772	135,825	188,408	75,976
1987	680,036	608,675	266,295	153,064	189,316	71,362
1988 [5]	729,121	662,553	285,364	174,269	202,921	66,568
1989	777,608	716,825	292,002	199,308	225,515	60,783
1990	793,978	735,338	284,993	222,950	227,395	58,640
1991	780,566	727,799	263,003	242,785	222,012	52,767
1991: Jan	792,534	732,760	283,318	222,262	227,181	59,774
Feb	792,338	732,436	281,120	225,320	225,996	59,903
Mar	792,268	733,182	279,277	228,749	225,156	59,085
Apr	792,701	733,227	276,963	230,437	225,827	59,475
May	792,032	731,724	273,389	232,297	226,038	60,309
June	789,996	730,109	270,789	233,399	225,922	59,887
July	788,095	728,823	268,897	234,654	225,273	59,272
Aug	785,414	727,311	266,620	236,294	224,396	58,103
Sept	783,993	727,449	264,621	238,987	223,842	56,543
Oct	781,129	729,225	264,420	241,436	223,369	51,904
Nov	781,242	727,960	262,383	242,573	223,004	53,283
Dec	780,566	727,799	263,003	242,785	222,012	52,767
1992: Jan	783,252	728,618	263,134	244,288	221,196	54,634
Feb	784,641	728,395	261,659	245,974	220,762	56,247
Mar	782,485	727,404	262,125	245,259	220,020	55,080
Apr	779,418	723,821	260,376	245,905	217,541	55,597
May	778,969	722,928	259,834	246,220	216,874	56,041
June	779,122	722,919	257,339	247,418	218,162	56,203
July	778,276	721,820	257,743	247,332	216,744	56,456
Aug	777,861	720,664	256,944	248,043	215,677	57,197
Sept	779,464	722,104	257,384	250,017	214,703	57,361
Oct	777,825	722,668	257,101	250,485	215,082	55,157
Nov [p]		723,890	257,809	250,585	215,496	

[1] Installment credit covers most short- and intermediate-term credit extended to individuals through regular business channels, usually to finance the purchase of consumer goods and services or to refinance debts incurred for such purposes, and scheduled to be repaid (or with the option of repayment) in two or more installments. Credit secured by real estate is generally excluded.
[2] Consists of credit cards at retailers, gasoline companies, and commercial banks, and check credit at commercial banks. Excludes 30-day charge credit held by travel and entertainment companies. Prior to 1968, included in "other," except gasoline companies included in noninstallment credit prior to 1971. Beginning 1977, includes open-end credit at retailers, previously included in "other." Also beginning 1977, some retail credit was reclassified from commercial into consumer credit.
[3] Includes mobile home loans and all other installment loans not included in autombile or revolving credit, such as loans for education, boats, trailers, or vacations. These loans may be secured or unsecured.
[4] Noninstallment credit is credit scheduled to be repaid in a lump sum, including single-payment loans, charge accounts, and service credit. Because of inconsistencies in the data and infrequent benchmarking, series is no longer published by the Federal Reserve Board on a regular basis. Data are shown here as a general indication of trends.
[5] Data newly available in January 1989 result in breaks in many series between December 1988 and subsequent months.

Source: Board of Governors of the Federal Reserve System.

434

GOVERNMENT FINANCE

TABLE B-74.—_Federal receipts, outlays, surplus or deficit, and debt, selected fiscal years, 1929–93_

[Billions of dollars; fiscal years]

Fiscal year or period	Total			On-budget			Off-budget			Gross Federal debt (end of period)		Addendum: Gross domestic product
	Receipts	Outlays	Surplus or deficit (−)	Receipts	Outlays	Surplus or deficit (−)	Receipts	Outlays	Surplus or deficit (−)	Total	Held by the public	
1929	3.9	3.1	0.7							[1] 16.9		
1933	2.0	4.6	−2.6							[1] 22.5		
1939	6.3	9.1	−2.8	5.8	9.2	−3.4	0.5	−0.0	0.5	48.2	41.4	87.8
1940	6.5	9.5	−2.9	6.0	9.5	−3.5	.6	−.0	.6	50.7	42.8	95.4
1941	8.7	13.7	−4.9	8.0	13.6	−5.6	.7	.0	.7	57.5	48.2	112.5
1942	14.6	35.1	−20.5	13.7	35.1	−21.3	.9	.1	.8	79.2	67.8	141.8
1943	24.0	78.6	−54.6	22.9	78.5	−55.6	1.1	.1	1.0	142.6	127.8	175.4
1944	43.7	91.3	−47.6	42.5	91.2	−48.7	1.3	.1	1.2	204.1	184.8	201.7
1945	45.2	92.7	−47.6	43.8	92.6	−48.7	1.3	.1	1.2	260.1	235.2	212.0
1946	39.3	55.2	−15.9	38.1	55.0	−17.0	1.2	.2	1.0	271.0	241.9	212.5
1947	38.5	34.5	4.0	37.1	34.2	2.9	1.5	.3	1.2	257.1	224.3	222.9
1948	41.6	29.8	11.8	39.9	29.4	10.5	1.6	.4	1.2	252.0	216.3	246.7
1949	39.4	38.8	.6	37.7	38.4	−.7	1.7	.4	1.3	252.6	214.3	262.7
1950	39.4	42.6	−3.1	37.3	42.0	−4.7	2.1	.5	1.6	256.9	219.0	265.8
1951	51.6	45.5	6.1	48.5	44.2	4.3	3.1	1.3	1.8	255.3	214.3	313.5
1952	66.2	67.7	−1.5	62.6	66.0	−3.4	3.6	1.7	1.9	259.1	214.8	340.5
1953	69.6	76.1	−6.5	65.5	73.8	−8.3	4.1	2.3	1.8	266.0	218.4	363.8
1954	69.7	70.9	−1.2	65.1	67.9	−2.8	4.6	2.9	1.7	270.8	224.5	368.0
1955	65.5	68.4	−3.0	60.4	64.5	−4.1	5.1	4.0	1.1	274.4	226.6	384.7
1956	74.6	70.6	3.9	68.2	65.7	2.5	6.4	5.0	1.5	272.7	222.2	416.3
1957	80.0	76.6	3.4	73.2	70.6	2.6	6.8	6.0	.8	272.3	219.3	438.3
1958	79.6	82.4	−2.8	71.6	74.9	−3.3	8.0	7.5	.5	279.7	226.3	448.1
1959	79.2	92.1	−12.8	71.0	83.1	−12.1	8.3	9.0	−.7	287.5	234.7	480.2
1960	92.5	92.2	.3	81.9	81.3	.5	10.6	10.9	−.2	290.5	236.8	504.6
1961	94.4	97.7	−3.3	82.3	86.0	−3.8	12.1	11.7	.4	292.6	238.4	517.0
1962	99.7	106.8	−7.1	87.4	93.3	−5.9	12.3	13.5	−1.3	302.9	248.0	555.2
1963	106.6	111.3	−4.8	92.4	96.4	−4.0	14.2	15.0	−.8	310.3	254.0	584.5
1964	112.6	118.5	−5.9	96.2	102.8	−6.5	16.4	15.7	.6	316.1	256.8	625.3
1965	116.8	118.2	−1.4	100.1	101.7	−1.6	16.7	16.5	.2	322.3	260.8	671.0
1966	130.8	134.5	−3.7	111.7	114.8	−3.1	19.1	19.7	−.6	328.5	263.7	735.4
1967	148.8	157.5	−8.6	124.4	137.0	−12.6	24.4	20.4	4.0	340.4	266.6	793.3
1968	153.0	178.1	−25.2	128.1	155.8	−27.7	24.9	22.3	2.6	368.7	289.5	847.2
1969	186.9	183.6	3.2	157.9	158.4	−.5	29.0	25.2	3.7	365.8	278.1	925.7
1970	192.8	195.6	−2.8	159.3	168.0	−8.7	33.5	27.6	5.9	380.9	283.2	985.4
1971	187.1	210.2	−23.0	151.3	177.3	−26.1	35.8	32.8	3.0	408.2	303.0	1,050.9
1972	207.3	230.7	−23.4	167.4	193.8	−26.4	39.9	36.9	3.1	435.9	322.4	1,147.8
1973	230.8	245.7	−14.9	184.7	200.1	−15.4	46.1	45.6	.5	466.3	340.9	1,274.0
1974	263.2	269.4	−6.1	209.3	217.3	−8.0	53.9	52.1	1.8	483.9	343.7	1,403.6
1975	279.1	332.3	−53.2	216.6	271.9	−55.3	62.5	60.4	2.0	541.9	394.7	1,509.8
1976	298.1	371.8	−73.7	231.7	302.2	−70.5	66.4	69.6	−3.2	629.0	477.4	1,684.2
Transition quarter	81.2	96.0	−14.7	63.2	76.6	−13.3	18.0	19.4	−1.4	643.6	495.5	445.0
1977	355.6	409.2	−53.7	278.7	328.5	−49.8	76.8	80.7	−3.9	706.4	549.1	1,917.2
1978	399.6	458.7	−59.2	314.2	369.1	−54.9	85.4	89.7	−4.3	776.6	607.1	2,155.0
1979	463.3	503.5	−40.2	365.3	403.5	−38.2	98.0	100.0	−2.0	828.9	639.8	2,429.5
1980	517.1	590.9	−73.8	403.9	476.6	−72.7	113.2	114.3	−1.1	908.5	709.3	2,644.1
1981	599.3	678.2	−79.0	469.1	543.1	−74.0	130.2	135.2	−5.0	994.3	784.8	2,964.4
1982	617.8	745.8	−128.0	474.3	594.4	−120.1	143.5	151.4	−7.9	1,136.8	919.2	3,122.2
1983	600.6	808.4	−207.8	453.2	661.3	−208.0	147.3	147.1	.2	1,371.2	1,131.0	3,316.5
1984	666.5	851.8	−185.4	500.4	686.0	−185.7	166.1	165.8	.3	1,564.1	1,300.0	3,695.0
1985	734.1	946.4	−212.3	547.9	769.6	−221.7	186.2	176.8	9.4	1,817.0	1,499.4	3,967.7
1986	769.1	990.3	−221.2	568.9	806.8	−238.0	200.2	183.5	16.7	2,120.1	1,736.2	4,219.0
1987	854.1	1,003.9	−149.8	640.7	810.1	−169.3	213.4	193.8	19.6	2,345.6	1,888.1	4,452.4
1988	909.0	1,064.1	−155.2	667.5	861.4	−194.0	241.5	202.7	38.8	2,600.8	2,050.3	4,808.4
1989	990.7	1,143.2	−152.5	727.0	932.3	−205.2	263.7	210.9	52.8	2,867.5	2,189.3	5,173.3
1990	1,031.3	1,252.7	−221.4	749.7	1,027.6	−278.0	281.7	225.1	56.6	3,206.3	2,410.4	5,467.1
1991	1,054.3	1,323.8	−269.5	760.4	1,082.1	−321.7	293.9	241.7	52.2	3,599.0	2,687.9	5,632.6
1992	1,091.6	1,381.8	−290.2	789.2	1,129.5	−340.3	302.4	252.3	50.1	4,002.7	2,998.6	5,868.6
1993 [2]	1,147.6	1,474.9	−327.3	828.2	1,208.1	−379.9	319.4	266.8	52.6	4,410.5	3,309.7	6,164.4

[1] Not strictly comparable with later data.
[2] Estimates.

Note.—Through fiscal year 1976, the fiscal year was on a July 1–June 30 basis; beginning October 1976 (fiscal year 1977), the fiscal year is on an October 1–September 30 basis. The 3-month period from July 1, 1976 through September 30, 1976 is a separate fiscal period known as the transition quarter.

Refunds of receipts are excluded from receipts and outlays.

See _Budget Baselines, Historical Data, and Alternatives for the Future_, January 1993, for additional information.

Sources: Department of Commerce (Bureau of Economic Analysis), Department of the Treasury, and Office of Management and Budget.

TABLE B-75.—*Federal receipts, outlays, and debt, fiscal years 1981-93*

[Millions of dollars; fiscal years]

Description	Actual						
	1981	1982	1983	1984	1985	1986	1987
RECEIPTS AND OUTLAYS:							
Total receipts	599,272	617,766	600,562	666,457	734,057	769,091	854,143
Total outlays	678,249	745,755	808,380	851,846	946,391	990,336	1,003,911
Total surplus or deficit (−)	−78,976	−127,989	−207,818	−185,388	−212,334	−221,245	−149,769
On-budget receipts	469,097	474,299	453,242	500,382	547,886	568,862	640,741
On-budget outlays	543,053	594,351	661,272	686,032	769,584	806,838	810,079
On-budget surplus or deficit (−)	−73,956	−120,052	−208,030	−185,650	−221,698	−237,976	−169,339
Off-budget receipts	130,176	143,467	147,320	166,075	186,171	200,228	213,402
Off-budget outlays	135,196	151,404	147,108	165,813	176,807	183,498	193,832
Off-budget surplus or deficit (−)	−5,020	−7,937	212	262	9,363	16,731	19,570
OUTSTANDING DEBT, END OF PERIOD:							
Gross Federal debt	994,298	1,136,798	1,371,164	1,564,110	1,816,974	2,120,082	2,345,578
Held by Government accounts	209,507	217,560	240,114	264,159	317,612	383,919	457,444
Held by the public	784,791	919,238	1,131,049	1,299,951	1,499,362	1,736,163	1,888,134
Federal Reserve System	124,466	134,497	155,527	155,122	169,806	190,855	212,040
Other	660,325	784,741	975,522	1,144,829	1,329,556	1,545,308	1,676,094
RECEIPTS: ON-BUDGET AND OFF-BUDGET	599,272	617,766	600,562	666,457	734,057	769,091	854,143
Individual income taxes	285,917	297,744	288,938	298,415	334,531	348,959	392,557
Corporation income taxes	61,137	49,207	37,022	56,893	61,331	63,143	83,926
Social insurance taxes and contributions	182,720	201,498	208,994	239,376	265,163	283,901	303,318
On-budget	52,545	58,031	61,674	73,301	78,992	83,673	89,916
Off-budget	130,176	143,467	147,320	166,075	186,171	200,228	213,402
Excise taxes	40,839	36,311	35,300	37,361	35,992	32,919	32,457
Estate and gift taxes	6,787	7,991	6,053	6,010	6,422	6,958	7,493
Customs duties and fees	8,083	8,854	8,655	11,370	12,079	13,327	15,085
Miscellaneous receipts:							
Deposits of earnings by Federal Reserve System	12,834	15,186	14,492	15,684	17,059	18,374	16,817
All other	956	975	1,108	1,347	1,480	1,510	2,490
OUTLAYS: ON-BUDGET AND OFF-BUDGET	678,249	745,755	808,380	851,846	946,391	990,336	1,003,911
National defense	157,513	185,309	209,903	227,413	252,748	273,375	281,999
International affairs	13,104	12,300	11,848	15,876	16,176	14,152	11,649
General science, space, and technology	6,469	7,200	7,935	8,317	8,627	8,976	9,216
Energy	15,166	13,527	9,353	7,086	5,685	4,735	4,115
Natural resources and environment	13,568	12,998	12,672	12,593	13,357	13,639	13,363
Agriculture	11,323	15,944	22,901	13,613	25,565	31,449	26,606
Commerce and housing credit	8,206	6,256	6,681	6,917	4,229	4,890	6,182
On-budget	8,206	6,256	6,681	6,917	4,229	4,890	6,182
Off-budget							
Transportation	23,379	20,625	21,334	23,669	25,838	28,117	26,222
Community and regional development	10,568	8,347	7,560	7,673	7,680	7,233	5,051
Education, training, employment, and social services	33,709	27,029	26,606	27,579	29,342	30,585	29,724
Health	26,866	27,445	28,641	30,417	33,542	35,936	39,967
Medicare	39,149	46,567	52,588	57,540	65,822	70,164	75,120
Income security	99,723	107,717	122,598	112,668	128,200	119,796	123,250
Social security	139,584	155,964	170,724	178,223	188,623	198,757	207,353
On-budget	670	844	19,993	7,056	5,189	8,072	4,930
Off-budget	138,914	155,120	150,731	171,167	183,434	190,684	202,422
Veterans benefits and services	22,991	23,958	24,846	25,614	26,292	26,356	26,782
Administration of justice	4,769	4,712	5,105	5,663	6,270	6,572	7,553
General government	11,429	10,914	11,235	11,817	11,588	12,564	7,565
Net interest	68,774	85,044	89,828	111,123	129,504	136,047	138,652
On-budget	71,062	87,114	91,673	114,432	133,622	140,377	143,942
Off-budget	−2,288	−2,071	−1,845	−3,310	−4,118	−4,329	−5,290
Undistributed offsetting receipts	−28,041	−26,099	−33,976	−31,957	−32,698	−33,007	−36,455
On-budget	−26,611	−24,453	−32,198	−29,913	−30,189	−30,150	−33,155
Off-budget	−1,430	−1,646	−1,778	−2,044	−2,509	−2,857	−3,300

Note.—Through fiscal year 1976, the fiscal year was on a July 1–June 30 basis; beginning October 1976 (fiscal year 1977), the fiscal year is on an October 1–September 30 basis. The 3-month period from July 1, 1976 through September 30, 1976 is a separate fiscal period known as the transition quarter.

Refunds of receipts are excluded from receipts and outlays.

See next page for continuation of table.

TABLE B-75.—*Federal receipts, outlays, and debt, fiscal years 1981-93*—Continued

[Millions of dollars; fiscal years]

Description	Actual					Estimates
	1988	1989	1990	1991	1992	1993
RECEIPTS AND OUTLAYS:						
Total receipts	908,954	990,691	1,031,308	1,054,264	1,091,631	1,147,588
Total outlays	1,064,140	1,143,172	1,252,691	1,323,785	1,381,791	1,474,935
Total surplus or deficit (−)	− 155,187	− 152,481	− 221,384	− 269,521	− 290,160	− 327,347
On-budget receipts	667,463	727,026	749,652	760,380	789,205	828,183
On-budget outlays	861,449	932,261	1,027,626	1,082,098	1,129,475	1,208,120
On-budget surplus or deficit (−)	− 193,986	− 205,235	− 277,974	− 321,719	− 340,270	− 379,937
Off-budget receipts	241,491	263,666	281,656	293,885	302,426	319,405
Off-budget outlays	202,691	210,911	225,065	241,687	252,316	266,815
Off-budget surplus or deficit (−)	38,800	52,754	56,590	52,198	50,110	52,590
OUTSTANDING DEBT, END OF PERIOD:						
Gross Federal debt	2,600,760	2,867,537	3,206,347	3,598,993	4,002,669	4,410,475
Held by Government accounts	550,507	678,210	795,990	911,060	1,004,039	1,100,758
Held by the public	2,050,252	2,189,327	2,410,357	2,687,933	2,998,630	3,309,717
Federal Reserve System	229,218	220,088	234,410	258,591	296,397	
Other	1,821,034	1,969,239	2,175,947	2,429,342	2,702,234	
RECEIPTS: ON-BUDGET AND OFF-BUDGET	908,954	990,691	1,031,308	1,054,264	1,091,631	1,147,588
Individual income taxes	401,181	445,690	466,884	467,827	476,465	510,388
Corporation income taxes	94,508	103,291	93,507	98,086	100,270	105,501
Social insurance taxes and contributions	334,335	359,416	380,047	396,016	413,689	435,831
On-budget	92,845	95,751	98,392	102,131	111,263	116,426
Off-budget	241,491	263,666	281,656	293,885	302,426	319,405
Excise taxes	35,227	34,386	35,345	42,402	45,569	47,539
Estate and gift taxes	7,594	8,745	11,500	11,138	11,143	12,594
Customs duties and fees	16,198	16,334	16,707	15,949	17,359	18,176
Miscellaneous receipts:						
Deposits of earnings by Federal Reserve System	17,163	19,604	24,319	19,158	22,920	13,090
All other	2,747	3,225	2,997	3,688	4,215	4,469
OUTLAYS: ON-BUDGET AND OFF-BUDGET	1,064,140	1,143,172	1,252,691	1,323,785	1,381,791	1,474,935
National defense	290,361	303,559	299,331	273,292	298,361	289,299
International affairs	10,471	9,573	13,764	15,851	16,106	18,704
General science, space, and technology	10,841	12,838	14,444	16,111	16,409	17,142
Energy	2,297	2,706	3,341	2,436	4,509	4,807
Natural resources and environment	14,606	16,182	17,067	18,552	20,017	21,462
Agriculture	17,210	16,919	11,958	15,183	14,997	21,533
Commerce and housing credit	18,815	29,211	67,142	75,639	9,514	22,141
On-budget	18,815	29,520	65,516	74,321	8,877	20,514
Off-budget		− 310	1,626	1,317	636	1,627
Transportation	27,272	27,608	29,485	31,099	33,337	36,380
Community and regional development	5,294	5,362	8,498	6,811	7,411	10,086
Education, training, employment, and social services	31,938	36,674	38,755	43,354	45,248	52,292
Health	44,487	48,390	57,716	71,183	89,570	104,979
Medicare	78,878	84,964	98,102	104,489	119,024	132,839
Income security	129,332	136,031	147,019	170,301	198,073	207,433
Social security	219,341	232,542	248,623	269,015	287,545	304,747
On-budget	4,852	5,069	3,625	2,619	6,127	6,023
Off-budget	214,489	227,473	244,998	266,395	281,418	298,724
Veterans benefits and services	29,428	30,066	29,112	31,349	34,133	35,575
Administration of justice	9,236	9,474	9,995	12,276	14,450	15,229
General government	9,464	9,017	10,734	11,661	12,939	14,728
Net interest	151,838	169,266	184,221	194,541	199,429	202,771
On-budget	159,253	180,661	200,212	214,763	223,066	229,793
Off-budget	− 7,416	− 11,395	− 15,991	− 20,222	− 23,637	− 27,022
Undistributed offsetting receipts	− 36,967	− 37,212	− 36,615	− 39,356	− 39,280	− 37,213
On-budget	− 32,585	− 32,354	− 31,048	− 33,553	− 33,179	− 30,698
Off-budget	− 4,382	− 4,858	− 5,567	− 5,804	− 6,101	− 6,515

See *Budget Baselines, Historical Data, and Alternatives for the Future,* January 1993, for additional information.

Sources: Department of the Treasury and Office of Management and Budget.

TABLE B-76.—*Federal budget receipts, outlays, surplus or deficit, and debt, as percentages of gross domestic product, 1934-93*

[Percent; fiscal years]

Fiscal year or period	Receipts	Outlays		Surplus or deficit (−)	Gross Federal debt (end of period)	
		Total	National defense		Total	Held by public
1934	4.9	10.8		−5.9		
1935	5.3	9.3		−4.1		
1936	5.1	10.6		−5.6		
1937	6.2	8.7		−2.5		
1938	7.7	7.8		−.1		
1939	7.2	10.4		−3.2		
1940	6.9	9.9	1.7	−3.1	53.1	44.8
1941	7.7	12.1	5.7	−4.4	51.1	42.9
1942	10.3	24.8	18.1	−14.5	55.9	47.8
1943	13.7	44.8	38.0	−31.1	81.3	72.8
1944	21.7	45.3	39.2	−23.6	101.2	91.6
1945	21.3	43.7	39.1	−22.4	122.7	110.9
1946	18.5	26.0	20.1	−7.5	127.5	113.8
1947	17.3	15.5	5.7	1.8	115.4	100.6
1948	16.8	12.1	3.7	4.8	102.2	87.7
1949	15.0	14.8	5.0	.2	96.2	81.6
1950	14.8	16.0	5.2	−1.2	96.6	82.4
1951	16.5	14.5	7.5	1.9	81.4	68.4
1952	19.4	19.9	13.5	−.4	76.1	63.1
1953	19.1	20.9	14.5	−1.8	73.1	60.0
1954	18.9	19.3	13.4	−.3	73.6	61.0
1955	17.0	17.8	11.1	−.8	71.3	58.9
1956	17.9	17.0	10.2	.9	65.5	53.4
1957	18.3	17.5	10.4	.8	62.1	50.0
1958	17.8	18.4	10.4	−.6	62.4	50.5
1959	16.5	19.2	10.2	−2.7	59.9	48.9
1960	18.3	18.3	9.5	.1	57.6	46.9
1961	18.3	18.9	9.6	−.6	56.6	46.1
1962	18.0	19.2	9.4	−1.3	54.6	44.7
1963	18.2	19.0	9.1	−.8	53.1	43.5
1964	18.0	19.0	8.8	−.9	50.5	41.1
1965	17.4	17.6	7.5	−.2	48.0	38.9
1966	17.8	18.3	7.9	−.5	44.7	35.9
1967	18.8	19.8	9.0	−1.1	42.9	33.6
1968	18.1	21.0	9.7	−3.0	43.5	34.2
1969	20.2	19.8	8.9	.4	39.5	30.0
1970	19.6	19.9	8.3	−.3	38.7	28.7
1971	17.8	20.0	7.5	−2.2	38.8	28.8
1972	18.1	20.1	6.9	−2.0	38.0	28.1
1973	18.1	19.3	6.0	−1.2	36.6	26.8
1974	18.8	19.2	5.7	−.4	34.5	24.5
1975	18.5	22.0	5.7	−3.5	35.9	26.1
1976	17.7	22.1	5.3	−4.4	37.3	28.3
Transition quarter	18.3	21.6	5.0	−3.3	36.2	27.8
1977	18.5	21.3	5.1	−2.8	36.8	28.6
1978	18.5	21.3	4.8	−2.7	36.0	28.2
1979	19.1	20.7	4.8	−1.7	34.1	26.3
1980	19.6	22.3	5.1	−2.8	34.4	26.8
1981	20.2	22.9	5.3	−2.7	33.5	26.5
1982	19.8	23.9	5.9	−4.1	36.4	29.4
1983	18.1	24.4	6.3	−6.3	41.3	34.1
1984	18.0	23.1	6.2	−5.0	42.3	35.2
1985	18.5	23.9	6.4	−5.4	45.8	37.8
1986	18.2	23.5	6.5	−5.2	50.3	41.2
1987	19.2	22.5	6.3	−3.4	52.7	42.4
1988	18.9	22.1	6.0	−3.2	54.1	42.6
1989	19.2	22.1	5.9	−2.9	55.4	42.3
1990	18.9	22.9	5.5	−4.0	58.6	44.1
1991	18.7	23.5	4.9	−4.8	63.9	47.7
1992	18.6	23.5	5.1	−4.9	68.2	51.1
1993 [1]	18.6	23.9	4.7	−5.3	71.5	53.7

[1] Estimates.

Note.—Through fiscal year 1976, the fiscal year was on a July 1–June 30 basis; beginning October 1976 (fiscal year 1977), the fiscal year is on an October 1–September 30 basis. The 3-month period from July 1, 1976 through September 30, 1976 is a separate fiscal period known as the transition quarter.

See *Budget Baselines, Historical Data, and Alternatives for the Future,* January 1993, for additional information.

Sources: Department of the Treasury and Office of Management and Budget.

TABLE B-77.—*Federal and State and local government receipts and expenditures, national income and product accounts, 1959–92*

[Billions of dollars; quarterly data at seasonally adjusted annual rates]

Year or quarter	Total government		Surplus or deficit (−), national income and product accounts	Federal Government		Surplus or deficit (−), national income and product accounts	State and local government		Surplus or deficit (−), national income and product accounts
	Receipts	Expenditures		Receipts	Expenditures		Receipts	Expenditures	
1959	128.8	131.9	−3.1	90.6	93.2	−2.6	45.0	45.5	−0.5
1960	138.8	135.2	3.6	97.0	93.4	3.5	48.3	48.3	.0
1961	144.1	147.1	−3.0	99.0	101.7	−2.6	52.4	52.7	−.4
1962	155.8	158.7	−2.9	107.2	110.6	−3.4	56.6	56.1	.5
1963	167.5	165.9	1.6	115.5	114.4	1.1	61.1	60.6	.4
1964	172.9	174.5	−1.6	116.2	118.8	−2.6	67.1	66.1	1.0
1965	187.0	185.8	1.2	125.8	124.6	1.3	72.3	72.3	.0
1966	210.7	211.6	−1.0	143.5	144.9	−1.4	81.5	81.1	.5
1967	226.4	240.2	−13.7	152.6	165.2	−12.7	89.8	90.9	−1.1
1968	260.9	265.5	−4.6	176.8	181.5	−4.7	102.7	102.6	.1
1969	294.0	284.0	10.0	199.6	191.0	8.5	114.8	113.3	1.5
1970	299.8	311.2	−11.5	195.2	208.5	−13.3	129.0	127.2	1.8
1971	318.9	338.1	−19.2	202.6	224.3	−21.7	145.3	142.8	2.5
1972	364.2	368.1	−3.9	232.0	249.3	−17.3	169.7	156.3	13.4
1973	408.5	401.6	6.9	263.7	270.3	−6.6	185.3	171.9	13.4
1974	450.7	455.2	−4.5	294.0	305.6	−11.6	200.6	193.5	7.1
1975	465.8	530.6	−64.8	294.8	364.2	−69.4	225.6	221.0	4.6
1976	532.6	570.9	−38.3	339.9	392.7	−52.9	253.9	239.3	14.6
1977	598.4	615.2	−16.8	384.0	426.4	−42.4	281.9	256.3	25.6
1978	673.2	670.3	2.9	441.2	469.3	−28.1	309.3	278.2	31.1
1979	754.7	745.3	9.4	504.7	520.3	−15.7	330.6	305.4	25.1
1980	825.7	861.0	−35.3	553.0	613.1	−60.1	361.4	336.6	24.8
1981	941.9	972.3	−30.3	639.0	697.8	−58.8	390.8	362.3	28.5
1982	960.5	1,069.1	−108.6	635.4	770.9	−135.5	409.0	382.1	26.9
1983	1,016.4	1,156.2	−139.8	660.0	840.0	−180.1	443.4	403.2	40.3
1984	1,123.6	1,232.4	−108.8	725.8	892.7	−166.9	492.2	434.1	58.1
1985	1,217.0	1,342.2	−125.3	788.6	969.9	−181.4	528.7	472.6	56.1
1986	1,290.8	1,437.5	−146.8	827.2	1,028.2	−201.0	571.2	517.0	54.3
1987	1,405.2	1,516.9	−111.7	913.8	1,065.6	−151.8	594.3	554.2	40.1
1988	1,492.4	1,590.7	−98.3	972.3	1,109.0	−136.6	631.3	593.0	38.4
1989	1,622.6	1,700.1	−77.5	1,059.3	1,181.6	−122.3	681.5	636.7	44.8
1990	1,704.4	1,840.5	−136.1	1,107.4	1,273.6	−166.2	729.3	699.2	30.1
1991	1,746.8	1,940.1	−193.3	1,122.2	1,332.7	−210.4	777.9	760.7	17.1
1982: IV	965.9	1,122.8	−156.9	632.3	815.7	−183.4	417.9	391.4	26.5
1983: IV	1,043.7	1,180.0	−136.3	671.1	855.7	−184.6	459.5	411.1	48.3
1984: IV	1,147.1	1,274.9	−127.8	739.8	926.6	−186.8	505.1	446.1	59.0
1985: IV	1,243.8	1,374.7	−130.9	803.6	990.8	−187.2	544.8	488.4	56.3
1986: IV	1,335.4	1,461.6	−126.2	856.8	1,034.3	−177.5	582.4	531.1	51.2
1987: IV	1,445.7	1,561.5	−115.8	943.5	1,096.3	−152.7	605.1	568.1	37.0
1988: IV	1,535.8	1,630.5	−94.7	1,000.6	1,135.5	−134.9	648.2	607.9	40.2
1989: I	1,597.9	1,664.0	−66.1	1,050.9	1,160.8	−110.0	662.8	618.9	43.9
II	1,625.4	1,686.9	−61.5	1,064.5	1,174.2	−109.7	678.0	629.8	48.2
III	1,622.8	1,705.1	−82.3	1,053.6	1,181.5	−128.0	687.4	641.7	45.7
IV	1,644.1	1,744.3	−100.2	1,068.3	1,209.8	−141.5	697.7	656.4	41.3
1990: I	1,671.7	1,803.4	−131.7	1,086.7	1,254.5	−167.8	713.1	677.0	36.1
II	1,699.5	1,822.6	−123.1	1,109.6	1,266.5	−156.9	722.1	688.3	33.8
III	1,724.1	1,839.4	−115.3	1,119.9	1,265.5	−145.6	735.4	705.0	30.3
IV	1,722.3	1,896.8	−174.4	1,113.3	1,307.9	−194.6	746.6	726.4	20.2
1991: I	1,724.3	1,859.6	−135.3	1,114.6	1,264.4	−149.9	754.0	739.4	14.6
II	1,734.7	1,930.4	−195.6	1,117.3	1,329.4	−212.2	769.3	752.8	16.5
III	1,757.8	1,963.3	−205.6	1,127.7	1,348.7	−221.0	783.5	768.1	15.4
IV	1,770.4	2,007.0	−236.6	1,129.4	1,388.1	−258.7	804.6	782.5	22.0
1992: I	1,796.0	2,068.6	−272.6	1,143.3	1,432.5	−289.2	817.8	801.2	16.6
II	1,809.6	2,094.9	−285.2	1,149.8	1,452.7	−302.9	834.0	816.3	17.7
III	1,821.5	2,116.6	−295.2	1,155.4	1,459.8	−304.4	840.0	830.8	9.2

Note.—Federal grants-in-aid to State and local governments are reflected in Federal expenditures and State and local receipts. Total government receipts and expenditures have been adjusted to eliminate this duplication.

Source: Department of Commerce, Bureau of Economic Analysis.

439

TABLE B-78.—*Federal and State and local government receipts and expenditures, national income and product accounts, by major type, 1959–92*

[Billions of dollars; quarterly data at seasonally adjusted annual rates]

Year or quarter	Receipts					Expenditures								Surplus or deficit (−), national income and product accounts	Addendum: Grants-in-aid to State and local governments
	Total	Personal tax and nontax receipts	Corporate profits tax accruals	Indirect business tax and nontax accruals	Contributions for social insurance	Total ¹	Purchases	Transfer payments	Net interest paid			Less: Dividends received by government ²	Subsidies less current surplus of government enterprises		
									Total	Interest paid	Less: Interest received				
1959	128.8	44.5	23.6	41.9	18.8	131.9	99.0	27.5	6.3				−0.9	−3.1	6.8
1960	138.8	48.7	22.7	45.5	21.9	135.2	99.8	29.3	6.9	10.1	3.3		−.8	3.6	6.5
1961	144.1	50.3	22.8	48.1	22.9	147.1	107.0	33.6	6.4	9.9	3.5		.2	−3.0	7.2
1962	155.8	54.8	24.0	51.7	25.4	158.7	116.8	34.7	6.9	10.8	3.9		.3	−2.9	8.0
1963	167.5	58.0	26.2	54.7	28.5	165.9	122.3	36.6	7.4	11.6	4.2		−.3	1.6	9.1
1964	172.9	56.0	28.0	58.8	30.1	174.5	128.3	38.1	7.9	12.5	4.6		.1	−1.6	10.4
1965	187.0	61.9	30.9	62.7	31.6	185.8	136.3	41.1	8.1	13.2	5.1		.3	1.2	11.1
1966	210.7	71.0	33.7	65.4	40.6	211.6	155.9	45.8	8.5	14.5	6.0		1.4	−1.0	14.4
1967	226.4	77.9	32.7	70.4	45.5	240.2	175.6	54.5	8.9	15.7	6.8		1.2	−13.7	15.9
1968	260.9	92.1	39.4	79.0	50.4	265.5	191.5	62.6	10.3	18.1	7.7	0.1	1.2	−4.6	18.6
1969	294.0	109.9	39.7	86.6	57.9	284.0	201.8	69.3	11.5	19.8	8.3	.2	1.5	10.0	20.3
1970	299.8	109.0	34.4	94.3	62.2	311.2	212.7	83.8	12.4	22.3	9.9	.2	2.6	−11.5	24.4
1971	318.9	108.7	37.7	103.6	68.9	338.1	224.3	99.4	12.5	23.1	10.6	.3	2.4	−19.2	29.0
1972	364.2	132.0	41.9	111.4	79.0	368.1	241.5	110.9	12.9	24.8	11.9	.3	3.4	−3.9	37.5
1973	408.5	140.6	49.3	121.0	97.6	401.6	257.7	126.6	15.2	29.6	14.4	.5	2.6	6.9	40.6
1974	450.7	159.1	51.8	129.3	110.5	455.2	288.3	150.5	16.3	33.6	17.3	.9	.4	−4.5	43.9
1975	465.8	156.4	50.9	140.0	118.5	530.6	321.4	189.2	18.5	37.7	19.2	.9	2.6	−64.8	54.6
1976	532.6	182.3	64.2	151.6	134.5	570.9	341.3	206.5	22.8	43.6	20.9	.9	1.4	−38.3	61.1
1977	598.4	210.0	73.0	165.5	149.8	615.2	368.0	220.9	24.4	47.9	23.5	1.3	3.3	−16.8	67.5
1978	673.2	240.1	83.5	177.8	171.8	670.3	403.6	238.6	26.5	56.8	30.3	1.7	3.6	2.9	77.3
1979	754.7	280.2	88.0	188.7	197.8	745.3	448.5	266.9	28.7	68.6	39.9	2.0	2.9	9.4	80.5
1980	825.7	312.4	84.8	212.0	216.6	861.0	507.1	317.6	33.4	83.9	50.5	1.9	4.8	−35.3	88.7
1981	941.9	360.2	81.1	249.3	251.3	972.3	561.1	360.7	48.1	110.2	62.1	2.3	4.7	−30.3	87.9
1982	960.5	371.4	63.1	256.4	269.6	1,069.1	607.6	402.7	55.5	130.6	75.0	2.9	6.2	−108.6	83.9
1983	1,016.4	368.8	77.2	280.1	290.2	1,156.2	652.3	433.4	61.8	146.6	84.8	3.4	11.7	−139.8	87.0
1984	1,123.6	395.1	94.0	309.5	325.0	1,232.4	700.8	447.2	79.1	174.6	95.6	3.9	9.5	−108.8	94.4
1985	1,217.0	436.8	96.5	329.9	353.8	1,342.2	772.3	479.5	88.3	195.9	107.6	4.5	6.4	−125.3	100.3
1986	1,290.8	459.0	106.5	345.5	379.8	1,437.5	833.0	509.4	90.6	207.9	117.3	5.1	9.7	−146.8	107.6
1987	1,405.2	512.5	127.1	365.0	400.7	1,516.9	881.5	531.8	95.4	215.9	120.5	5.9	14.1	−111.7	102.8
1988	1,492.4	527.7	137.0	385.3	442.3	1,590.7	918.7	566.2	101.8	229.9	128.1	6.9	10.9	−98.3	111.3
1989	1,622.6	593.3	141.3	414.7	473.2	1,700.1	975.2	615.1	112.4	251.0	138.6	8.1	5.4	−77.5	118.2
1990	1,704.4	621.3	136.7	444.2	502.3	1,840.5	1,043.2	678.0	124.2	269.9	145.7	9.0	4.2	−136.1	132.3
1991	1,746.8	618.7	124.0	475.2	528.8	1,940.1	1,090.5	720.0	138.5	284.6	146.1	9.5	.5	−193.3	153.3
1982: IV	965.9	372.1	58.7	262.3	272.8	1,122.8	631.6	428.1	56.6	135.6	79.0	3.1	9.6	−156.9	84.3
1983: IV	1,043.7	371.6	82.2	291.7	298.3	1,180.0	657.6	439.1	67.7	156.1	88.4	3.5	19.2	−136.3	86.9
1984: IV	1,147.1	413.4	83.8	317.7	332.2	1,274.9	727.0	456.2	86.7	186.5	99.8	4.1	9.7	−127.8	97.7
1985: IV	1,243.8	448.8	97.6	335.1	362.3	1,374.7	799.2	488.3	89.2	201.6	112.3	4.7	2.6	−130.9	104.5
1986: IV	1,335.4	478.5	116.6	351.6	388.7	1,461.6	849.7	518.6	90.5	208.7	118.2	5.4	8.2	−126.2	103.8
1987: IV	1,445.7	528.6	135.2	372.3	409.6	1,561.5	901.4	542.6	101.3	222.9	121.6	6.1	22.0	−115.8	102.9
1988: IV	1,535.8	542.0	146.2	394.2	453.5	1,630.5	937.6	578.6	105.0	236.0	131.0	7.2	16.5	−94.7	113.0
1989: I	1,597.9	575.2	154.8	401.7	466.3	1,664.0	950.4	595.9	110.2	244.5	134.3	7.6	15.2	−66.1	115.7
II	1,625.4	599.1	143.7	411.6	471.0	1,686.9	970.2	605.0	113.9	250.9	137.1	8.0	5.8	−61.5	117.1
III	1,622.8	593.8	132.6	421.0	475.3	1,705.1	985.6	620.6	110.9	252.6	141.8	8.2	−3.9	−82.3	118.2
IV	1,644.1	605.1	134.2	424.4	480.4	1,744.3	994.5	639.0	114.8	256.0	141.2	8.5	4.4	−100.2	121.9
1990: I	1,671.7	609.4	132.4	436.0	493.9	1,803.4	1,024.7	660.1	117.8	260.2	142.4	8.7	9.5	−131.7	128.1
II	1,699.5	624.6	137.6	437.7	499.6	1,822.6	1,034.3	670.6	124.0	266.5	142.4	9.0	2.7	−123.1	132.2
III	1,724.1	627.3	143.0	447.3	506.5	1,839.4	1,042.4	680.4	131.3	274.5	143.2	9.0	−5.6	−115.3	131.2
IV	1,722.3	623.8	133.7	455.7	509.1	1,896.8	1,071.3	700.8	123.8	278.7	154.8	9.3	10.3	−174.4	137.6
1991: I	1,724.3	616.8	121.3	464.7	521.5	1,859.6	1,087.5	646.4	132.7	280.6	148.0	9.3	2.5	−135.3	144.3
II	1,734.7	617.2	122.9	468.2	526.5	1,930.4	1,090.8	708.0	139.2	284.5	145.3	9.5	1.6	−195.6	151.9
III	1,757.8	618.6	127.0	480.0	532.1	1,963.3	1,093.3	747.8	138.9	285.4	146.5	9.5	−7.1	−205.6	153.4
IV	1,770.4	622.3	125.0	487.9	535.2	2,007.0	1,090.3	777.8	143.5	288.0	144.5	9.6	5.1	−236.6	163.6
1992: I	1,796.0	619.6	136.4	493.8	546.2	2,068.6	1,103.1	830.6	141.4	285.7	144.3	9.7	3.2	−272.6	165.1
II	1,809.6	617.1	144.1	497.6	550.8	2,094.9	1,109.1	848.9	143.2	288.1	144.9	10.0	3.6	−285.2	174.1
III	1,821.5	628.8	131.8	506.4	554.4	2,116.6	1,124.2	861.3	144.5	287.9	143.4	10.1	−3.4	−295.2	174.0

¹ Includes an item for the difference between wage accruals and disbursements, not shown separately.
² Prior to 1968, dividends received is included in interest received.

Source: Department of Commerce, Bureau of Economic Analysis.

TABLE B-79.—*Federal Government receipts and expenditures, national income and product accounts,*
1976-92

[Billions of dollars; quarterly data at seasonally adjusted annual rates]

Year or quarter	Receipts					Expenditures								Surplus or deficit (−), national income and product accounts
	Total	Personal tax and nontax receipts	Corporate rate profits tax accruals	Indirect business tax and nontax accruals	Contributions for social insurance	Total[1]	Purchases		Transfer payments		Grants-in-aid to State and local governments	Net interest paid	Subsidies less current surplus of government enterprises	
							Total	National defense	To persons	To rest of the world (net)				
Fiscal: [2]														
1976	322.0	136.5	51.7	24.6	109.2	379.0	132.6	91.5	154.3	3.1	57.5	25.1	6.5	−57.0
1977	375.4	165.2	59.8	25.0	125.4	417.1	144.7	99.2	167.1	3.4	66.3	28.5	7.2	−41.7
1978	423.8	185.5	67.4	27.9	143.0	458.0	158.1	106.3	179.3	3.5	74.7	33.1	9.4	−34.1
1979	490.5	221.6	75.3	29.9	163.7	505.4	174.5	117.7	198.5	4.0	79.1	40.2	9.1	−14.9
1980	538.1	249.1	70.4	36.2	182.3	587.1	201.0	136.9	235.4	4.3	86.7	50.1	9.6	−49.0
1981	623.0	287.9	69.3	54.3	211.5	679.9	232.9	160.9	274.6	5.2	90.1	66.1	11.0	−56.9
1982	642.7	308.4	51.6	51.5	231.2	747.6	259.5	187.3	305.6	5.8	83.4	81.8	11.5	−105.0
1983	646.4	290.7	56.4	52.0	247.3	829.2	289.8	210.2	339.8	6.5	86.2	89.6	16.8	−182.8
1984	711.7	300.4	75.1	57.0	279.3	875.3	302.2	228.2	342.4	8.7	91.5	107.5	23.0	−163.6
1985	777.0	337.0	75.0	59.1	305.9	952.9	335.2	251.7	360.7	11.5	98.6	125.2	21.6	−175.9
1986	813.8	353.1	80.4	53.8	326.5	1,017.6	363.7	274.3	380.6	12.5	108.3	130.5	22.1	−203.9
1987	899.1	396.3	99.4	57.9	345.5	1,051.0	379.9	287.6	399.4	9.9	103.4	133.6	24.9	−151.9
1988	955.1	403.8	107.6	59.6	384.1	1,098.5	386.3	295.1	420.7	10.2	108.4	143.8	28.9	−143.3
1989	1,050.1	456.9	119.2	62.2	411.8	1,164.5	399.4	299.5	449.6	11.6	115.8	160.5	27.6	−114.3
1990	1,089.6	473.2	113.8	63.8	438.7	1,249.5	417.6	308.9	490.5	14.0	128.3	175.1	23.9	−159.9
1991	1,114.9	472.1	104.4	74.8	463.5	1,310.9	447.1	326.6	536.1	−25.4	146.9	183.1	23.1	−196.1
1992	1,144.5	470.1	110.5	80.3	483.6	1,433.3	446.5	314.9	594.8	9.7	169.2	188.1	25.1	−288.8
Calendar:														
1976	339.9	146.6	54.6	23.8	115.0	392.7	135.8	93.4	159.3	3.7	61.1	26.8	6.2	−52.9
1977	384.0	169.1	61.6	25.6	127.7	426.4	147.9	100.9	170.1	3.4	67.5	29.1	8.4	−42.4
1978	441.2	193.8	71.4	28.9	147.1	469.3	162.2	108.9	182.4	3.8	77.3	34.6	9.2	−28.1
1979	504.7	229.7	74.4	30.1	170.4	520.3	179.3	121.9	205.7	4.1	80.5	42.1	8.7	−15.7
1980	553.0	256.2	70.3	39.6	186.8	613.1	209.1	142.7	247.0	5.0	88.7	52.7	10.6	−60.1
1981	639.0	297.2	65.7	57.3	218.8	697.8	240.8	167.5	282.1	5.0	87.9	71.7	10.3	−58.8
1982	635.4	302.9	49.0	49.7	233.8	770.9	266.6	193.8	316.4	6.4	83.9	84.4	13.3	−135.5
1983	660.0	292.6	61.3	53.5	252.6	840.0	292.0	214.4	340.2	7.3	87.0	92.7	20.4	−180.1
1984	725.8	308.0	75.2	57.8	284.8	892.7	310.9	233.1	344.3	9.4	94.4	113.1	20.8	−166.9
1985	788.6	342.8	76.3	58.6	310.9	969.9	344.3	258.6	366.8	11.4	100.3	127.0	19.9	−181.4
1986	827.2	357.4	83.8	53.5	332.5	1,028.2	367.8	276.7	386.2	12.3	107.6	131.0	23.4	−201.0
1987	913.8	400.6	103.2	58.4	351.5	1,065.6	384.9	292.1	401.8	10.4	102.8	136.6	29.1	−151.8
1988	972.3	410.1	111.0	60.9	390.4	1,109.0	387.0	295.6	425.9	10.4	111.3	146.0	28.4	−136.6
1989	1,059.3	461.9	117.1	61.9	418.5	1,181.6	401.6	299.9	460.2	11.3	118.2	164.8	25.5	−122.3
1990	1,107.4	482.6	113.9	66.0	444.9	1,273.6	426.4	314.0	499.9	13.4	132.3	176.6	25.1	−166.2
1991	1,122.2	473.4	102.5	78.2	468.2	1,332.7	447.3	323.8	550.2	−28.3	153.3	186.9	23.1	−210.4
1982: IV	632.3	301.6	45.5	49.2	235.9	815.7	281.4	205.5	337.8	8.2	84.3	86.8	17.3	−183.4
1983: IV	671.1	290.5	65.4	55.4	259.8	855.7	289.7	222.8	340.0	11.0	86.9	99.2	28.8	−184.6
1984: IV	739.8	323.5	67.0	58.2	291.1	926.6	324.7	242.9	346.2	13.9	97.7	122.3	22.2	−186.8
1985: IV	803.6	351.8	77.0	56.8	318.0	990.8	356.9	268.6	370.3	13.5	104.5	129.2	16.4	−187.2
1986: IV	856.8	371.7	91.4	54.8	338.8	1,034.3	373.1	278.6	391.4	12.8	103.8	131.1	22.1	−177.5
1987: IV	943.5	414.8	109.7	59.5	359.4	1,096.3	392.5	295.8	405.1	14.6	102.9	143.1	37.8	−152.7
1988: IV	1,000.6	420.0	118.5	61.4	400.7	1,135.5	392.0	296.8	429.4	15.1	113.0	151.2	34.9	−134.9
1989: I	1,050.9	449.4	127.8	61.0	412.6	1,160.8	392.3	293.5	448.5	10.0	115.7	159.8	34.6	−110.0
II	1,064.5	467.3	119.1	61.6	416.5	1,174.2	401.6	298.2	455.1	8.6	117.1	165.8	25.9	−109.7
III	1,053.6	460.6	110.0	62.8	420.1	1,181.5	407.3	305.3	463.6	11.5	118.2	164.4	16.6	−128.0
IV	1,068.3	470.1	111.3	62.2	424.7	1,209.8	405.1	302.5	473.7	15.1	121.9	168.9	25.0	−141.5
1990: I	1,086.7	474.0	110.3	64.8	437.6	1,254.5	420.3	311.6	492.8	12.0	128.1	171.4	29.9	−167.8
II	1,109.6	487.2	114.6	65.2	442.7	1,266.5	424.4	312.9	494.2	15.5	132.2	176.9	23.2	−156.9
III	1,119.9	486.6	119.2	65.4	448.8	1,265.5	422.6	308.4	499.8	13.3	131.2	183.3	15.3	−145.6
IV	1,113.3	482.5	111.7	68.5	450.6	1,307.9	438.3	323.2	512.7	12.8	137.6	174.8	32.0	−194.6
1991: I	1,114.6	474.7	100.3	77.3	462.2	1,264.4	451.3	332.4	538.0	−76.4	144.3	182.7	24.8	−149.9
II	1,117.3	473.1	101.6	76.3	466.3	1,329.4	449.9	325.9	546.6	−31.8	151.9	188.1	24.4	−212.2
III	1,127.7	473.4	104.9	78.3	471.1	1,348.7	447.2	321.9	551.7	−6.2	153.4	186.8	15.7	−221.0
IV	1,129.4	472.2	103.3	80.8	473.2	1,388.1	440.8	314.7	564.7	1.3	163.6	190.1	27.7	−258.7
1992: I	1,143.3	468.4	112.2	79.2	483.5	1,432.5	445.0	313.6	597.8	12.0	165.1	186.8	25.7	−289.2
II	1,149.8	464.2	118.3	79.8	487.4	1,452.7	444.8	311.7	605.9	13.6	174.1	187.5	26.9	−302.9
III	1,155.4	475.5	108.2	81.3	490.4	1,459.8	455.2	319.6	610.6	12.0	174.0	187.8	20.2	−304.4

[1] Includes an item for the difference between wage accruals and disbursements, not shown separately.
[2] Through fiscal year 1976, the fiscal year was on a July 1–June 30 basis; beginning October 1976 (fiscal year 1977), the fiscal year is on an October 1–September 30 basis. The 3-month period from July 1, 1976 through September 30, 1976 is a separate fiscal period known as the transition quarter. Data are not seasonally adjusted.

Sources: Department of Commerce (Bureau of Economic Analysis) and Office of Management and Budget.

TABLE B–80.—*State and local government receipts and expenditures, national income and product accounts, 1959–92*

[Billions of dollars; quarterly data at seasonally adjusted annual rates]

Year or quarter	Receipts						Expenditures					Surplus or deficit (−), national income and product accounts
	Total	Personal tax and nontax receipts	Corporate rate profits tax accruals	Indirect business tax and nontax accruals	Contributions for social insurance	Federal grants-in-aid	Total [1]	Purchases	Transfer payments to persons	Net interest paid less dividends received	Subsidies less current surplus of government enterprises	
1959	45.0	4.6	1.2	29.3	3.1	6.8	45.5	41.8	5.6	0.1	−2.0	−0.5
1960	48.3	5.2	1.2	32.0	3.4	6.5	48.3	44.5	5.9	.1	−2.2	.0
1961	52.4	5.7	1.3	34.4	3.7	7.2	52.7	48.4	6.5	.1	−2.3	−.4
1962	56.6	6.3	1.5	37.0	3.9	8.0	56.1	51.4	7.0	.2	−2.5	.5
1963	61.1	6.7	1.7	39.4	4.2	9.1	60.6	55.8	7.5	.1	−2.8	.4
1964	67.1	7.5	1.8	42.6	4.7	10.4	66.1	60.9	8.2	−.1	−2.8	1.0
1965	72.3	8.1	2.0	46.1	5.0	11.1	72.3	66.8	8.8	−.3	−3.0	.0
1966	81.5	9.5	2.2	49.7	5.7	14.4	81.1	74.6	10.1	−.6	−3.0	.5
1967	89.8	10.6	2.6	53.9	6.7	15.9	90.9	82.7	12.1	−.9	−3.1	−1.1
1968	102.7	12.7	3.3	60.8	7.2	18.6	102.6	92.3	14.5	−1.1	−3.2	.1
1969	114.8	15.2	3.6	67.4	8.3	20.3	113.3	101.3	16.7	−1.3	−3.3	1.5
1970	129.0	16.7	3.7	74.8	9.2	24.4	127.2	112.6	20.1	−2.0	−3.6	1.8
1971	145.3	18.7	4.3	83.1	10.2	29.0	142.8	124.3	24.0	−1.6	−3.7	2.5
1972	169.7	24.2	5.3	91.2	11.5	37.5	156.3	134.7	27.5	−1.8	−4.2	13.4
1973	185.3	26.3	6.0	99.5	13.0	40.6	171.9	149.2	30.4	−3.3	−4.3	13.4
1974	200.6	28.2	6.7	107.2	14.6	43.9	193.5	170.7	32.3	−5.2	−4.4	7.1
1975	225.6	31.0	7.3	115.8	16.8	54.6	221.0	192.0	38.9	−5.4	−4.5	4.6
1976	253.9	35.8	9.6	127.8	19.5	61.1	239.3	205.5	43.6	−5.0	−4.8	14.6
1977	281.9	41.0	11.4	139.9	22.1	67.5	256.3	220.1	47.4	−6.0	−5.1	25.6
1978	309.3	46.3	12.1	148.9	24.7	77.3	278.2	241.4	52.4	−9.8	−5.6	31.1
1979	330.6	50.5	13.6	158.6	27.4	80.5	305.4	269.2	57.2	−15.3	−5.7	25.1
1980	361.4	56.2	14.5	172.3	29.7	88.7	336.6	298.0	65.7	−21.2	−5.8	24.8
1981	390.8	63.0	15.4	192.0	32.5	87.9	362.3	320.3	73.6	−25.9	−5.6	28.5
1982	409.0	68.5	14.0	206.8	35.8	83.9	382.1	341.1	79.9	−31.8	−7.1	26.9
1983	443.4	76.2	15.9	226.6	37.7	87.0	403.2	360.3	85.9	−34.3	−8.7	40.3
1984	492.2	87.1	18.8	251.7	40.2	94.4	434.1	389.9	93.5	−37.9	−11.4	58.1
1985	528.7	94.0	20.2	271.4	42.8	100.3	472.6	428.1	101.2	−43.2	−13.5	56.1
1986	571.2	101.6	22.7	292.0	47.3	107.6	517.0	465.3	110.9	−45.6	−13.7	54.3
1987	594.3	111.8	23.9	306.5	49.2	102.8	554.2	496.6	119.6	−47.0	−14.9	40.1
1988	631.3	117.6	26.0	324.5	51.9	111.3	593.0	531.7	130.0	−51.1	−17.5	38.4
1989	681.5	131.4	24.2	352.8	54.8	118.2	636.7	573.6	143.6	−60.4	−20.1	44.8
1990	729.3	138.7	22.7	378.2	57.3	132.3	699.2	616.8	164.7	−61.4	−20.9	30.1
1991	777.9	145.4	21.5	397.0	60.6	153.3	760.7	643.2	198.0	−57.9	−22.6	17.1
1982: IV	417.9	70.5	13.1	213.1	36.8	84.3	391.4	350.3	82.1	−33.2	−7.7	26.5
1983: IV	459.5	81.1	16.8	236.3	38.4	86.9	411.1	367.9	88.0	−35.1	−9.6	48.3
1984: IV	505.1	89.9	16.8	259.6	41.1	97.7	446.1	402.2	96.1	−39.7	−12.5	59.0
1985: IV	544.8	97.0	20.6	278.3	44.3	104.5	488.4	442.4	104.5	−44.7	−13.8	56.3
1986: IV	582.4	106.8	25.2	296.8	49.8	103.8	531.1	476.6	114.4	−45.9	−13.9	51.2
1987: IV	605.1	113.8	25.5	312.8	50.2	102.9	568.1	509.0	122.9	−48.0	−15.8	37.0
1988: IV	648.2	122.0	27.7	332.7	52.8	113.0	607.9	545.7	134.2	−53.4	−18.5	40.2
1989: I	662.8	128.5	26.9	340.7	53.7	115.7	618.9	558.1	137.3	−57.2	−19.4	43.9
II	678.0	131.8	24.6	350.0	54.5	117.1	629.8	568.6	141.3	−60.0	−20.0	48.2
III	687.4	133.2	22.6	358.2	55.2	118.2	641.7	578.4	144.5	−61.8	−20.5	45.7
IV	697.7	135.0	22.8	362.2	55.8	121.9	656.4	589.3	150.2	−62.6	−20.6	41.3
1990: I	713.1	135.5	22.1	371.2	56.3	128.1	677.0	604.3	155.4	−62.3	−20.4	36.1
II	722.1	137.4	23.0	372.5	56.9	132.2	688.3	610.0	160.8	−61.9	−20.6	33.8
III	735.4	140.7	23.8	382.0	57.7	131.2	705.0	619.7	167.3	−61.0	−21.0	30.3
IV	746.6	141.3	22.0	387.2	58.5	137.6	726.4	633.0	175.4	−60.3	−21.6	20.2
1991: I	754.0	142.1	21.0	387.4	59.2	144.3	739.4	636.3	184.8	−59.4	−22.3	14.6
II	769.3	144.1	21.3	391.9	60.2	151.9	752.8	640.8	193.2	−58.5	−22.8	16.5
III	783.5	145.2	22.1	401.7	61.0	153.4	768.1	646.0	202.3	−57.4	−22.9	15.4
IV	804.6	150.1	21.7	407.1	62.0	163.6	782.5	649.5	211.8	−56.2	−22.6	22.0
1992: I	817.8	151.1	24.2	414.6	62.7	165.1	801.2	658.0	220.8	−55.1	−22.5	16.6
II	834.0	152.9	25.8	417.8	63.4	174.1	816.3	664.3	229.4	−54.3	−23.2	17.7
III	840.0	153.3	23.6	425.1	64.0	174.0	830.8	669.0	238.7	−53.4	−23.6	9.2

[1] Includes an item for the difference between wage accruals and disbursements, not shown separately.

Source: Department of Commerce, Bureau of Economic Analysis.

TABLE B-81.—*State and local government revenues and expenditures, selected fiscal years, 1927–91*

[Millions of dollars]

Fiscal year[1]	General revenues by source[2]							General expenditures by function[2]				
	Total	Property taxes	Sales and gross receipts taxes	Individual income taxes	Corporation net income taxes	Revenue from Federal Government	All other[3]	Total	Education	Highways	Public welfare	All other[4]
1927	7,271	4,730	470	70	92	116	1,793	7,210	2,235	1,809	151	3,015
1932	7,267	4,487	752	74	79	232	1,643	7,765	2,311	1,741	444	3,269
1934	7,678	4,076	1,008	80	49	1,016	1,449	7,181	1,831	1,509	889	2,952
1936	8,395	4,093	1,484	153	113	948	1,604	7,644	2,177	1,425	827	3,215
1938	9,228	4,440	1,794	218	165	800	1,811	8,757	2,491	1,650	1,069	3,547
1940	9,609	4,430	1,982	224	156	945	1,872	9,229	2,638	1,573	1,156	3,862
1942	10,418	4,537	2,351	276	272	858	2,123	9,190	2,586	1,490	1,225	3,889
1944	10,908	4,604	2,289	342	451	954	2,269	8,863	2,793	1,200	1,133	3,737
1946	12,356	4,986	2,986	422	447	855	2,661	11,028	3,356	1,672	1,409	4,591
1948	17,250	6,126	4,442	543	592	1,861	3,685	17,684	5,379	3,036	2,099	7,170
1950	20,911	7,349	5,154	788	593	2,486	4,541	22,787	7,177	3,803	2,940	8,867
1952	25,181	8,652	6,357	998	846	2,566	5,763	26,098	8,318	4,650	2,788	10,342
1953	27,307	9,375	6,927	1,065	817	2,870	6,252	27,910	9,390	4,987	2,914	10,619
1954	29,012	9,967	7,276	1,127	778	2,966	6,897	30,701	10,557	5,527	3,060	11,557
1955	31,073	10,735	7,643	1,237	744	3,131	7,584	33,724	11,907	6,452	3,168	12,197
1956	34,667	11,749	8,691	1,538	890	3,335	8,465	36,711	13,220	6,953	3,139	13,399
1957	38,164	12,864	9,467	1,754	984	3,843	9,252	40,375	14,134	7,816	3,485	14,940
1958	41,219	14,047	9,829	1,759	1,018	4,865	9,699	44,851	15,919	8,567	3,818	16,547
1959	45,306	14,983	10,437	1,994	1,001	6,377	10,516	48,887	17,283	9,592	4,136	17,876
1960	50,505	16,405	11,849	2,463	1,180	6,974	11,634	51,876	18,719	9,428	4,404	19,325
1961	54,037	18,002	12,463	2,613	1,266	7,131	12,563	56,201	20,574	9,844	4,720	21,063
1962	58,252	19,054	13,494	3,037	1,308	7,871	13,489	60,206	22,216	10,357	5,084	22,549
1963	62,890	20,089	14,456	3,269	1,505	8,722	14,850	64,816	23,776	11,136	5,481	24,423
1962–63	62,269	19,833	14,446	3,267	1,505	8,663	14,556	63,977	23,729	11,150	5,420	23,678
1963–64	68,443	21,241	15,762	3,791	1,695	10,002	15,951	69,302	26,286	11,664	5,766	25,586
1964–65	74,000	22,583	17,118	4,090	1,929	11,029	17,250	74,678	28,563	12,221	6,315	27,579
1965–66	83,036	24,670	19,085	4,760	2,038	13,214	19,269	82,843	33,287	12,770	6,757	30,029
1966–67	91,197	26,047	20,530	5,825	2,227	15,370	21,197	93,350	37,919	13,932	8,218	33,281
1967–68	101,264	27,747	22,911	7,308	2,518	17,181	23,598	102,411	41,158	14,481	9,857	36,915
1968–69	114,550	30,673	26,519	8,908	3,180	19,153	26,118	116,728	47,238	15,417	12,110	41,963
1969–70	130,756	34,054	30,322	10,812	3,738	21,857	29,971	131,332	52,718	16,427	14,679	47,508
1970–71	144,927	37,852	33,233	11,900	3,424	26,146	32,374	150,674	59,413	18,095	18,226	54,940
1971–72	167,541	42,877	37,518	15,227	4,416	31,342	36,162	168,549	65,814	19,021	21,117	62,597
1972–73	190,222	45,283	42,047	17,994	5,425	39,264	40,210	181,357	69,714	18,615	23,582	69,446
1973–74	207,670	47,705	46,098	19,491	6,015	41,820	46,541	198,959	75,833	19,946	25,085	78,096
1974–75	228,171	51,491	49,815	21,454	6,642	47,034	51,735	230,721	87,858	22,528	28,155	92,180
1975–76	256,176	57,001	54,547	24,575	7,273	55,589	57,191	256,731	97,216	23,907	32,604	103,004
1976–77	285,157	62,527	60,641	29,246	9,174	62,444	61,124	274,215	102,780	23,058	35,906	112,472
1977–78	315,960	66,422	67,596	33,176	10,738	69,592	68,436	296,984	110,758	24,609	39,140	122,477
1978–79	343,279	64,944	74,247	36,932	12,128	75,164	79,864	327,517	119,448	28,440	41,898	137,731
1979–80	382,322	68,499	79,927	42,080	13,321	83,029	95,466	369,086	133,211	33,311	47,288	155,277
1980–81	423,404	74,969	85,971	46,426	14,143	90,294	111,599	407,449	145,784	34,603	54,105	172,957
1981–82	457,654	82,067	93,613	50,738	15,028	87,282	128,926	436,733	154,282	34,520	57,996	189,935
1982–83	486,753	89,105	100,247	55,129	14,258	90,007	138,008	466,516	163,876	36,655	60,906	205,079
1983–84	542,730	96,457	114,097	64,529	17,141	96,935	153,570	505,008	176,108	39,419	66,414	223,068
1984–85	598,121	103,757	126,376	70,361	19,152	106,158	172,317	553,899	192,686	44,989	71,479	244,745
1985–86	641,486	111,709	135,005	74,365	19,994	113,099	187,314	605,623	210,819	49,368	75,868	269,568
1986–87	686,860	121,203	144,091	83,935	22,425	114,857	200,350	657,134	226,619	52,355	82,650	295,510
1987–88	726,762	132,212	156,452	88,350	23,663	117,602	208,482	704,921	242,683	55,621	89,090	317,528
1988–89	786,129	142,400	166,336	97,806	25,926	125,824	227,838	762,360	263,898	58,105	97,879	342,479
1989–90	849,502	155,613	177,885	105,640	23,566	136,802	249,996	834,818	288,148	61,057	110,518	375,095
1990–91 ᵖ	902,189	167,926	185,570	109,341	22,242	154,097	263,013	908,635	309,667	64,937	130,402	403,629

[1] Fiscal years not the same for all governments. See Note.
[2] Excludes revenues or expenditures of publicly owned utilities and liquor stores, and of insurance-trust activities. Intergovernmental receipts and payments between State and local governments are also excluded.
[3] Includes other taxes and charges and miscellaneous revenues.
[4] Includes expenditures for libraries, hospitals, health, employment security administration, veterans' services, air transportation, water transport and terminals, parking facilities, and transit subsidies, police protection, fire protection, correction, protective inspection and regulation, sewerage, natural resources, parks and recreation, housing and community development, solid waste management, financial administration, judicial and legal, general public buildings, other governmental administration, interest on general debt, and general expenditures, n.e.c.

Note.—Data for fiscal years listed from 1962–63 to 1990–91 are the aggregations of data for government fiscal years that ended in the 12-month period from July 1 to June 30 of those years. Data for 1963 and earlier years include data for government fiscal years ending during that particular calendar year.

Data are not available for intervening years.

Source: Department of Commerce, Bureau of the Census.

443

TABLE B-82.—*Interest-bearing public debt securities by kind of obligation, 1967-92*

[Millions of dollars]

End of year or month	Total interest-bearing public debt securities	Marketable				Nonmarketable				
		Total [1]	Treasury bills	Treasury notes	Treasury bonds	Total	U.S. savings bonds	Foreign government and public series [2]	Government account series	Other [3]
Fiscal year:										
1967	322,286	[4] 210,672	58,535	49,108	97,418	111,614	51,213	1,514	56,155	2,731
1968	344,401	226,592	64,440	71,073	91,079	117,808	51,712	3,741	59,526	2,828
1969	351,729	226,107	68,356	78,946	78,805	125,623	51,711	4,070	66,790	3,051
1970	369,026	232,599	76,154	93,489	62,956	136,426	51,281	4,755	76,323	4,068
1971	396,289	245,473	86,677	104,807	53,989	150,816	53,003	9,270	82,784	5,759
1972	425,360	257,202	94,648	113,419	49,135	168,158	55,921	18,985	89,598	3,654
1973	456,353	262,971	100,061	117,840	45,071	193,382	59,418	28,524	101,738	3,701
1974	473,238	266,575	105,019	128,419	33,137	206,663	61,921	25,011	115,442	4,289
1975	532,122	315,606	128,569	150,257	36,779	216,516	65,482	23,216	124,173	3,644
1976	619,254	392,581	161,198	191,758	39,626	226,673	69,733	21,500	130,557	4,883
1977	697,629	443,508	156,091	241,692	45,724	254,121	75,411	21,799	140,113	16,797
1978	766,971	485,155	160,936	267,865	56,355	281,816	79,798	21,680	153,271	27,067
1979	819,007	506,693	161,378	274,242	71,073	312,314	80,440	28,115	176,360	27,400
1980	906,402	594,506	199,832	310,903	83,772	311,896	72,727	25,158	189,848	24,164
1981	996,495	683,209	223,388	363,643	96,178	313,286	68,017	20,499	201,052	23,718
1982	1,140,883	824,422	277,900	442,890	103,631	316,461	67,274	14,641	210,462	24,085
1983	1,375,751	1,024,000	340,733	557,525	125,742	351,751	70,024	11,450	234,684	35,593
1984	1,559,570	1,176,556	356,798	661,687	158,070	383,015	72,832	8,806	259,534	41,843
1985	1,821,010	1,360,179	384,220	776,449	199,510	460,831	77,011	6,638	313,928	63,255
1986	2,122,684	[1] 1,564,329	410,730	896,884	241,716	558,355	85,551	4,128	365,872	102,804
1987	2,347,750	[1] 1,675,980	378,263	1,005,127	277,590	671,769	97,004	4,350	440,658	129,758
1988	2,599,877	[1] 1,802,905	398,451	1,089,578	299,875	796,972	106,176	6,320	536,455	148,023
1989	2,836,309	[1] 1,892,763	406,597	1,133,193	337,974	943,546	114,025	6,818	663,677	159,025
1990	3,210,943	[1] 2,092,759	482,454	1,218,081	377,224	1,118,184	122,152	36,041	779,412	180,581
1991	3,662,759	[1] 2,390,660	564,589	1,387,717	423,354	1,272,099	133,512	41,639	908,406	188,541
1992	4,061,801	[1] 2,677,476	634,287	1,566,349	461,840	1,384,325	148,266	37,039	1,011,020	188,000
1991: Jan	3,408,637	[1] 2,221,746	537,383	1,281,200	388,164	1,186,891	125,294	43,211	828,789	189,598
Feb	3,455,910	[1] 2,257,098	541,742	1,301,087	399,270	1,198,811	126,524	42,665	839,760	189,862
Mar	3,441,367	[1] 2,227,914	533,262	1,280,385	399,270	1,213,453	127,726	42,788	853,086	189,853
Apr	3,442,402	[1] 2,237,682	504,404	1,319,015	399,263	1,204,719	129,145	42,680	842,527	190,368
May	3,494,576	[1] 2,278,545	512,912	1,339,419	411,214	1,216,031	130,246	42,621	852,749	190,415
June	3,516,066	[1] 2,268,060	521,544	1,320,313	411,203	1,248,006	131,268	42,101	883,188	191,450
July	3,574,226	[1] 2,327,812	538,211	1,363,403	411,199	1,246,414	132,062	42,118	886,229	186,004
Aug	3,600,603	[1] 2,347,629	551,555	1,357,715	423,359	1,252,974	132,744	42,024	889,893	188,315
Sept	3,662,759	[1] 2,390,660	564,589	1,387,717	423,354	1,272,099	133,512	41,639	908,406	188,541
Oct	3,714,592	[1] 2,429,226	585,908	1,404,975	423,343	1,285,367	134,545	41,472	920,079	189,269
Nov	3,732,281	[1] 2,439,406	589,735	1,399,195	435,476	1,292,875	135,402	41,736	926,101	189,636
Dec	3,798,859	[1] 2,471,646	590,389	1,430,784	435,473	1,327,213	135,924	41,940	959,185	190,165
1992: Jan	3,806,526	[1] 2,486,097	586,759	1,448,869	435,470	1,320,429	137,293	42,025	954,823	186,287
Feb	3,814,147	[1] 2,493,416	591,223	1,443,400	443,793	1,320,731	138,656	41,971	952,963	187,140
Mar	3,878,494	[1] 2,552,261	615,818	1,477,653	443,789	1,326,233	139,924	41,966	956,123	188,219
Apr	3,889,211	[1] 2,554,175	598,383	1,497,003	443,789	1,335,036	141,320	42,164	961,491	190,060
May	3,919,096	[1] 2,572,961	620,107	1,483,559	454,295	1,346,135	142,217	42,259	970,957	190,702
June	3,961,791	[1] 2,605,058	618,218	1,517,548	454,292	1,376,733	143,215	38,698	1,002,534	192,285
July	4,007,778	[1] 2,637,918	632,322	1,536,306	454,289	1,369,861	144,503	38,456	999,957	186,945
Aug	4,046,065	[1] 2,672,225	637,025	1,558,359	461,841	1,373,840	146,083	37,023	1,002,969	187,765
Sept	4,061,801	[1] 2,677,476	634,287	1,566,349	461,840	1,384,325	148,266	37,039	1,011,020	188,000
Oct	4,050,814	[1] 2,661,374	627,762	1,556,785	461,827	1,389,441	151,147	36,526	1,016,380	185,388
Nov	4,130,034	[1] 2,734,642	644,964	1,602,153	472,525	1,395,392	153,528	37,370	1,019,979	184,516

[1] Includes Federal Financing Bank securities, not shown separately, in the amount of 15,000 million dollars.
[2] Nonmarketable certificates of indebtedness, notes, bonds, and bills in the Treasury foreign series of dollar-denominated and foreign-currency denominated issues.
[3] Includes depository bonds, retirement plan bonds, Rural Electrification Administration bonds, State and local bonds, and special issues held only by U.S. Government agencies and trust funds and the Federal home loan banks.
[4] Includes $5,610 million in certificates not shown separately.

Note.—Through fiscal year 1976, the fiscal year was on a July 1–June 30 basis; beginning October 1976 (fiscal year 1977), the fiscal year is on an October 1–September 30 basis.

Source: Department of the Treasury.

444

TABLE B-83.—*Maturity distribution and average length of marketable interest-bearing public debt securities held by private investors, 1967-92*

End of year or month	Amount out-standing, privately held	Within 1 year	1 to 5 years	5 to 10 years	10 to 20 years	20 years and over	Average length Years	Months
		Millions of dollars					Years	Months
Fiscal year:								
1967	150,321	56,561	53,584	21,057	6,153	12,968	5	1
1968	159,671	66,746	52,295	21,850	6,110	12,670	4	5
1969	156,008	69,311	50,182	18,078	6,097	12,337	4	2
1970	157,910	76,443	57,035	8,286	7,876	8,272	3	8
1971	161,863	74,803	58,557	14,503	6,357	7,645	3	6
1972	165,978	79,509	57,157	16,033	6,358	6,922	3	3
1973	167,869	84,041	54,139	16,385	8,741	4,564	3	1
1974	164,862	87,150	50,103	14,197	9,930	3,481	2	11
1975	210,382	115,677	65,852	15,385	8,857	4,611	2	8
1976	279,782	150,296	90,578	24,169	8,087	6,652	2	7
1977	326,674	161,329	113,319	33,067	8,428	10,531	2	11
1978	356,501	163,819	132,993	33,500	11,383	14,805	3	3
1979	380,530	181,883	127,574	32,279	18,489	20,304	3	7
1980	463,717	220,084	156,244	38,809	25,901	22,679	3	9
1981	549,863	256,187	182,237	48,743	32,569	30,127	4	0
1982	682,043	314,436	221,783	75,749	33,017	37,058	3	11
1983	862,631	379,579	294,955	99,174	40,826	48,097	4	1
1984	1,017,488	437,941	332,808	130,417	49,664	66,658	4	6
1985	1,185,675	472,661	402,766	159,383	62,853	88,012	4	11
1986	1,354,275	506,903	467,348	189,995	70,664	119,365	5	3
1987	1,445,366	483,582	526,746	209,160	72,862	153,016	5	9
1988	1,555,208	524,201	552,993	232,453	74,186	171,375	5	9
1989	1,654,660	546,751	578,333	247,428	80,616	201,532	6	0
1990	1,841,903	626,297	630,144	267,573	82,713	235,176	6	1
1991	2,113,799	713,778	761,243	280,574	84,900	273,304	6	0
1992	2,363,802	808,705	866,329	295,921	84,706	308,141	5	11
1991: Jan	1,954,246	677,365	679,371	270,662	86,129	240,719	5	11
Feb	1,987,388	686,639	699,981	265,683	84,446	250,639	6	0
Mar	1,970,519	678,000	685,842	268,356	85,136	253,185	6	0
Apr	1,974,883	647,282	720,023	269,257	85,136	253,185	6	0
May	2,012,127	662,538	736,577	264,523	87,198	261,291	6	2
June	2,003,121	673,231	717,100	264,344	87,198	261,248	6	1
July	2,054,782	688,269	752,002	266,065	87,198	261,248	6	0
Aug	2,075,255	702,752	733,723	280,576	84,900	273,304	6	1
Sept	2,113,799	713,778	761,243	280,574	84,900	273,304	6	0
Oct	2,143,244	736,169	769,530	280,645	84,394	272,506	5	11
Nov	2,157,159	743,407	769,070	276,457	87,461	280,764	6	1
Dec	2,171,507	742,609	788,493	274,221	87,203	278,980	6	0
1992: Jan	2,201,642	749,495	806,162	278,275	87,297	280,413	5	11
Feb	2,211,963	758,592	785,152	291,657	85,798	290,764	6	1
Mar	2,266,806	786,988	812,044	291,507	85,708	290,559	5	11
Apr	2,268,375	769,874	828,118	293,819	85,798	290,765	5	11
May	2,284,866	786,584	816,200	295,318	85,788	300,976	6	0
June	2,310,321	784,194	845,264	294,745	85,793	300,326	5	11
July	2,344,094	800,084	861,247	296,644	85,793	300,326	5	10
Aug	2,372,764	811,729	868,080	297,830	85,572	309,553	5	11
Sept	2,363,802	808,705	866,329	295,921	84,706	308,141	5	11
Oct	2,362,075	806,345	860,918	299,422	85,529	309,861	5	11
Nov	2,425,550	825,445	893,133	303,863	92,798	310,311	5	11

Note.—All issues classified to final maturity.
Through fiscal year 1976, the fiscal year was on a July 1–June 30 basis; beginning October 1976 (fiscal year 1977), the fiscal year is on an October 1–September 30 basis.

Source: Department of the Treasury.

445

[Par values; [1] billions of dollars]

End of month	Total	Commercial banks [2]	Held by private investors — Nonbank investors — Total	Individuals [3] Total	Savings bonds [4]	Other securities	Insurance companies	Money market funds	Corporations [5]	State and local governments [6]	Foreign and international [7]	Other investors [8]
1976: June............	376.4	92.5	283.9	96.1	69.6	26.5	10.7	0.8	23.3	32.7	69.8	50.5
Dec............	409.5	103.8	305.7	101.6	72.0	29.6	12.7	1.1	23.5	39.3	78.1	49.4
1977: June............	421.0	102.9	318.1	104.9	74.4	30.5	13.0	.8	22.1	49.6	87.9	39.8
Dec............	461.3	102.0	359.3	107.8	76.7	31.1	15.1	.9	18.2	59.1	109.6	48.6
1978: June............	477.8	99.6	378.2	109.0	79.1	29.9	14.2	1.3	17.3	69.6	119.5	47.3
Dec............	508.6	95.3	413.3	114.0	80.7	33.3	15.3	1.5	17.3	81.1	133.1	51.0
1979: June............	516.6	94.6	422.0	115.5	80.6	34.9	16.0	3.8	18.6	86.2	114.9	67.0
Dec............	540.5	95.6	444.9	118.0	79.9	38.1	15.6	5.6	17.0	86.2	119.0	83.5
1980: June............	558.2	98.5	459.7	116.5	73.4	43.1	15.3	5.3	14.0	85.1	118.2	105.3
Dec............	616.4	111.5	504.9	117.1	72.5	44.6	18.1	3.5	19.3	90.3	129.7	126.9
1981: June............	651.2	115.0	536.2	107.4	69.2	38.2	19.9	9.0	19.9	95.9	136.6	147.5
Dec............	694.5	113.8	580.7	110.8	68.1	42.7	21.6	21.5	17.9	99.9	136.6	172.4
1982: June............	740.9	114.7	626.2	114.1	67.4	46.7	24.4	22.4	17.6	106.0	137.2	204.5
Dec............	848.4	134.0	714.4	116.5	68.3	48.2	30.6	42.6	24.5	118.6	149.5	232.1
1983: June............	948.6	167.4	781.2	121.3	69.7	51.6	37.8	28.3	32.8	138.1	160.1	262.8
Dec............	1,022.6	179.5	843.1	133.4	71.5	61.9	46.0	22.8	39.7	153.0	166.3	281.9
1984: June............	1,102.2	180.6	921.6	142.2	72.9	69.3	51.2	14.9	45.3	168.5	171.6	327.9
Dec............	1,212.5	181.5	1,031.0	143.8	74.5	69.3	64.5	25.9	50.1	188.4	205.9	352.4
1985: June............	1,292.0	195.6	1,096.4	148.7	76.7	72.0	69.1	24.8	54.9	213.4	213.8	371.7
Dec............	1,417.2	189.4	1,227.8	154.8	79.8	75.0	80.5	25.1	59.0	303.6	224.8	380.0
1986: June............	1,502.7	194.3	1,308.4	159.5	83.8	75.7	87.9	22.8	61.2	319.5	250.9	406.6
Dec............	1,602.0	197.5	1,404.5	162.7	92.3	70.4	101.6	28.6	68.8	346.6	263.4	432.8
1987: Mar	1,641.4	193.4	1,448.0	163.0	94.7	68.3	106.3	18.8	73.5	365.3	272.8	448.3
June............	1,658.1	192.3	1,465.8	165.6	96.8	68.8	104.7	20.6	79.7	383.9	281.1	430.2
Sept............	1,680.7	198.3	1,482.4	167.7	98.5	69.2	106.2	15.5	81.8	397.6	279.5	434.1
Dec............	1,731.4	194.2	1,537.2	172.4	101.1	71.3	108.1	14.6	84.6	418.4	299.7	439.4
1988: Mar	1,779.6	195.6	1,584.0	178.1	104.0	74.1	110.2	15.2	86.3	432.5	332.5	429.2
June............	1,786.7	190.7	1,596.0	182.0	106.2	75.8	111.0	13.4	87.6	446.9	345.4	409.7
Sept............	1,821.2	191.2	1,630.0	186.8	107.8	79.0	115.9	11.1	85.9	457.7	345.9	426.7
Dec............	1,858.5	184.9	1,673.6	190.4	109.6	80.8	118.6	11.8	86.0	471.6	362.2	433.0
1989: Mar	1,903.4	192.0	1,711.4	204.2	112.2	92.0	119.7	13.0	89.4	477.9	376.6	430.6
June............	1,909.1	178.0	1,731.1	211.7	114.0	97.7	120.3	11.3	91.0	483.5	369.1	444.2
Sept............	1,958.3	166.6	1,791.7	213.5	115.7	97.8	121.4	12.9	90.9	487.1	394.9	471.0
Dec............	2,015.8	164.9	1,850.9	216.4	117.7	98.7	125.1	14.9	93.4	487.5	392.9	520.7
1990: Mar	2,115.1	178.4	1,936.7	222.8	119.9	102.9	134.9	31.3	94.9	493.8	385.0	574.0
June............	2,141.8	176.9	1,964.9	229.6	121.9	107.7	137.6	28.0	96.9	494.5	390.5	587.8
Sept............	2,207.3	179.5	2,027.8	232.5	123.9	108.6	141.2	34.0	102.0	492.1	403.5	622.5
Dec............	2,288.3	171.5	2,116.8	233.8	126.2	107.6	142.0	45.5	108.9	490.4	421.7	674.5
1991: Mar	2,360.6	188.5	2,172.1	238.3	129.7	108.6	145.3	65.4	114.9	510.4	427.6	670.2
June............	2,397.9	197.3	2,200.6	243.5	133.2	110.3	151.7	55.4	130.8	510.8	436.9	671.6
Sept............	2,489.4	218.6	2,270.8	257.5	135.4	122.1	163.0	64.5	142.0	512.9	440.6	690.3
Dec............	2,563.2	233.4	2,329.8	263.9	138.1	125.8	168.7	80.0	150.8	520.3	455.0	691.1
1992: Mar	2,664.0	256.6	2,407.4	268.1	142.0	126.1	176.9	84.0	166.0	521.8	471.2	719.5
June............	2,712.4	267.2	2,445.2	275.1	145.4	129.7	181.3	79.4	175.0	528.5	492.9	713.1
Sept............	2,765.5	270.0	2,495.5	281.2	150.3	130.9	185.0	79.4	180.8	530.0	499.0	740.0

[1] U.S. savings bonds, series A–F and J, are included at current redemption value.

[2] Includes domestically chartered banks, U.S. branches and agencies of foreign banks, New York investment companies majority owned by foreign banks, and Edge Act corporations owned by domestically chartered and foreign banks.

[3] Includes partnerships and personal trust accounts.

[4] Includes U.S. savings notes. Sales began May 1, 1967, and were discontinued June 30, 1970.

[5] Exclusive of banks and insurance companies.

[6] State and local government securities have been redefined to include their fully defeased debt that is backed by nonmarketable Federal securities. Includes State and local pension funds.

[7] Consists of the investment of foreign balances and international accounts in the United States.

[8] Includes savings and loan associations, credit unions, nonprofit institutions, mutual savings banks, corporate pension trust funds, dealers and brokers, certain Government deposit accounts, and Government-sponsored agencies.

Source: Department of the Treasury.

CORPORATE PROFITS AND FINANCE

TABLE B-85.—*Corporate profits with inventory valuation and capital consumption adjustments, 1959–92*

[Billions of dollars; quarterly data at seasonally adjusted annual rates]

Year or quarter	Corporate profits with inventory valuation and capital consumption adjustments	Corporate profits tax liability	Corporate profits after tax with inventory valuation and capital consumption adjustments		Undistributed profits with inventory valuation and capital consumption adjustments
			Total	Dividends	
1959	52.3	23.6	28.6	12.7	15.9
1960	50.7	22.7	28.0	13.4	14.6
1961	51.6	22.8	28.8	14.0	14.8
1962	59.6	24.0	35.6	15.0	20.6
1963	65.1	26.2	38.9	16.1	22.8
1964	72.1	28.0	44.1	18.0	26.1
1965	82.9	30.9	52.0	20.2	31.8
1966	88.6	33.7	54.9	20.9	34.0
1967	86.0	32.7	53.3	22.1	31.2
1968	92.6	39.4	53.2	24.6	28.6
1969	89.6	39.7	49.9	25.2	24.7
1970	77.5	34.4	43.1	23.7	19.4
1971	90.3	37.7	52.6	23.7	28.8
1972	103.2	41.9	61.3	25.8	35.5
1973	116.4	49.3	67.1	28.1	39.0
1974	104.5	51.8	52.7	30.4	22.3
1975	121.9	50.9	71.0	30.1	40.9
1976	147.1	64.2	82.8	35.6	47.2
1977	175.7	73.0	102.6	40.7	61.9
1978	199.7	83.5	116.2	45.9	70.3
1979	202.5	88.0	114.5	52.4	62.1
1980	177.7	84.8	92.9	59.0	33.9
1981	182.0	81.1	100.9	69.2	31.7
1982	151.5	63.1	88.4	70.0	18.4
1983	212.7	77.2	135.4	81.2	54.2
1984	264.2	94.0	170.2	82.7	87.5
1985	280.8	96.5	184.2	92.4	91.9
1986	271.6	106.5	165.1	109.8	55.4
1987	319.8	127.1	192.8	106.2	86.5
1988	365.0	137.0	228.0	115.3	112.6
1989	362.8	141.3	221.5	134.6	86.9
1990	361.7	136.7	225.1	149.3	75.7
1991	346.3	124.0	222.3	146.5	75.8
1982: IV	150.3	58.7	91.7	72.5	19.2
1983: IV	229.1	82.2	146.9	84.2	62.7
1984: IV	261.3	83.8	177.5	83.4	94.1
1985: IV	284.9	97.6	187.2	97.4	89.9
1986: IV	264.6	116.6	148.1	111.0	37.1
1987: IV	343.3	135.2	208.1	106.3	101.8
1988: IV	378.3	146.2	232.2	121.0	111.2
1989: I	369.4	154.8	214.7	127.8	86.9
II	369.9	143.7	226.3	132.2	94.1
III	357.3	132.6	224.7	136.9	87.8
IV	354.5	134.2	220.3	141.3	79.0
1990: I	367.6	132.4	235.2	146.1	89.1
II	384.0	137.6	246.4	148.7	97.7
III	351.4	143.0	208.4	150.6	57.8
IV	344.0	133.7	210.2	151.9	58.3
1991: I	349.6	121.3	228.3	150.6	77.7
II	347.3	122.9	224.4	146.2	78.1
III	341.2	127.0	214.2	145.1	69.0
IV	347.1	125.0	222.2	143.9	78.3
1992: I	384.0	136.4	247.6	143.6	104.0
II	388.4	144.1	244.3	146.6	97.7
III	374.1	131.8	242.3	151.1	91.2

Source: Department of Commerce, Bureau of Economic Analysis.

447

TABLE B-86.—*Corporate profits by industry, 1959-92*

[Billions of dollars; quarterly data at seasonally adjusted annual rates]

Year or quarter	Total	Corporate profits with inventory valuation adjustment and without capital consumption adjustment									Rest of the world
		Domestic industries									
		Financial[1]			Nonfinancial						
		Total	Federal Reserve banks	Other	Total	Manufacturing[2]	Transportation and public utilities	Wholesale and retail trade	Other		
1959	53.1	50.4	7.0	0.7	6.3	43.4	26.5	7.1	6.2	3.6	2.7
1960	51.0	47.8	7.7	.9	6.7	40.2	23.8	7.5	5.2	3.6	3.1
1961	51.3	48.0	7.5	.8	6.8	40.4	23.4	7.9	5.5	3.6	3.3
1962	56.4	52.6	7.6	.9	6.8	45.0	26.3	8.5	6.3	3.9	3.8
1963	61.2	57.1	7.3	1.0	6.4	49.8	29.6	9.5	6.4	4.4	4.1
1964	67.5	63.0	7.5	1.1	6.4	55.5	32.4	10.2	7.9	5.1	4.5
1965	77.6	72.9	7.9	1.3	6.5	65.0	39.7	11.0	8.6	5.6	4.7
1966	83.0	78.5	9.2	1.7	7.5	69.3	42.4	11.9	8.8	6.2	4.5
1967	80.3	75.5	9.5	2.0	7.6	66.0	39.0	10.9	9.7	6.4	4.8
1968	86.9	81.3	10.9	2.5	8.4	70.4	41.7	11.0	10.9	6.8	5.6
1969	83.2	76.6	11.6	3.1	8.5	65.0	37.0	10.6	11.2	6.2	6.6
1970	71.8	64.7	13.1	3.5	9.6	51.6	27.1	8.2	10.3	5.9	7.1
1971	85.5	77.7	15.2	3.3	11.9	62.5	34.8	8.9	12.3	6.6	7.9
1972	97.9	88.4	16.4	3.3	13.1	72.0	41.4	9.4	14.1	7.1	9.5
1973	110.9	96.0	17.5	4.5	13.0	78.5	46.7	9.0	14.6	8.2	14.9
1974	103.4	85.9	16.2	5.7	10.5	69.7	40.7	7.6	13.7	7.7	17.5
1975	129.4	114.8	15.9	5.6	10.3	98.9	54.5	10.9	21.9	11.6	14.6
1976	158.8	142.3	19.9	5.9	14.0	122.4	70.7	15.3	23.1	13.3	16.5
1977	186.7	167.7	25.7	6.1	19.6	142.0	78.5	18.5	27.8	17.1	18.9
1978	212.8	190.2	31.8	7.6	24.1	158.4	89.6	21.7	27.7	19.4	22.6
1979	219.8	185.6	31.6	9.4	22.2	153.9	88.3	16.9	28.3	20.5	34.3
1980	197.8	162.9	24.3	11.8	12.6	138.5	75.8	18.3	22.8	21.6	35.0
1981	203.2	174.0	18.7	14.4	4.3	155.3	87.4	20.1	31.6	16.2	29.2
1982	166.4	138.6	15.6	15.2	.4	123.0	63.1	20.8	31.9	7.2	27.8
1983	202.2	171.9	24.5	14.6	9.9	147.4	71.4	28.9	38.7	8.4	30.4
1984	236.4	205.2	20.3	16.4	3.9	185.0	86.7	39.9	49.7	8.7	31.2
1985	225.3	194.5	28.7	16.3	12.4	165.8	80.1	34.1	43.1	8.5	30.8
1986	227.6	194.6	35.8	15.5	20.3	158.9	59.0	36.5	46.3	17.1	32.9
1987	273.4	233.9	36.4	15.7	20.7	197.5	87.0	43.4	39.9	27.2	39.5
1988	320.3	271.2	41.8	17.6	24.2	229.4	117.5	47.5	37.1	27.3	49.1
1989	325.4	266.0	50.6	20.1	30.5	215.3	108.0	42.1	39.7	25.5	59.4
1990	341.2	275.5	56.7	21.4	35.3	218.8	106.9	43.9	35.8	32.1	65.7
1991	337.8	271.3	60.9	20.2	40.7	210.4	89.3	46.1	44.0	31.1	66.5
1982: IV	160.0	130.8	23.0	14.6	8.3	107.8	50.1	18.2	33.8	5.7	29.2
1983: IV	216.2	182.6	22.1	15.2	6.9	160.5	90.5	19.1	40.7	10.2	33.6
1984: IV	223.6	192.9	20.3	17.2	3.2	172.6	79.2	33.5	50.8	9.0	30.7
1985: IV	228.0	193.5	29.0	16.0	13.0	164.5	83.3	31.3	39.0	11.0	34.5
1986: IV	225.0	192.5	34.7	15.2	19.5	157.8	63.9	34.2	43.1	16.6	32.6
1987: IV	293.4	246.3	39.4	16.1	23.3	207.0	98.7	43.1	39.3	25.8	47.0
1988: IV	340.5	285.9	46.1	18.9	27.2	239.7	129.3	47.6	39.3	23.5	54.6
1989: I	331.3	274.9	51.9	19.7	32.2	223.0	119.7	43.1	37.4	22.8	56.4
II	330.0	272.5	50.9	20.8	30.1	221.6	111.4	45.1	39.3	25.8	57.5
III	319.8	261.7	47.2	19.7	27.5	214.5	106.5	41.4	42.9	23.7	58.1
IV	320.6	254.8	52.5	20.4	32.1	202.3	94.5	38.8	39.2	29.8	65.8
1990: I	337.4	275.0	57.0	20.6	36.5	218.0	104.4	46.3	36.7	30.6	62.4
II	359.6	297.0	57.8	21.3	36.5	239.2	116.6	49.1	41.7	31.8	62.6
III	334.4	269.7	56.9	22.1	34.8	212.8	110.6	41.7	30.0	30.5	64.7
IV	333.5	260.2	55.1	21.5	33.6	205.1	96.3	38.6	35.0	35.3	73.3
1991: I	344.2	269.4	59.7	20.9	38.8	209.7	87.6	46.9	44.1	31.1	74.8
II	342.2	275.9	60.7	20.2	40.5	215.1	90.3	49.6	45.5	29.8	66.3
III	331.9	270.0	63.6	20.0	43.6	206.4	91.8	42.2	41.7	30.7	61.9
IV	333.1	270.2	59.7	19.8	39.9	210.5	87.5	45.6	44.5	32.9	62.9
1992: I	360.7	292.0	70.1	18.8	51.3	221.9	97.5	49.4	39.9	35.1	68.7
II	361.4	300.4	61.3	18.5	42.8	239.0	115.2	42.2	46.7	35.0	61.0
III	344.4	279.3	40.3	17.2	23.1	239.0	118.0	40.6	43.7	36.7	65.1

[1] Consists of the following industries: Depository institutions; nondepository credit institutions; security and commodity brokers; insurance carriers; regulated investment companies; small business investment companies; and real estate investment trusts.
[2] See Table B-87 for industry detail.

Note.—The industry classification is on a company basis and is based on the 1987 Standard Industrial Classification (SIC) beginning 1987, and on the 1972 SIC for earlier years shown.

Source: Department of Commerce, Bureau of Economic Analysis.

TABLE B–87.—*Corporate profits of manufacturing industries, 1959–92*

[Billions of dollars; quarterly data at seasonally adjusted annual rates]

Year or quarter	Total manufacturing	Corporate profits with inventory valuation adjustment and without capital consumption adjustment											
		Durable goods							Nondurable goods				
		Total	Primary metal industries	Fabricated metal products	Industrial machinery and equipment	Electronic and other electric equipment	Motor vehicles and equipment	Other	Total	Food and kindred products	Chemicals and allied products	Petroleum and coal products	Other
1959	26.5	13.7	2.3	1.1	2.2	1.7	3.0	3.5	12.8	2.5	3.5	2.6	4.3
1960	23.8	11.7	2.0	.8	1.8	1.3	3.0	2.8	12.1	2.2	3.1	2.6	4.2
1961	23.4	11.4	1.6	1.0	1.9	1.3	2.5	3.1	12.0	2.4	3.3	2.2	4.2
1962	26.3	14.1	1.6	1.2	2.4	1.5	4.0	3.5	12.2	2.4	3.2	2.2	4.4
1963	29.6	16.4	2.0	1.3	2.5	1.6	4.9	4.0	13.2	2.7	3.7	2.2	4.7
1964	32.4	18.0	2.5	1.4	3.3	1.7	4.6	4.5	14.4	2.7	4.1	2.3	5.3
1965	39.7	23.2	3.1	2.1	4.0	2.7	6.2	5.2	16.4	2.8	4.6	2.9	6.1
1966	42.4	23.9	3.6	2.4	4.5	3.0	5.1	5.3	18.4	3.3	4.9	3.4	6.8
1967	39.0	21.2	2.7	2.5	4.1	3.0	4.0	5.0	17.8	3.2	4.3	3.9	6.4
1968	41.7	22.4	1.9	2.3	4.1	2.9	5.5	5.7	19.2	3.2	5.2	3.7	7.0
1969	37.0	19.0	1.4	2.0	3.7	2.3	4.8	4.9	18.0	3.0	4.6	3.3	7.0
1970	27.1	10.4	.8	1.1	3.0	1.3	1.3	3.0	16.8	3.2	3.9	3.6	6.1
1971	34.8	16.6	.8	1.5	3.0	1.9	5.1	4.2	18.2	3.5	4.5	3.7	6.5
1972	41.4	22.6	1.6	2.2	4.3	2.8	5.9	5.7	18.8	2.9	5.2	3.2	7.5
1973	46.7	25.0	2.3	2.6	4.7	3.2	5.9	6.3	21.7	2.5	6.1	5.2	7.9
1974	40.7	15.1	5.0	1.8	3.1	.5	.7	4.1	25.7	2.6	5.2	10.7	7.2
1975	54.5	20.3	2.7	3.2	4.8	2.6	2.2	4.8	34.1	8.6	6.3	9.8	9.4
1976	70.7	31.2	2.1	3.9	6.7	3.8	7.4	7.4	39.5	7.1	8.2	13.3	11.0
1977	78.5	37.6	1.0	4.5	8.3	5.8	9.3	8.6	41.0	6.8	7.7	12.9	13.6
1978	89.6	45.0	3.6	5.0	10.4	6.6	8.9	10.5	44.6	6.1	8.2	15.5	14.8
1979	88.3	36.5	3.5	5.2	9.1	5.4	4.6	8.6	51.8	5.8	7.1	24.5	14.6
1980	75.8	17.9	2.6	4.3	7.5	5.0	-4.3	2.8	57.8	6.0	5.5	33.6	12.9
1981	87.4	18.1	3.0	4.4	8.2	4.9	.2	-2.7	69.3	9.0	7.6	38.6	14.2
1982	63.1	4.8	-4.7	2.6	3.4	1.3	-.4	2.6	58.3	7.2	4.7	31.6	14.8
1983	71.4	18.4	-4.9	3.1	4.4	3.4	5.2	7.2	53.0	5.8	6.8	22.1	18.3
1984	86.7	37.2	-.4	4.5	6.3	4.8	8.9	13.1	49.5	7.3	7.3	15.9	19.1
1985	80.1	29.0	-.9	4.7	5.3	2.4	7.3	10.1	51.1	8.4	6.0	17.1	19.7
1986	59.0	30.0	.9	5.3	3.2	2.6	4.4	13.7	29.0	7.5	8.0	-8.5	21.9
1987	87.0	42.2	2.6	5.2	7.3	6.2	3.7	17.3	44.8	11.4	15.1	-3.6	21.9
1988	117.5	52.2	5.9	6.4	10.5	7.6	5.7	16.1	65.3	11.8	19.3	10.4	23.8
1989	108.0	49.3	6.1	6.6	10.3	9.3	2.3	14.6	58.8	10.7	18.5	5.7	23.9
1990	106.9	40.5	3.1	6.3	11.3	7.5	-2.6	14.9	66.5	13.2	16.2	14.6	22.5
1991	89.3	25.8	1.1	5.4	8.9	6.6	-6.9	10.8	63.5	16.6	16.1	7.7	23.1
1982: IV	50.1	-5.3	-5.2	1.1	1.0	-1.0	-2.9	1.7	55.5	6.7	3.1	29.0	16.6
1983: IV	90.5	33.4	-3.7	4.9	6.5	6.6	9.4	9.7	57.1	6.1	7.7	24.1	19.2
1984: IV	79.2	34.2	-1.0	5.2	5.0	4.1	8.5	12.4	45.0	7.3	6.0	13.0	18.6
1985: IV	83.3	28.8	-1.3	4.0	7.0	2.0	7.3	9.7	54.5	7.8	3.5	24.1	19.2
1986: IV	63.9	34.2	1.7	4.7	2.6	3.3	4.5	17.4	29.7	8.2	9.5	-13.3	25.3
1987: IV	98.7	35.2	3.3	6.0	6.3	2.9	.6	16.2	63.4	13.4	18.5	7.4	24.1
1988: IV	129.3	56.4	6.5	6.4	8.0	9.7	9.6	16.2	72.9	12.3	24.0	14.2	22.4
1989: I	119.7	55.2	6.4	7.6	9.2	9.2	7.6	15.2	64.5	13.6	19.2	5.8	25.9
II	111.4	51.6	7.1	6.7	10.2	9.4	4.0	14.2	59.8	9.5	21.1	4.6	24.5
III	106.5	47.4	6.8	7.0	9.1	7.9	.6	16.0	59.1	9.7	18.7	7.6	23.1
IV	94.5	43.0	4.1	5.3	12.6	10.9	-3.1	13.2	51.6	9.8	15.0	4.6	22.2
1990: I	104.4	46.3	4.7	7.9	12.4	9.8	-4.3	15.8	58.1	8.5	16.3	10.2	23.1
II	116.6	44.4	3.4	6.9	10.9	8.3	-.4	15.3	72.2	14.5	19.2	14.0	24.5
III	110.6	41.4	2.0	5.8	11.0	7.1	.5	15.0	69.2	15.0	16.2	14.4	23.6
IV	96.3	29.8	2.3	4.8	10.7	4.8	-6.1	13.3	66.4	14.8	13.0	19.6	19.0
1991: I	87.6	23.3	1.5	4.1	9.9	7.2	-10.9	11.5	64.3	16.6	13.2	14.5	20.0
II	90.3	29.0	1.2	5.5	9.7	6.9	-7.5	13.2	61.3	16.6	14.1	6.8	23.8
III	91.8	26.2	.2	5.8	6.8	5.5	-4.3	12.2	65.7	18.4	17.1	4.2	25.9
IV	87.5	24.8	1.4	6.0	9.2	6.8	-4.9	6.2	62.7	14.6	20.1	5.1	22.9
1992: I	97.5	31.8	.8	6.1	8.6	7.2	1.8	7.4	65.7	15.2	17.8	8.2	24.5
II	115.2	38.3	1.1	7.8	9.5	6.4	4.5	9.0	76.9	19.5	17.1	11.1	29.2
III	118.0	43.8	.3	7.8	9.3	10.4	1.9	14.0	74.2	17.1	17.5	10.1	29.4

Note.—The industry classification is on a company basis and is based on the 1987 Standard Industrial Classification (SIC) beginning 1987 and on the 1972 SIC for earlier years shown. In the 1972 SIC, the categories shown here as "industrial machinery and equipment" and "electronic and other electric equipment" were identified as "machinery, except electrical" and "electric and electronic equipment," respectively.

Source: Department of Commerce, Bureau of Economic Analysis.

449

TABLE B–88.—*Sales, profits, and stockholders' equity, all manufacturing corporations, 1950–92*

[Billions of dollars]

Year or quarter	All manufacturing corporations				Durable goods industries				Nondurable goods industries			
	Sales (net)	Profits Before income taxes [1]	Profits After income taxes	Stock-holders' equity [2]	Sales (net)	Profits Before income taxes [1]	Profits After income taxes	Stock-holders' equity [2]	Sales (net)	Profits Before income taxes [1]	Profits After income taxes	Stock-holders' equity [2]
1950	181.9	23.2	12.9	83.3	86.8	12.9	6.7	39.9	95.1	10.3	6.1	43.5
1951	245.0	27.4	11.9	98.3	116.8	15.4	6.1	47.2	128.1	12.1	5.7	51.1
1952	250.2	22.9	10.7	103.7	122.0	12.9	5.5	49.8	128.0	10.0	5.2	53.9
1953	265.9	24.4	11.3	108.2	137.9	14.0	5.8	52.4	128.0	10.4	5.5	55.7
1954	248.5	20.9	11.2	113.1	122.8	11.4	5.6	54.9	125.7	9.6	5.6	58.2
1955	278.4	28.6	15.1	120.1	142.1	16.5	8.1	58.8	136.3	12.1	7.0	61.3
1956	307.3	29.8	16.2	131.6	159.5	16.5	8.3	65.2	147.8	13.2	7.8	66.4
1957	320.0	28.2	15.4	141.1	166.0	15.8	7.9	70.5	154.1	12.4	7.5	70.6
1958	305.3	22.7	12.7	147.4	148.6	11.4	5.8	72.8	156.7	11.3	6.9	74.6
1959	338.0	29.7	16.3	157.1	169.4	15.8	8.1	77.9	168.5	13.9	8.3	79.2
1960	345.7	27.5	15.2	165.4	173.9	14.0	7.0	82.3	171.8	13.5	8.2	83.1
1961	356.4	27.5	15.3	172.6	175.2	13.6	6.9	84.9	181.2	13.9	8.5	87.7
1962	389.4	31.9	17.7	181.4	195.3	16.8	8.6	89.1	194.1	15.1	9.2	92.3
1963	412.7	34.9	19.5	189.7	209.0	18.5	9.5	93.3	203.6	16.4	10.0	96.3
1964	443.1	39.6	23.2	199.8	226.3	21.2	11.6	98.5	216.8	18.3	11.6	101.3
1965	492.2	46.5	27.5	211.7	257.0	26.2	14.5	105.4	235.2	20.3	13.0	106.3
1966	554.2	51.8	30.9	230.3	291.7	29.2	16.4	115.2	262.4	22.6	14.6	115.1
1967	575.4	47.8	29.0	247.6	300.6	25.7	14.6	125.0	274.8	22.0	14.4	122.6
1968	631.9	55.4	32.1	265.9	335.5	30.6	16.5	135.6	296.4	24.8	15.5	130.3
1969	694.6	58.1	33.2	289.9	366.5	31.5	16.9	147.6	328.1	26.6	16.4	142.3
1970	708.8	48.1	28.6	306.8	363.1	23.0	12.9	155.1	345.7	25.2	15.7	151.7
1971	751.1	52.9	31.0	320.8	381.8	26.5	14.5	160.4	369.3	26.5	16.5	160.5
1972	849.5	63.2	36.5	343.4	435.8	33.6	18.4	171.4	413.7	29.6	18.0	172.0
1973	1,017.2	81.4	48.1	374.1	527.3	43.6	24.8	188.7	489.9	37.8	23.3	185.4
1973: IV	275.1	21.4	13.0	386.4	140.1	10.8	6.3	194.7	135.0	10.6	6.7	191.7
New series:												
1973: IV	236.6	20.6	13.2	368.0	122.7	10.1	6.2	185.8	113.9	10.5	7.0	182.1
1974	1,060.6	92.1	58.7	395.0	529.0	41.1	24.7	196.0	531.6	51.0	34.1	199.0
1975	1,065.2	79.9	49.1	423.4	521.1	35.3	21.4	208.1	544.1	44.6	27.7	215.3
1976	1,203.2	104.9	64.5	462.7	589.6	50.7	30.8	224.3	613.7	54.3	33.7	238.4
1977	1,328.1	115.1	70.4	496.7	657.3	57.9	34.8	239.9	670.8	57.2	35.5	256.8
1978	1,496.4	132.5	81.1	540.5	760.7	69.6	41.8	262.6	735.7	62.9	39.3	277.9
1979	1,741.8	154.2	98.7	600.5	865.7	72.4	45.2	292.5	876.1	81.8	53.5	308.0
1980	1,912.8	145.8	92.6	668.1	889.1	57.4	35.6	317.7	1,023.7	88.4	56.9	350.4
1981	2,144.7	158.6	101.3	743.4	979.5	67.2	41.6	350.4	1,165.2	91.3	59.6	393.0
1982	2,039.4	108.2	70.9	770.2	913.1	34.7	21.7	355.5	1,126.4	73.6	49.3	414.7
1983	2,114.3	133.1	83.8	812.8	973.5	48.7	30.0	372.4	1,140.8	84.4	55.8	440.4
1984	2,335.0	165.6	107.6	864.2	1,107.6	75.5	48.9	395.6	1,227.5	90.0	58.8	468.5
1985	2,331.4	137.0	87.6	866.2	1,142.6	61.5	38.6	420.9	1,188.8	75.6	49.1	445.3
1986	2,220.9	129.3	83.1	874.7	1,125.5	52.1	32.6	436.3	1,095.4	77.2	50.5	438.4
1987	2,378.2	173.0	115.6	900.9	1,178.0	78.0	53.0	444.3	1,200.3	95.1	62.6	456.6
1988	2,596.2	216.1	154.6	957.6	1,284.7	91.7	67.1	468.7	1,311.5	124.4	87.5	488.9
1989	2,745.1	188.8	136.3	999.0	1,356.6	75.2	55.7	501.3	1,388.5	113.5	80.6	497.7
1990	2,810.7	159.6	111.6	1,043.8	1,357.2	57.6	40.9	515.0	1,453.5	102.0	70.6	528.9
1991	2,761.1	99.8	67.5	1,063.8	1,304.0	14.1	7.4	506.8	1,457.1	85.7	60.1	557.0
1990: I	671.4	40.1	28.1	1,026.6	325.8	16.3	11.8	506.4	345.6	23.8	16.3	520.2
II	706.9	50.0	35.1	1,039.8	354.0	22.0	15.7	517.0	352.9	28.0	19.5	522.7
III	705.1	42.1	29.6	1,054.6	337.7	12.8	9.4	519.0	367.5	29.2	20.2	535.6
IV	727.3	27.4	18.8	1,054.4	339.8	6.4	4.1	517.5	387.5	21.0	14.7	537.0
1991: I	655.1	27.0	18.3	1,050.4	303.9	3.4	1.4	503.5	351.2	23.6	16.8	546.8
II	698.8	32.8	23.1	1,057.6	335.3	10.7	7.6	507.8	363.5	22.1	15.4	549.8
III	698.7	27.8	17.6	1,069.1	328.0	3.2	1.1	505.9	370.7	24.6	16.5	563.2
IV	708.4	12.2	8.5	1,078.2	336.8	-3.2	-2.8	509.9	371.7	15.3	11.3	568.3
1992: I	677.0	34.1	24.7	1,084.2	324.2	10.9	7.8	510.1	352.9	23.2	17.0	574.1
II	731.9	42.2	29.9	1,105.5	354.9	15.1	10.5	523.9	377.0	27.2	19.4	581.6
III	728.4	38.6	28.9	1,124.7	344.9	12.3	10.1	532.1	383.5	26.3	18.8	592.6

[1] In the old series, "income taxes" refers to Federal income taxes only, as State and local income taxes had already been deducted. In the new series, no income taxes have been deducted.
[2] Annual data are average equity for the year (using four end-of-quarter figures).

Note.—Data are not necessarily comparable from one period to another due to changes in accounting procedures, industry classifications, sampling procedures, etc. For explanatory notes concerning compilation of the series, see "Quarterly Financial Report for Manufacturing, Mining, and Trade Corporations," Department of Commerce, Bureau of the Census.

Source: Department of Commerce, Bureau of the Census.

Year or quarter	Ratio of profits after income taxes (annual rate) to stockholders' equity—percent [1]			Profits after income taxes per dollar of sales—cents		
	All manufacturing corporations	Durable goods industries	Nondurable goods industries	All manufacturing corporations	Durable goods industries	Nondurable goods industries
1947	15.6	14.4	16.6	6.7	6.7	6.7
1948	16.0	15.7	16.2	7.0	7.1	6.8
1949	11.6	12.1	11.2	5.8	6.4	5.4
1950	15.4	16.9	14.1	7.1	7.7	6.5
1951	12.1	13.0	11.2	4.9	5.3	4.5
1952	10.3	11.1	9.7	4.3	4.5	4.1
1953	10.5	11.1	9.9	4.3	4.2	4.3
1954	9.9	10.3	9.6	4.5	4.6	4.4
1955	12.6	13.8	11.4	5.4	5.7	5.1
1956	12.3	12.8	11.8	5.3	5.2	5.3
1957	10.9	11.3	10.6	4.8	4.8	4.9
1958	8.6	8.0	9.2	4.2	3.9	4.4
1959	10.4	10.4	10.4	4.8	4.8	4.9
1960	9.2	8.5	9.8	4.4	4.0	4.8
1961	8.9	8.1	9.6	4.3	3.9	4.7
1962	9.8	9.6	9.9	4.5	4.4	4.7
1963	10.3	10.1	10.4	4.7	4.5	4.9
1964	11.6	11.7	11.5	5.2	5.1	5.4
1965	13.0	13.8	12.2	5.6	5.7	5.5
1966	13.4	14.2	12.7	5.6	5.6	5.6
1967	11.7	11.7	11.8	5.0	4.8	5.3
1968	12.1	12.2	11.9	5.1	4.9	5.2
1969	11.5	11.4	11.5	4.8	4.6	5.0
1970	9.3	8.3	10.3	4.0	3.5	4.5
1971	9.7	9.0	10.3	4.1	3.8	4.5
1972	10.6	10.8	10.5	4.3	4.2	4.4
1973	12.8	13.1	12.6	4.7	4.7	4.8
1973: IV	13.4	12.9	14.0	4.7	4.5	5.0
New series:						
1973: IV	14.3	13.3	15.3	5.6	5.0	6.1
1974	14.9	12.6	17.1	5.5	4.7	6.4
1975	11.6	10.3	12.9	4.6	4.1	5.1
1976	13.9	13.7	14.2	5.4	5.2	5.5
1977	14.2	14.5	13.8	5.3	5.3	5.3
1978	15.0	16.0	14.2	5.4	5.5	5.3
1979	16.4	15.4	17.4	5.7	5.2	6.1
1980	13.9	11.2	16.3	4.8	4.0	5.6
1981	13.6	11.9	15.2	4.7	4.2	5.1
1982	9.2	6.1	11.9	3.5	2.4	4.4
1983	10.6	8.1	12.7	4.1	3.1	4.9
1984	12.5	12.4	12.5	4.6	4.4	4.8
1985	10.1	9.2	11.0	3.8	3.4	4.1
1986	9.5	7.5	11.5	3.7	2.9	4.6
1987	12.8	11.9	13.7	4.9	4.5	5.2
1988	16.1	14.3	17.9	6.0	5.2	6.7
1989	13.6	11.1	16.2	5.0	4.1	5.8
1990	10.7	8.0	13.4	4.0	3.0	4.9
1991	6.3	1.5	10.8	2.4	.6	4.1
1990: I	10.9	9.3	12.5	4.2	3.6	4.7
II	13.5	12.1	14.9	5.0	4.4	5.5
III	11.2	7.2	15.1	4.2	2.8	5.5
IV	7.1	3.2	10.9	2.6	1.2	3.8
1991: I	7.0	1.2	12.3	2.8	.5	4.8
II	8.7	6.0	11.2	3.3	2.3	4.2
III	6.6	.9	11.7	2.5	.3	4.4
IV	3.2	−2.2	8.0	1.2	−.8	3.0
1992: I	9.1	6.1	11.8	3.7	2.4	4.8
II	10.8	8.0	13.3	4.1	3.0	5.1
III	10.3	7.6	12.7	4.0	2.9	4.9

[1] Annual ratios based on average equity for the year (using four end-of-quarter figures). Quarterly ratios based on equity at end of quarter only.

Note.—Based on data in millions of dollars.

See Note, Table B-88.

Source: Department of Commerce, Bureau of the Census.

Table B-90.—*Sources and uses of funds, nonfarm nonfinancial corporate business, 1947–92*

[Billions of dollars; quarterly data at seasonally adjusted annual rates]

Year or quarter	Sources											Uses			Discrepancy (sources less uses)
	Total	Internal					External					Total	Capital expenditures[3]	Increase in financial assets	
		Total	U.S. undistributed profits	Inventory valuation and capital consumption adjustments	Capital consumption allowances	Foreign earnings retained abroad[1]	Total	Credit market funds			Other[2]				
								Total	Securities and mortgages	Loans and short-term paper					
1947....	27.4	13.3	12.7	−8.7	9.0	0.3	14.0	8.6	5.6	3.0	5.4	33.0	24.7	8.3	−5.7
1948....	29.7	19.7	14.0	−5.2	10.4	.4	10.1	7.7	7.0	.7	2.4	33.8	28.9	4.9	−4.1
1949....	21.3	20.0	9.6	−1.0	11.2	.3	1.3	3.8	5.6	−1.9	−2.5	26.4	22.9	3.5	−5.1
1950....	42.9	18.5	14.1	−7.9	12.0	.3	24.4	8.7	4.8	3.9	15.7	49.6	33.2	16.3	−6.7
1951....	37.3	20.8	10.8	−4.4	13.8	.6	16.6	11.5	7.1	4.4	5.1	47.3	40.0	7.3	−10.0
1952....	30.4	22.5	8.9	−2.0	14.8	.8	8.0	9.3	8.2	1.1	−1.3	30.0	25.5	4.5	.4
1953....	29.0	22.3	9.2	−3.3	15.9	.7	6.7	6.3	6.7	−.4	.4	28.1	25.9	2.2	.9
1954....	30.0	24.4	9.0	−1.9	16.8	.5	5.6	6.4	6.9	−.5	−.9	27.9	23.1	4.8	2.0
1955....	53.2	29.9	13.4	−2.0	17.8	.8	23.3	10.6	6.9	3.7	12.7	48.8	32.3	16.4	4.5
1956....	46.1	30.0	12.7	−3.7	20.0	1.0	16.1	13.4	8.1	5.3	2.7	40.9	37.1	3.9	5.2
1957....	44.2	32.0	11.5	−2.7	22.0	1.2	12.3	12.8	10.8	1.9	−.5	39.7	35.5	4.1	4.6
1958....	42.8	30.7	8.3	−1.5	23.1	.8	12.2	11.0	11.1	−.1	1.2	38.3	27.6	10.7	4.5
1959....	57.0	37.0	13.0	−1.0	24.1	.9	20.0	12.4	8.4	4.0	7.6	51.2	37.2	14.1	5.8
1960....	50.3	36.5	10.6	−.4	25.1	1.2	13.8	12.2	8.3	3.9	1.5	41.4	37.6	3.8	8.9
1961....	56.0	37.5	10.2	.6	25.8	1.0	18.5	12.4	10.9	1.5	6.1	50.6	36.5	14.1	5.4
1962....	61.9	44.0	13.0	3.2	26.8	1.1	17.9	13.4	9.5	3.9	4.5	54.6	42.2	12.3	7.4
1963....	70.2	47.8	14.5	4.0	27.9	1.4	22.3	12.9	9.1	3.8	9.5	59.9	44.4	15.5	10.3
1964....	76.0	53.0	18.4	4.0	29.3	1.3	23.0	15.0	9.0	6.0	8.0	64.5	49.8	14.7	11.4
1965....	94.4	60.1	23.4	4.0	31.3	1.4	34.4	19.7	7.8	11.9	14.7	82.4	60.8	21.6	12.0
1966....	100.6	64.3	25.0	3.5	34.1	1.7	36.3	26.4	16.0	10.4	9.8	91.0	74.5	16.5	9.6
1967....	96.4	65.3	22.2	4.2	37.3	1.6	31.1	27.2	19.0	8.2	3.9	87.3	71.2	16.2	9.1
1968....	115.0	66.7	21.3	1.9	41.1	2.3	48.3	29.4	16.8	12.6	18.9	107.3	76.8	30.5	7.7
1969....	122.1	66.5	18.4	.4	45.0	2.8	55.6	35.7	17.8	17.8	19.9	116.8	85.5	31.3	5.3
1970....	106.5	64.0	12.6	−1.1	49.4	3.2	42.5	36.7	28.8	7.8	5.9	100.2	82.0	18.3	6.3
1971....	130.6	76.1	18.7	−.1	54.2	3.2	54.5	39.2	34.7	4.6	15.3	124.3	88.2	36.1	6.4
1972....	159.0	88.1	24.6	−1.6	60.5	4.7	70.9	45.3	29.3	16.0	25.6	149.8	100.4	49.4	9.3
1973....	221.4	95.5	36.9	−15.2	65.6	8.1	126.0	81.3	49.4	31.9	44.7	195.1	125.2	69.8	26.4
1974....	188.9	91.0	45.3	−38.8	76.8	7.7	97.9	58.5	25.0	33.5	39.4	195.0	143.7	51.3	−6.1
1975....	155.0	125.0	43.4	−18.6	92.2	8.1	30.0	23.9	40.2	−16.3	6.1	157.1	117.4	39.7	−2.1
1976....	208.6	140.5	56.5	−26.1	102.5	7.6	68.1	50.1	41.8	8.3	18.0	210.5	158.8	51.7	−1.9
1977....	257.4	162.7	66.9	−27.0	114.8	8.1	94.7	68.7	43.9	24.8	26.0	245.5	185.2	60.3	11.9
1978....	316.3	183.6	78.7	−37.8	131.1	11.7	132.7	73.0	39.7	33.2	59.7	328.7	223.1	105.7	−12.4
1979....	332.5	198.5	86.4	−58.0	151.6	18.6	134.0	67.2	16.0	51.3	66.8	373.2	245.6	127.6	−40.7
1980....	330.3	199.7	69.2	−61.4	173.2	18.7	130.6	76.5	35.9	40.6	54.1	352.8	255.8	97.1	−22.5
1981....	381.9	238.9	64.2	−44.8	205.3	14.2	143.1	97.9	30.7	67.2	45.2	408.9	313.0	95.9	−26.9
1982....	316.6	247.5	30.6	−22.4	227.5	11.8	69.1	54.0	−.7	54.7	15.1	332.9	285.3	47.6	−16.3
1983....	423.3	292.3	30.5	2.9	240.1	18.8	131.0	80.1	44.6	35.5	50.9	420.5	300.1	120.4	2.8
1984....	493.1	336.3	46.4	24.1	246.1	19.7	156.8	98.0	−7.5	105.5	58.8	502.3	398.5	103.8	−9.2
1985....	465.7	351.9	21.7	54.4	256.0	19.8	113.9	58.5	1.9	56.6	55.4	457.8	374.9	83.0	7.9
1986....	515.9	336.7	−2.1	53.4	269.2	16.2	179.2	129.8	64.6	65.2	49.4	502.4	351.9	150.4	13.5
1987....	540.7	375.9	41.3	30.6	279.2	24.8	164.8	67.6	32.8	34.9	97.1	473.4	365.1	108.4	67.3
1988....	588.7	404.3	73.6	15.7	295.1	19.9	184.4	69.3	−6.7	76.0	115.1	554.2	394.4	159.8	34.4
1989....	532.2	399.9	32.2	19.8	315.1	32.8	132.3	49.4	−34.2	83.7	82.9	512.2	406.0	106.2	20.0
1990....	511.4	407.5	22.0	12.9	327.0	45.7	103.9	23.4	−11.5	34.9	80.5	482.4	395.1	87.3	29.0
1991....	444.2	416.5	8.9	20.9	338.5	48.3	27.6	18.8	87.5	−68.7	8.8	427.6	363.9	63.7	16.5
1990:															
I......	540.5	412.4	17.8	27.5	322.4	44.7	128.0	54.9	−24.7	79.6	73.1	490.6	398.7	91.9	49.8
II......	583.5	423.0	28.8	33.8	324.7	35.7	160.5	63.4	21.4	42.0	97.1	553.4	417.7	135.7	30.1
III......	511.5	391.9	30.0	−8.7	328.4	42.1	119.6	5.4	−48.9	54.4	114.2	524.9	401.8	123.0	−13.4
IV.....	410.1	402.7	11.5	−1.3	332.3	60.2	7.4	−30.0	6.3	−36.4	37.4	360.7	362.2	−1.5	49.4
1991:															
I......	366.2	417.5	5.0	21.3	336.0	55.2	−51.3	8.0	71.8	−63.8	−59.3	345.0	353.5	−8.6	21.3
II......	476.3	418.9	9.4	24.5	338.2	46.8	57.4	39.2	111.9	−72.7	18.2	436.9	351.3	85.5	39.4
III......	490.4	407.0	14.2	13.7	338.7	40.4	83.4	28.7	78.6	−49.9	54.8	489.7	371.5	118.2	.7
IV.....	443.7	422.8	7.0	24.0	341.0	50.8	20.9	−.7	87.7	−88.4	21.6	439.0	379.2	59.8	4.7
1992:															
I......	542.0	439.1	30.5	27.0	339.8	41.8	102.9	103.7	109.7	−6.0	−.8	523.8	354.1	169.6	18.2
II......	568.7	442.2	40.9	20.3	344.4	36.6	126.5	71.2	103.2	−32.0	55.4	566.2	390.8	175.3	2.6
III.....	553.1	463.3	34.1	28.5	360.2	40.6	89.8	48.4	48.7	−.4	41.4	530.6	399.0	131.6	22.5

[1] Foreign branch profits, dividends, and subsidiaries' earnings retained abroad.
[2] Consists of tax liabilities, trade debt, and direct foreign investment in the United States.
[3] Plant and equipment, residential structures, inventory investment, and mineral rights from U.S. Government.

Source: Board of Governors of the Federal Reserve System.

TABLE B–91.—*Common stock prices and yields, 1955–92*

| Year or month | Common stock prices [1] | | | | | | | Common stock yields (percent) [5] | |
| | New York Stock Exchange indexes (Dec. 31, 1965=50) [2] | | | | | Dow Jones industrial average [3] | Standard & Poor's composite index (1941–43=10) [4] | Dividend-price ratio [6] | Earnings-price ratio [7] |
	Composite	Industrial	Transportation	Utility	Finance				
1955	21.54					442.72	40.49	4.08	7.95
1956	24.40					493.01	46.62	4.09	7.55
1957	23.67					475.71	44.38	4.35	7.89
1958	24.56					491.66	46.24	3.97	6.23
1959	30.73					632.12	57.38	3.23	5.78
1960	30.01					618.04	55.85	3.47	5.90
1961	35.37					691.55	66.27	2.98	4.62
1962	33.49					639.76	62.38	3.37	5.82
1963	37.51					714.81	69.87	3.17	5.50
1964	43.76					834.05	81.37	3.01	5.32
1965	47.39					910.88	88.17	3.00	5.59
1966	46.15	46.18	50.26	45.41	44.45	873.60	85.26	3.40	6.63
1967	50.77	51.97	53.51	45.43	49.82	879.12	91.93	3.20	5.73
1968	55.37	58.00	50.58	44.19	65.85	906.00	98.70	3.07	5.67
1969	54.67	57.44	46.96	42.80	70.49	876.72	97.84	3.24	6.08
1970	45.72	48.03	32.14	37.24	60.00	753.19	83.22	3.83	6.45
1971	54.22	57.92	44.35	39.53	70.38	884.76	98.29	3.14	5.41
1972	60.29	65.73	50.17	38.48	78.35	950.71	109.20	2.84	5.50
1973	57.42	63.08	37.74	37.69	70.12	923.88	107.43	3.06	7.12
1974	43.84	48.08	31.89	29.79	49.67	759.37	82.85	4.47	11.59
1975	45.73	50.52	31.10	31.50	47.14	802.49	86.16	4.31	9.15
1976	54.46	60.44	39.57	36.97	52.94	974.92	102.01	3.77	8.90
1977	53.69	57.86	41.09	40.92	55.25	894.63	98.20	4.62	10.79
1978	53.70	58.23	43.50	39.22	56.65	820.23	96.02	5.28	12.03
1979	58.32	64.76	47.34	38.20	61.42	844.40	103.01	5.47	13.46
1980	68.10	78.70	60.61	37.35	64.25	891.41	118.78	5.26	12.66
1981	74.02	85.44	72.61	38.91	73.52	932.92	128.05	5.20	11.96
1982	68.93	78.18	60.41	39.75	71.99	884.36	119.71	5.81	11.60
1983	92.63	107.45	89.36	47.00	95.34	1,190.34	160.41	4.40	8.03
1984	92.46	108.01	85.63	46.44	89.28	1,178.48	160.46	4.64	10.02
1985	108.09	123.79	104.11	56.75	114.21	1,328.23	186.84	4.25	8.12
1986	136.00	155.85	119.87	71.36	147.20	1,792.76	236.34	3.49	6.09
1987	161.70	195.31	140.39	74.30	146.48	2,275.99	286.83	3.08	5.48
1988	149.91	180.95	134.12	71.77	127.26	2,060.82	265.79	3.64	8.01
1989	180.02	216.23	175.28	87.43	151.88	2,508.91	322.84	3.45	7.41
1990	183.46	225.78	158.62	90.60	133.26	2,678.94	334.59	3.61	6.47
1991	206.33	258.14	173.99	92.66	150.82	2,929.33	376.18	3.24	4.81
1992	229.01	284.62	201.09	99.46	179.26	3,284.29	415.74	2.99	....
1991: Jan	177.95	220.69	145.89	88.59	121.39	2,587.60	325.49	3.82	....
Feb	197.75	246.74	166.06	92.08	141.03	2,863.04	362.26	3.35	....
Mar	203.57	255.36	166.26	92.29	145.42	2,920.11	372.28	3.26	5.58
Apr	207.71	260.15	166.90	92.92	152.64	2,925.54	379.68	3.19	....
May	206.93	260.13	170.77	90.76	151.32	2,928.42	377.99	3.23	....
June	207.32	261.16	177.05	89.01	152.31	2,968.14	378.29	3.23	5.23
July	208.29	262.48	177.15	90.05	151.60	2,978.19	380.23	3.20	....
Aug	213.33	268.22	178.52	92.38	157.70	3,006.09	389.40	3.10	....
Sept	212.55	266.21	177.99	93.72	157.69	3,010.35	387.20	3.15	4.59
Oct	213.10	265.68	187.31	95.25	158.94	3,019.74	386.88	3.14	....
Nov	213.25	264.89	188.52	96.78	159.78	2,986.12	385.92	3.15	....
Dec	214.26	266.01	185.47	98.08	159.96	2,958.64	388.51	3.11	3.83
1992: Jan	229.34	286.62	201.55	99.31	174.50	3,227.06	416.08	2.90	....
Feb	228.12	286.09	205.53	96.18	174.08	3,257.27	412.56	2.94	....
Mar	225.21	282.36	204.07	94.16	173.49	3,247.42	407.36	3.01	4.01
Apr	224.55	281.60	201.28	94.92	171.10	3,294.08	407.41	3.02	....
May	228.61	285.25	207.93	98.26	175.90	3,376.79	414.81	2.99	....
June	224.68	279.54	202.02	97.23	174.82	3,337.79	408.27	3.06	4.18
July	228.17	281.90	198.36	101.18	181.00	3,329.41	415.05	3.00	....
Aug	230.07	284.44	191.31	103.41	180.47	3,307.45	417.93	2.97	....
Sept	230.13	285.76	191.61	102.26	178.27	3,293.92	418.48	3.00	4.32
Oct	226.97	279.70	192.30	101.62	181.36	3,198.70	412.50	3.07	....
Nov	232.84	287.30	204.78	101.13	189.27	3,238.49	422.84	2.98	....
Dec	239.47	294.86	212.35	103.85	196.87	3,303.15	435.64	2.90	....

[1] Averages of daily closing prices, except New York Stock Exchange data through May 1964 are averages of weekly closing prices.
[2] Includes all the stocks (more than 1,500) listed on the New York Stock Exchange.
[3] Includes 30 stocks.
[4] Includes 500 stocks.
[5] Standard & Poor's series, based on 500 stocks in the composite index.
[6] Aggregate cash dividends (based on latest known annual rate) divided by aggregate market value based on Wednesday closing prices. Monthly data are averages of weekly figures; annual data are averages of monthly figures.
[7] Quarterly data are ratio of earnings (after taxes) for 4 quarters ending with particular quarter to price index for last day of that quarter. Annual data are averages of quarterly ratios.

Note.—All data relate to stocks listed on the New York Stock Exchange.

Sources: New York Stock Exchange, Dow Jones & Co., Inc., and Standard & Poor's Corporation.

453

TABLE B–92.—*Business formation and business failures, 1950–92*

Year or month	Index of net business formation (1967=100)	New business incorporations (number)	Business failure rate [2]	Business failures [1] Number of failures Total	Under $100,000	$100,000 and over	Amount of current liabilities (millions of dollars) Total	Under $100,000	$100,000 and over
1950	87.7	93,092	34.3	9,162	8,746	416	248.3	151.2	97.1
1951	86.7	83,778	30.7	8,058	7,626	432	259.5	131.6	128.0
1952	90.8	92,946	28.7	7,611	7,081	530	283.3	131.9	151.4
1953	89.7	102,706	33.2	8,862	8,075	787	394.2	167.5	226.6
1954	88.8	117,411	42.0	11,086	10,226	860	462.6	211.4	251.2
1955	96.6	139,915	41.6	10,969	10,113	856	449.4	206.4	243.0
1956	94.6	141,163	48.0	12,686	11,615	1,071	562.7	239.8	322.9
1957	90.3	137,112	51.7	13,739	12,547	1,192	615.3	267.1	348.2
1958	90.2	150,781	55.9	14,964	13,499	1,465	728.3	297.6	430.7
1959	97.9	193,067	51.8	14,053	12,707	1,346	692.8	278.9	413.9
1960	94.5	182,713	57.0	15,445	13,650	1,795	938.6	327.2	611.4
1961	90.8	181,535	64.4	17,075	15,006	2,069	1,090.1	370.1	720.0
1962	92.6	182,057	60.8	15,782	13,772	2,010	1,213.6	346.5	867.1
1963	94.4	186,404	56.3	14,374	12,192	2,182	1,352.6	321.0	1,031.6
1964	98.2	197,724	53.2	13,501	11,346	2,155	1,329.2	313.6	1,015.6
1965	99.8	203,897	53.3	13,514	11,340	2,174	1,321.7	321.7	1,000.0
1966	99.3	200,010	51.6	13,061	10,833	2,228	1,385.7	321.5	1,064.1
1967	100.0	206,569	49.0	12,364	10,144	2,220	1,265.2	297.9	967.3
1968	108.3	233,635	38.6	9,636	7,829	1,807	941.0	241.1	699.9
1969	115.8	274,267	37.3	9,154	7,192	1,962	1,142.1	231.3	910.8
1970	108.8	264,209	43.8	10,748	8,019	2,729	1,887.8	269.3	1,618.4
1971	111.1	287,577	41.7	10,326	7,611	2,715	1,916.9	271.3	1,645.6
1972	119.3	316,601	38.3	9,566	7,040	2,526	2,000.2	258.8	1,741.5
1973	119.1	329,358	36.4	9,345	6,627	2,718	2,298.6	235.6	2,063.0
1974	113.2	319,149	38.4	9,915	6,733	3,182	3,053.1	256.9	2,796.3
1975	109.9	326,345	42.6	11,432	7,504	3,928	4,380.2	298.6	4,081.6
1976	120.4	375,766	34.8	9,628	6,176	3,452	3,011.3	257.8	2,753.4
1977	130.8	436,170	28.4	7,919	4,861	3,058	3,095.3	208.3	2,887.0
1978	138.1	478,019	23.9	6,619	3,712	2,907	2,656.0	164.7	2,491.3
1979	138.3	524,565	27.8	7,564	3,930	3,634	2,667.4	179.9	2,487.5
1980	129.9	533,520	42.1	11,742	5,682	6,060	4,635.1	272.5	4,362.6
1981	124.8	581,242	61.3	16,794	8,233	8,561	6,955.2	405.8	6,549.3
1982	116.4	566,942	89.0	24,908	11,509	13,399	15,610.8	541.7	15,069.1
1983	117.5	600,400	110.0	31,334	15,509	15,825	16,072.9	635.1	15,437.8
1984	121.3	634,991	107.0	52,078	19,618	32,460	29,268.6	409.8	28,858.8
1985	120.9	662,047	115.0	57,253	36,539	20,714	36,937.4	423.9	36,513.5
1986	120.4	702,738	120.0	61,616	38,908	22,708	44,724.0	838.3	43,885.7
1987	121.2	685,572	102.0	61,111	38,949	22,162	34,723.8	746.0	33,977.8
1988	124.1	685,095	98.0	57,097	38,300	18,797	39,573.0	686.9	38,886.1
1989	124.8	676,565	65.0	50,361	33,312	17,049	42,328.8	670.5	41,658.2
1990	120.7	647,366	76.0	60,747	40,643	20,104	56,130.1	735.6	55,394.5
1991	115.3	628,580	106.0	88,215	60,672	27,543	107,905.1	1,046.9	106,858.2
Seasonally adjusted									
1991: Jan	115.5	51,991		6,751	4,481	2,270	8,949.9	81.5	8,868.4
Feb	114.7	50,384		6,911	4,549	2,362	13,257.4	80.8	13,176.7
Mar	114.2	51,536		7,397	4,989	2,408	7,876.8	87.5	7,789.3
Apr	115.0	52,235		7,505	5,135	2,370	9,920.9	90.0	9,830.9
May	115.7	52,327		7,830	5,399	2,431	12,637.7	95.4	12,542.4
June	116.0	52,071		6,984	4,896	2,088	15,763.9	89.9	15,673.9
July	115.4	52,767		7,690	5,313	2,377	5,919.9	95.7	5,824.2
Aug	116.0	53,313		7,471	5,243	2,228	3,015.9	83.6	2,932.3
Sept	115.4	52,284		6,899	4,805	2,094	7,114.9	77.3	7,073.6
Oct	115.3	53,892		8,563	6,064	2,499	8,628.3	98.1	8,530.3
Nov	115.9	54,165		7,192	4,953	2,239	5,180.3	84.6	5,095.7
Dec	115.1	52,898		7,022	4,845	2,177	9,639.2	82.5	9,556.7
1992: Jan	116.9	58,132		8,586	6,041	2,545	7,725.3	93.2	7,632.1
Feb	115.7	55,057		8,059	5,661	2,398	6,839.3	93.8	6,745.5
Mar	115.7	57,403		9,136	6,364	2,772	6,273.6	106.9	6,166.7
Apr	115.0	54,462		8,682	6,055	2,627	7,939.2	97.3	7,841.8
May	112.6	48,673		5,741	5,409	2,332	12,020.3	88.4	11,931.9
June	117.0	58,718		8,446	6,049	2,397	13,637.0	97.0	13,540.0
July	116.8			8,625	6,129	2,496	3,568.2	97.1	3,471.2
Aug	116.9			7,946	5,559	2,387	9,317.3	89.2	9,228.0
Sept	118.6			7,557	5,373	2,184	3,204.9	87.6	3,117.3
Oct [p]	119.9			7,973	5,615	2,358	7,876.4	87.2	7,789.3

[1] Commercial and industrial failures only through 1983, excluding failures of banks, railroads, real estate, insurance, holding, and financial companies, steamship lines, travel agencies, etc.

Data beginning 1984 are based on expanded coverage and new methodology and are therefore not generally comparable with earlier data. Data for 1991 and 1992 are subject to revision due to amended court filings.

[2] Failure rate per 10,000 listed enterprises.

Sources: Department of Commerce (Bureau of Economic Analysis) and The Dun & Bradstreet Corporation.

TABLE B–93.—*Farm income, 1940–92*

[Billions of dollars; quarterly data at seasonally adjusted annual rates]

Year or quarter	Income of farm operators from farming						Net farm income	
	Gross farm income							
	Total¹	Cash marketing receipts			Value of inventory changes²	Production expenses	Current dollars	1987 dollars³
		Total	Livestock and products	Crops				
1940	11.3	8.4	4.9	3.5	0.3	6.9	4.5	40.7
1941	14.3	11.1	6.5	4.6	.4	7.8	6.5	55.5
1942	19.9	15.6	9.0	6.5	1.1	10.0	9.9	80.1
1943	23.3	19.6	11.5	8.1	−.1	11.6	11.7	93.9
1944	24.0	20.5	11.4	9.2	−.4	12.3	11.7	92.9
1945	25.4	21.7	12.0	9.7	−.4	13.1	12.3	92.6
1946	29.6	24.8	13.8	11.0	.0	14.5	15.1	90.2
1947	32.4	29.6	16.5	13.1	−1.8	17.0	15.4	82.1
1948	36.5	30.2	17.1	13.1	1.7	18.8	17.7	88.3
1949	30.8	27.8	15.4	12.4	−.9	18.0	12.8	64.2
1950	33.1	28.5	16.1	12.4	.8	19.5	13.6	67.6
1951	38.3	32.9	19.6	13.2	1.2	22.3	15.9	74.8
1952	37.8	32.5	18.2	14.3	.9	22.8	15.0	69.6
1953	34.4	31.0	16.9	14.1	−.6	21.5	13.0	59.0
1954	34.2	29.8	16.3	13.6	.5	21.8	12.4	55.7
1955	33.5	29.5	16.0	13.5	.2	22.2	11.3	49.4
1956	34.0	30.4	16.4	14.0	−.5	22.7	11.3	47.7
1957	34.8	29.7	17.4	12.3	.6	23.7	11.1	45.4
1958	39.0	33.5	19.2	14.2	.8	25.8	13.2	52.9
1959	37.9	33.6	18.9	14.7	.0	27.2	10.7	41.9
1960	38.6	34.0	19.0	15.0	.4	27.4	11.2	43.1
1961	40.5	35.2	19.5	15.7	.3	28.6	12.0	45.5
1962	42.3	36.5	20.2	16.3	.6	30.3	12.1	44.8
1963	43.4	37.5	20.0	17.4	.6	31.6	11.8	43.3
1964	42.3	37.3	19.9	17.4	−.8	31.8	10.5	37.9
1965	46.5	39.4	21.9	17.5	1.0	33.6	12.9	45.4
1966	50.5	43.4	25.0	18.4	−.1	36.5	14.0	47.5
1967	50.5	42.8	24.4	18.4	.7	38.2	12.3	40.7
1968	51.8	44.2	25.5	18.7	.1	39.5	12.3	38.8
1969	56.4	48.2	28.6	19.6	.1	42.1	14.3	42.8
1970	58.8	50.5	29.5	21.0	.0	44.5	14.4	40.8
1971	62.1	52.7	30.5	22.3	1.4	47.1	15.0	40.5
1972	71.1	61.1	35.6	25.5	.9	51.7	19.5	50.1
1973	98.9	86.9	45.8	41.1	3.4	64.6	34.4	83.2
1974	98.2	92.4	41.3	51.1	−1.6	71.0	27.3	60.7
1975	100.6	88.9	43.1	45.8	3.4	75.0	25.5	51.9
1976	102.9	95.4	46.3	49.0	−1.5	82.7	20.2	38.6
1977	108.8	96.2	47.6	48.6	1.1	88.9	19.9	35.6
1978	128.4	112.4	59.2	53.2	1.9	103.3	25.2	41.8
1979	150.7	131.5	69.2	62.3	5.0	123.3	27.4	41.9
1980	149.3	139.7	68.0	71.7	−6.3	133.1	16.1	22.5
1981	166.3	141.6	69.2	72.5	6.5	139.4	26.9	34.1
1982	164.1	142.6	70.3	72.3	−1.4	140.3	23.8	28.4
1983	153.9	136.8	69.6	67.2	−10.9	139.6	14.2	16.3
1984	168.0	142.8	72.9	69.9	6.0	141.9	26.1	28.7
1985	161.2	144.1	69.8	74.3	−2.3	132.4	28.8	30.5
1986	156.1	135.4	71.6	63.8	−2.2	125.1	31.1	32.0
1987	168.5	141.8	76.0	65.9	−2.3	128.8	39.7	39.7
1988	175.4	151.1	79.4	71.7	−3.4	134.3	41.1	39.6
1989	191.1	161.0	84.1	76.9	4.8	141.2	49.9	46.0
1990	196.0	169.9	89.9	80.0	3.5	145.1	51.0	45.0
1991	189.5	167.3	86.7	80.5	.4	144.9	44.6	37.9
1990: I	200.0	166.0	89.7	76.2	5.2	142.8	57.2	51.4
II	192.4	166.7	88.2	78.5	4.1	144.4	48.0	42.6
III	189.3	173.6	91.1	82.6	2.8	144.7	44.6	39.1
IV	202.4	173.3	90.6	82.7	1.7	148.3	54.1	47.1
1991: I	189.1	165.1	89.6	75.6	1.2	145.8	43.3	37.1
II	189.7	165.4	87.6	77.9	.6	147.2	42.5	36.2
III	185.2	170.6	84.9	85.8	.1	143.1	42.0	35.6
IV	194.1	167.9	85.0	83.0	−.1	143.4	50.6	42.6
1992: I	199.2	165.2	83.8	81.4	10.8	145.1	54.1	45.2
II	195.7	170.3	85.6	84.7	1.4	146.5	49.2	40.8
III ᵖ	190.8	174.8	84.9	89.9	.2	142.5	48.3	39.9

¹ Cash marketing receipts and inventory changes plus Government payments, other farm cash income, and nonmoney income furnished by farms.
² Physical changes in end-of-period inventory of crop and livestock commodities valued at average prices during the period.
³ Income in current dollars divided by the GDP implicit price deflator (Department of Commerce).

Note.—Data include net Commodity Credit Corporation loans and operator households.

Source: Department of Agriculture, except as noted.

[1977 = 100]

Year	Farm output						Productivity indicators		
	Total [1]	Crops [2]				Livestock and products [2]	Farm output		Crop production per acre [5]
		Total [3]	Feed grains	Food grains	Oil crops		Per unit of total input	Per hour of farm work [4]	
1947	58	56	39	64	22	65	55	18	57
1948	63	64	57	62	27	64	60	21	64
1949	62	61	50	53	26	67	57	20	60
1950	61	59	51	49	26	70	58	22	59
1951	63	60	47	49	26	73	60	24	59
1952	66	62	50	63	26	74	62	26	62
1953	66	62	49	57	26	74	64	28	62
1954	66	61	51	51	28	77	65	29	61
1955	69	63	54	48	30	79	66	30	63
1956	69	63	54	50	34	79	67	31	64
1957	67	62	58	47	33	78	67	33	65
1958	73	69	64	69	39	79	74	39	73
1959	74	68	66	55	36	83	73	39	72
1960	76	72	69	66	38	82	76	42	77
1961	76	70	62	60	43	86	78	44	78
1962	77	71	62	56	44	86	78	46	81
1963	80	74	68	59	46	89	82	51	83
1964	79	72	59	65	46	91	81	52	81
1965	82	76	70	67	53	89	84	56	85
1966	79	73	70	67	55	91	83	59	83
1967	83	77	79	76	56	94	85	64	86
1968	85	79	75	80	64	94	87	68	89
1969	85	80	78	74	65	95	88	72	91
1970	84	77	71	69	66	99	87	74	88
1971	92	86	92	81	68	100	95	85	96
1972	91	87	88	77	74	101	94	83	99
1973	93	92	91	86	87	99	95	86	99
1974	88	84	74	91	71	100	90	81	88
1975	95	93	91	108	86	95	99	90	96
1976	97	92	96	107	74	99	98	97	94
1977	100	100	100	100	100	100	100	100	100
1978	104	102	108	93	105	101	101	104	105
1979	111	113	116	108	129	104	105	113	113
1980	104	101	97	121	99	108	101	109	100
1981	118	117	121	144	114	109	116	123	115
1982	116	117	122	138	121	107	119	125	116
1983	96	88	67	117	91	109	100	99	100
1984	112	111	116	129	106	107	118	121	112
1985	118	118	134	121	117	110	129	139	120
1986	111	109	123	107	110	110	124	139	116
1987	110	108	106	107	108	113	124	142	123
1988	102	92	73	98	89	116	116	135	106
1989	114	107	108	107	106	116	130	147	119
1990	119	114	112	136	107	118	135	142	127
1991	120	111	106	104	114	119	....	....	125

[1] Farm output measures the annual volume of net farm production available for eventual human use through sales from farms or consumption in farm households.
[2] Gross production.
[3] Includes items not included in groups shown.
[4] Survey-based labor productivity time series; not comparable with data published in the issues of the *Economic Report of the President* prior to January 1989.
[5] Computed from variable weights for individual crops produced each year.

Source: Department of Agriculture.

TABLE B-95.—*Farm input use, selected inputs, 1947–91*

Year	Farm population, April [1]		Farm employment (thousands) [3]			Crops harvested (millions of acres) [4]	Selected indexes of input use (1977=100)					
	Number (thousands)	As percent of total population [2]	Total	Family workers	Hired workers		Total	Farm labor	Farm real estate	Mechanical power and machinery	Agricultural chemicals [5]	Feed, seed, and livestock purchases [6]
1947	25,829	17.9	10,382	8,115	2,267	355	104	297	106	54	15	51
1948	24,383	16.6	10,363	8,026	2,337	356	104	285	107	62	16	52
1949	24,194	16.2	9,964	7,712	2,252	360	108	285	108	68	18	56
1950	23,048	15.2	9,926	7,597	2,329	345	106	265	109	72	19	58
1951	21,890	14.2	9,546	7,310	2,236	344	106	251	109	77	21	62
1952	21,748	13.9	9,149	7,005	2,144	349	105	237	108	81	23	63
1953	19,874	12.5	8,864	6,775	2,089	348	103	220	108	82	24	63
1954	19,019	11.7	8,651	6,570	2,081	346	102	214	108	82	24	65
1955	19,078	11.5	8,381	6,345	2,036	340	104	220	108	83	26	66
1956	18,712	11.1	7,852	5,900	1,952	324	103	212	106	84	27	69
1957	17,656	10.3	7,600	5,660	1,940	324	100	196	105	83	27	68
1958	17,128	9.8	7,503	5,521	1,982	324	98	182	104	83	28	73
1959	16,592	9.3	7,342	5,390	1,952	324	101	183	105	84	32	77
1960	15,635	8.7	7,057	5,172	1,885	324	99	177	103	83	32	77
1961	14,803	8.1	6,919	5,029	1,890	302	98	167	103	80	35	81
1962	14,313	7.7	6,700	4,873	1,827	295	98	163	104	80	38	83
1963	13,367	7.1	6,518	4,738	1,780	298	98	155	104	79	43	83
1964	12,954	6.7	6,110	4,506	1,604	298	98	148	104	80	46	85
1965	12,363	6.4	5,610	4,128	1,482	298	97	144	103	80	49	86
1966	11,595	5.9	5,214	3,854	1,360	294	96	132	102	82	56	89
1967	10,875	5.5	4,903	3,650	1,253	306	98	128	104	85	66	92
1968	10,454	5.2	4,749	3,535	1,213	300	97	124	102	86	69	89
1969	10,307	5.1	4,596	3,419	1,176	290	96	118	102	86	73	93
1970	9,712	4.7	4,523	3,348	1,175	293	96	112	105	85	75	96
1971	9,425	4.5	4,436	3,275	1,161	305	97	108	103	87	81	102
1972	9,610	4.6	4,373	3,228	1,146	294	97	110	102	86	86	104
1973	9,472	4.5	4,337	3,169	1,168	321	98	109	100	90	90	107
1974	9,264	4.3	4,389	3,075	1,314	328	98	109	99	92	92	99
1975	8,864	4.1	4,342	3,026	1,317	336	97	106	97	96	83	93
1976	8,253	3.8	4,374	2,997	1,377	337	98	100	98	98	96	101
1977	[7] 6,194	[7] 2.8	4,155	2,859	1,296	345	100	100	100	100	100	100
1978	[7] 6,501	[7] 2.9	3,957	2,689	1,268	338	102	100	100	104	107	108
1979	[7] 6,241	[7] 2.8	3,774	2,501	1,273	348	105	99	103	104	123	· 115
1980	[7] 6,051	[7] 2.7	3,705	2,402	1,303	352	103	96	103	101	123	114
1981	[7] 5,850	[7] 2.5	[8] 3,552	[8] 2,267	[8] 1,285	366	102	96	104	98	129	108
1982	[7] 5,628	[7] 2.4	[8] 3,400	[8] 2,136	[8] 1,264	362	98	93	102	89	118	107
1983	[7] 5,787	[7] 2.5	[8] 3,247	[8] 2,007	[8] 1,240	306	96	97	101	86	102	103
1984	5,754	2.4	[8] 3,094	[8] 1,976	[8] 1,118	348	95	92	99	85	120	103
1985	5,355	2.2	2,941	1,904	1,037	342	91	85	97	80	115	102
1986	5,226	2.2	2,749	1,768	981	325	89	80	96	77	109	109
1987	4,986	2.1	2,734	1,743	992	302	89	78	95	74	111	116
1988	4,951	2.1	2,789	1,810	979	297	87	75	94	74	112	111
1989	4,801	2.0	2,873	1,926	947	318	87	76	93	73	119	113
1990	4,591	1.9	2,869	1,965	904	322	88	80	93	71	122	113
1991	4,632	1.9	2,877	1,967	910	318						

[1] Farm population as defined by Department of Agriculture and Department of Commerce, i.e., civilian population living on farms in rural areas, regardless of occupation. See also footnote 7.

[2] Total population of United States including Armed Forces overseas, as of July 1.

[3] Includes persons doing farmwork on all farms. These data, published by the Department of Agriculture, differ from those on agricultural employment by the Department of Labor (see Table B-30) because of differences in the method of approach, in concepts of employment, and in time of month for which the data are collected.

[4] Acreage harvested plus acreages in fruits, tree nuts, and farm gardens.

[5] Fertilizer, lime, and pesticides.

[6] Nonfarm constant dollar value of feed, seed, and livestock purchases.

[7] Based on new definition of a farm. Under old definition of a farm, farm population (in thousands and as percent of total population) for 1977, 1978, 1979, 1980, 1981, 1982, and 1983 is 7,806 and 3.6; 8,005 and 3.6; 7,553 and 3.4; 7,241 and 3.2; 7,014 and 3.1; 6,880 and 3.0; 7,029 and 3.0, respectively.

[8] Basis for farm employment series was discontinued for 1981 through 1984. Employment is estimated for these years.

Note.—Population includes Alaska and Hawaii beginning 1960.

Sources: Department of Agriculture and Department of Commerce (Bureau of the Census).

TABLE B-96.—*Indexes of prices received and prices paid by farmers, 1950–92*

[1977 = 100]

Year or month	Prices received by farmers			Prices paid by farmers						Addendum: Average farm real estate value per acre [3]
	All farm products	Crops	Livestock and products	All commodities, services, interest, taxes, and wage rates [1]	Production items				Wage rates	
					Total [2]	Tractors and self-propelled machinery	Fertilizer	Fuels and energy		
1950	56	54	58	37	42		54		22	14
1951	66	61	70	41	47		57		25	16
1952	63	62	64	42	47		59		26	18
1953	56	55	56	40	44		59		27	18
1954	54	56	52	40	44		59		27	18
1955	51	53	49	40	43		58		27	19
1956	50	54	47	40	43		57		28	19
1957	51	52	51	42	44		58		29	21
1958	55	52	57	43	46		58		30	22
1959	53	51	53	43	46		57		32	23
1960	52	51	53	44	46		57		33	24
1961	53	52	52	44	46		58		33	25
1962	53	54	53	45	47		58		34	26
1963	53	55	51	45	47		57		35	27
1964	52	55	49	45	47		57		36	29
1965	54	53	54	47	48	39	57	49	38	31
1966	58	55	60	49	50	40	56	49	41	33
1967	55	52	57	49	50	42	55	50	44	35
1968	56	52	60	51	50	44	52	50	48	38
1969	59	50	67	53	52	47	48	51	53	40
1970	60	52	67	55	54	49	48	52	57	42
1971	62	56	67	58	57	51	50	53	59	43
1972	69	60	77	62	61	54	52	54	63	47
1973	98	91	104	71	73	58	56	57	69	53
1974	105	117	94	81	83	68	92	79	79	66
1975	101	105	98	89	91	82	120	88	85	75
1976	102	102	101	95	97	91	102	93	93	86
1977	100	100	100	100	100	100	100	100	100	100
1978	115	105	124	108	108	109	100	105	107	109
1979	132	116	147	123	125	122	108	137	117	125
1980	134	125	144	138	138	136	134	188	127	145
1981	139	134	143	150	148	152	144	213	138	158
1982	133	121	145	159	153	165	144	210	144	157
1983	135	128	141	161	152	174	137	202	148	148
1984	142	138	146	164	155	181	143	201	151	146
1985	128	120	136	162	151	178	135	201	154	128
1986	123	107	138	159	144	174	124	162	158	112
1987	127	106	146	162	148	174	118	164	166	103
1988	138	126	150	170	157	181	130	167	171	106
1989	147	134	160	178	165	193	137	180	185	111
1990	149	127	170	184	171	202	131	204	191	112
1991	146	130	161	189	173	211	134	203	201	115
1992 ᵖ	139	121	157	191	174	219	131	199	210	115
1991: Jan	144	121	166	188	173	208	132	219	204	115
Feb	145	122	166							
Mar	148	128	168							
Apr	149	131	166	189	175	210	136	198	203	
May	151	137	165							
June	152	142	162							
July	148	135	162	189	173	210	136	196	203	
Aug	146	133	158							
Sept	147	137	157							
Oct	142	126	158	189	172	216	132	200	194	
Nov	139	124	153							
Dec	137	120	153							
1992: Jan	138	123	152	189	171	216	132	192	216	115
Feb	142	128	156							
Mar	143	131	155							
Apr	141	126	155	191	174	217	132	194	212	
May	141	123	157							
June	140	122	157							
July	138	117	158	192	175	217	132	206	212	
Aug	139	117	160							
Sept	138	117	158							
Oct	139	116	160	192	174	224	128	205	201	
Nov	136	115	156							
Dec	138	117	157							

[1] Includes items used for family living, not shown separately.
[2] Includes other production items not shown separately.
[3] Average for 48 States. Annual data are for March 1 of each year through 1975, February 1 for 1976–81, April 1 for 1982–85, February 1 for 1986–89, and January 1 for 1990, 1991 and 1992.

Source: Department of Agriculture.

TABLE B-97.—U.S. exports and imports of agricultural commodities, 1940–92

[Billions of dollars]

Year	Exports Total¹	Feed grains	Food grains²	Oilseeds and products	Cotton	Tobacco	Animals and products	Imports Total¹	Crops, fruits, and vegetables³	Animals and products	Coffee	Cocoa beans and products	Agricultural trade balance
1940	0.5	(⁴)	(⁴)	(⁴)	0.2	(⁴)	0.1	1.3	(⁴)	0.2	0.1	(⁴)	−0.8
1941	.7	(⁴)	0.1	(⁴)	.1	0.1	.3	1.7	0.1	.3	.2	(⁴)	−1.0
1942	1.2	(⁴)	(⁴)	(⁴)	.1	.1	.8	1.3	(⁴)	.5	.2	(⁴)	−.1
1943	2.1	(⁴)	.1	0.1	.2	.2	1.2	1.5	.1	.4	.3	(⁴)	.6
1944	2.1	(⁴)	.1	.1	.1	.1	1.3	1.8	.1	.3	.3	(⁴)	.3
1945	2.3	(⁴)	.4	(⁴)	.3	.2	.9	1.7	.1	.4	.3	(⁴)	.5
1946	3.1	0.1	.7	(⁴)	.5	.4	.9	2.3	.2	.4	.5	0.1	.8
1947	4.0	.4	1.4	.1	.4	.3	.7	2.8	.1	.4	.6	.2	1.2
1948	3.5	.1	1.5	.2	.5	.2	.5	3.1	.2	.6	.7	.2	.3
1949	3.6	.3	1.1	.3	.9	.3	.4	2.9	.2	.4	.8	.1	.7
1950	2.9	.2	.6	.2	1.0	.3	.3	4.0	.2	.7	1.1	.2	−1.1
1951	4.0	.3	1.1	.3	1.1	.3	.5	5.2	.2	1.1	1.4	.2	−1.1
1952	3.4	.3	1.1	.2	.9	.2	.3	4.5	.2	.7	1.4	.2	−1.1
1953	2.8	.3	.7	.2	.5	.3	.4	4.2	.2	.6	1.5	.2	−1.3
1954	3.1	.2	.5	.3	.8	.3	.5	4.0	.2	.5	1.5	.3	−.9
1955	3.2	.3	.6	.4	.5	.4	.6	4.0	.2	.5	1.4	.2	−.8
1956	4.2	.4	1.0	.5	.7	.3	.7	4.0	.2	.4	1.4	.2	.2
1957	4.5	.3	1.0	.5	1.0	.4	.7	4.0	.2	.5	1.4	.2	.6
1958	3.9	.5	.8	.4	.7	.4	.5	3.9	.2	.7	1.2	.2	(⁴)
1959	4.0	.6	.9	.6	.4	.3	.6	4.1	.2	.8	1.1	.2	−.1
1960	4.8	.5	1.2	.6	1.0	.4	.6	3.8	.2	.6	1.0	.2	1.0
1961	5.0	.5	1.4	.6	.9	.4	.6	3.7	.2	.7	1.0	.2	1.3
1962	5.0	.8	1.3	.7	.5	.4	.6	3.9	.2	.9	1.0	.2	1.2
1963	5.6	.8	1.5	.8	.6	.4	.7	4.0	.3	.9	1.0	.2	1.6
1964	6.3	.9	1.7	1.0	.7	.4	.8	4.1	.3	.8	1.2	.2	2.3
1965	6.2	1.1	1.4	1.2	.5	.4	.8	4.1	.3	.9	1.1	.1	2.1
1966	6.9	1.3	1.8	1.2	.4	.5	.7	4.5	.4	1.2	1.1	.1	2.4
1967	6.4	1.1	1.5	1.3	.5	.5	.7	4.5	.4	1.1	1.0	.2	1.9
1968	6.3	.9	1.4	1.3	.5	.5	.7	5.0	.5	1.3	1.2	.2	1.3
1969	6.0	.9	1.2	1.3	.3	.6	.8	5.0	.5	1.4	.9	.2	1.1
1970	7.3	1.1	1.4	1.9	.4	.5	.9	5.8	.5	1.6	1.2	.3	1.5
1971	7.7	1.0	1.3	2.2	.6	.5	1.0	5.8	.6	1.5	1.2	.2	1.9
1972	9.4	1.5	1.8	2.4	.5	.7	1.1	6.5	.7	1.8	1.3	.2	2.9
1973	17.7	3.5	4.7	4.3	.9	.7	1.6	8.4	.8	2.6	1.7	.3	9.3
1974	21.9	4.6	5.4	5.7	1.3	.8	1.8	10.2	.8	2.2	1.6	.5	11.7
1975	21.9	5.2	6.2	4.5	1.0	.9	1.7	9.3	.8	1.8	1.7	.5	12.6
1976	23.0	6.0	4.7	5.1	1.0	.9	2.4	11.0	.9	2.3	2.9	.6	12.0
1977	23.6	4.9	3.6	6.6	1.5	1.1	2.7	13.4	1.2	2.3	4.2	1.0	10.2
1978	29.4	5.9	5.5	8.2	1.7	1.4	3.0	14.8	1.5	3.1	4.0	1.4	14.6
1979	34.7	7.7	6.3	8.9	2.2	1.2	3.8	16.7	1.7	3.9	4.2	1.2	18.0
1980	41.2	9.8	7.9	9.4	2.9	1.3	3.8	17.4	1.6	3.8	4.2	.9	23.9
1981	43.3	9.4	9.6	9.6	2.3	1.5	4.2	16.8	2.0	3.5	2.9	.9	26.6
1982	36.6	6.4	7.9	9.1	2.0	1.5	3.9	15.4	2.3	3.7	2.9	.7	21.2
1983	36.1	7.3	7.4	8.7	1.8	1.5	3.8	16.6	2.3	3.8	2.8	.8	19.5
1984	37.8	8.1	7.5	8.4	2.4	1.5	4.2	19.3	3.1	4.1	3.3	1.1	18.5
1985	29.0	6.0	4.5	5.8	1.6	1.5	4.1	20.0	3.5	4.2	3.3	1.4	9.1
1986	26.2	3.1	3.8	6.5	.8	1.2	4.5	21.5	3.6	4.5	4.6	1.1	4.7
1987	28.7	3.8	3.8	6.4	1.6	1.1	5.2	20.4	3.6	4.9	2.9	1.2	8.3
1988	37.1	5.9	5.9	7.7	2.0	1.3	6.4	21.0	3.8	5.2	2.5	1.0	16.1
1989	39.9	7.7	7.1	6.3	2.3	1.3	6.4	21.7	4.2	5.1	2.4	1.0	18.2
1990	39.4	7.0	4.8	5.7	2.8	1.4	6.7	22.8	4.9	5.6	1.9	1.1	16.6
1991	39.2	5.8	4.2	6.4	2.5	1.4	7.0	22.7	4.8	5.5	1.9	1.1	16.5
Jan–Oct:													
1991	31.3	4.8	3.3	4.7	2.0	1.1	5.7	18.9	4.0	4.6	1.5	.9	12.4
1992	35.3	4.6	4.4	5.8	1.7	1.3	6.6	20.6	4.0	4.7	1.4	.9	14.7

¹ Total includes items not shown separately.
² Rice, wheat, and wheat flour.
³ Includes nuts, fruits, and vegetable preparations.
⁴ Less than $50 million.

Note.—Data derived from official estimates released by the Bureau of the Census, Department of Commerce. Agricultural commodities are defined as (1) nonmarine food products and (2) other products of agriculture which have not passed through complex processes of manufacture. Export value, at U.S. port of exportation, is based on the selling price and includes inland freight, insurance, and other charges to the port. Import value, defined generally as the market value in the foreign country, excludes import duties, ocean freight, and marine insurance.

Source: Department of Agriculture.

459

[Billions of dollars]

End of year	Assets									Claims			
	Total assets	Physical assets						Financial assets		Total claims	Real estate debt [5]	Non-real estate debt [6]	Propri-etors' equity
		Real estate	Nonreal estate					Invest-ments in cooper-atives	Other [4]				
			Live-stock and poul-try [1]	Machin-ery and motor vehicles	Crops [2]	Pur-chased in-puts [3]	House-hold equip-ment and furnish-ings						
1939	52.6	33.6	5.1	3.1	2.2		4.2	0.8	3.5	52.6	6.6	3.0	43.0
1940	53.7	34.0	5.3	3.3	2.3		4.1	.9	3.9	53.7	6.5	3.3	43.8
1941	61.4	36.6	7.1	4.0	3.2		4.8	.9	4.7	61.4	6.4	3.5	51.5
1942	72.9	41.5	9.6	4.9	4.3		4.8	1.0	6.5	72.9	6.0	3.2	63.7
1943	82.9	47.7	9.7	5.4	5.5		4.7	1.1	8.8	82.9	5.4	2.9	74.5
1944	92.1	52.9	9.0	6.5	6.0		5.2	1.2	11.3	92.1	4.9	2.7	84.4
1945	102.4	60.5	9.7	5.4	6.0		5.6	1.7	13.5	102.4	4.8	2.9	94.8
1946	116.4	68.7	11.9	5.3	7.0		7.2	1.9	14.4	116.4	4.9	3.5	108.1
1947	127.4	73.5	13.3	7.4	8.9		8.1	2.0	14.3	127.4	5.1	4.1	118.3
1948	133.2	76.0	14.4	10.1	7.4		8.9	2.2	14.2	133.2	5.3	4.9	123.0
1949	130.7	75.1	12.9	12.2	5.9		8.4	2.4	13.8	130.7	5.6	5.2	119.9
1950	153.3	88.9	17.1	14.1	7.1		9.6	2.7	13.8	153.3	6.1	6.1	141.1
1951	170.1	98.7	19.5	16.7	8.2		10.0	2.9	14.1	170.1	6.7	7.4	156.0
1952	166.8	100.0	14.8	17.4	7.9		9.6	3.2	14.1	166.8	7.3	7.7	151.9
1953	162.8	98.9	11.7	18.4	6.8		9.5	3.3	14.2	162.8	7.8	6.8	148.2
1954	167.5	102.5	11.2	18.7	7.5		9.7	3.5	14.4	167.5	8.3	7.2	152.0
1955	173.0	108.2	10.6	19.3	6.5		10.0	3.7	14.6	173.0	9.0	7.9	156.0
1956	182.2	116.1	11.0	20.2	6.8		9.6	4.0	14.4	182.2	9.9	8.0	164.4
1957	191.5	122.7	13.9	20.1	6.4		9.6	4.2	14.6	191.5	10.4	8.8	172.3
1958	207.0	131.5	17.7	21.8	6.9		9.4	4.5	15.1	207.0	11.1	10.1	185.8
1959	210.4	138.4	15.2	22.7	6.2		9.2	4.8	13.8	210.4	12.1	11.5	186.8
1960	210.0	139.7	15.6	22.2	6.2		8.7	4.2	13.3	210.0	12.9	12.0	185.1
1961	217.8	145.8	16.4	22.5	6.3		8.9	4.5	13.3	217.8	14.0	12.7	191.1
1962	225.6	151.5	17.3	23.5	6.3		8.8	4.6	13.6	225.6	15.2	14.2	196.2
1963	233.9	159.7	15.9	23.9	7.2		8.8	5.0	13.5	233.9	16.9	15.7	201.4
1964	242.2	168.7	14.4	24.8	6.8		8.4	5.2	13.8	242.2	18.9	16.4	206.8
1965	259.9	180.8	17.6	26.0	7.7		8.4	5.4	14.1	259.9	21.2	18.1	220.6
1966	273.3	190.7	19.0	27.4	7.9		8.3	5.7	14.2	273.3	23.1	19.8	230.4
1967	287.2	201.4	18.8	29.8	7.7		8.8	5.8	14.7	287.2	25.2	20.8	241.1
1968	300.4	211.0	20.2	31.3	7.2		9.4	6.1	15.2	300.4	27.5	20.4	252.5
1969	311.6	217.1	22.5	32.3	8.1		9.6	6.4	15.6	311.6	29.4	21.2	261.0
1970	324.3	224.5	23.7	34.4	8.5		10.0	7.2	16.0	324.3	30.5	22.3	271.5
1971	350.1	240.9	27.3	36.7	9.7		10.8	7.9	16.8	350.1	32.4	25.1	292.6
1972	393.0	268.7	33.7	39.3	12.7		11.9	8.7	18.0	393.0	35.4	28.0	329.7
1973	477.9	329.2	42.4	44.2	21.2		12.3	9.7	19.0	477.9	39.8	33.1	405.0
1974 [7]	513.2	369.5	24.6	53.6	22.5		14.0	11.2	17.8	513.2	44.9	36.7	431.6
1975	579.5	421.0	29.4	63.1	20.5		14.2	13.0	18.4	579.5	49.9	41.6	488.0
1976	667.7	499.8	29.0	70.1	20.6		15.2	14.3	18.7	667.7	55.4	47.8	564.6
1977	735.0	556.5	31.9	76.4	20.5		17.2	13.5	19.0	735.0	63.9	55.0	616.1
1978	862.0	656.0	50.1	76.4	23.8		20.0	16.1	19.7	862.0	72.8	63.8	725.4
1979	1,001.5	767.8	61.4	82.9	29.9		21.5	18.1	19.9	1,001.5	86.8	75.7	839.1
1980	1,089.0	850.1	60.6	86.9	32.7		19.4	19.3	20.0	1,089.0	97.5	81.2	910.3
1981	1,088.9	851.7	53.5	92.5	29.5		20.8	20.6	20.3	1,088.9	107.2	88.2	893.5
1982	1,056.2	819.1	53.0	92.6	25.8		23.0	21.9	20.8	1,056.2	111.3	91.8	853.1
1983	1,063.6	829.3	49.5	92.1	23.6		24.4	22.8	21.8	1,063.6	113.7	92.7	857.1
1984	975.7	735.0	49.5	91.1	26.1	2.0	24.3	24.3	23.4	975.7	112.3	92.0	771.4
1985	892.8	657.0	46.3	88.3	22.9	1.2	27.8	24.3	25.0	892.8	105.7	82.2	704.9
1986	847.7	613.0	47.8	86.1	16.3	2.1	28.7	24.4	29.4	847.7	95.9	70.8	681.0
1987	911.3	658.6	58.0	84.5	17.5	3.2	32.9	25.3	31.4	911.3	87.7	66.0	757.6
1988	951.5	682.2	62.2	86.1	23.3	3.5	37.0	25.1	32.1	951.5	83.0	65.6	802.9
1989	985.8	703.9	66.2	89.2	23.4	2.6	42.2	26.3	32.0	985.8	80.5	65.5	839.8
1990	1,003.6	711.4	70.9	88.6	22.8	2.8	46.4	27.5	33.3	1,003.6	78.4	66.7	858.5
1991	1,004.1	705.6	68.4	88.0	23.6	2.5	50.4	28.4	37.2	1,004.1	79.1	67.8	857.1
1992 [f]	1,011	705	72	88	23	3	53	29	39	1,011	80	68	863

[f] Forecast.
[1] Excludes commercial broilers; also excludes horses and mules beginning 1959, and turkeys beginning 1986.
[2] Non-Commodity Credit Corporation (CCC) crops held on farms plus value above loan rate for crops held under CCC.
[3] Includes fertilizer, chemicals, fuels, parts, feed, seed, and other supplies.
[4] Sum of currency, demand deposits, time deposits, and U.S. savings bonds.
[5] Includes CCC storage and drying facilities loans.
[6] Does not include CCC crop loans.
[7] Beginning 1974, data are for farms included in the new farm definition, that is, places with sales of $1,000 or more annually.
Note.—Data include operator households.
Beginning 1959, data include Alaska and Hawaii.
Source: Department of Agriculture.

TABLE B-99.—*International investment position of the United States at year-end, 1983–91*

[Billions of dollars]

Type of investment	1983	1984	1985	1986	1987	1988	1989	1990	1991
NET INTERNATIONAL INVESTMENT POSITION OF THE UNITED STATES:									
With direct investment at current cost	337.4	232.9	139.0	18.7	−26.6	−183.7	−312.3	−294.8	−361.5
With direct investment at market value	267.6	175.9	142.2	109.1	54.2	−38.0	−158.8	−272.0	−381.8
U.S. ASSETS ABROAD:									
With direct investment at current cost	1,169.2	1,177.5	1,252.5	1,410.2	1,564.7	1,654.6	1,794.7	1,884.2	1,960.3
With direct investment at market value	1,068.3	1,081.8	1,244.5	1,507.7	1,648.4	1,817.5	2,049.8	1,977.1	2,107.0
U.S. official reserve assets	123.1	105.0	117.9	139.9	162.4	144.2	168.7	174.7	159.2
Gold [1]	100.5	81.2	85.8	102.4	127.6	107.4	105.2	102.4	92.6
Special drawing rights	5.0	5.6	7.3	8.4	10.3	9.6	10.0	11.0	11.2
Reserve position in the International Monetary Fund	11.3	11.5	11.9	11.7	11.3	9.7	9.0	9.1	9.5
Foreign currencies	6.3	6.7	12.9	17.3	13.1	17.4	44.6	52.2	45.9
U.S. Government assets other than official reserves	79.6	85.0	87.8	89.6	88.9	85.9	84.6	82.2	78.7
U.S. credits and other long-term assets	77.8	82.9	85.8	88.7	88.1	85.4	84.2	81.8	77.4
Repayable in dollars	76.0	81.1	84.1	87.1	86.5	83.9	82.7	80.5	76.1
Other	1.8	1.8	1.7	1.6	1.6	1.5	1.5	1.3	1.2
U.S. foreign currency holdings and U.S. short-term assets	1.8	2.1	1.9	.9	.8	.5	.3	.4	1.4
U.S. private assets:									
With direct investment at current cost	966.4	987.5	1,046.9	1,180.7	1,313.5	1,424.5	1,541.5	1,627.3	1,722.3
With direct investment at market value	865.5	891.8	1,038.8	1,278.2	1,397.1	1,587.5	1,796.5	1,720.2	1,869.1
Direct investment abroad:									
At current cost	371.7	361.6	387.2	421.2	493.3	515.7	552.8	623.6	655.3
At market value	270.8	265.8	379.1	518.7	577.0	678.6	807.9	716.4	802.0
Foreign securities	84.7	88.8	114.7	145.9	164.7	183.1	220.9	241.7	305.9
Bonds	58.6	62.8	73.7	82.9	95.1	97.1	101.0	131.7	147.6
Corporate stocks	26.2	26.0	41.0	63.0	69.6	86.0	119.9	110.0	158.3
U.S. claims on unaffiliated foreigners reported by U.S. nonbanking concerns	75.5	91.5	97.6	106.3	106.0	117.7	106.1	109.8	104.4
U.S. claims reported by U.S. banks, not included elsewhere	434.5	445.6	447.4	507.3	549.5	608.0	661.7	652.1	656.8
FOREIGN ASSETS IN THE UNITED STATES:									
With direct investment at current cost	831.8	944.7	1,113.6	1,391.5	1,591.4	1,838.3	2,107.0	2,179.0	2,321.8
With direct investment at market value	800.7	905.9	1,102.3	1,398.6	1,594.1	1,855.5	2,208.6	2,249.1	2,488.9
Foreign official assets in the United States	194.5	199.7	202.5	241.2	283.1	322.0	337.3	371.1	396.6
U.S. Government securities	137.0	144.7	145.1	178.9	220.5	260.9	265.7	297.0	318.0
U.S. Treasury securities	129.7	138.2	138.4	173.3	213.7	253.0	256.1	286.7	305.9
Other	7.3	6.5	6.6	5.6	6.8	8.0	9.6	10.3	12.1
Other U.S. Government liabilities	14.2	15.0	15.8	18.0	15.7	15.2	15.3	17.2	18.8
U.S. liabilities reported by U.S. banks, not included elsewhere	25.5	26.1	26.7	27.9	31.8	31.5	36.5	39.9	38.4
Other foreign official assets	17.7	14.0	14.9	16.4	15.0	14.4	19.7	17.0	21.4
Other foreign assets in the United States:									
With direct investment at current cost	637.3	745.0	911.1	1,150.2	1,308.3	1,516.3	1,769.7	1,807.9	1,925.2
With direct investment at market value	606.2	706.2	899.8	1,157.4	1,311.1	1,533.4	1,871.3	1,878.0	2,092.3
Direct investment in the United States:									
At current cost	184.4	211.2	231.3	265.8	313.5	374.3	433.2	466.5	487.0
At market value	153.3	172.4	220.0	273.0	316.2	391.5	534.7	536.6	654.1
U.S. Treasury securities	33.8	62.1	88.0	96.1	82.6	100.9	134.5	130.7	154.7
U.S. securities other than U.S. Treasury securities	113.8	128.5	207.9	309.8	341.7	392.3	484.4	471.9	559.7
Corporate and other bonds	17.5	32.4	82.3	140.9	166.1	191.3	223.8	240.7	277.0
Corporate stocks	96.4	96.1	125.6	168.9	175.6	201.0	260.6	231.2	282.6
U.S. liabilities to unaffiliated foreigners reported by U.S. nonbanking concerns	26.9	31.0	29.5	26.9	29.8	35.0	40.5	45.4	43.8
U.S. liabilities reported by U.S. banks, not included elsewhere	278.3	312.2	354.5	451.6	540.7	613.7	677.1	693.4	680.1

[1] Valued at market price.

Note.—For details regarding these data, see *Survey of Current Business*, June 1991 and June 1992.

Source: Department of Commerce, Bureau of Economic Analysis.

TABLE B-100.—U.S. international transactions, 1946–92

[Millions of dollars; quarterly data seasonally adjusted, except as noted. Credits (+), debits (−)]

Year or quarter	Merchandise [1][2]			Services			Investment income			Balance on goods, services, and income	Unilateral transfers, net [4]	Balance on current account
	Exports	Imports	Net	Net military transactions [3][4]	Net travel and transportation receipts	Other services, net	Receipts on U.S. assets abroad	Payments on foreign assets in U.S.	Net			
1946	11,764	−5,067	6,697	−424	733	310	772	−212	560	7,876	−2,991	4,885
1947	16,097	−5,973	10,124	−358	946	145	1,102	−245	857	11,714	−2,722	8,992
1948	13,265	−7,557	5,708	−351	374	175	1,921	−437	1,484	7,390	−4,973	2,417
1949	12,213	−6,874	5,339	−410	230	208	1,831	−476	1,355	6,722	−5,849	873
1950	10,203	−9,081	1,122	−56	−120	242	2,068	−559	1,509	2,697	−4,537	−1,840
1951	14,243	−11,176	3,067	169	298	254	2,633	−583	2,050	5,838	−4,954	884
1952	13,449	−10,838	2,611	528	83	309	2,751	−555	2,196	5,727	−5,113	614
1953	12,412	−10,975	1,437	1,753	−238	307	2,736	−624	2,112	5,371	−6,657	−1,286
1954	12,929	−10,353	2,576	902	−269	305	2,929	−582	2,347	5,861	−5,642	219
1955	14,424	−11,527	2,897	−113	−297	299	3,406	−676	2,730	5,516	−5,086	430
1956	17,556	−12,803	4,753	−221	−361	447	3,837	−735	3,102	7,720	−4,990	2,730
1957	19,562	−13,291	6,271	−423	−189	482	4,180	−796	3,384	9,525	−4,763	4,762
1958	16,414	−12,952	3,462	−849	−633	486	3,790	−825	2,965	5,431	−4,647	784
1959	16,458	−15,310	1,148	−831	−821	573	4,132	−1,061	3,071	3,140	−4,422	−1,282
1960	19,650	−14,758	4,892	−1,057	−964	639	4,616	−1,238	3,379	6,886	−4,062	2,824
1961	20,108	−14,537	5,571	−1,131	−978	732	4,999	−1,245	3,755	7,949	−4,127	3,822
1962	20,781	−16,260	4,521	−912	−1,152	912	5,618	−1,324	4,294	7,664	−4,277	3,387
1963	22,272	−17,048	5,224	−742	−1,309	1,036	6,157	−1,560	4,596	8,806	−4,392	4,414
1964	25,501	−18,700	6,801	−794	−1,146	1,161	6,824	−1,783	5,041	11,063	−4,240	6,823
1965	26,461	−21,510	4,951	−487	−1,280	1,480	7,437	−2,088	5,350	10,014	−4,583	5,431
1966	29,310	−25,493	3,817	−1,043	−1,331	1,497	7,528	−2,481	5,047	7,987	−4,955	3,031
1967	30,666	−26,866	3,800	−1,187	−1,750	1,742	8,021	−2,747	5,274	7,878	−5,294	2,583
1968	33,626	−32,991	635	−596	−1,548	1,759	9,367	−3,378	5,990	6,240	−5,629	611
1969	36,414	−35,807	607	−718	−1,763	1,964	10,913	−4,869	6,044	6,135	−5,735	399
1970	42,469	−39,866	2,603	−641	−2,038	2,330	11,748	−5,515	6,233	8,486	−6,156	2,331
1971	43,319	−45,579	−2,260	653	−2,345	2,649	12,707	−5,435	7,272	5,969	−7,402	−1,433
1972	49,381	−55,797	−6,416	1,072	−3,063	2,965	14,765	−6,572	8,192	2,749	−8,544	−5,795
1973	71,410	−70,499	911	740	−3,158	3,406	21,808	−9,655	12,153	14,053	−6,913	7,140
1974	98,306	−103,811	−5,505	165	−3,184	4,231	27,587	−12,084	15,503	11,210 [5]	−9,249	1,962
1975	107,088	−98,185	8,903	1,461	−2,812	4,854	25,351	−12,564	12,787	25,191	−7,075	18,116
1976	114,745	−124,228	−9,483	931	−2,558	5,027	29,375	−13,311	16,063	9,982	−5,686	4,295
1977	120,816	−151,907	−31,091	1,731	−3,565	5,680	32,354	−14,217	18,137	−9,109	−5,226	−14,335
1978	142,075	−176,002	−33,927	857	−3,573	6,879	42,088	−21,680	20,408	−9,355	−5,788	−15,143
1979	184,439	−212,007	−27,568	−1,313	−2,935	7,251	63,834	−32,961	30,873	6,308	−6,593	−285
1980	224,250	−249,750	−25,500	−1,822	−997	8,912	72,606	−42,532	30,073	10,666	−8,349	2,317
1981	237,044	−265,067	−28,023	−844	144	12,552	86,529	−53,626	32,903	16,732	−11,702	5,030
1982	211,157	−247,642	−36,485	112	−992	13,209	86,200	−56,412	29,788	5,632	−17,075	−11,443
1983	201,799	−268,901	−67,102	−563	−4,227	14,095	85,614	−53,700	31,915	−25,882	−17,741	−43,623
1984	219,926	−332,418	−112,492	−2,547	−8,293	14,277	100,415	−69,572	30,843	−78,212	−20,612	−98,824
1985	215,915	−338,088	−122,173	−4,390	−9,709	14,266	91,110	−67,875	23,235	−98,771	−22,950	−121,721
1986	223,344	−368,425	−145,081	−5,181	−7,324	18,855	88,998	−73,620	15,378	−123,354	−24,176	−147,529
1987	250,208	−409,765	−159,557	−3,812	−6,398	18,400	96,574	−85,629	10,945	−140,421	−23,052	−163,474
1988	320,230	−447,189	−126,959	−6,354	−1,370	20,430	119,456	−106,991	12,466	−101,787	−24,869	−126,656
1989	361,697	−477,365	−115,668	−6,838	5,851	26,752	140,692	−126,326	14,366	−75,537	−25,606	−101,143
1990	388,705	−497,558	−108,853	−7,818	10,142	29,730	143,547	−124,261	19,287	−57,511	−32,916	−90,428
1991	415,962	−489,398	−73,436	−5,524	17,118	33,701	125,315	−108,886	16,429	−11,710	8,028	−3,682
1990:												
I	94,981	−122,360	−27,379	−1,873	2,093	6,984	35,004	−30,676	4,328	−15,847	−6,538	−22,385
II	96,654	−121,461	−24,807	−1,627	2,073	7,237	34,586	−31,386	3,200	−13,924	−7,401	−21,325
III	96,544	−125,434	−28,890	−1,692	2,120	7,461	35,137	−30,913	4,224	−16,777	−7,201	−23,978
IV	100,526	−128,303	−27,777	−2,627	3,855	8,051	38,821	−31,289	7,532	−10,966	−11,778	−22,744
1991:												
I	100,636	−118,962	−18,326	−2,564	3,755	8,164	35,498	−28,533	6,965	−2,006	14,199	12,193
II	103,324	−119,721	−16,397	−1,427	3,929	8,280	31,215	−27,284	3,931	−1,684	4,115	2,431
III	104,151	−124,325	−20,174	−994	4,358	8,660	29,904	−26,828	3,076	−5,075	−6,012	−11,087
IV	107,851	−126,390	−18,539	−539	5,080	8,596	28,698	−26,240	2,458	−2,945	−4,273	−7,218
1992:												
I	107,946	−125,168	−17,222	−625	4,401	10,067	28,499	−24,025	4,474	1,096	−6,999	−5,903
II	107,464	−132,022	−24,558	−623	4,216	9,045	28,452	−26,522	1,930	−9,990	−7,812	−17,802
III p	110,812	−137,350	−26,538	−548	4,024	12,149	27,756	−24,205	3,551	−7,362	−6,876	−14,238

[1] Excludes military.
[2] Adjusted from Census data for differences in valuation, coverage, and timing.
[3] Quarterly data are not seasonally adjusted.
[4] Includes transfers of goods and services under U.S. military grant programs.

See next page for continuation of table.

TABLE B-100.—*U.S. international transactions, 1946-92*—Continued

[Millions of dollars; quarterly data seasonally adjusted, except as noted]

Year or quarter	U.S. assets abroad, net [increase/capital outflow (−)]				Foreign assets in the U.S., net [increase/capital inflow (+)]			Allocations of special drawing rights (SDRs)	Statistical discrepancy	
	Total	U.S. official reserve assets [3][6]	Other U.S. Government assets	U.S. private assets	Total	Foreign official assets [3]	Other foreign assets		Total (sum of the items with sign reversed)	Of which: Seasonal adjustment discrepancy
1946		−623								
1947		−3,315								
1948		−1,736								
1949		−266								
1950		1,758								
1951		−33								
1952		−415								
1953		1,256								
1954		480								
1955		182								
1956		−869								
1957		−1,165								
1958		2,292								
1959		1,035								
1960	−4,099	2,145	−1,100	−5,144	2,294	1,473	821		−1,019	
1961	−5,538	607	−910	−5,235	2,705	765	1,939		−989	
1962	−4,174	1,535	−1,085	−4,623	1,911	1,270	641		−1,124	
1963	−7,270	378	−1,662	−5,986	3,217	1,986	1,231		−360	
1964	−9,560	171	−1,680	−8,050	3,643	1,660	1,983		−907	
1965	−5,716	1,225	−1,605	−5,336	742	134	607		−457	
1966	−7,321	570	−1,543	−6,347	3,661	−672	4,333		629	
1967	−9,757	53	−2,423	−7,386	7,379	3,451	3,928		−205	
1968	−10,977	−870	−2,274	−7,833	9,928	−774	10,703		438	
1969	−11,585	−1,179	−2,200	−8,206	12,702	−1,301	14,002		−1,516	
1970	−9,337	2,481	−1,589	−10,229	6,359	6,908	−550	867	−219	
1971	−12,475	2,349	−1,884	−12,940	22,970	26,879	−3,909	717	−9,779	
1972	−14,497	−4	−1,568	−12,925	21,461	10,475	10,986	710	−1,879	
1973	−22,874	158	−2,644	−20,388	18,388	6,026	12,362		−2,654	
1974	−34,745	−1,467	[5] 366	−33,643	34,241	10,546	23,696		−1,458	
1975	−39,703	−849	−3,474	−35,380	15,670	7,027	8,643		5,917	
1976	−51,269	−2,558	−4,214	−44,498	36,518	17,693	18,826		10,455	
1977	−34,785	−375	−3,693	−30,717	51,319	36,816	14,503		−2,199	
1978	−61,130	732	−4,660	−57,202	64,036	33,678	30,358		12,236	
1979	−66,054	−1,133	−3,746	−61,176	38,752	−13,665	52,416	1,139	26,449	
1980	−86,967	−8,155	−5,162	−73,651	58,112	15,497	42,615	1,152	25,386	
1981	−114,147	−5,175	−5,097	−103,875	83,032	4,960	78,072	1,093	24,992	
1982	−122,335	−4,965	−6,131	−111,239	92,418	3,593	88,826		41,359	
1983	−58,856	−1,196	−5,006	−52,654	83,380	5,845	77,534		19,099	
1984	−29,224	−3,131	−5,489	−20,605	102,010	3,140	98,870		26,038	
1985	−34,069	−3,858	−2,821	−27,391	130,966	−1,119	132,084		24,825	
1986	−91,069	312	−2,022	−89,360	223,191	35,648	187,543		15,407	
1987	−62,402	9,149	1,006	−72,556	229,972	45,387	184,585		−4,096	
1988	−92,708	−3,912	2,967	−91,762	219,489	39,758	179,731		−126	
1989	−114,944	−25,293	1,271	−90,922	213,693	8,489	205,204		2,394	
1990	−56,321	−2,158	2,304	−56,467	99,379	33,908	65,471		47,370	
1991	−62,220	5,763	3,397	−71,379	66,980	18,407	48,573		−1,078	
1990:										
I	42,141	−3,177	−743	46,061	−30,965	−6,450	−24,515		11,209	4,489
II	−30,682	371	−794	−30,259	30,853	6,134	24,719		21,154	518
III	−30,964	1,739	−337	−32,366	51,386	14,097	37,289		3,556	−5,605
IV	−36,816	−1,091	4,179	−39,903	48,108	20,127	27,981		11,452	600
1991:										
I	−640	−353	1,073	−1,360	−7,840	5,650	−13,490		−3,713	4,636
II	−7,050	1,014	−420	−7,644	2,959	−4,178	7,137		1,660	883
III	−10,368	3,877	3,180	−17,426	22,933	4,115	18,818		−1,478	−6,137
IV	−44,158	1,225	−437	−44,947	48,929	12,819	36,110		2,447	613
1992:										
I	−4,250	−1,057	−38	−3,155	18,563	21,192	−2,629		−8,410	4,023
II	37	1,464	−277	−1,150	47,415	20,895	26,520		−29,650	410
III [p]	−20,157	1,952	−385	−21,724	17,286	−7,738	25,024		17,109	−7,680

[5] Includes extraordinary U.S. Government transactions with India.
[6] Consists of gold, special drawing rights, foreign currencies, and the U.S. reserve position in the International Monetary Fund (IMF).

Source: Department of Commerce, Bureau of Economic Analysis.

463

[Billions of dollars; quarterly data seasonally adjusted]

Year or quarter	Exports Total	Agricultural products	Nonagricultural products Total	Industrial supplies and materials	Capital goods except automotive	Automotive	Other	Imports Total	Petroleum and products	Nonpetroleum products Total	Industrial supplies and materials	Capital goods except automotive	Automotive	Other
1965	26.5	6.3	20.2	7.6	8.1	1.9	2.6	21.5	2.0	19.5	9.1	1.5	0.9	8.0
1966	29.3	6.9	22.4	8.2	8.9	2.4	2.9	25.5	2.1	23.4	10.2	2.2	1.8	9.2
1967	30.7	6.5	24.2	8.5	9.9	2.8	3.0	26.9	2.1	24.8	10.0	2.5	2.4	9.9
1968	33.6	6.3	27.3	9.6	11.1	3.5	3.2	33.0	2.4	30.6	12.0	2.8	4.0	11.8
1969	36.4	6.1	30.3	10.3	12.4	3.9	3.7	35.8	2.6	33.2	11.8	3.4	4.9	13.0
1970	42.5	7.4	35.1	12.3	14.7	3.9	4.3	39.9	2.9	36.9	12.4	4.0	5.5	15.0
1971	43.3	7.8	35.5	10.9	15.4	4.7	4.5	45.6	3.7	41.9	13.8	4.3	7.4	16.4
1972	49.4	9.5	39.9	11.9	16.9	5.5	5.6	55.8	4.7	51.1	16.3	5.9	8.7	20.2
1973	71.4	18.0	53.4	17.0	22.0	6.9	7.6	70.5	8.4	62.1	19.6	8.3	10.3	23.9
1974	98.3	22.4	75.9	26.3	30.9	8.6	10.0	103.8	26.6	77.2	27.8	9.8	12.0	27.5
1975	107.1	22.2	84.8	26.8	36.6	10.6	10.8	98.2	27.0	71.2	24.0	10.2	11.7	25.3
1976	114.7	23.4	91.4	28.4	39.1	12.1	11.7	124.2	34.6	89.7	29.8	12.3	16.2	31.4
1977	120.8	24.3	96.5	29.8	39.8	13.4	13.5	151.9	45.0	106.9	35.7	14.0	18.6	38.6
1978 [1]	142.1	29.9	112.2	34.2	47.5	15.2	15.3	176.0	42.6	133.4	40.7	19.3	25.0	48.4
1979	184.4	35.5	149.0	52.2	60.2	17.9	18.7	212.0	60.4	151.6	47.5	24.6	26.6	52.8
1980	224.3	42.0	182.2	65.1	76.3	17.4	23.4	249.8	79.5	170.2	53.0	31.6	28.3	57.4
1981	237.0	44.1	193.0	63.6	84.2	19.7	25.5	265.1	78.4	186.7	56.1	37.1	31.0	62.4
1982	211.2	37.3	173.9	57.7	76.5	17.2	22.4	247.6	62.0	185.7	48.6	38.4	34.3	64.3
1983	201.8	37.1	164.7	52.7	71.7	18.5	21.8	268.9	55.1	213.8	53.7	43.7	43.0	73.3
1984	219.9	38.4	181.5	56.8	77.0	22.4	25.3	332.4	58.1	274.4	66.1	60.4	56.5	91.4
1985	215.9	29.6	186.3	54.8	79.3	24.9	27.2	338.1	51.4	286.7	62.6	61.3	64.9	97.9
1986	223.3	27.2	196.2	59.4	82.8	25.1	28.9	368.4	34.3	334.1	69.9	72.0	78.1	114.2
1987	250.2	29.5	220.7	63.7	92.7	27.6	36.8	409.8	42.9	366.8	70.8	85.1	85.2	125.7
1988	320.2	38.2	282.0	82.6	119.1	33.4	46.9	447.2	39.6	407.6	83.1	102.2	87.9	134.4
1989	361.7	42.2	319.5	91.9	139.6	34.9	53.1	477.4	50.9	426.4	84.2	112.5	87.4	142.4
1990	388.7	40.2	348.5	97.1	153.3	36.5	61.7	497.6	62.3	435.3	82.5	116.0	87.7	149.0
1991	416.0	40.1	375.8	101.8	167.0	40.0	66.9	489.4	51.2	438.2	80.9	120.7	84.9	151.7
1990: I	95.0	10.7	84.2	23.2	37.7	8.8	14.6	122.4	15.8	106.6	20.2	28.4	21.2	36.7
II	96.7	10.1	86.5	23.3	38.6	9.5	15.1	121.5	12.8	108.6	20.5	28.8	22.2	37.1
III	96.5	9.9	86.7	24.0	38.3	9.3	15.1	125.4	15.5	110.0	20.8	28.9	22.6	37.7
IV	100.5	9.5	91.1	26.6	38.8	8.8	16.9	128.3	18.2	110.1	20.9	30.0	21.7	37.5
1991: I	100.6	9.8	90.8	26.4	38.9	8.8	16.8	119.0	12.9	106.0	19.9	29.8	20.3	36.0
II	103.3	9.4	94.0	25.3	42.3	9.9	16.4	119.7	12.9	106.8	20.1	30.1	19.8	36.8
III	104.2	10.2	94.0	25.1	41.7	10.9	16.3	124.3	13.1	111.2	20.0	30.3	22.7	38.2
IV	107.9	10.8	97.1	25.0	44.1	10.4	17.6	126.4	12.2	114.2	20.8	30.5	22.2	40.7
1992: I	107.9	10.8	97.1	24.9	44.1	10.7	17.4	125.2	10.4	114.8	21.1	31.3	22.0	40.5
II	107.5	10.5	97.0	25.1	43.5	11.5	16.9	132.0	12.9	119.1	22.1	32.8	22.4	41.8
III	110.8	11.6	99.2	25.8	43.6	12.2	17.5	137.4	14.2	123.1	22.0	34.5	22.8	43.8

[1] End-use categories beginning 1978 are not strictly comparable with data for earlier periods. See *Survey of Current Business*, June 1988.

Note.—Data are on an international transactions basis and exclude military.

In June 1990, end-use categories for merchandise exports were redefined to include reexports; beginning with data for 1978, reexports (exports of foreign merchandise) are assigned to detailed end-use categories in the same manner as exports of domestic merchandise.

Source: Department of Commerce, Bureau of Economic Analysis.

TABLE B–102.—U.S. merchandise exports and imports by area, 1983–92

[Billions of dollars]

Item	1983	1984	1985	1986	1987	1988	1989	1990	1991	1992 first 3 quarters at annual rate [1]
Exports............................	201.8	219.9	215.9	223.3	250.2	320.2	361.7	388.7	416.0	435.0
Industrial countries...........	128.3	141.0	140.5	150.3	165.6	207.3	233.8	253.2	260.4	263.8
Canada..........................	44.5	53.0	55.4	56.5	62.0	74.3	80.7	82.9	85.0	90.4
Japan	21.8	23.2	22.1	26.4	27.6	37.2	43.9	47.8	47.2	47.2
Western Europe..............	55.4	56.9	56.0	60.4	68.6	86.4	98.4	111.4	116.8	114.4
Australia, New Zealand, and South Africa.......	6.6	7.8	7.0	7.1	7.4	9.4	10.9	11.2	11.4	11.8
Australia....................	3.9	4.9	5.1	5.1	5.3	6.8	8.1	8.3	8.3	8.3
Other countries, except Eastern Europe..............	70.4	74.6	71.9	71.0	82.3	109.1	122.2	130.6	150.3	165.9
OPEC [2]...........................	15.3	13.8	11.4	10.4	10.7	13.8	13.3	13.4	18.4	20.7
Other [3]	55.2	60.8	60.5	60.6	71.6	95.3	108.9	117.2	131.9	145.2
Eastern Europe..................	3.0	4.3	3.2	2.1	2.3	3.8	5.5	4.3	4.8	5.3
International organizations and unallocated....................	.1	.0	.2			.1	.2	.6	.4	
Imports............................	268.9	332.4	338.1	368.4	409.8	447.2	477.4	497.6	489.4	526.1
Industrial countries...........	160.1	205.5	219.0	245.4	259.7	283.2	292.5	299.1	293.3	309.0
Canada..........................	55.2	67.6	70.2	69.7	73.6	84.6	89.9	93.1	93.0	100.2
Japan	43.3	60.2	65.7	80.8	84.6	89.8	93.5	89.6	91.5	94.0
Western Europe..............	56.2	72.1	77.5	89.0	96.1	102.6	102.4	109.2	101.9	108.1
Australia, New Zealand, and South Africa.......	5.4	5.6	5.6	5.9	5.4	6.2	6.6	7.3	6.9	6.8
Australia....................	2.2	2.8	2.7	2.6	3.0	3.5	3.9	4.4	4.0	3.7
Other countries, except Eastern Europe..............	107.4	124.7	117.3	121.1	148.2	161.8	182.8	196.1	194.3	215.1
OPEC [2]...........................	24.9	26.9	22.8	18.9	24.4	23.0	30.7	38.2	33.1	32.5
Other [3]	82.5	97.8	94.5	102.2	123.8	138.8	152.1	157.9	161.2	182.6
Eastern Europe..................	1.4	2.2	1.8	2.0	1.9	2.2	2.1	2.3	1.8	2.0
International organizations and unallocated...............										
Balance (excess of exports +).......................	−67.1	−112.5	−122.2	−145.1	−159.6	−127.0	−115.7	−108.9	−73.4	−91.1
Industrial countries...........	−31.8	−64.5	−78.4	−95.1	−94.1	−75.9	−58.7	−45.9	−32.9	−45.2
Canada..........................	−10.7	−14.6	−14.8	−13.2	−11.6	−10.3	−9.3	−10.2	−8.0	−9.8
Japan	−21.6	−37.0	−43.5	−54.4	−56.9	−52.6	−49.7	−41.8	−44.3	−46.8
Western Europe..............	−.8	−15.2	−21.4	−28.6	−27.5	−16.2	−4.0	2.2	14.9	6.3
Australia, New Zealand, and South Africa.......	1.2	2.2	1.4	1.1	2.0	3.2	4.2	3.9	4.5	5.0
Australia....................	1.7	2.1	2.4	2.5	2.3	3.3	4.2	3.9	4.3	4.5
Other countries, except Eastern Europe..............	−37.0	−50.1	−45.3	−50.1	−65.8	−52.7	−60.6	−65.6	−43.9	−49.2
OPEC [2]...........................	−9.7	−13.1	−11.4	−8.5	−13.7	−9.2	−17.4	−24.8	−14.6	−11.8
Other [3]	−27.3	−37.0	−33.9	−41.6	−52.1	−43.5	−43.2	−40.7	−29.3	−37.4
Eastern Europe..................	1.6	2.1	1.4	.1	.3	1.6	3.5	2.1	3.0	3.3
International organizations and unallocated....................	.1	.0	.2			.1	.2	.6	.4	

[1] Preliminary; seasonally adjusted.
[2] Organization of Petroleum Exporting Countries, consisting of Algeria, Ecuador, Gabon, Indonesia, Iran, Iraq, Kuwait, Libya, Nigeria, Qatar, Saudi Arabia, United Arab Emirates, and Venezuela.
[3] Latin America, other Western Hemisphere, and other countries in Asia and Africa, less members of OPEC.

Note.—Data are on an international transactions basis and exclude military.

Source: Department of Commerce, Bureau of Economic Analysis.

465

TABLE B–103.—*U.S. merchandise exports, imports, and trade balance, 1972–92*

[Billions of dollars; monthly data seasonally adjusted]

Year or month	Merchandise exports (f.a.s. value)[1] — Principal end-use commodity category							General merchandise imports (customs value)[3] — Principal end-use commodity category							Trade balance		
	Total[2]	Foods, feeds, and beverages	Industrial supplies and materials	Capital goods except automotive	Automotive vehicles, parts, and engines	Consumer goods (nonfood)	Other[2]	Total	Foods, feeds, and beverages	Industrial supplies and materials	Capital goods except automotive	Automotive vehicles, parts, and engines	Consumer goods (nonfood)	Other	General merchandise imports (c.i.f. value)[4]	Exports (f.a.s.) less imports (customs value)	Exports (f.a.s.) less imports (c.i.f.)
	F.a.s. value[5]							Customs value									
1972	49.9							55.6							58.9	−5.7	−9.0
1973	71.9							69.5							73.2	2.4	−1.3
								F.a.s. value[5]									
1974	99.4							103.3							110.9	−3.9	−11.4
1975	108.9							99.3							105.9	9.6	3.0
1976	116.8							124.6							132.5	−7.8	−15.7
1977	123.2							151.5							160.4	−28.4	−37.2
1978	145.8							176.1							186.0	−30.2	−40.2
1979	186.4							210.3							222.2	−23.9	−35.9
1980	225.6							245.3							257.0	−19.7	−31.4
								Customs value									
1981	238.7							261.0							273.4	−22.3	−34.6
1982	216.4	31.3	61.7	72.7	15.7	14.3	20.7	244.0	17.1	112.0	35.4	33.3	39.7	6.5	254.9	−27.5	−38.4
1983	205.6	30.9	56.7	67.2	16.8	13.4	20.5	258.0	18.2	107.0	40.9	40.8	44.9	6.3	269.9	−52.4	−64.2
1984	224.0	31.5	61.7	72.0	20.6	13.3	24.0	[6]330.7	21.0	123.7	59.8	53.5	60.0	7.8	346.4	−106.7	−122.4
1985	[7]218.8	24.0	58.5	73.9	22.9	12.6	27.3	[6]336.5	21.9	113.9	65.1	66.8	68.3	9.4	352.5	−117.7	−133.6
1986	[7]227.2	22.3	57.3	75.8	21.7	14.2	35.9	365.4	24.4	101.3	71.8	78.2	79.4	10.4	382.3	−138.3	−155.1
1987	254.1	24.3	66.7	86.2	24.6	17.7	34.6	406.2	24.8	111.0	84.5	85.2	88.7	12.1	424.4	−152.1	−170.3
1988	322.4	32.3	85.1	109.2	29.3	23.1	43.4	441.0	24.8	118.3	101.4	87.7	95.9	12.8	459.5	−118.5	−137.1
1989	363.8	37.2	99.3	138.8	34.8	36.4	17.2	473.2	25.1	132.3	113.3	86.1	102.9	13.6	493.2	−109.4	−129.4
1990	393.6	35.1	104.4	152.7	37.4	43.3	20.7	495.3	26.6	143.2	116.4	87.3	105.7	16.1	517.0	−101.7	−123.4
1991	421.7	35.7	109.7	166.7	40.0	45.9	23.7	487.1	26.5	131.0	120.7	84.9	108.0	15.9	508.4	−65.4	−86.6
1991:																	
Jan	34.3	2.7	9.5	13.0	3.3	3.9	1.9	41.2	2.2	12.2	9.8	7.2	8.6	1.3	43.0	−6.9	−8.7
Feb	33.7	3.0	9.9	12.4	2.6	3.8	1.9	39.0	2.1	10.6	9.9	6.7	8.5	1.2	40.7	−5.3	−7.0
Mar	34.2	3.0	9.0	13.5	3.0	3.8	1.9	38.5	2.2	10.1	10.1	6.6	8.3	1.3	40.2	−4.3	−6.1
Apr	35.5	2.9	9.2	14.3	3.4	3.8	1.9	39.7	2.3	10.8	10.1	6.8	8.5	1.3	41.6	−4.3	−6.1
May	35.0	2.9	9.4	13.7	3.4	3.7	2.0	40.0	2.3	11.3	9.9	6.6	8.5	1.5	41.8	−5.0	−6.8
June	34.7	2.7	8.7	14.3	3.5	3.7	1.9	39.4	2.3	10.6	10.0	6.6	8.4	1.5	41.1	−4.7	−6.4
July	35.2	3.1	9.1	13.7	3.6	3.7	2.0	40.8	2.2	10.7	10.2	7.4	9.1	1.3	42.6	−5.6	−7.4
Aug	34.5	3.0	9.1	13.4	3.3	3.7	1.9	41.1	2.1	10.9	10.0	7.9	8.9	1.3	42.8	−6.6	−8.4
Sept	35.3	3.1	8.6	14.4	3.5	3.8	1.9	41.8	2.2	11.1	10.2	7.4	9.4	1.3	43.6	−6.5	−8.3
Oct	36.8	3.2	9.3	14.4	3.7	4.1	2.1	42.7	2.1	11.1	10.3	7.7	10.0	1.4	44.5	−5.9	−7.6
Nov	37.3	3.2	8.9	15.4	3.6	4.1	2.1	41.4	2.2	10.8	9.9	7.2	9.8	1.4	43.1	−4.1	−5.8
Dec	36.1	3.3	8.9	14.3	3.3	3.8	2.3	41.7	2.3	10.8	10.3	7.2	9.8	1.4	43.4	−5.6	−7.4
1992:																	
Jan	35.5	3.1	9.3	13.9	3.2	3.9	2.0	41.3	2.3	10.6	10.3	7.3	9.5	1.3	43.1	−5.8	−7.6
Feb	37.7	3.6	8.9	15.3	3.6	4.1	2.1	41.0	2.2	10.4	10.3	7.1	9.6	1.5	42.6	−3.3	−5.0
Mar	37.1	3.3	8.8	14.9	3.9	4.0	2.3	42.7	2.3	10.7	10.7	7.5	9.9	1.6	44.5	−5.6	−7.4
Apr	36.4	3.5	8.8	14.3	4.0	3.9	2.0	43.5	2.4	11.3	10.8	7.7	9.8	1.4	45.3	−7.1	−8.9
May	35.7	3.0	8.9	13.9	3.8	4.0	2.1	42.9	2.2	11.4	10.8	7.3	9.8	1.3	44.6	−7.2	−8.9
June	38.2	3.1	9.3	15.3	4.0	4.2	2.2	45.0	2.6	12.0	11.2	7.4	10.2	1.5	46.7	−6.8	−8.5
July	37.8	3.5	9.6	14.5	3.9	4.3	2.0	45.1	2.5	12.0	11.3	7.4	10.5	1.5	46.9	−7.3	−9.1
Aug	35.8	3.3	8.7	14.0	3.7	4.1	2.1	44.8	2.3	11.8	11.5	7.6	10.3	1.3	46.6	−9.0	−10.8
Sept	37.9	3.7	9.1	15.0	3.8	4.5	2.0	46.5	2.3	12.0	11.7	7.8	11.2	1.4	48.3	−8.6	−10.4
Oct	39.2	3.7	9.6	15.4	3.8	4.6	2.2	46.2	2.3	12.3	11.8	7.6	10.7	1.5	48.0	−7.0	−8.9

[1] Department of Defense shipments of grant-aid military supplies and equipment under the Military Assistance Program are excluded from total exports through 1985 and included beginning 1986.

[2] Includes undocumented exports to Canada through 1988. Beginning 1989, undocumented exports to Canada are included in the appropriate end-use category.

[3] Total arrivals of imported goods other than intransit shipments.

[4] C.i.f. (cost, insurance, and freight) import value at first port of entry into United States. Data for 1967–73 are estimates.

[5] F.a.s. (free alongside ship) value basis at U.S. port of exportation for exports and at foreign port of exportation for imports.

[6] Total includes revisions not reflected in detail.

[7] Total exports are on a revised statistical month basis; end-use categories are on a statistical month basis.

Note.—Data are as reported by the Bureau of the Census adjusted to include silver ore and bullion reported separately prior to 1969. Trade in gold is included beginning 1974. Export statistics cover all merchandise shipped from the U.S. customs area, except supplies for the U.S. Armed Forces. Exports include shipments under Agency for International Development and Food for Peace programs as well as other private relief shipments.

Data beginning 1974 include trade of the U.S. Virgin Islands.

Source: Department of Commerce, Bureau of the Census.

[Millions of SDRs; end of period]

Area and country	1952	1962	1972	1982	1989	1990	1991	1992 Oct	1992 Nov
All countries..	49,388	62,851	146,658	361,253	624,122	670,727	704,977	731,351	....
Industrial countries [1]	39,280	53,502	113,362	214,014	410,113	441,924	428,417	417,788	....
United States	24,714	17,220	12,112	29,918	57,525	59,958	55,769	54,082	53,529
Canada	1,944	2,561	5,572	3,428	12,781	13,060	11,816	9,349	7,466
Australia..	920	1,168	5,656	6,053	10,763	11,710	11,837	8,241	8,246
Japan...	1,101	2,021	16,916	22,001	64,735	56,027	51,224	51,592	52,644
New Zealand..	183	251	767	577	2,303	2,902	2,062	....	....
Austria...	116	1,081	2,505	5,544	7,266	7,305	7,924	9,635	9,455
Belgium..	1,133	1,753	3,564	4,757	9,250	9,599	9,573	9,055	....
Denmark...	150	256	787	2,111	4,925	7,502	5,234	6,630	6,361
Finland...	132	237	664	1,420	3,959	6,849	5,389	4,778	5,138
France	686	4,049	9,224	17,850	21,592	28,716	24,735	....	....
Germany...	960	6,958	21,908	43,909	49,527	51,060	47,375	66,207	65,360
Greece...	94	287	950	916	2,572	2,517	3,747	3,163	3,380
Iceland...	8	32	78	133	258	308	316	364	393
Ireland...	318	359	1,038	2,390	3,100	3,684	4,026	2,809	2,479
Italy..	722	4,068	5,605	15,108	37,884	46,565	36,365	18,398	21,163
Netherlands...	953	1,943	4,407	10,723	14,100	13,827	13,980	16,301	16,152
Norway	164	304	1,220	6,272	10,531	10,819	9,292	11,862	....
Portugal...	603	680	2,129	1,179	8,135	10,736	14,977	14,930	15,087
Spain	134	1,045	4,618	7,450	32,104	36,555	46,562	37,765	31,409
Sweden...	504	802	1,453	3,397	7,487	12,856	13,028	....	....
Switzerland..	1,667	2,919	6,961	16,930	22,148	23,456	23,191	22,701	24,304
United Kingdom	1,956	3,308	5,201	11,904	27,121	25,864	29,948	28,058	27,910
Developing countries: Total [2]	9,648	9,349	33,295	147,239	214,009	228,802	276,560	313,564	....
By area:									
Africa..	1,786	2,110	3,962	7,734	9,439	12,053	14,586	15,778	....
Asia [2]	3,793	2,772	8,129	44,490	121,690	128,826	157,535	180,841	....
Europe	269	381	2,680	5,359	14,931	15,535	15,634	15,561	....
Middle East	1,183	1,805	9,436	64,094	42,288	38,011	41,859	42,603	....
Western Hemisphere................................	2,616	2,282	9,089	25,563	25,660	34,376	46,946	58,781	....
Memo:									
Oil-exporting countries	1,699	2,030	9,956	67,163	44,363	43,930	48,938	47,098	....
Non-oil developing countries [2]	7,949	7,319	23,339	80,076	169,645	184,872	227,621	266,460	....

[1] Includes data for Luxembourg.
[2] Includes data for Taiwan Province of China.

Note.—International reserves is comprised of monetary authorities' holdings of gold (at SDR 35 per ounce), special drawing rights (SDRs), reserve positions in the International Monetary Fund, and foreign exchange. Data exclude U.S.S.R., other Eastern European countries, and Cuba (after 1960).

U.S. dollars per SDR (end of period) are: 1952 and 1962—1.00000; 1972—1.08571; 1982—1.10311; 1989—1.31416; 1990—1.42266; 1991—1.43043; October 1992—1.40595; and November 1992—1.37896.

Source: International Monetary Fund, *International Financial Statistics.*

TABLE B-105.—*Industrial production and consumer prices, major industrial countries, 1967–92*

Year or quarter	United States	Canada	Japan	European Community [1]	France	Germany [2]	Italy	United Kingdom
			Industrial production (1987=100) [3]					
1967	57.5	51.1	36.2	59.3	61	57.6	58.5	70.5
1968	60.7	54.3	41.7	63.7	62	62.9	61.9	75.9
1969	63.5	58.1	48.3	69.6	69	70.9	64.2	78.5
1970	61.4	58.8	55.0	73.1	72	75.5	68.3	78.9
1971	62.2	62.0	56.5	74.7	77	77.0	68.0	78.5
1972	68.3	66.7	59.6	78.0	81	79.9	70.8	79.9
1973	73.8	73.8	67.9	83.7	87	85.0	77.7	87.0
1974	72.7	76.1	66.4	84.3	90	84.8	81.2	85.4
1975	66.3	71.6	59.4	78.7	83	79.6	73.7	80.8
1976	72.4	76.0	66.0	84.5	90	86.8	82.9	83.4
1977	78.2	79.3	68.6	86.6	92	88.0	83.8	87.6
1978	82.6	82.1	73.0	95.4	94	90.4	85.4	90.1
1979	85.7	86.1	78.1	93.1	99	94.7	91.1	93.6
1980	84.1	82.8	81.7	92.8	98.9	95.0	96.2	87.5
1981	85.7	84.5	82.6	91.1	98.3	93.2	94.7	84.8
1982	81.9	76.2	82.9	89.9	97.3	90.3	91.7	86.4
1983	84.9	81.2	85.5	90.8	96.5	90.9	88.9	89.6
1984	92.8	91.0	93.4	92.8	97.1	93.5	91.8	89.7
1985	94.4	96.1	96.8	95.8	97.2	97.7	92.9	94.6
1986	95.3	95.4	96.6	98.0	98.0	99.6	96.2	96.9
1987	100.0	100.0	100.0	100.0	100.0	100.0	100.0	100.0
1988	105.4	105.3	109.3	104.2	104.6	103.9	105.9	103.6
1989	108.1	104.9	115.9	108.1	108.8	108.8	109.2	104.0
1990	109.2	100.5	121.4	110.2	110.9	114.5	109.4	103.4
1991	107.1	96.4	124.1	110.2	111.2	118.0	107.1	100.4
1991: I	105.8	95.5	124.8	110.1	110.3	118.4	108.5	100.9
II	106.4	96.5	124.3	109.9	110.9	119.0	106.5	99.5
III	108.1	97.2	124.5	109.4	112.1	117.8	106.2	100.5
IV	107.9	96.4	123.1	109.3	111.0	116.2	107.4	100.4
1992: I	107.1	96.2	119.9	110.6	110.5	119.3	110.1	99.6
II	108.5	96.6	117.1	109.4	111.0	117.1	107.0	99.3
III [p]	109.1	97.3	117.7			114.8		99.9
			Consumer prices (1982–84=100)					
1967	33.4	31.3	32.2	23.2	24.6	49.3	16.0	18.5
1968	34.8	32.5	34.0	24.0	25.7	50.1	16.2	19.4
1969	36.7	34.0	35.8	25.0	27.4	51.0	16.6	20.4
1970	38.8	35.1	38.5	26.3	28.7	52.9	16.8	21.8
1971	40.5	36.1	40.9	28.0	30.3	55.6	17.6	23.8
1972	41.8	37.9	42.9	29.8	32.2	58.7	18.7	25.5
1973	44.4	40.7	47.9	32.4	34.5	62.8	20.6	27.9
1974	49.3	45.2	59.0	37.0	39.3	67.2	24.6	32.3
1975	53.8	50.1	66.0	42.4	43.9	71.2	28.8	40.2
1976	56.9	53.8	72.1	47.6	48.1	74.2	33.6	46.8
1977	60.6	58.1	78.0	53.5	52.7	76.9	40.1	54.2
1978	65.2	63.3	81.3	58.6	57.5	79.0	45.1	58.7
1979	72.6	69.1	84.3	65.0	63.6	82.3	52.1	66.6
1980	82.4	76.1	91.0	74.0	72.2	86.8	63.2	78.5
1981	90.9	85.6	95.3	83.1	81.8	92.2	75.4	87.9
1982	96.5	94.9	98.0	92.2	91.7	97.0	87.7	95.4
1983	99.6	100.4	99.8	100.2	100.3	100.3	100.8	99.8
1984	103.9	104.8	102.1	107.5	108.0	102.7	111.5	104.8
1985	107.6	108.9	104.1	114.2	114.3	104.8	121.1	111.1
1986	109.6	113.4	104.8	118.5	117.2	104.7	128.5	114.9
1987	113.6	118.4	104.9	122.5	121.1	104.9	134.4	119.7
1988	118.3	123.2	105.7	126.9	124.4	106.3	141.1	125.6
1989	124.0	129.3	108.0	133.4	128.9	109.2	150.4	135.4
1990	130.7	135.5	111.4	140.9	133.2	112.1	159.6	148.2
1991	136.2	143.1	115.0	148.1	137.2	116.0	169.7	156.9
1991: I	134.8	141.9	113.8	145.4	135.7	114.2	166.5	153.7
II	135.6	143.0	114.9	147.3	136.6	115.2	169.2	156.9
III	136.7	143.8	114.9	149.0	137.7	116.9	170.9	157.6
IV	137.7	143.6	116.3	150.7	138.9	117.7	173.3	159.2
1992: I	138.7	144.2	115.9	152.3	139.8	119.1	175.9	160.0
II	139.8	144.9	117.5	154.2	140.8	120.4	178.2	163.5
III	140.9	145.6	117.0	155.0	141.5	121.0	179.4	163.4

[1] Consists of Belgium-Luxembourg, Denmark, France, Greece, Ireland, Italy, Netherlands, United Kingdom, Germany, Portugal, and Spain. Industrial production prior to July 1981 excludes data for Greece, which joined the EC in 1981. Data for Portugal and Spain, which became members on January 1, 1986 are excluded prior to 1982.
[2] Former West Germany.
[3] All data exclude construction. Quarterly data are seasonally adjusted.

Sources: National sources as reported by Department of Commerce (International Trade Administration, Office of Trade and Economic Analysis, Trade and Industry Statistics Division), Department of Labor (Bureau of Labor Statistics), and Board of Governors of the Federal Reserve System.

TABLE B–106.—*Civilian unemployment rate, and hourly compensation, major industrial countries, 1965–92*

[Quarterly data seasonally adjusted]

Year or quarter	United States	Canada	Japan	France	Germa- ny [1]	Italy	United Kingdom
	Civilian unemployment rate (percent)[2]						
1965	4.5	3.6	1.2	1.6	0.3	3.5	2.1
1966	3.8	3.4	1.4	1.6	.3	3.7	2.3
1967	3.8	3.8	1.3	2.1	1.3	3.4	3.3
1968	3.6	4.5	1.2	2.7	1.1	3.5	3.2
1969	3.5	4.4	1.1	2.3	.6	3.5	3.1
1970	4.9	5.7	1.2	2.5	.5	3.2	3.1
1971	5.9	6.2	1.3	2.8	.6	3.3	3.9
1972	5.6	6.2	1.4	2.9	.7	3.8	4.2
1973	4.9	5.5	1.3	2.8	.7	3.7	3.2
1974	5.6	5.3	1.4	2.9	1.6	3.1	3.1
1975	8.5	6.9	1.9	4.1	3.4	3.4	4.6
1976	7.7	7.1	2.0	4.5	3.4	3.9	5.9
1977	7.1	8.1	2.0	5.1	3.4	4.1	6.4
1978	6.1	8.3	2.3	5.3	3.3	4.1	6.3
1979	5.8	7.4	2.1	6.0	2.9	4.4	5.4
1980	7.1	7.5	2.0	6.4	2.8	4.4	7.0
1981	7.6	7.5	2.2	7.6	4.0	4.9	10.5
1982	9.7	11.0	2.4	8.3	5.6	5.4	11.3
1983	9.6	11.8	2.7	8.5	3 6.9	5.9	11.8
1984	7.5	11.2	2.8	10.0	7.1	5.9	11.8
1985	7.2	10.5	2.6	10.4	7.2	6.0	11.2
1986	7.0	9.5	2.8	10.6	6.6	3 7.5	11.2
1987	6.2	8.8	2.9	10.7	6.3	7.9	10.3
1988	5.5	7.8	2.5	10.2	6.3	7.9	8.6
1989	5.3	7.5	2.3	9.6	5.7	7.8	7.1
1990	5.5	8.1	2.1	9.1	p5.0	p7.0	6.9
1991 p	6.7	10.3	2.1	9.6	4.4	3 6.9	8.8
1992	7.4						
1991: I	6.5	10.2	2.1	9.1	4.5	6.9	7.9
II	6.7	10.3	2.1	9.5	4.4	7.0	8.6
III	6.7	10.4	2.2	9.7	4.4	6.7	9.2
IV	7.0	10.3	2.1	9.9	4.4	6.9	9.4
1992: I	7.3	10.7	2.1	10.0	4.4	7.0	9.6
II	7.5	11.3	2.1	10.2	4.6	6.9	9.8
III	7.5	11.5	2.2	10.2	4.8	6.9	10.2
	Manufacturing hourly compensation in U.S. dollars (1982=100)[4]						
1965		22.8	8.5	15.5	13.2	15.1	15.8
1966		24.7	9.3	16.4	14.3	16.0	17.1
1967		26.1	10.5	17.6	15.2	17.7	17.3
1968		28.2	12.2	19.8	16.3	18.9	16.2
1969		30.4	14.6	20.1	18.1	20.6	17.6
1970		33.9	17.4	21.2	22.9	25.1	20.4
1971		37.7	20.7	24.0	27.0	29.4	24.0
1972		41.3	27.3	28.9	32.5	34.9	28.4
1973		44.3	37.4	37.8	44.2	41.2	31.7
1974		52.2	45.6	41.4	51.6	48.1	36.3
1975		57.3	52.1	57.3	59.7	60.5	45.9
1976		67.7	56.2	59.3	62.9	59.0	43.1
1977	62.6	69.5	68.6	65.6	74.5	65.7	47.2
1978	67.7	69.8	94.0	81.0	92.8	78.8	60.5
1979	74.2	74.8	95.5	97.3	109.1	97.4	79.7
1980	83.1	83.0	98.3	113.5	119.3	111.1	106.1
1981	91.4	93.1	107.6	102.0	102.2	100.9	105.9
1982	100.0	100.0	100.0	100.0	100.0	100.0	100.0
1983	102.5	106.2	107.7	95.3	99.9	104.3	92.7
1984	105.7	105.9	111.0	90.4	93.9	103.5	87.7
1985	111.0	105.6	115.0	95.6	96.0	107.0	92.2
1986	115.4	107.8	171.2	129.3	135.6	142.7	112.2
1987	118.0	116.3	204.2	154.7	171.4	173.3	133.2
1988	122.6	130.9	234.4	162.4	182.1	179.9	152.6
1989	127.3	143.2	231.2	158.0	178.4	188.5	152.6
1990	133.8	154.8	238.1	192.4	222.2	239.4	184.6
1991	140.6	168.0	272.2	193.6	231.4	253.5	199.3

[1] Former West Germany.

[2] Civilian unemployment rates, approximating U.S. concepts. Quarterly data for France, Germany, and United Kingdom should be viewed as less precise indicators of unemployment under U.S. concepts than the annual data. Many Italians reported as unemployed did not actively seek work in the past 30 days, and they have been excluded for comparability with U.S. concepts. Inclusion of such persons would about double the unemployment rate for Italy through 1985, and increase it to 11–12 percent for 1986 forward.

[3] There are breaks in the series for Germany (1983) and Italy (1986 and 1991). Based on the prior series, the rate for Germany was 7.4 percent in 1983 and the rate for Italy was 6.3 percent in 1986. Based on the new series beginning in 1991, the rate for Italy for 1990 would be approximately 7.3 percent.

[4] Hourly compensation in manufacturing, U.S. dollar basis. Data relate to all employed persons (wage and salary earners and the self-employed) in the United States and Canada, and to all employees (wage and salary earners) in the other countries. For France and United Kingdom, compensation adjusted to include changes in employment taxes that are not compensation to employees, but are labor costs to employers.

Source: Department of Labor, Bureau of Labor Statistics.

TABLE B-107.—*Foreign exchange rates, 1967-92*

[Currency units per U.S. dollar, except as noted]

Period	Belgium (franc)	Canada (dollar)	France (franc)	Germany (mark)	Italy (lira)	Japan (yen)
March 1973	39.408	0.9967	4.5156	2.8132	568.17	261.90
1967	49.689	1.0789	4.9206	3.9865	624.09	362.13
1968	49.936	1.0776	4.9529	3.9920	623.38	360.55
1969	50.142	1.0769	5.1999	3.9251	627.32	358.36
1970	49.656	1.0444	5.5288	3.6465	627.12	358.16
1971	48.598	1.0099	5.5100	3.4830	618.34	347.79
1972	44.020	.9907	5.0444	3.1886	583.70	303.13
1973	38.955	1.0002	4.4535	2.6715	582.41	271.31
1974	38.959	.9780	4.8107	2.5868	650.81	291.84
1975	36.800	1.0175	4.2877	2.4614	653.10	296.78
1976	38.609	.9863	4.7825	2.5185	833.58	296.45
1977	35.849	1.0633	4.9161	2.3236	882.78	268.62
1978	31.495	1.1405	4.5091	2.0097	849.13	210.39
1979	29.342	1.1713	4.2567	1.8343	831.11	219.02
1980	29.238	1.1693	4.2251	1.8175	856.21	226.63
1981	37.195	1.1990	5.4397	2.2632	1138.58	220.63
1982	45.781	1.2344	6.5794	2.4281	1354.00	249.06
1983	51.123	1.2325	7.6204	2.5539	1519.32	237.55
1984	57.752	1.2952	8.7356	2.8455	1756.11	237.46
1985	59.337	1.3659	8.9800	2.9420	1908.88	238.47
1986	44.664	1.3896	6.9257	2.1705	1491.16	168.35
1987	37.358	1.3259	6.0122	1.7981	1297.03	144.60
1988	36.785	1.2306	5.9595	1.7570	1302.39	128.17
1989	39.409	1.1842	6.3802	1.8808	1372.28	138.07
1990	33.424	1.1668	5.4467	1.6166	1198.27	145.00
1991	34.195	1.1460	5.6468	1.6610	1241.28	134.59
1992	32.148	1.2085	5.2935	1.5618	1232.17	126.78
1991: I	31.626	1.1561	5.2229	1.5357	1150.42	133.98
II	35.658	1.1493	5.8715	1.7336	1286.27	138.32
III	35.870	1.1440	5.9202	1.7421	1300.75	136.38
IV	33.482	1.1350	5.5497	1.6256	1222.85	129.50
1992: I	33.347	1.1775	5.5137	1.6204	1218.54	128.77
II	33.220	1.1940	5.4416	1.6146	1217.23	130.37
III	30.170	1.2016	4.9628	1.4643	1135.18	124.93
IV	31.915	1.2617	5.2671	1.5509	1362.89	123.02

Period	Netherlands (guilder)	Sweden (krona)	Switzerland (franc)	United Kingdom (pound) [1]	Multilateral trade-weighted value of the U.S. dollar (March 1973=100)	
					Nominal	Real [2]
March 1973	2.8714	4.4294	3.2171	247.24	100.0	100.0
1967	3.6024	5.1621	4.3283	275.04	120.0	
1968	3.6198	5.1683	4.3163	239.35	122.1	
1969	3.6240	5.1701	4.3131	239.01	122.4	
1970	3.6166	5.1862	4.3106	239.59	121.1	
1971	3.4953	5.1051	4.1171	244.42	117.8	
1972	3.2098	4.7571	3.8186	250.34	109.1	
1973	2.7946	4.3619	3.1688	245.25	99.1	98.9
1974	2.6879	4.4387	2.9805	234.03	101.4	99.4
1975	2.5293	4.1531	2.5839	222.17	98.5	94.1
1976	2.6449	4.3580	2.5002	180.48	105.7	97.6
1977	2.4548	4.4802	2.4065	174.49	103.4	93.3
1978	2.1643	4.5207	1.7907	191.84	92.4	84.4
1979	2.0073	4.2893	1.6644	212.24	88.1	83.2
1980	1.9875	4.2310	1.6772	232.46	87.4	84.9
1981	2.4999	5.0660	1.9675	202.43	103.4	100.9
1982	2.6719	6.2839	2.0327	174.80	116.6	111.8
1983	2.8544	7.6718	2.1007	151.59	125.3	117.3
1984	3.2085	8.2708	2.3500	133.68	138.2	128.8
1985	3.3185	8.6032	2.4552	129.74	143.0	132.4
1986	2.4485	7.1273	1.7979	146.77	112.2	103.6
1987	2.0264	6.3469	1.4918	163.98	96.9	90.9
1988	1.9778	6.1370	1.4643	178.13	92.7	88.2
1989	2.1219	6.4559	1.6369	163.82	98.6	94.4
1990	1.8215	5.9231	1.3901	178.41	89.1	86.0
1991	1.8720	6.0521	1.4356	176.74	89.8	86.5
1992	1.7587	5.8258	1.4064	176.63	86.6	83.3
1991: I	1.7312	5.7029	1.3119	190.48	84.7	81.9
II	1.9533	6.2260	1.4740	170.95	92.9	89.6
III	1.9633	6.3239	1.5173	168.61	93.3	89.7
IV	1.8322	5.9357	1.4335	177.57	88.2	84.7
1992: I	1.8243	5.8854	1.4573	176.92	88.2	84.8
II	1.8182	5.8302	1.4780	180.70	88.0	84.4
III	1.6506	5.3523	1.3041	190.30	81.9	78.8
IV	1.7448	6.2581	1.3888	157.81	88.5	85.1

[1] Cents per unit of foreign currency.
[2] Adjusted by changes in consumer prices.
Source: Board of Governors of the Federal Reserve System.

470

TABLE B–108.—*Growth rates in real gross national product/gross domestic product, 1971-91*

[Percent change]

Area and country	1971-75 annual average	1976-80 annual average	1981-85 annual average	1986	1987	1988	1989	1990	1991
OECD countries [1]	3.1	3.4	2.4	2.8	3.2	4.4	3.3	2.4	0.8
United States	2.4	3.2	2.6	2.9	3.1	3.9	2.5	.8	−1.2
Canada	5.2	4.0	2.9	3.3	4.2	5.0	2.3	−.5	−1.7
Japan	4.5	4.6	3.8	2.6	4.1	6.2	4.7	5.2	4.4
European Community [2]	2.9	3.2	1.4	2.8	2.7	4.1	3.4	2.9	1.5
France	3.5	3.1	1.5	2.5	2.3	4.5	4.1	2.2	1.2
Germany [3]	2.2	3.3	1.1	2.2	1.3	3.6	3.3	4.8	3.7
Italy	2.8	4.8	1.4	2.9	3.1	4.1	2.9	2.2	1.4
United Kingdom	2.1	1.9	2.0	4.1	4.8	4.4	2.1	.5	−2.2
Western Hemisphere (other than countries listed above)	6.4	5.4	.4	3.6	3.7	.6	.2	−.6	....
U.S.S.R. [4]	3.0	1.8	1.7	4.1	1.3	2.1	1.5	−3.7	−13.0
China	5.5	6.2	10.0	7.7	10.2	11.3	3.6	4.8	....
Africa	4.0	2.7	.9	2.6	1.6	6.3	4.2	3.7	....
Asia	5.0	5.8	6.7	6.3	8.1	8.9	5.9	6.2	....
Middle East	9.7	4.0	1.7	−2.6	.3	.8	....	....	....

[1] OECD (Organization for Economic Cooperation and Development) includes Australia, Austria, Belgium, Denmark, Finland, France, Germany, Greece, Iceland, Ireland, Italy, Luxembourg, Netherlands, New Zealand, Norway, Portugal, Spain, Sweden, Switzerland, Turkey, and United Kingdom, not shown separately.

[2] Includes Belgium, Denmark, Greece, Ireland, Luxembourg, Netherlands, Portugal, and Spain, not shown separately.

[3] Former West Germany.

[4] Data for U.S.S.R. as published in last year's *Economic Report of the President*; data for individual countries are not available.

Sources: Department of Commerce, Organization for Economic Cooperation and Development, International Monetary Fund, and Council of Economic Advisers.

NATIONAL WEALTH

TABLE B-109.—National wealth, 1960-91

[Billions of dollars]

End of year	Total net worth [1]	Private net worth [2]							Government net financial assets		
		Total	Tangible wealth [3]			Financial wealth			Total [7]	Federal	State and local
			Total [4]	Owner-occupied real estate	Consumer durables	Total [5]	Corporate equity [6]	Noncorporate equity			
1960	1,579.0	1,833.6	730.0	488.2	193.7	1,103.6	395.4	347.2	−254.6	−213.6	−41.9
1961	1,735.9	1,998.6	761.2	512.5	196.8	1,237.4	500.8	355.6	−262.7	−218.0	−45.7
1962	1,726.2	1,994.9	794.5	535.9	202.3	1,200.4	437.1	365.0	−268.7	−220.9	−48.8
1963	1,870.4	2,142.9	833.0	559.2	212.8	1,309.9	513.5	374.9	−272.5	−222.1	−51.5
1964	2,001.2	2,280.3	874.9	584.6	223.7	1,405.4	564.1	387.8	−279.1	−225.8	−54.5
1965	2,169.5	2,449.5	919.2	609.6	236.1	1,530.3	634.9	409.0	−280.0	−224.3	−57.0
1966	2,234.8	2,520.8	991.8	651.9	258.5	1,529.0	574.8	433.0	−286.0	−226.5	−60.9
1967	2,513.8	2,810.3	1,059.4	688.2	283.2	1,750.9	719.3	452.6	−296.5	−232.1	−66.0
1968	2,846.4	3,153.4	1,182.0	768.7	314.2	1,971.4	856.4	487.6	−307.0	−238.3	−70.5
1969	2,901.1	3,211.1	1,286.8	830.7	343.7	1,924.3	744.7	514.7	−310.0	−233.9	−78.2
1970	3,029.5	3,358.2	1,368.4	872.0	372.4	1,989.8	727.2	538.0	−328.7	−243.9	−87.3
1971	3,338.2	3,695.2	1,483.4	950.9	393.7	2,211.8	831.0	584.1	−357.0	−263.7	−96.2
1972	3,757.3	4,128.4	1,673.5	1,091.4	424.7	2,454.9	918.4	656.1	−371.1	−279.2	−95.1
1973	3,944.2	4,315.9	1,894.3	1,241.5	470.5	2,421.6	707.3	788.4	−371.7	−285.5	−90.6
1974	4,126.4	4,510.6	2,154.0	1,402.4	544.2	2,356.6	492.0	866.7	−384.2	−296.5	−94.3
1975	4,681.6	5,146.2	2,399.1	1,580.2	595.7	2,747.1	639.2	948.4	−464.6	−373.2	−99.8
1976	5,265.1	5,790.3	2,692.5	1,799.2	652.8	3,097.8	758.1	1,060.8	−525.2	−433.2	−102.0
1977	5,774.4	6,341.9	3,098.0	2,104.4	725.5	3,243.9	708.9	1,180.8	−567.5	−488.2	−89.7
1978	6,601.4	7,200.6	3,612.3	2,489.3	815.2	3,588.3	705.0	1,399.2	−599.2	−525.9	−84.8
1979	7,720.9	8,334.8	4,191.0	2,909.5	924.4	4,143.8	857.0	1,633.1	−613.9	−547.3	−79.3
1980	8,968.6	9,644.3	4,719.4	3,305.9	1,014.3	4,924.9	1,163.4	1,865.0	−675.7	−607.5	−81.6
1981	9,576.1	10,337.3	5,115.9	3,592.1	1,086.2	5,221.4	1,103.8	2,017.9	−761.2	−683.5	−92.3
1982	10,194.0	11,102.4	5,378.7	3,778.6	1,133.7	5,723.7	1,195.1	2,018.6	−908.4	−829.0	−95.6
1983	10,907.0	12,001.5	5,693.8	4,004.9	1,193.8	6,307.7	1,365.8	2,065.4	−1,094.5	−1,022.4	−89.4
1984	11,533.3	12,802.2	6,181.3	4,370.6	1,281.5	6,620.9	1,382.2	2,033.3	−1,268.9	−1,204.6	−84.0
1985	12,612.6	14,072.3	6,625.8	4,672.6	1,391.1	7,446.5	1,818.3	2,059.3	−1,459.7	−1,410.5	−68.4
1986	13,546.3	15,231.6	7,121.8	4,999.6	1,527.5	8,109.8	2,107.6	2,121.8	−1,685.3	−1,644.4	−60.7
1987	14,216.6	16,099.7	7,677.7	5,390.5	1,659.5	8,422.0	2,006.6	2,253.1	−1,883.1	−1,826.4	−78.3
1988	15,120.6	17,199.1	8,126.4	5,643.1	1,808.4	9,072.7	2,136.9	2,373.1	−2,078.5	−2,019.1	−84.1
1989	16,631,9	18,917.2	8,731.9	6,081.9	1,929.6	10,185.3	2,495.7	2,524.9	−2,285.3	−2,193.8	−119.0
1990	16,320.6	18,839.3	8,747.4	6,005.1	2,030.7	10,091.9	2,356.0	2,449.4	−2,518.7	−2,386.7	−162.7
1991	17,630.9	20,428.2	9,256.2	6,468.6	2,122.7	11,172.0	3,060.9	2,372.6	−2,797.3	−2,627.6	−203.5

[1] Sum of private net worth and government net financial assets.
[2] Referred to as household net worth in the *Balance Sheets*.
[3] Held by households and nonprofit institutions.
[4] Also includes nonprofit institutions' real estate.
[5] Also includes credit market instruments, life insurance and pension reserves, security credit, and miscellaneous assets, and is net of liabilities.
[6] Includes households and nonprofit institutions' direct (or through mutual funds) holdings of corporate equity. Equity held through pension and life insurance reserves is not included.
[7] Also includes sponsored credit agencies and the Federal Reserve. Some tangible wealth is included for these agencies.

Note.—Data are from *Balance Sheets for the U.S. Economy, 1960-91*, September 1992.
Data are measured at market value where available. For example, corporate equity and land are measured at market value, but bonds are measured at par value.

Source: Board of Governors of the Federal Reserve System.

TABLE B-110.—*National wealth in 1987 dollars, 1960-91*

[Billions of 1987 dollars]

End of year	Total net worth [1]	Private net worth [2]							Government net financial assets		
		Total	Tangible wealth [3]			Financial wealth			Total [7]	Federal	State and local
			Total [4]	Owner-occupied real estate	Consumer durables	Total [5]	Corporate equity [6]	Non-corporate equity			
1960	6,049.8	7,025.3	2,796.9	1,870.5	742.1	4,228.4	1,514.9	1,330.3	−975.5	−818.4	−160.5
1961	6,525.9	7,513.5	2,861.7	1,926.7	739.8	4,651.9	1,882.7	1,336.8	−987.6	−819.5	−171.8
1962	6,369.7	7,361.3	2,931.7	1,977.5	746.5	4,429.5	1,612.9	1,346.9	−991.5	−815.1	−180.1
1963	6,801.5	7,792.4	3,029.1	2,033.5	773.8	4,763.3	1,867.3	1,363.3	−990.9	−807.6	−187.3
1964	7,121.7	8,114.9	3,113.5	2,080.4	796.1	5,001.4	2,007.5	1,380.1	−993.2	−803.6	−194.0
1965	7,506.9	8,475.8	3,180.6	2,109.3	817.0	5,295.2	2,196.9	1,415.2	−968.9	−776.1	−197.2
1966	7,449.3	8,402.7	3,306.0	2,173.0	861.7	5,096.7	1,916.0	1,443.3	−953.3	−755.0	−203.0
1967	8,109.0	9,065.5	3,417.4	2,220.0	913.5	5,648.1	2,320.3	1,460.0	−956.5	−748.7	−212.9
1968	8,731.3	9,673.0	3,625.8	2,358.0	963.8	6,047.2	2,627.0	1,495.7	−941.7	−731.0	−216.3
1969	8,458.0	9,361.8	3,751.6	2,421.9	1,002.0	5,610.2	2,171.1	1,500.6	−903.8	−681.9	−228.0
1970	8,392.0	9,302.5	3,790.6	2,415.5	1,031.6	5,511.9	2,014.4	1,490.3	−910.5	−675.6	−241.8
1971	8,784.7	9,724.2	3,903.7	2,502.4	1,036.1	5,820.5	2,186.8	1,537.1	−939.5	−693.9	−253.2
1972	9,416.8	10,346.9	4,194.2	2,735.3	1,064.4	6,152.6	2,301.8	1,644.4	−930.1	−699.7	−238.3
1973	9,172.6	10,037.0	4,405.3	2,887.2	1,094.2	5,631.6	1,644.9	1,833.5	−864.4	−664.0	−210.7
1974	8,723.9	9,536.2	4,553.9	2,964.9	1,150.5	4,982.2	1,040.2	1,832.3	−812.3	−626.8	−199.4
1975	9,197.6	10,110.4	4,713.4	3,104.5	1,170.3	5,397.1	1,255.8	1,863.3	−912.8	−733.2	−196.1
1976	9,750.2	10,722.8	4,986.1	3,331.9	1,208.9	5,736.7	1,403.9	1,964.4	−972.6	−802.2	−188.9
1977	9,990.3	10,972.1	5,359.9	3,640.8	1,255.2	5,612.3	1,226.5	2,042.9	−981.8	−844.6	−155.2
1978	10,495.1	11,447.7	5,742.9	3,957.6	1,296.0	5,704.8	1,120.8	2,224.5	−952.6	−836.1	−134.8
1979	11,287.9	12,185.4	6,127.2	4,253.7	1,351.5	6,058.2	1,252.9	2,387.6	−897.5	−800.1	−115.9
1980	11,878.9	12,773.9	6,250.9	4,378.7	1,343.4	6,523.0	1,540.9	2,470.2	−895.0	−804.6	−108.1
1981	11,692.4	12,621.9	6,246.5	4,386.0	1,326.3	6,375.3	1,347.7	2,463.9	−929.4	−834.6	−112.7
1982	11,922.8	12,985.3	6,290.9	4,419.4	1,326.0	6,694.4	1,397.8	2,360.9	−1,062.5	−969.6	−111.8
1983	12,241.3	13,469.7	6,390.3	4,494.8	1,339.8	7,079.3	1,532.9	2,318.1	−1,228.4	−1,147.5	−100.3
1984	12,428.1	13,795.5	6,660.9	4,709.7	1,380.9	7,134.6	1,489.4	2,191.1	−1,367.3	−1,298.1	−90.5
1985	13,165.6	14,689.2	6,916.3	4,877.5	1,452.1	7,773.0	1,898.0	2,149.6	−1,523.7	−1,472.3	−71.4
1986	13,766.6	15,479.3	7,237.6	5,080.9	1,552.3	8,241.7	2,141.9	2,156.3	−1,712.7	−1,671.1	−61.7
1987	13,979.0	15,830.6	7,549.4	5,300.4	1,631.8	8,281.2	1,973.1	2,215.4	−1,851.6	−1,795.9	−77.0
1988	14,237.9	16,195.0	7,652.0	5,313.7	1,702.8	8,543.0	2,012.1	2,234.6	−1,957.2	−1,901.2	−79.2
1989	15,024.3	17,088.7	7,887.9	5,494.0	1,743.1	9,200.8	2,254.5	2,280.8	−2,064.4	−1,981.8	−107.5
1990	14,093.8	16,268.8	7,553.9	5,185.8	1,753.6	8,714.9	2,034.5	2,115.2	−2,175.0	−2,061.1	−140.5
1991	14,766.2	17,109.0	7,752.3	5,417.6	1,777.8	9,356.8	2,563.6	1,987.1	−2,342.8	−2,200.7	−170.4

[1] Sum of private net worth and government net financial assets.
[2] Referred to as household net worth in the *Balance Sheets*.
[3] Held by households and nonprofit institutions.
[4] Also includes nonprofit institutions' real estate.
[5] Also includes credit market instruments, life insurance and pension reserves, security credit, and miscellaneous assets, and is net of liabilities.
[6] Includes households and nonprofit institutions' direct (or through mutual funds) holdings of corporate equity. Equity held through pension and life insurance reserves is not included.
[7] Also includes sponsored credit agencies and the Federal Reserve. Some tangible wealth is included for these agencies.

Note.—Data are from *Balance Sheets for the U.S. Economy, 1960-91*, September 1992; deflated by the GDP implicit deflator. (The deflator was averaged for fourth quarter of year shown and first quarter of following year.)

Data are measured at market value where available. For example, corporate equity and land are measured at market value, but bonds are measured at par value.

Sources: Board of Governors of the Federal Reserve System and Department of Commerce, Bureau of Economic Analysis.

SUPPLEMENTARY TABLE

TABLE B-111.—Selected historical series on gross domestic product and related series, 1929–58

[Billions of dollars; except as noted]

Year	Gross domestic product — Current dollars	Gross domestic product — 1987 dollars	Gross domestic product — Implicit price deflator (1987=100)	Percent change from preceding period — Current dollars	Percent change from preceding period — 1987 dollars	Percent change from preceding period — Implicit price deflator	Constant 1987 dollars — Personal consumption expenditures	Constant 1987 dollars — Gross private domestic investment	Constant 1987 dollars — Net exports	Constant 1987 dollars — Government purchases	Disposable personal income — Total	Disposable personal income — Per capita (dollars)	Saving as percent of disposable personal income [1]	Population (thousands) [2]
1929	103.1	821.8	12.5				554.5	152.8	1.9	112.6	585.8	4,807	3.0	121,878
1930	90.4	748.9	12.1	−12.4	−8.9	−3.2	520.0	107.2	−.3	122.0	542.2	4,402	2.5	123,188
1931	75.8	691.3	11.0	−16.2	−7.7	−9.1	501.0	67.2	−2.3	125.5	519.7	4,186	2.1	124,149
1932	58.0	599.7	9.7	−23.5	−13.3	−11.8	456.6	25.0	−2.4	120.5	449.8	3,600	−3.1	124,949
1933	55.6	587.1	9.5	−4.1	−2.1	−2.1	447.4	26.6	−3.0	116.1	437.0	3,477	−3.9	125,690
1934	65.1	632.6	10.3	17.1	7.7	8.4	461.1	41.1	−1.0	131.4	462.0	3,652	−1.1	126,485
1935	72.3	681.3	10.6	11.1	7.7	2.9	487.6	65.2	−7.2	135.7	505.2	3,967	2.3	127,362
1936	82.7	777.9	10.6	14.4	14.2	.0	534.4	89.9	−5.1	158.6	565.9	4,415	4.4	128,181
1937	90.8	811.4	11.2	9.8	4.3	5.7	554.6	106.4	−1.9	152.2	585.5	4,540	4.0	128,961
1938	84.9	778.9	10.9	−6.5	−4.0	−2.7	542.2	69.9	4.2	162.5	547.6	4,213	−.3	129,969
1939	90.8	840.7	10.8	7.0	7.9	−.9	568.7	93.4	4.6	174.0	590.3	4,505	2.4	131,028
1940	100.0	906.0	11.0	10.2	7.8	1.9	595.2	121.8	8.2	180.7	627.2	4,747	3.8	132,122
1941	125.0	1,070.6	11.7	25.0	18.2	6.4	629.3	149.4	2.8	289.1	713.9	5,352	10.7	133,402
1942	158.5	1,284.9	12.3	26.8	20.0	5.1	628.7	81.4	−11.1	586.0	824.7	6,115	23.1	134,860
1943	192.4	1,540.5	12.5	21.3	19.9	1.6	647.3	53.5	−28.1	867.7	863.8	6,317	24.5	136,739
1944	211.0	1,670.0	12.6	9.7	8.4	.8	671.2	59.8	−29.0	968.0	901.8	6,516	25.0	138,397
1945	213.1	1,602.6	13.3	1.0	−4.0	5.6	714.6	82.6	−23.9	829.4	890.9	6,367	19.2	139,928
1946	211.9	1,272.1	16.7	−.6	−20.6	25.6	779.1	195.5	26.5	271.0	860.0	6,083	8.5	141,389
1947	234.3	1,252.8	18.7	10.6	−1.5	12.0	793.3	198.8	41.9	218.8	826.1	5,732	3.0	144,126
1948	260.3	1,300.0	20.0	11.1	3.8	7.0	813.0	229.8	16.6	240.6	872.9	5,953	5.8	146,631
1949	259.3	1,305.5	19.9	−.4	.4	−.5	831.4	187.4	17.3	269.3	874.5	5,862	3.7	149,188
1950	287.0	1,418.5	20.2	10.7	8.7	1.5	874.3	256.4	3.2	284.5	942.5	6,214	5.9	151,684
1951	331.6	1,558.4	21.3	15.5	9.9	5.4	894.7	255.6	11.1	397.0	978.2	6,340	7.3	154,287
1952	349.7	1,624.9	21.5	5.4	4.3	.9	923.4	231.6	2.3	467.6	1,009.7	6,433	7.2	156,954
1953	370.0	1,685.5	22.0	5.8	3.7	2.3	962.5	240.3	−7.1	489.8	1,053.5	6,603	7.0	159,565
1954	370.9	1,673.8	22.2	.2	−.7	.9	987.3	234.1	−2.3	454.7	1,071.5	6,598	6.2	162,391
1955	404.3	1,768.3	22.9	9.0	5.6	3.2	1,047.0	284.8	−5.2	441.7	1,130.8	6,842	5.7	165,275
1956	426.2	1,803.6	23.6	5.4	2.0	3.1	1,078.7	282.2	−1.2	444.0	1,185.2	7,046	7.1	168,221
1957	448.6	1,838.2	24.4	5.2	1.9	3.4	1,104.4	266.9	1.6	465.3	1,214.6	7,091	7.2	171,274
1958	454.7	1,829.1	24.9	1.4	−.5	2.0	1,122.2	245.7	−14.9	476.0	1,236.0	7,098	7.4	174,141

[1] Percents based on data in millions of dollars.
[2] Population of the United States including Armed Forces overseas; includes Alaska and Hawaii beginning 1960.

Source: Department of Commerce, Bureau of Economic Analysis.

ISBN 0-16-041592-6